PROFESSIONAL ENGINEER'S EXAMINATION QUESTIONS AND ANSWERS

PROFESSIONAL ENGINEER'S EXAMINATION QUESTIONS AND ANSWERS

WILLIAM S. LA LONDE, JR.
Licensed Professional Engineer, New Jersey, New York
Chairman, Department of Civil Engineering
Newark College of Engineering, Newark, N.J.

McGRAW-HILL BOOK COMPANY, INC.
NEW YORK TORONTO LONDON
1956

PROFESSIONAL ENGINEER'S EXAMINATION
QUESTIONS AND ANSWERS

Library of Congress Catalog Card Number: 55-5689

VI

THE MAPLE PRESS COMPANY, YORK, PA.

PREFACE

This book has been prepared to help both the newly graduated engineer and the older practicing engineer in their review of engineering fundamentals in preparation for the professional engineer examinations as part requirement for the engineer-in-training certificate or the professional engineer license.

About 80 per cent of the problems appearing in this book were taken directly from sample question sheets or past professional engineer examinations as given by the many state boards of professional engineer examiners throughout the United States. These problems may be considered a composite of the many examinations which have been given in the past, but they purposely do not represent the examination questions of any state. The problems that have been added were included so as to give better coverage of some of the subject matter for those preparing to take future professional engineer examinations.

Grateful acknowledgement is given to the many state boards of professional engineers or engineering examiners and to the National Council of State Boards of Engineering Examiners for contributing specimen or sample questions or information on the scope of examinations and of registration; and to professional engineers R. E. Anderson, J. Joffe, W. Jordan, G. C. Keeffe, F. G. Lehman, R. D. Mangasarian, E. Miller, A. A. Nims, J. M. Robbins, F. A. Russell, and L. Shapiro, all of the faculty of the Newark College of Engineering, for the services which they contributed toward the solutions of the problems in their fields of specialization.

William S. La Londe, Jr.

HOW TO USE THIS BOOK

It is suggested that the General Information in Part One be reviewed to estimate your eligibility and qualifications for making application for the engineer-in-training certificate or professional engineer's license.

The definitions set forth in the Model Law for the Registration of Professional Engineers and Land Surveyors should be helpful. Your professional experience should be carefully scrutinized and compared with the Experience Qualification Guide prepared by the Committee on Qualifying Experience of the National Council of State Boards of Engineering Examiners. After you have done this and you feel that you have had the prerequisite training and years of professional experience to qualify you to apply for the professional engineer's license, then write to the secretary of your state board of registration for professional engineers and land surveyors and request an application blank and information with respect to the laws covering the requirements. After you have filled out and submitted your application blank, you will be informed by the license board whether there will be any written examinations or not. Some license boards will give bona fide applicants sample or specimen questions, and all will at least inform the applicant as to the scope of the examinations.

Having at least learned the scope of your examination, you will find many problems worked out in this book that will be helpful to you in reviewing the engineering fundamentals with which you should be familiar. It is the intent here only to help you review what you know. Space limitations prevent the derivation of formulas or explanations concerning the subject material which may be found in standard engineering texts. Formulas and symbols will be identified as well as source material taken from special tables. The solutions to these problems should be studied and used as a guide for minimum clarity and explanation when later working out the problems of your particular examination. So often engineers, when taking these examinations, present their work so non-understandingly as to make it difficult for the examiner to follow the specific solutions.

In studying for the examinations, you should have a sufficient duplication of problems to do a certain number with the solutions as practice and a certain number without the solutions to test yourself for competency and speed. There is no equal in the preparation for these license examinations to the working of a sufficiently large number of these problems.

In practically all the state board examinations, the applicant will be permitted some choice. It is desirable at the beginning of each examination to calmly and thoughtfully read over all the questions and to pick out those you wish to do; and it might be a good idea to do first those problems which you can do readily. If eight problems are to be done in four hours, try first to budget your time with not over 15 or 20 minutes per problem. This will allow an opportunity to go back and review the problems afterwards. It is also better to answer six problems correctly than to try to get all eight problems answered with only part scores. Sometimes if one has difficulty with a problem, it is well not to work on it too long as a suggestion in another problem or the feeling of confidence gained from the solution of a number of problems will stimulate the thinking or relax the pressure, and the solution may be obtained when one returns to the problem. Neatness and carefulness in the arithmetical work and in making tabulations will insure the best results. Never omit a check if it is possible to make one.

Sometimes needed information is purposely omitted from the examination question to test the examinee's ability to size up the situation and to supply reasonable data. In answering such a question, merely indicate your assumptions and proceed from that point. It is well to be careful, however, not to make assumptions where none are needed.

A satisfactory speed for the solution of these problems, indicative of reasonable familiarity with the fundamentals of any given section, is to be able to work two or three problems per hour. As much work as possible should be done without the use of texts or notes, as in many cases their use or the use of books such as this one are not permitted at the examinations. It is best not to bank on the use of more than a handbook of tables and formulas, and where the necessary information is supplied to the questions, perhaps not more than a slide rule will be permitted. Where books are permitted, the questions may be more searching, and unless one has a knowledge of his subject, much time can be lost browsing in books looking for the answer. The solutions to the problems in this book are purposely separated from the questions in order to encourage the reviewer as far as it may be possible to do his own thinking and work.

CONTENTS

PART ONE

General Information

LEGAL REGISTRATION

The office of the National Council of State Boards of Engineering Examiners will furnish upon request any specific information available regarding the legal registration or licensing of professional engineers that may be required in addition to the following.

Engineers who wish to secure legal registration or professional license in any particular state must communicate directly with the state board or department in that state and request its application form and regulations. All the states, Alaska, Hawaii, Puerto Rico, and the provinces of Canada have registration laws regulating the practice of engineering.

The engineering registration laws are not uniform due to local conditions, date of enactment, etc. Most state laws, however, require either graduation in an accredited engineering curriculum, a written engineering examination, adequate and satisfactory engineering experience, or a combination of these.

INTERSTATE REGISTRATION

Legal registration or professional license in any one state or certification by the National Bureau of Engineering Registration does not permit or authorize the practice of engineering in other states. Most states, however, grant registration to registrants of other states or temporary permits to practice, provided they have the required qualifications and comply with the regulations of those states.

NATIONAL BUREAU OF ENGINEERING REGISTRATION

The National Bureau of Engineering Registration is operated as a function of the National Council of State Boards of Engineering Examiners. It was established primarily to minimize the effort and expense of registered engineers desiring to secure registration or license in more than one state. The registration laws or regulations of most states specifically provide for acceptance of the Certificates of Qualification as competent evidence. However, such certification is not binding upon the State Boards and is not a form of registration or license. The "Information Pamphlet" of the Registration Bureau containing the procedure, requirements, and fees can be secured from the Executive Secretary at P.O. Drawer 1404, Columbia, S.C.

A MODEL LAW FOR THE REGISTRATION OF PROFESSIONAL ENGINEERS AND LAND SURVEYORS AND PROVIDING FOR THE CERTIFICATION OF ENGINEERS-IN-TRAINING

DEFINITIONS

Engineer The term Engineer as used in this Act should mean a Professional Engineer as hereinafter defined.

Professional Engineer The term Professional Engineer within the meaning and intent of this Act shall mean a person who, by reason of his special knowledge of the mathematical and physical sciences and the principles and methods of engineering analysis and design, acquired by professional education and practical experience, is qualified to practice engineering as hereinafter defined, as attested by his legal registration as a Professional Engineer.

Engineer-in-Training The term Engineer-in-Training as used in this Act shall mean a candidate for registration as Professional Engineer who is a graduate in an approved engineering curriculum of four years or more from a school or college approved by the Board as of satisfactory standing, or who has had four years or more of experience in engineering work of a character satisfactory to the Board; and who, in addition, has successfully passed the examination in the fundamental engineering subjects prior to completion of the requisite years of experience in engineering work, as provided in Section 14 of this Act, and who shall have received from the Board, as hereinafter defined, a certificate stating that he has successfully passed this portion of the professional examinations.

Practice of Engineering The term Practice of Engineering within the meaning and intent of this Act shall mean any professional service or creative work requiring engineering education, training, and experience and the application of special knowledge of the mathematical, physical, and engineering sciences to such professional services or creative work as consultation, investigation, evaluation, planning, design, and supervision of construction for the purpose of assuring compliance with specifications and design, in connection with any public or private utilities, structures, buildings, machines, equipment, processes, works, or projects.

A person shall be construed to practice or offer to practice engineering, within the meaning and intent of this Act, who practices any branch of the profession of engineering; or who, by verbal claim, sign, advertisement, letterhead, card, or in any other way represents himself to be a professional engineer, or through the use of some other title implies that he is a professional engineer; or who holds himself out as able to perform, or who does perform any engineering service or work or any other professional service designated by the practitioner or recognized by educational authorities as engineering.

Land Surveyor The term Land Surveyor as used in this Act shall mean a person who engages in the practice of land surveying as hereinafter defined.

Land Surveying The practice of land surveying within the meaning and intent of this Act includes surveying of areas for their correct determination and description and for conveyancing, or for the establishment or reestablishment of land boundaries and the plotting of lands and subdivisions thereof.

SUGGESTED EXPERIENCE QUALIFICATION GUIDE

CHEMICAL ENGINEERING

Professional Experience

Design, Specifications and/or Construction: Equipment for chemical enterprises; processing plants; plant layouts; equipment; economic balances; production planning; pilot plants; heat-transmission apparatus.

Development: Processes; pilot plants; refrigeration systems for food processing.

Research: Laboratory; pilot plants; director; markets; unit operations; kinetics; processes; calculation and correlation of physical properties.

Responsible charge of broader fields of chemical engineering; executive.

Consultation; appraisals; evaluations; reports; economics; chemical patent laws.

Operation of pilot plants; product testing; technical service; technical sales.

Teaching full time, at college level; editing and writing.

Subprofessional Experience

Construction: Process equipment; pilot plants; piping systems.

Operation: Shift operator; special chemicals manufacture (solutions); pilot plants; trouble shooting; glass blower.

Drafting: Flow-sheet layout.

Instrument making and servicing; routine analyses; routine sampling and tests; latheman.

Analyst: Routine, under direction; laboratory assistant (commercial, college); computations, under direction; data taking.

Sales: Routine, of standard equipment.

CIVIL ENGINEERING

Professional Experience

Design and/or Construction: Highways; streets; subways; tunnels; drainage; drainage structures; sewerage; sewage-disposal structures; railroad spurs and turnouts; railroads; rivers, harbors, and waterfront; waterworks; water supply; water power; airports and/or airways; bridges; dams; irrigation; irrigation structures; water purification systems; incinerators; storage elevators and structures; flood control.

Development: Structures for regions; ports; wharves and docks; irrigation works; flood control; drainage.

Investigations; appraisals and evaluations; cost analysis; consultations; testing; research and economic studies; reports.

Teaching at college level, full time in an accredited college of engineering.

Editing and writing.

Surveys: Topographic; hydrographic; earthwork; triangulation; railroad; irrigation; drainage; water power.

Independent responsibility and supervision of the work of others.

Subprofessional Experience

Fieldwork: Instrumentman; chainman; rodman; chief of party; recorder; surveyman; levelman; staking out foundations; staking out dredging ranges; railroad lines and turnouts; sounding; instrumental observations.

Drafting: Plotting field notes; map drafting and tracing; tracing designs; structural detailing; plotting soundings.

Construction: Inspection; timekeeping; supervision, without authority to change designs.

Computations: Routine, under direction; taking off quantities; monthly estimates.

Cost Data: Routine assembling and computing; estimating, under direction.

Testing: Routine testing of materials of construction; water.

Teaching: As an associate without full responsibility in an engineering college.

ELECTRICAL ENGINEERING

Professional Experience

Design, Specifications and/or Construction: Power plants; electronic and transmission equipment; application of electrical equipment to industry; electric service and supply; communication systems; control systems and servomechanisms; manufacturing plants; operating procedures; distribution networks; transportation; radio circuits; major electrical installations.

Development and Production: New techniques and devices; electrical and electronic devices.

Supervision and/or Management: Power plants; manufacturing plants.

Research and investigations in electrical fields; water, steam, and electric power; electronics; new techniques and devices; high-voltage cables.

Consultation; appraisals; valuations; estimates; cost analysis; reports; determination of rates; economics and cost figures; calculations of system and device performance.

Sales and application of equipment to industry; service engineering; testing, when not of a routine character.

Editing and writing on electrical-engineering subjects.

Teaching full time, at college level, in an accredited school.

Subprofessional Experience

Construction and Installation: Construction of electrical installations, under competent direction; electronic and radio equipment; wiring, lineman; switchboard wiring; electrician; meterman; armature winding.

Inspection: Routine, under direction.

Installation: Heating, ventilating, and air conditioning; radio equipment.

Drafting: Elementary layout; circuit drafting; detailing.

Testing: Routine; performance of electrical machinery.

Operation: Radio; power stations; substations; switchboards.

Repairs: Motors; generators; electrical devices; electronic and radio devices.

Maintenance: Electronic and radio devices; radio and television technician.

Apprentice: Work as junior in fields of illumination, communication, and transportation.

Sales: Routine; almost all customer service; inventory.

Teaching: Manual skills; instructor in accredited school.

MECHANICAL ENGINEERING

Professional Experience

Design and/or Construction: Machines; machinery and mill layouts; heating, ventilating, and air conditioning; power plants; power-plant equipment; industrial layouts; refrigeration; tools and processes; designs involving application of existing equipment and principles; internal-combustion engines.

Development of industrial plants and processes; consultation.

Appraisals; investigations; research and economic studies; cost analyses; reports.

Operation: Major mechanical installations; manufacturing plants; power plants; testing; application of instruments and control to manufacturing processes.

Editing and writing on mechanical-engineering subjects.

Teaching full time, at college level, in accredited schools.

Subprofessional Experience

Construction and Installation: Machinery; heating; ventilating and air conditioning; mechanical structures.

Operation: Heating, ventilating, and air-conditioning equipment; power plants; mechanical manufacturing plant; stationary machinery (small operations); foundry and machine shops.

Drafting: Detailing; shop drawings; checking shop drawings; tracing; layout work; design of tools, jigs, and fixtures.

Recording; routine computing under competent direction; laboratory assistant; routine testing under competent direction; inspection of materials, etc.

Maintenance; repairs; welding.

Teaching as an assistant without full responsibility, in an accredited college.

SANITARY ENGINEERING

Professional Experience

Design, Specifications, and/or Construction: Water-treatment plants; sewage-disposal plants; waterworks; sewers; incinerators; distribution systems; sewage- and industrial-waste-treatment plants.

Consultations; reports for proposed works; original research for processes and equipment; review of plans for works for state and Federal authorities; planning and analysis of surveys and pollution data; advising on water-purification plants; counseling municipal officials concerning needed sanitary facilities; planning and supervising environmental sanitation work in sanitation of food, milk, etc.; investigations; studies; reports and evaluation of proposed or existing water systems or sewerage; industrial-hygiene surveys and reports; research in sanitary engineering or public health.

Abatement procedures on stream pollution; supervision of works for large cities; supervision of pollution surveys; control of rodents and insects.

Teaching full time, at college level, in an accredited school.

Editing and writing.

Subprofessional Experience

Routine laboratory tests; installation of machinery; gathering records for reports; stream gaging; surveying; plant operation and maintenance; record keeping; sanitarian's inspection; mapping; inspection; routine chemical and bacteriological tests; pest control; collection of data; take off; sampling; establishing of lines and grades; inspection of eating and drinking establishments; routine vessel-sanitation inspections; routine watering-point inspections; orientation periods in public-health agencies; inspection of construction.

Maintenance and operation of filter and sewage plant; routine laboratory examinations.

Same as Civil Engineering.

STRUCTURAL ENGINEERING

Professional Experience

Design, specifications, and/or construction on structures; hydraulic design; stress analysis; soils analysis; mechanical analysis.

Research on structures; testing; layout studies and comparisons; new design procedures and methods of analysis; reports; consultations; investigation evaluations.

Project supervision; field execution of projects; senior structural draftsman; senior stress analyst; senior engineer on materials testing; senior concrete laboratory technician; resident (field) engineer on bridges, dams, and buildings; research engineer.

Same as Civil Engineering.

Teaching full time, at college level, in an accredited school.

Subprofessional Experience

Structural drafting, detailing; drafting layout and details; junior stress analyst; computer; checking detail drawings; checking design computations; collection of data for reports; inspector; junior laboratory engineer; research assistant; junior concrete technician.

TRAFFIC ENGINEERING

Professional Experience

Design of traffic islands; design of new and augmented control systems; design of relief systems; design of highway lighting; traffic-engineering planning and roadway design; design of mechanical traffic control.

Planning and analyzing surveys and traffic counts; interpretation of field data; computing earning power of proposed routes; establishing traffic-count stations; transportation studies (major or complete); traffic-education programs.

Traffic-engineering organization and administration. Teaching, at college level.

Subprofessional Experience

Traffic counts; compiling of data; timing of automatic signals; plotting traffic-flow charts; plotting traffic-dispersion charts; origin and destination data; weighting stations; accident study and tabulation; sign and signal checking.

ADDRESSES OF REGISTRATION BOARDS

Alabama State Board of Registration for Professional Engineers and Land Surveyors
711 High Street, Montgomery 5, Alabama

Alaska Territorial Board of Engineers and Architects Examiners
Box 854, Anchorage, Alaska

Arizona State Board of Technical Registration
Room 403, 128 North 1st Avenue, Phoenix, Arizona

Arkansas State Board of Registration for Professional Engineers
P.O. Box 175, Pulaski Heights Station, Little Rock, Arkansas

California State Board of Registration for Civil and Professional Engineers
529 Business and Professions Building
1020 N Street, Sacramento 14, California

Canal Zone Board of Registration for Architects and Professional Engineers
P.O. Box 223, Balboa Heights, Canal Zone

Colorado State Board of Registration for Professional Engineers
20 Capitol Building, Denver, Colorado

Connecticut State Board of Registration for Professional Engineers and Land Surveyors
30 Oak Street, Hartford 6, Connecticut

Delaware State Board of Registration for Professional Engineers and Land Surveyors
11 East 12th Street, Wilmington, Delaware

District of Columbia Board of Registration for Professional Engineers
1740 Massachusetts Avenue, N.W., Washington 6, D.C.

Florida State Board of Engineer Examiners
408 John F. Seagle Building, Gainesville, Florida

Georgia State Board of Registration for Professional Engineers and Surveyors
224 State Capitol, Atlanta, Georgia

Hawaii Board of Registration for Professional Engineers, Architects, and Land Surveyors
1909 Aleo Place, Honolulu 14, Hawaii

Idaho State Board of Engineering Examiners
623½ Main Street, Boise, Idaho

Illinois State Department of Registration and Education, Professional Engineer's Examining Committee
State Capitol, Springfield, Illinois

Indiana State Board of Registration for Professional Engineers and Land Surveyors
145 W. Washington St., Indianapolis, Indiana

Iowa State Board of Engineering Examiners
State House, Des Moines 19, Iowa

Kansas State Board of Engineering Examiners
422 Garlinghouse Building, Topeka, Kansas

Kentucky State Board of Registration for Professional Engineers
University of Kentucky, Lexington 29, Kentucky

Louisiana State Board of Registration for Professional Engineers and Land Surveyors
Civil Engineering Building, Tulane University
New Orleans 18, Louisiana

Maine State Board of Registration for Professional Engineers
Box 103, Waterville, Maine

Maryland State Board of Registration for Professional Engineers and Land Surveyors
1101 Key Highway, Baltimore 30, Maryland

Massachusetts State Board of Registration of Professional Engineers and of Land Surveyors
Room 34, State House, Boston, Massachusetts

Michigan State Board of Registration for Architects, Professional Engineers, and Land Surveyors
1604 Cadillac Square Building, Detroit 26, Michigan

Minnesota State Board of Registration for Architects, Engineers, and Land Surveyors
316 New York Building, St. Paul 1, Minnesota

Mississippi State Board of Registration for Professional Engineers
P.O. Box 3, Jackson, Mississippi

Missouri State Board of Registration for Architects and Professional Engineers
Box 184, Jefferson City, Missouri

Montana State Board of Registration for Civil Engineers and Land Surveyors, Montana State College
Bozeman, Montana

Nebraska State Board of Examiners for Professional Engineers and Architects
210 Ferguson Hall, University of Nebraska
Lincoln 8, Nebraska

Nevada State Board of Registered Professional Engineers
University of Nevada, Reno, Nevada

New Hampshire State Board of Registration for Professional Engineers
92 Rockingham St., Concord, New Hampshire

New Jersey State Board of Professional Engineers and Land Surveyors
1100 Raymond Blvd, Newark, New Jersey

New Mexico State Board of Registration for Professional Engineers and Land Surveyors
P.O. Box 2074, Santa Fe, New Mexico

New York State Board of Examiners of Professional Engineers and Land Surveyors
23 South Pearl Street, Albany, New York

North Carolina State Board of Registration for Engineers and Land Surveyors
P.O. Box 5131,
North Carolina State College, Raleigh, North Carolina

North Dakota State Board of Registration for Professional Engineers
P.O. Box 1265, Minot, North Dakota

Ohio State Board of Registration for Professional Engineers and Surveyors
21 West Broad Street, Columbus 15, Ohio

Oklahoma State Board of Registration for Professional Engineers
2901 Classen Boulevard, Oklahoma City 6, Oklahoma

Oregon State Board of Engineering Examiners
717 Board of Trade Building, Portland, Oregon

Pennsylvania State Registration Board for Professional Engineers
324 Education Building, Harrisburg, Pennsylvania

Puerto Rico Board of Examiners of Engineers, Architects, and Surveyors
P.O. Box 3271, San Juan, Fortaleza 54, Puerto Rico

Rhode Island State Board of Registration for Professional Engineers and Land Surveyors
245 State Office Building, Providence, Rhode Island

South Carolina State Board of Engineering Examiners
P.O. Drawer 1404, Columbia, South Carolina

South Dakota State Board of Engineering and Architectural Examiners
School of Mines and Technology, Rapid City, South Dakota

Tennessee State Board of Architectural and Engineering Examiners
503 Nashville Trust Building, Nashville 3, Tennessee

Texas State Board of Registration for Professional Engineers
308 West 15th Street, Austin, Texas

Utah Professional Engineers and Land Surveyors Examining Committee, Dept. of Registration
324 State Capitol Building, Salt Lake City 1, Utah

Vermont State Board of Registration for Professional Engineers
Norwich University, Northfield, Vermont

Virginia State Board for Examination and Certification of Architects, Professional Engineers, and Land Surveyors
P.O. Box 1-X, Richmond, Virginia

Washington State Board of Engineering Examiners
Department of Licenses, Professional Division
Transportation Building, Olympia, Washington

West Virginia State Registration Board for Professional Engineers
301 Morrison Building, Charleston, West Virginia

Wisconsin State Registration Board of Architects and Professional Engineers
1140 State Office Building, Madison 2, Wisconsin

Wyoming State Board of Examining Engineers
201 State Capitol Building, Cheyenne, Wyoming

PART TWO

Questions from Professional Engineer's Examinations

SECTION ONE

1.101–1.725

BASIC FUNDAMENTALS

CHEMISTRY, SCIENCE, AND MATERIALS

1.101 Calculate the weight of sulfuric acid and of sodium chloride that would be required to prepare 1 liter of hydrochloric acid, density 1.201. HCl of density 1.201 contains 40.09 per cent by weight HCl. Chemical equation and atomic weights are as indicated.

$$2NaCl + H_2SO_4 \rightarrow Na_2SO_4 + 2HCl$$

Atomic weights: Na, 23; Cl, 35.46; H, 1.008; O, 16; S, 32.

1.102 Explain:

a. Oxidation and reduction
b. The periodic law of the chemical elements
c. Radioactivity
d. Acidity

1.103 Cupric sulfide (CuS) ore may be roasted in air, the sulfur driven off as sulfur dioxide and later converted to sulfuric acid. How many pounds acid (93 per cent H_2SO_4) can be made from 1 ton ore that shows 60 per cent copper, allowing for 10 per cent loss sulfur during the process?

Atomic weights: Cu, 63.6; H, 1.00; S, 32; O, 16.

1.104 Describe the commercial method for the production of sodium hydroxide (caustic soda) from soda ash and indicate the type of equipment used for each step in the process. What engineering problems are involved?

1.105 A solution of 4.00 grams of an unknown substance in 200 grams benzene is found to freeze at 4.82°C; the benzene freezes at 5.49°C. Calculate the molecular weight of the substance.

1.106 An aqueous solution of sodium sulfate is saturated at 32°C. Calculate the temperature to which the solution must be cooled to crystallize 60 per cent of the solution as $Na_2SO_4 \cdot 10H_2O$.

1.107 It has been determined by trial mixing that a 1:1½:3 mixture (by volume) with 5 gal water per sack of cement produces a satisfactory mixture of concrete with a 2-in. slump. What quantity of mixed concrete in cubic feet will a barrel of cement produce if the following is known about the cement, sand, and stone aggregate?

	Voids	Unit weight, lb
Cement	0.513	94
Sand	0.360	120
Stone	0.330	105

1.108 How many cubic feet of a gas composed of 28 per cent CO and 72 per cent N_2 (by volume) and measured at 85°F and 100 psig would be required to reduce 1 ton of ore which is 84 per cent Fe_3O_4 to metallic iron? The reactions are:

$$Fe_3O_4 + CO \rightarrow 3FeO + CO_2$$
$$FeO + CO \rightarrow Fe + CO_2$$

Atomic weights: C, 12.00; Fe, 55.84; O, 16.00; N, 14.008

1.109 Balance the chemical equation given below. Atomic weights: Al, 26.97; Fe, 55.84; S, 32.06; O, 16.00.

$$?Al + ?Fe_2(SO_4)_3 \rightarrow Al_2(SO_4)_3 + ?Fe\,SO_4$$

In each of the following questions, 1.110 *to* 1.119, *select one, and only one, correct answer:*

1.110 The chemical most commonly used to speed sedimentation of sewage is: (1) sulfuric acid; (2) copper sulfate; (3) lime; (4) methylene blue; (5) sodium permanganate.

1.111 The gas from sludge digestion tanks is mainly composed of: (1) nitrogen; (2) hydrogen sulfide; (3) carbon dioxide; (4) carbon monoxide; (5) methane.

1.112 The quantity of chlorine in parts per million required to satisfactorily chlorinate sewage is usually: (1) 0–25; (2) 30–60; (3) 65–90; (4) 95–120; (5) 125–150.

1.113 The ratio of oxygen available to the oxygen required for stabilization of sewage is called: (1) biochemical oxygen demand; (2) oxygen-ion concentration; (3) relative stability; (4) bacterial-stability factor; (5) concentration factor.

1.114 Most of the bacteria in sewage are: (1) parasitic; (2) saprophytic; (3) pathogenic; (4) anaerobic; (5) dangerous.

1.115 In the design of grit chambers: (1) temperature is an important factor; (2) baffles are essential; (3) there should be a 5 to 1 ratio of length to depth; (4) the detention period should be at least 30 min; (5) the maximum velocity of flow is 1 ft per sec.

1.116 In an Imhoff tank: (1) the effluent contains very little dissolved oxygen; (2) there are no settling compartments; (3) the sludge and fresh sewage are well mixed to give complete digestion; (4) the sludge and raw sewage are not mixed; (5) much larger settling compartments are required than for an equivalent septic tank.

1.117 The per cent of total solids in most domestic sewage is approximately: (1) 0.01; (2) 0.1; (3) 1.0; (4) 10; (5) 100.

1.118 Intermittent sand filters are primarily used to: (1) remove offensive odors; (2) supply fertilizer to farmers; (3) oxidize putrescible matter; (4) neutralize sludge; (5) remove solids from sewage.

1.119 To divert excessive flow from combined sewers designers often use: (1) a Cipoletti weir; (2) a V-notch weir; (3) a broad-crested weir; (4) a submerged weir; (5) a leaping weir.

1.120 A batch of concrete consisted of 200 lb fine aggregate, 350 lb coarse aggregate, 94 lb cement, and 5 gal water. The specific gravity of the sand and gravel may be taken as 2.65 and that of the cement as 3.10.

a. What was the total volume of concrete produced?

b. What was the weight of concrete in place per cubic foot?

c. How much by weight of each ingredient is required to produce 1 cu yd concrete?

1.121 Explain (with chemical equations) the action of chlorine when applied as a disinfectant in the form of gas. Give details of the OT-A test for chlorine residual.

1.122 Give with brief explanations the various procedures that may be used for removal of color and odor. What are commonly used coagulants? State advantages of each. State aids used in coagulation such as additional "chemicals" and mechanical devices.

1.123 Hardness, alkalinity, and acidity are generally reported as ppm of calcium carbonate; turbidity and color as ppm; pH as a number. Explain these and describe the test procedures used in each case.

1.124 Determine the quantities *by weight* of cement, sand, and broken stone required for a 1-cu-yd batch of concrete of 1:2:3 mix if 6 gal water per bag of cement are used. The materials used have the following characteristics:

1 bag cement (1 cu ft) weighs	94 lb
1 cu ft sand weighs	105 lb
1 cu ft broken stone weighs	100 lb
Specific gravity of the cement is	3.1
Specific gravity of the sand is	2.7
Specific gravity of the broken stone is	2.7

1.125 In designing a concrete mix, what factors should be considered?

ELECTRICITY

1.201 An electric truck is propelled by a d-c motor driven by a 110-volt storage battery. The truck is required to exert a tractive effort of 200 lb at a speed of 5 mph. The over-all efficiency of the motor and drive is 70 per cent. What current is taken from the battery?

1.202 In the electric circuit shown, if the total resistance from A to B is 16 ohms, find the resistance R_2.

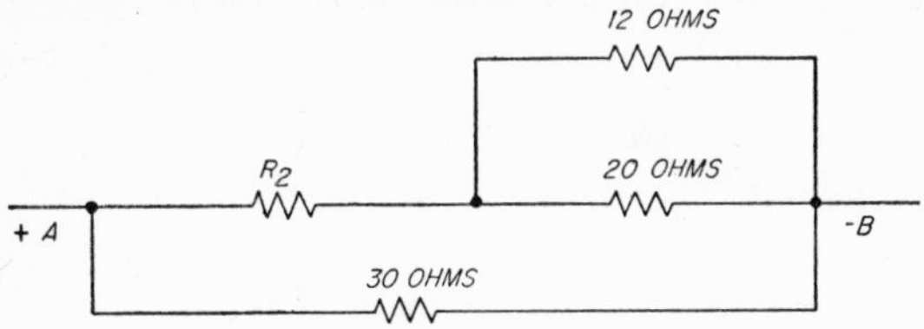

Fig. 1.202

1.203 Determine the current supplied by the battery in the network shown. Resistance in ohms are as indicated.

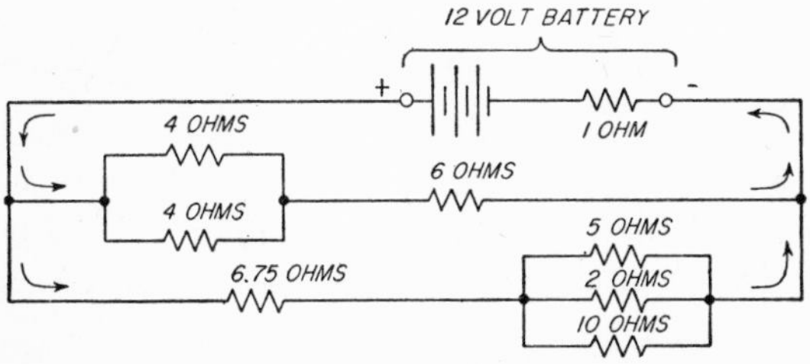

Fig. 1.203

1.204 Two coils of wire have resistance of 5 and 17 ohms respectively. Find the voltage used by each and the current flowing through each if the two are connected in parallel to the terminals of a 6-volt battery.

1.205 In the electrolytic refining of copper, the original weight of the cathode is 15.0 lb. After 15 days in a bath of $CuSO_4$ and free H_2SO_4, the weight of the electrode is 300 lb. Assuming 100 per cent efficiency, what total ampere-hours are required and what is the current flow? If the cathode is 40 by 36 in., what is the current density?

1.206 A 50-kva 2,300/230-volt 60-cycle single-phase transformer has a core loss of 400 watts and a full-load copper loss of 600 watts. Calculate its efficiency at 100 per cent load and 90 per cent power factor. At what per cent load will maximum efficiency occur?

1.207 Two groups of electric lights are connected in series across a 220-volt line. The first group has 25 lights in parallel, and the second group has 15 lights in parallel. Each light will carry 0.9 amp at 110 volts. Assuming the resistance of the lights to be constant at varying voltages, what is the potential difference across each group? What is the current in each light?

1.208 A d-c load of 10 kw at 120 volts is to be supplied from a copper line which has a diameter of 0.204 in. The distance from generator to load is 500 ft. What is the required voltage of the generator and the power loss in the line?

1.209 Two condensers of 2 and 10 μf capacitance are connected in parallel, and this combination is connected in series with a third condenser of 8 μf capacitance across a 120-volt d-c supply circuit. Find the charge of each condenser and the voltage across each. What is the total energy stored in the three condensers?

1.210 *a.* Two storage cells connected in parallel supply jointly a current of 20 amp to an external circuit. One cell has an emf of 2.1 volts and the other an emf of 2.0 volts, and each has an internal resistance of 0.05 ohm. Find the current flowing through each cell.

b. Explain why the specific gravity of the electrolyte of a lead storage cell decreases as it discharges.

1.211 A d-c generator has four poles with faces 6 in. square and has a flux density in the air gap of 40,000 lines per sq in. The machine has 360 conductors arranged in four parallel paths through the armature. Compute the emf of the generator when driven at 1,200 rpm.

1.212 Two storage batteries of 10 and 15 volts and an internal resistance of 1 and 2 ohms respectively have their positive terminals attached to one end of a variable resistance and their negative terminals to the other end. What must be the value of this resistance in order that the same current will flow from each battery?

1.213 Could two 30-watt and one 60-watt 120-volt lamps be connected across a 240-volt circuit in such a way as to give normal illumination? If so, show circuit diagram and explain.

1.214 Electrical resistances of 7 ohms and of 11 ohms are connected in parallel and the combination is then placed in series with a resistance of 15 ohms. The whole combination is connected across 110-volt d-c mains. What current flows through each resistance?

1.215 A d-c motor having an efficiency of 85 per cent is rated 5 hp and 220 volts. It is located 150 ft from the supply lines. If a maximum voltage drop of 5 per cent based on rated voltage is permitted, recommend the wire size for overhead wiring.

1.216 How many 100-watt lamps can be placed in a 115-volt circuit, as shown, which is protected by a 15-amp fuse? (The fuse "burns out" and opens the circuit when the current through it rises to a value of 15 amp.)

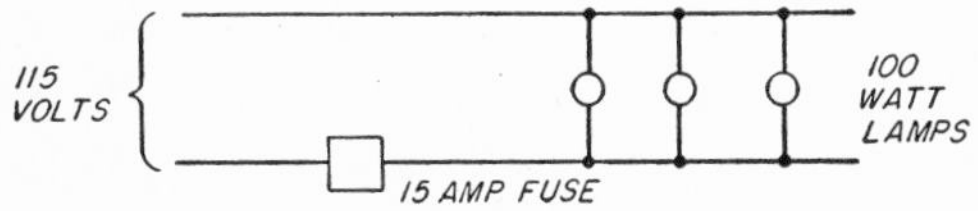

FIG. 1.216

1.217 If two voltmeters are connected in series to a power line and the first voltmeter, which has a resistance of 16,000 ohms, reads 60 volts, what is the voltage between the wires of the power lines provided the second voltmeter's resistance is 20,000 ohms?

1.218 A circuit consists of three devices and a 30-volt battery having an internal resistance of 1 ohm. One of the devices, which has 7 ohms resistance, is connected in series with the other two, and these, one of 3 ohms and the other of 6 ohms resistance, are connected in parallel. Find:

a. The voltage drop on the 7-ohm device
b. The power expended in the 3-ohm device
c. The current in the 6-ohm device

1.219 A 10-hp 220-volt d-c shunt motor has armature and field resistances of 0.25 and 100 ohms respectively. The full-load efficiency is 83 per cent. Determine the value of the starting resistance in order that the starting current will not exceed 200 per cent of the full-load value.

1.220 A circuit consisting of a 63-ohm resistance, a 0.15-henry inductance, and a 15-μf capacitor connected in series, is placed on a 110-volt 60-cycle supply line. Find the value of the current in the circuit.

1.221 A three-phase Y-connected induction motor operating on 220 volts has a power factor of 70 per cent and an efficiency of 82 per cent when delivering 8 hp. What is the current in the phase windings and what is the voltage across each?

1.222 Explain how the plate resistance, the amplification factor, and the mutual conductance may be calculated for a three-element electron tube from a family of plate-characteristic curves for the tube.

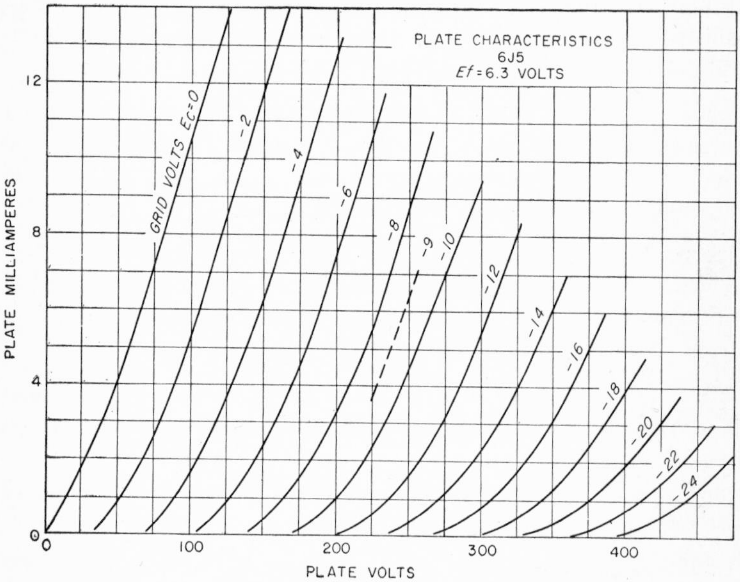

FIG. 1.222

1.223 If the current from a short-circuited 1.5-volt dry cell is 25 amp, what is the internal resistance of the cell? The resistance of the short circuit is negligible. If this cell is connected through a 1-ohm external circuit, find the current and the reading of a voltmeter connected to its terminals.

1.224 A series *L-C-R* circuit with inductance of 100 henrys has a transient resonant frequency of 5 cps.

a. What is the period?

b. The capacitance?

Neglect effect of *R* on frequency.

1.225 Same circuit as in 1.224. The condenser is given an initial charge Q, and at time $t = 0$, is switched to discharge through L and R in series.

a. Write the differential equation.

b. What is the physical meaning of each term?

HYDRAULICS

1.301 Compute the total normal pressure on the interior sides and bottom of a cylindrical water tower 40 ft in diameter containing water to a depth of 60 ft.

1.302 A vertical gate 4 ft wide and 6 ft high hinged at the upper edge is kept closed by the pressure of water standing 8 ft deep over its top edge. What force applied normally at the bottom of the gate would be required to open it?

1.303 How far below the water surface is it necessary to immerse a vertical plane surface 3 ft square, two edges of square being horizontal, in order that center of pressure shall be but 1 in. from center of gravity?

1.304 A wood-stave pipe 48 in. in inside diameter is to resist a maximum water pressure of 150 psi. If the staves are bound together by flat steel bands 4 in. wide by ¾ in. thick find the spacing distance of the latter in order that they may not be stressed above 15,000 psi.

1.305 A rectangular caisson is to be sunk, in which to build the foundation for a bridge pier. It is in the form of an open box, 50 by 20 ft in plan, and 23-ft deep. If it weighs 75 tons, how deep will it sink when launched? The water being 20 ft deep, what additional load will sink it to the bottom?

1.306 A flat-bottomed scow is built with vertical sides and straight sloping ends. Its length on deck is 80 ft, and on the bottom, 65 ft; its width is 20 ft, and its vertical depth is 12 ft. How much water will it draw if it weighs 250 tons?

1.307 A tank with vertical sides is 4 ft square, 10 ft deep, and is filled to a depth of 9 ft with water. By how much, if at all, will the pressure on one side of the tank be changed if a cube of wood, specific gravity 0.5, measuring 2 ft on an edge is placed in the water so as to float with one face horizontal?

1.308 Water from a reservoir is pumped over a hill through a pipe 3 ft in diameter, and a pressure of 30 psi is maintained at the summit, where the pipe is 300 ft above the reservoir. The quantity pumped is 49.5 cfs, and by reason of friction in the pump and pipe there is 10 ft of head lost between reservoir and summit. What amount of energy must be furnished the water each second by the pump?

1.309 A centrifugal pump draws water from a pit through a vertical 12-in. pipe which extends below the water surface. It discharges into a 6-in. horizontal pipe 15 ft above the water surface. While pumping 2 cfs, a pressure gage on the discharge pipe reads 24 psi, and a gage on the suction pipe registers 5 psi below atmosphere. Both gages are close to the pump and are separated by a vertical distance of 5 ft. What is the horsepower output of the pump?

1.310 A steel box, rectangular in plan, floats with a draft of 4 ft. If the box is 20 ft long, 10 ft wide, and 6 ft deep, compute the time necessary to sink it to its top edge by opening a standard orifice, 6 in. in diameter, in its bottom. Neglect the thickness of the vertical sides, and assume $c = 0.60$.

1.311 A rectangular weir with end contractions has a crest 10 ft long and 1.00 ft above the bottom of the channel. If the channel width be 16 ft, what amount of water will be discharged under a head of 0.875 ft? Neglect the velocity of approach.

1.312 A suppressed weir having a crest length of 7.00 ft, a height of 1.00 ft, discharges under a head of 0.875 ft. Compute the rate of discharge. Neglect the velocity of approach.

1.313 Two reservoirs with a difference in level of 100 ft are connected by 12,000 ft of 12-in. cast-iron pipe. Compute the rate of discharge.

1.314 An 18-in. cast-iron pipe is discharging 7,500 gpm. At a point 4,000 ft from the supplying reservoir (measured on pipe) the center of the pipe is 180 ft below the reservoir surface. What pressure, in pounds per square inch, is to be expected there?

1.315 A pump at elevation 1,000 is pumping 2.00 cfs through 8,000 ft of 6-in. pipe to a reservoir whose level is at elevation 1,250. What pressure will be found in the pipe at a point where the elevation is 1,100 ft above datum and the distance (measured along the pipe) from the pump is 3,200 ft? Assume $f = 0.0225$.

1.316 From a reservoir *A* whose surface is at elevation 800 water is pumped through 4,000 ft of 12-in. pipe across a valley to a second reservoir *B* whose level is at elevation 900. If, during pumping, the pressure is 100 psi at a point *M* on the pipe, midway of its length and at elevation 700, compute the rate of discharge and the horsepower exerted by the pumps ($f = 0.02$).

1.317 Reservoir *A* is at elevation 1,000 ft above datum. From reservoir *A* an 8-in. pipeline leads 3,000 ft to point *Y* at elevation 800, at which point it branches into two lines: a 6-in. line running 2,000 ft to reservoir *B*, elevation 850, and a 6-in. line running 1,000 ft to reservoir *C*, elevation 875. At what rate will water be delivered to each reservoir? Assume $f = 0.02$ in all cases.

1.318 Reservoir *R* is at grade 400. From reservoir *R* an 18-in. pipe, which is to carry 7 cfs of water, leads 2,000 ft to grade 300 at point *Y*. It there divides and branch *A*, 12 in. in diameter, leads 13,000 ft to reservoir *A*, which is at grade 250. Branch *B* leads 4,000 ft to reservoir *B*, which is at grade 50.

Neglect all losses except from friction, assume f as 0.02 in each case, and find the diameter of branch *B*.

1.319 A 48-in. main, carrying 75.4 cfs, branches at a point *A* into two pipes, one 2,000 ft long, 3 ft in diameter, and one 6,000 ft long, 2 ft in diameter. Both pipes come together at a point *B* and continue as a single 48-in. pipe. The following value of f may be assumed: $f = 0.0210$, 0.022, and 0.023 respectively for the 48-in., 36-in., and 24-in. pipes. Compute the rate of flow in the branch pipes.

1.320 A pipeline 25,000 ft long and 5 ft in diameter supplies eight nozzles with water from a reservoir whose level is 600 ft above the nozzles. Each nozzle has an opening 3 in. in diameter and a coefficient of discharge and velocity of 0.95. Assuming $f = 0.017$, find the aggregate horsepower available in the jets.

1.321 A venturi meter has an area ratio of 9 to 1, the larger diameter being 24 in. During flow the recorded pressure head in the large section is 36 ft, and that at the throat 9 ft. If c is 0.99, what rate of discharge through the meter is indicated?

1.322 A canal has a bottom width of 30 ft and side slopes of 3 horizontal to 1 vertical. If the water depth is 4 ft and the slope 1 in 1,000, compute the probable velocity and discharge, using Kutter's C and $n = 0.02$.

1.323 A circular brick conduit 5 ft in diameter flows half full with a slope of 1 in 1,000. Compute its probable discharge using Manning's coefficient ($n = 0.015$).

1.324 A rectangular timber flume 10 ft wide by 5 ft deep discharges 200 cfs. If the same material had been used for a trapezoidal section having the same perimeter, what would have been the greatest discharge possible with the same hydraulic slope?

1.325 Compute the probable rate of flow of water in cubic feet per second in a 10-in. vitrified-tile circular pipe with water $7\frac{1}{2}$ in. deep over the invert. The pipe is laid on a slope of 1 ft per 100 ft.

MATHEMATICS AND MEASUREMENTS

1.401 An observer wishes to determine the height of a tower. He takes sights at the top of the tower from points A and B, which are 50 ft apart, at the same elevation, and on a direct line with the tower. The vertical angle at point A is 30° and at point B is 40°. What is the height of the tower?

1.402 Express the equation of the straight line passing through points $x_1 = 2, y_1 = 2$ and $x_2 = 4, y_2 = 3$ in the form $y = mx + b$.

1.403 Solve

$$x^2 + y^2 = 5z$$
$$x^2 - y^2 = 3z$$

How many and what numerical values for x, y, and z will satisfy these simultaneous equations?

1.404 The area of a circle is 89.42 sq in. What is

a. The diameter of the circle?

b. The circumference?

c. The length of a side of a regular hexagon inscribed in this circle?

1.405 A vein of ore has a strike of N45°E., i.e., it intersects level ground along a line having this bearing. The vein dips westerly at an angle of 15° with the horizontal. A drift (slightly sloping mine opening following the vein) has been opened in the vein on a bearing of N30°E. Determine the per cent of grade of this drift.

1.406 The distance between two points measured with a steel tape was recorded as 916.58 ft. Later, the tape was checked and found to be only 99.9 ft long. What is the true distance between the points?

1.407 Solve for x (show all work):

$$4 + \frac{x+3}{x-3} - \frac{4x^2}{x^2-9} = \frac{x+9}{x+3}$$

1.408 A circular piece of tin 24 in. in diameter has a triangular hole 9 by 12 by 15 in. The vertex of the triangle at the intersection of the 9- and 12-in. sides is at the center of the circle. Find the position of the center of gravity of the piece of tin.

1.409 Compute the moment of inertia of the area shown with respect to its centroidal x and y axes.

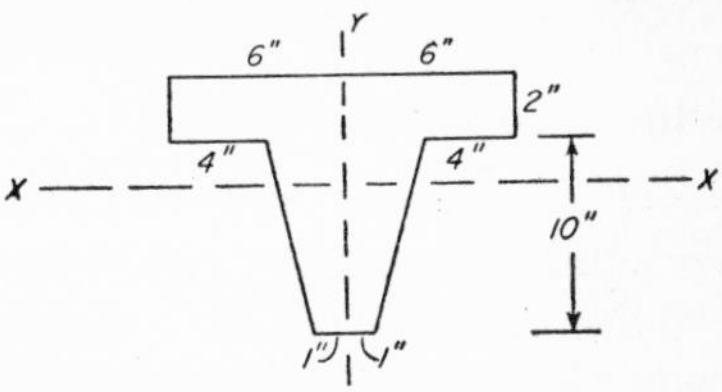

FIG. 1.409

1.410 Locate the centroids of the accompanying figure with respect to the axes shown and determine the moments of inertia with respect to the axes shown.

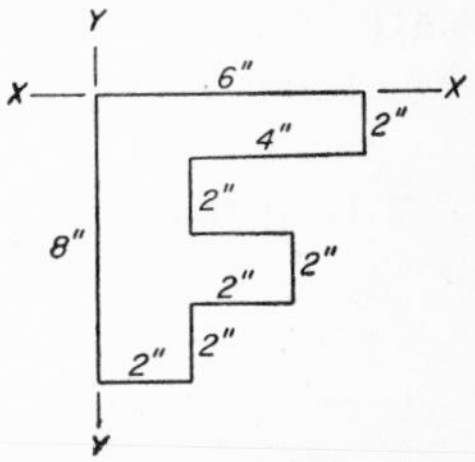

FIG. 1.410

1.411 Two planes leave Cleveland for Jacksonville, a distance of 900 miles. The four-motored plane (A) travels at a ground speed of 90 mph faster than the two-motored plane (B). Plane A arrives in Jacksonville 2 hr 15 min ahead of plane B. What were the respective ground speeds of the two planes?

1.412 Twice the sum of two numbers is 28. The sum of the squares of the two numbers is 100. What is the product of the two numbers?

1.413 A computer was told that a survey had been made of a certain rectangular field but the dimensions had been lost. An assistant remembered that if the field had been 100 ft longer and 25 ft narrower, the area would have been increased 2,500 sq ft, and that if it had been 100 ft shorter and 50 ft wider, the area would have been decreased 5,000 sq ft. What was the area of the field and what were its dimensions?

1.414 If the outside diameter of a locomotive driving wheel minus its steel tire is 62.378 in. and the inside diameter of the steel tire at 65°F is 62.263 in., to what temperature (Fahrenheit) must the tire be heated to just fit the wheel?

1.415 A certain steel tape is known to be 100.000 ft long at a temperature of 70°F. When the tape is at a temperature of 10°F, what tape reading corresponds to a distance of 90.000 ft?

1.416 Eight men can dig 150 ft of trench in 7 hr. Three men can backfill 100 ft of the trench in 4 hr. How long will it take 10 men to dig and fill 200 ft of trench?

1.417 A man owns two square lots of unequal size, together containing 15,025 sq ft. If the lots were contiguous, it would require 530 ft of fence to embrace them in a single enclosure of six sides. Find the area of each lot.

1.418 Given the semicubical parabola $y^3 = x^3$.

a. Find the area of the part enclosed by the line $x = 4$ and the x axis.

b. Find the area under the curve $y = x^3 + 3x^2$ and the x axis between $x = 1$ and $x = 3$.

c. Differentiate the following:

$$4x^2 + 17x$$

and

$$ax^2 + b^{1/2}$$

d. Integrate the following:

$$(7x^3 + 4x^2)\ dx$$

and

$$x \cos (2x^2 + 7)\ dx$$

1.419 A line was measured with a steel tape when the temperature was 30°C. The measured length of the line was found to be 1,256.271 ft. The tape was afterward tested when the temperature was 10°C and it was found to be 100.042 ft long. What was the true length of the line if the coefficient of linear expansion of tape was 0.000011 per °C?

1.420 The sum of three numbers in arithmetical progression is 45. If 2 is added to the first number, 3 to the second, and 7 to the third, the new numbers are in geometrical progression. Find the numbers.

1.421 Solve algebraically:

a.

$$\begin{aligned} 4x^2 + 7y^2 &= 32 \\ 11y^2 - 3x^2 &= 41 \end{aligned}$$

b.

$$\begin{aligned} x + 2y - z &= 6 \\ 2x - y + 3z &= -13 \\ 3x - 2y + 3z &= -16 \end{aligned}$$

1.422 *a.* Given $\cos 2A = 2 \cos^2 A - 1$, find: cos 75°

b. In a circle of unit radius, sketch a central angle B in the second quadrant and show lines that are equal in length to sin A; cos A; tan A; in *a*.

1.423 A box is to be constructed from a piece of zinc 20 in. square by cutting equal squares from each corner and turning up the zinc to form the sides. What is the volume of the largest box that can be so constructed? Solve by use of calculus.

1.424 Determine the volume of a right-truncated triangular prism with the following dimensions: let the corners of the triangular base be defined by a, b, and c; the length of $ab = 10$ ft, $bc = 9$ ft, and $ca = 12$ ft. The sides at a, b, and c are perpendicular to the triangular base and have heights of 8.6 ft, 7.1 ft, and 5.5 ft, respectively.

1.425 A 6 per cent upgrade meets a 3 per cent downgrade at elevation 100.00 at station 10 + 00. If the parabolic vertical curve is 600 ft long, find the station of the high point of the curve. Plot the profile of the curve, giving all pertinent information thereon.

MECHANICS (KINETICS)

1.501 An elevator weighing 2,000 lb attains an upward velocity of 16 fps in 4 sec with uniform acceleration. What is the tension in the supporting cables?

1.502 Solve for the tension in the cables of the elevator described in problem 1.501 if the tension is reduced so that the elevator comes to rest in a distance of 5 ft.

1.503 A body weighing 40 lb starts from rest and slides down a plane at an angle of 30° with the horizontal for which the coefficient of friction $f = 0.3$. How far will it move during the third second? How long will it require for it to move 60 ft?

1.504 A car and its load weigh 6,000 lb and the center of gravity is 2 ft from the ground and midway between the front and rear wheels, which are 120 in. apart. The car is brought to rest from a speed of 30 mph in 5 sec by means of the brakes. Compute the normal pressures on each of the front wheels and on each of the rear wheels.

1.505 A body weighing 1,000 lb falls 6 in. and strikes a 2,000-lb (per in.) spring. What is the deformation of the spring?

1.506 A freight car weighing 100,000 lb is moving with a velocity of 2 fps when it strikes a bumping post. Assuming the drawbar spring on the car to take all of the compression, what must be the scale of the spring in order that the compression shall not exceed 2.5 in.?

1.507 If the coefficient of friction under the blocks M and N is 0.20, what is the acceleration of the blocks, the tension in the cord, and the time to move 15 ft from rest?

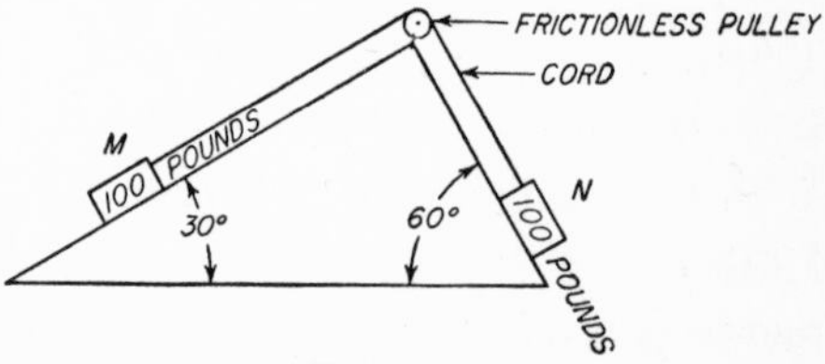

FIG. 1.507

1.508 The three bodies, X, Y, and Z, weigh 10, 20, and 30 lb, respectively. If they are supported in the position shown and then released simultaneously, what will be the velocity and position of each body 1 sec later? (Neglect mass of cords and pulleys.)

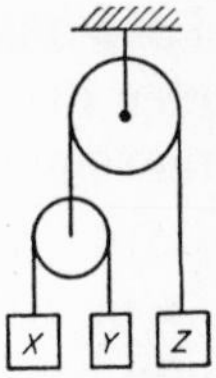

FIG. 1.508

1.509 A 60-ton freight car starts from rest and runs 100 ft down a 1 per cent grade, then strikes a bumping post. If train resistance is 10 lb per ton, what is the velocity of striking? If the drawbar spring has a scale of 100,000 lb per in. and is assumed to take all of the impact, how much will it be shortened?

1.510 A car weighing 40 tons is switched to a 2 per cent upgrade with a velocity of 30 mph. If train resistance is 10 lb per ton, how far up the grade will it go? If the car is then allowed to run back, what velocity will it have at the foot of the grade? If the track is then level, how far from the foot of the grade will it run?

1.511 Determine the superelevation of the outer rail of a railroad track on a 10° curve to give equal rail pressures on a car when moving with a speed of 45 mph. If a car weighing 100,000 lb with its center of gravity 5 ft above the track has a speed of 60 mph on this curve, and if the track now has a superelevation of only 8 in., what is the pressure of the outer rail on the car normal to the ties? (A 10° curve is one on which a chord 100 ft long subtends an angle of 10° at the center.)

1.512 A concrete highway curve with a radius of 500 ft is banked to give lateral pressure equivalent to $f = 0.15$. For what coefficient of friction will skidding impend for a speed of 60 mph?

1.513 A girder weighing 20,000 lb is suspended by a cable 100 ft long. What horizontal pull is necessary to hold it 5 ft from the vertical position? What is the tension in the cable as the girder is allowed to swing back through its vertical position?

1.514 A shot is fired at an angle of 45° with the horizontal and a velocity of 300 ft per sec. Find the height and the range of the projectile.

1.515 Compute the theoretical muzzle velocity required to give a projectile a maximum range of 40 miles. Compute the maximum height to which the projectile will rise.

1.516 A cast-iron governor ball 3 in. in diameter has its center 18 in. from the point of support. Neglecting the weight of the arm itself, find the tension in the arm and the speed of rotation if the angle with the vertical axis is 60°.

1.517 A car is moving on a horizontal track around a curve of 1,000 ft radius with a speed of 60 mph. A weight of 25 lb is suspended from the ceiling by a 6 ft cord. What is the tension in the cord, the angle the cord makes with the vertical, and the horizontal displacement of the weight?

1.518 The muzzle velocity of a projectile is 1,500 fps and the distance of the target is 10 miles. What must be the angle of elevation of the gun?

1.519 Determine the moment of inertia of a cast-iron cylinder 24 in. in outside diameter and 16 in. high with respect to its geometric axis. The cylinder wall is 1 in. thick. Cast iron weighs 450 lb per cu ft.

1.520 A steel disk 40 in. in diameter and 4 in. thick has a cylindrical hole 10 in. in diameter at the center and another 12 in. in diameter, 12 in. from the center. What is the moment of inertia with respect to the geometric axis of the 40-in. disk? Steel weighs 490 lb per cu ft.

1.521 A flywheel is brought from rest up to a speed of 1,500 rpm in 1 min. What is the average angular acceleration α, and the number of revolutions until the wheel stops? What is the velocity at the end of 40 sec?

1.522 The rim of a 36-in. wheel on a brake-shoe testing machine has a speed of 60 mph when the brake is dropped. It comes to rest when the rim has traveled a tangential distance of 500 ft. What is the angular acceleration and the number of revolutions?

1.523 A steel hemisphere 6 in. in diameter is to rotate about an axis parallel to its axis of symmetry and 12 in. distant from it. The axis of the rod which connects it to the axis of rotation is 0.5 in. from the diametral plane. Compute the induced bending moment in the rod when the hemisphere is rotating at a speed of 300 rpm. How far from the diametral plane should the rod be attached so that there will be no bending moment in it?

1.524 A steel rod 24 in. long is rotating about a vertical axis through one end. If it stands at an angle of 60° with the axis, at what speed is it rotating?

1.525 A cast-iron flywheel 12 ft in outside diameter has a rim 4 in. thick and 18 in. wide. If the flywheel is rotating at 240 rpm, what is the unit of centrifugal tensile stress in the rim if the tension in the arms is neglected? Cast iron weighs 450 lb per cu ft.

MECHANICS (STATICS)

1.601 Find the magnitude and direction of the resultant of a set of four vertical forces in the same plane. The first force is 10 lb upward; the next force, 5 ft away, is 10 lb downward; the third, 4 ft beyond the second, is 10 lb downward; the fourth, 3 ft beyond the third, is 10 lb upward.

1.602 A long wall stands on three rows of piles with the rows spaced 3 ft center to center. The spacings of piles parallel to the wall are 2 ft 6 in., 4 ft 0 in., and 6 ft 0 in. center to center in the first, second, and third rows, respectively. The resultant of the vertical loads is located midway between the first and second rows and amounts to 20,000 lb per lin ft of wall. What are the loads per pile in each row?

1.603 A beam 12 ft long and simply supported at each end, has a uniformly distributed load of 1,000 lb per ft extending from the left end to a point 4 ft away. There is also a clockwise couple of 10,000 ft-lb applied at the center of the beam. Draw the shear and moment diagrams for the beam and give all the necessary values. Neglect the weight of the beam.

1.604 Draw shear and moment diagrams for a 20-ft beam, simply supported at the ends. The beam carries a uniform load of 1,000 lb per ft (including its own weight) and three concentrated loads of 2,000, 4,000, and 6,000 lb acting respectively at the left quarter point, the center point, and the right quarter point.

1.605 A beam 20 ft long carries a uniform load of 2,000 lb per lin ft, including its own weight, on two supports 14 ft apart.

The right end of the beam cantilevers 2 ft and the left end cantilevers 4 ft. Draw the shear and moment diagrams and compute the positions and amounts of maximum bending moments.

1.606 A beam 24 ft long rests on two supports, one at its right end and the other 6 ft from its left end. The beam carries a uniform load of 1,000 lb per lin ft over its entire length and a concentrated load of 15,000 lb at the middle of the 18-ft span. Calculate the reactions, draw the shear and moment diagrams, and calculate the position and amount of maximum bending moment.

1.607 The left-hand half of a beam on a 30-ft span has a uniform load of 4,000 lb per lin ft. A concentrated load of 30,000 lb is located 10 ft from the right end. Draw the shear and moment diagrams.

1.608 Draw shear and moment diagrams for this beam and pick out a timber beam that will satisfy the maximum moment and shear. *Notice carefully:* use a dressed timber having a width equal to one-half the depth. Maximum allowable unit stresses are to be: in bending, 1,750 psi, and in shear, 128 psi.

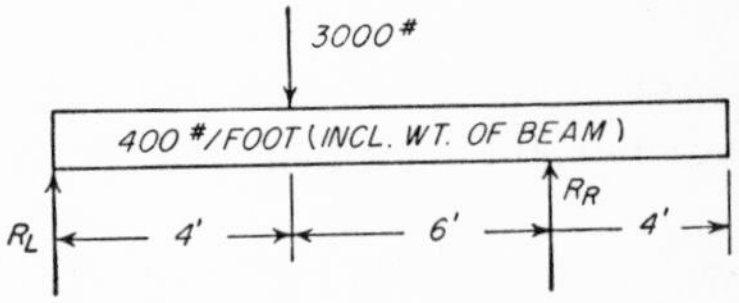

Fig. 1.608

1.609 Find the maximum plus and minus moments. I is uniform throughout.

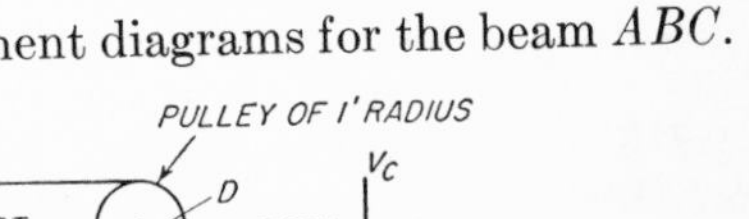

Fig. 1.609

1.610 Draw the shear and moment diagrams for the beam ABC.

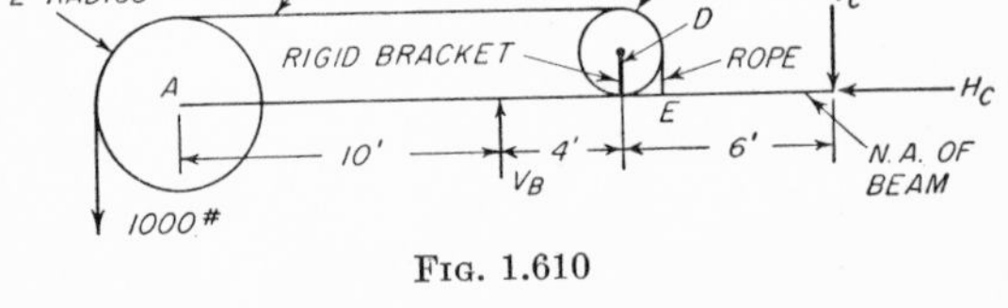

Fig. 1.610

1.611 A 1,000-lb weight A is to be supported by two wires. The first wire BA runs to a ring at point B, 3 ft above A and 4 ft to the left. The second wire CA runs to a ring at C, 4 ft above

A and 3 ft to the right. If points *A*, *B*, and *C* are in the same vertical plane, find the horizontal and vertical components of the stress in the wires at points *B* and *C* and the stress in each wire.

1.612 A painter's scaffold 20 ft long and weighing 150 lb is supported in a horizontal position by vertical ropes attached at equal distances from the ends of the scaffold. Find the greatest distance from the ends that the ropes may be attached so as to permit a 200-lb man to stand safely at one end of the scaffold.

1.613 A 20-ft ladder stands on a rough horizontal floor and leans against a vertical, smooth wall, the foot of the ladder being 8 ft out from the wall. Halfway up the ladder is a weight of 150 lb. What are the horizontal and vertical components of the reactions against the top end and the bottom end of the ladder? Neglect the weight of the ladder.

1.614 To what height could the water rise behind a rectangular masonry wall 6 ft thick and 15 ft high without causing an intensity of pressure at the toe greater than twice the average pressure on the base? Assume that concrete weighs 150 lb per cu ft and there is no seepage causing uplift against the bottom of the wall. Water weighs 62.5 lb per cu ft.

1.615 Is this wall safe against overturning about point *A* if the masonry weighs 150 lb per cu ft and the earth weighs 100 lb per cu ft? The horizontal pressure of the earth against the masonry wall is equal to *cwh*, where *cw* is equal to 30 psf and *h* is the distance down from the top of the wall in feet.

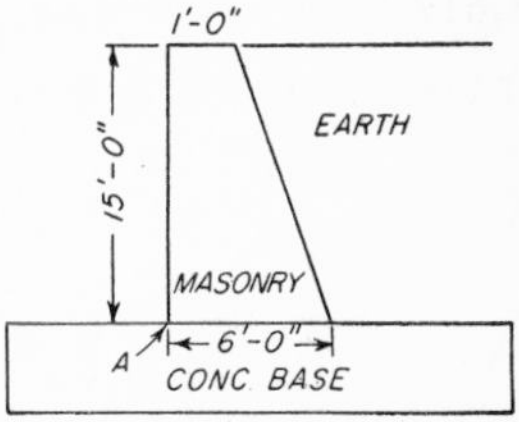

FIG. 1.615

1.616 Where shall a truck be placed on a 30-ft span to give the greatest bending moment? The loads are 4 tons on the front axle and 16 tons on the rear axle. The distance between axles is 14 ft. Calculate the maximum shear that this truck will induce in the bridge.

1.617 A tractor and semitrailer with axle loads as shown is a live load on a 100-ft simple span bridge girder.

a. How far is the 8-kip load from the end of the span when this load gives maximum moment?

b. Calculate the maximum moment due to this loading.
c. Determine the maximum shear due to this load.

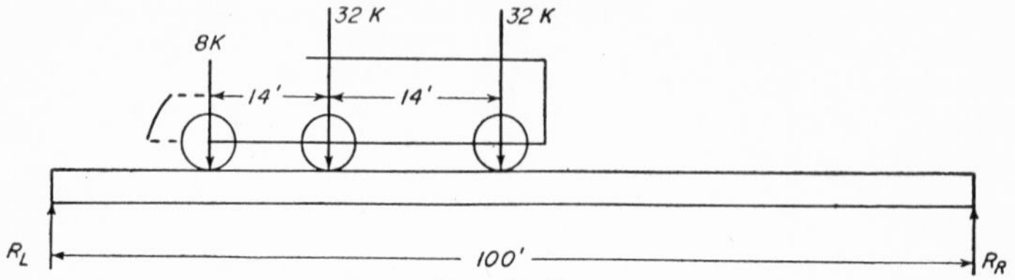

FIG. 1.617

1.618 Draw shear and moment diagrams for beams *AB*, *CD*, and *EF*. Assume all beams as "simple beams."

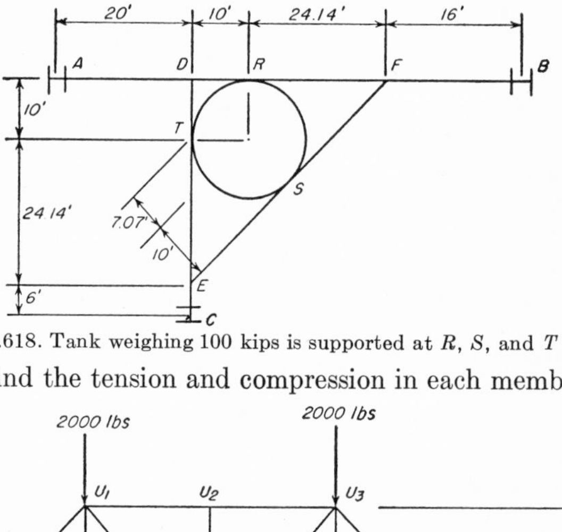

FIG. 1.618. Tank weighing 100 kips is supported at *R*, *S*, and *T* only.

1.619 Find the tension and compression in each member.

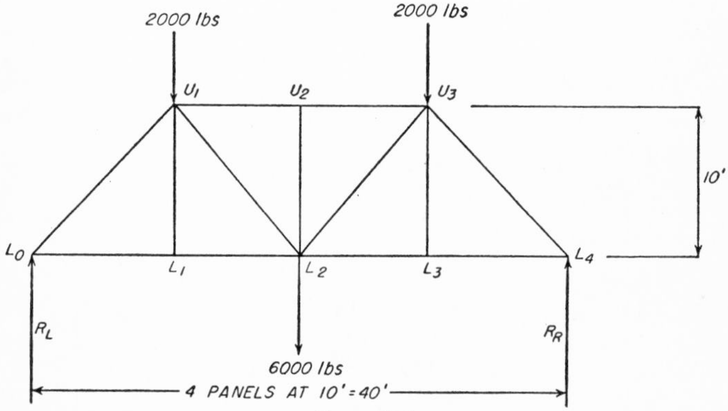

FIG. 1.619

1.620 In the roof truss shown, determine the stresses in members L_0L_1, U_1U_2, and U_1L_2. State which members are in tension or compression.

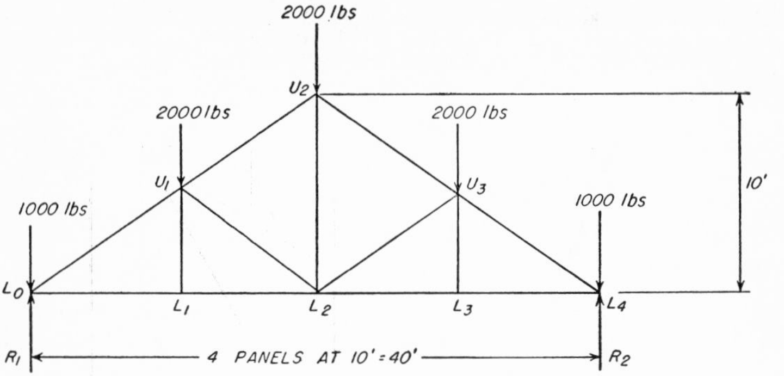

FIG. 1.620

1.621 Determine the stress in the members of the roof truss shown.

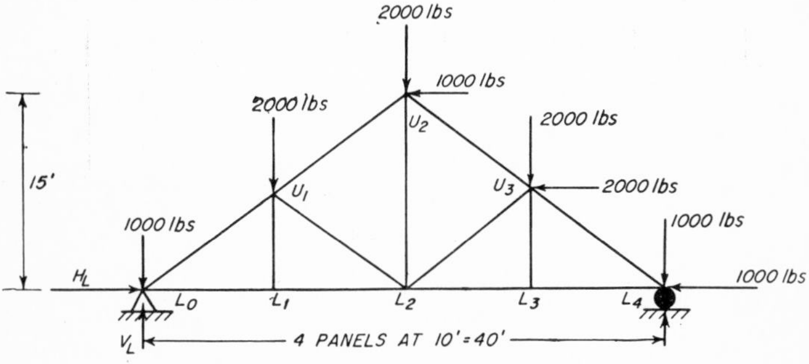

FIG. 1.621

1.622 For the deck truss shown compute the magnitude and direction (tension or compression) of the stress in the member U_2U_3, and in the diagonals U_0L_1 and U_1L_2.

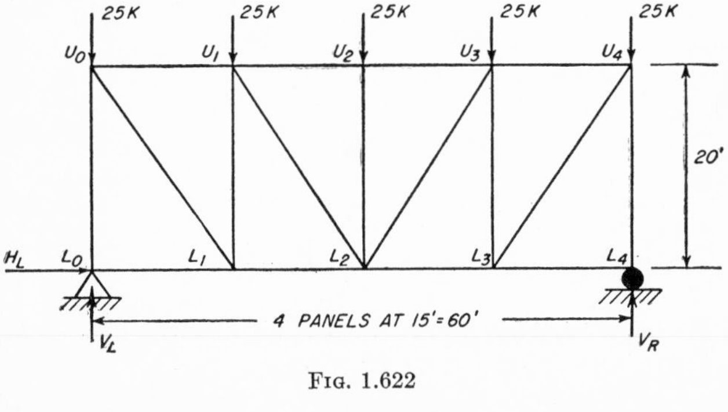

FIG. 1.622

1.623 Determine the amount and character of the stress in each member of the truss shown. Place answers on your sketch of truss.

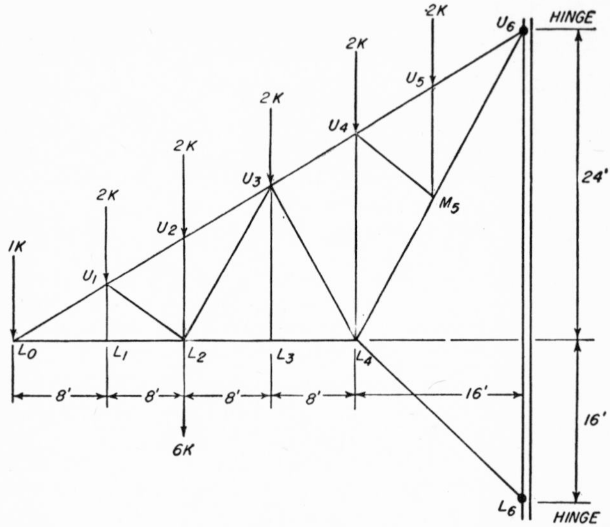

FIG. 1.623

1.624 Determine the kind and amount of stress in each member of this truss.

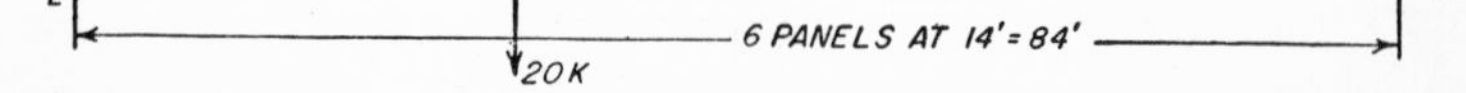

FIG. 1.624

1.625 The space structure shown in Fig. 1.625 supports a 2,400-lb horizontal load. Determine:

a. The vertical component of stresses in member *AB*
b. The *X* component of stress in member *AD*
c. The *Y* component of stress in member *AC*
d. The total stress in member *AD*

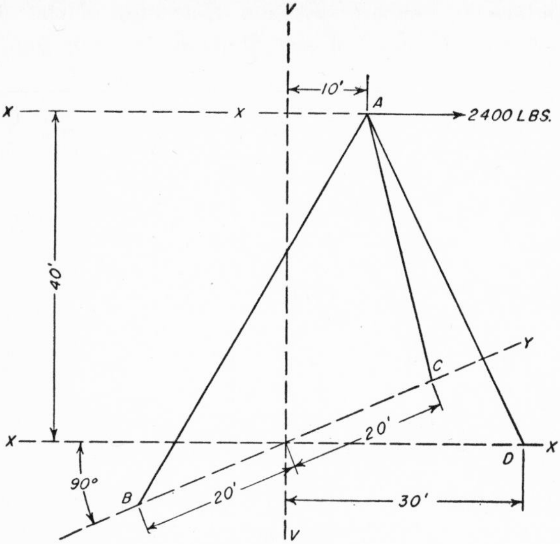

FIG. 1.625

THERMODYNAMICS

1.701 Define: (*a*) latent heat (*b*) specific heat (*c*) heat of fusion (*d*) Btu (*e*) absolute temperature (*f*) calorie (*g*) watt.

1.702 Thirty pounds of ice at 32°F is placed in 100 lb of water at 100°F. If no heat is lost or added to the mixture, what will be the temperature when equilibrium is reached? (The latent heat of ice may be taken as 144 Btu per lb.)

1.703 A small swimming pool 25 by 75 ft is to be filled with water at a temperature of 70°F to a depth of 5 ft. Hot water at 160°F and cold water at 40°F are available. How many cubic feet of each (neglecting the thermal capacity of the tank itself) should be used in filling the tank?

1.704 A partly filled barrel contains 300 lb of water and 100 lb of ice at 32°F. How many pounds of steam at 212°F must be run into the barrel to bring its contents up to 80°F?

1.705 Air is compressed in a diesel engine from an initial pressure of 13 psia and a temperature of 120°F to one-twelfth of its initial volume. Calculate the final temperature and pressure assuming the compression to be adiabatic.

1.706 An automobile tire is inflated to 32 psig pressure at 50°F. After being driven, the temperature rises to 75°F. Assuming that the volume remains constant, what is the final gage pressure?

1.707 If 100 cu ft of atmospheric air (pressure 14.7 psi) at zero Fahrenheit temperature are compressed to a volume of 1 cu ft at temperature 200°F, what will be the pressure of the compressed air in pounds per square inch?

1.708 *a.* Distinguish between higher heating value and lower heating value of fuel.

b. Why does the lower heating value at constant volume differ from that at constant pressure?

1.709 Air at 90°F dry bulb and 65°F wet bulb travels across the surface of a pond of water which is at 70°F. Will any of the 70°F water be evaporated into the air stream or will any of the water vapor in the air be condensed? Explain fully the physical laws upon which your answer is based.

1.710 *a.* If you wished the temperature distribution within a room to be as even as possible, would you blow hot air into the room near the floor or the ceilings? Reasons.

b. To heat the room most effectively, should the steam radiators be painted black or with aluminum paint? Reasons.

1.711 A steam turbine carrying a full load of 50,000 kw uses 569,000 lb steam per hour. The engine efficiency is 75 per cent and its exhaust steam is at 1 in. Hg abs and it has an enthalpy of 950 Btu per lb. What is the temperature and pressure of the steam at the throttle?

1.712 The use of electricity for melting snow in a driveway 10 ft wide by 50 ft long is being considered. At 2 cents a kilowatt-hour, what would be the cost of melting 6 in. of snow? (Assume the following data: weight of snow, 10 lb per cu ft; temperature, 32°; efficiency of operation, 50 per cent.)

1.713 A steam boiler on test generates 885,000 lb of steam in a 4-hr period. The average steam pressure is 400 psia, the average steam temperature is 700°F, and the average temperature of the feedwater supplied to the boiler is 280°F. If the boiler efficiency for the period is 82.5 per cent, and if the coal has a heating value of 13,850 Btu per lb as fired, find the average amount of coal burned in short tons per hour.

1.714 A hot-water heater consists of a 20-ft length of copper pipe of ½-in. average diameter and 1/16-in. thickness. The outer surface of the pipe is maintained at 212°. What is the capacity of the coil in gallons of water per minute, if water is fed into the coil at 40° and is expected to emerge heated to 150°? [Assume the conductivity of copper to be 2100 Btu/(sq ft)(deg)(hr)(in.) thickness.]

1.715 If coal having a heat of combustion of 14,000 Btu per lb is used in a heating plant of 50 per cent efficiency, how many pounds of steam of 50 per cent quality and 212°F temperature can be made per pound of this coal from water whose initial temperature is 70°F?

1.716 A single-cylinder, double-acting, reciprocating steam engine has a 6-in. bore, and 8-in. stroke, and a piston-rod diameter of 1¼ in. The average mean effective pressure found from the indicator cards is 62 psi for each end of the cylinder. The engine operates at 300 rpm and with a mechanical efficiency of 83 per cent. If the engine is directly coupled to a generator having an efficiency of 92 per cent, find the generator output in kilowatts.

1.717 Steam is admitted to the cylinder of an engine in such a manner that the average pressure is 120 psi. The diameter of the piston is 10 in. and the length of stroke is 12 in. How much work can be done during one revolution, assuming that steam is admitted to each side of the piston in succession? What is the horsepower of the engine when it is making 300 rpm?

1.718 A volume of 400 cc of air is measured at a pressure of 740 mm Hg abs and a temperature of 18°C. What will be the volume at 760 mm abs and 0°C?

1.719 What is the temperature of 2 liters of water at 30°C after 500 cal of heat have been added to it?

1.720 A heat engine (Carnot cycle) has its intake and exhaust temperatures 157°C and 100°C, respectively. What is its efficiency?

1.721 A 300-watt water heater is attached to a water faucet. If the water runs at a rate that permits it to be heated from 60 to 120°F, how long will it take to obtain a gallon and what will be the cost at 5 cents a kilowatt-hour? Assume that 75 per cent of the electrical energy will be utilized in heating the water.

1.722 By means of insulation, the loss in heat through a roof per square foot is reduced from 0.40 to 0.18 Btu per hr for each degree of difference between inside and outside temperatures. The area of the roof is 10,000 sq ft and the average difference between inside and outside temperatures is 35° during the heating season of 5,000 hr. If the heating value of coal is 13,000 Btu per lb and the efficiency of the heating plant is 60 per cent, find the value of the coal saved per season at $15 per ton.

1.723 What is the quality of steam that gives up 475 Btu per lb while condensing to water at a constant pressure of 20 psig?

1.724 A single-cylinder, double-acting, reciprocating steam engine has a 12-in. diameter piston with an 18-in. stroke. The piston-rod diameter is 2 in. Indicator cards show a mean effective pressure of 70 psi for both the head end and the crank end. The engine operates at 350 rpm with an efficiency of 92 per cent. Determine the horsepower output.

1.725 A 300-hp engine is given a brake test. The brakes are water cooled. At what rate must water at 80°F flow through the brakes if the water must not rise above 180°F?

SECTION TWO

2.01–2.50

CHEMICAL ENGINEERING

2.01 A boiler is fired with a coal containing 75 per cent carbon and 8 per cent ash, burned under such conditions that the elimination of combustible matter from the refuse is complete. The air enters the furnace at 90°F with a relative humidity of 80 per cent. The vapor pressure of water at 90°F is 36 mm Hg. The flue gases go to the stack at 680°F. The average flue-gas analysis shows 12.6 per cent CO_2, 6.2 per cent O_2, and 1 per cent CO.

Calculate:

a. The per cent of excess air

b. The complete analysis of the fuel

c. The cubic feet of stack gas per pound of coal

d. The cubic feet of air per pound of coal

2.02 A mixture of ammonia and air at a pressure of 745 mm Hg and a temperature of 40°C contains 4.9 per cent NH_3 by volume. The gas is passed at a rate of 100 cfm through an absorption tower in which only ammonia is removed. The gases leave the tower at a pressure of 740 mm Hg, a temperature of 20°C, and contain 0.13 per cent NH_3 by volume.

Using the simple gas law, calculate:

a. The rate of flow of gas leaving the tower in cubic feet per minute.

b. The weight of ammonia absorbed in the tower per minute.

2.03 A fractionating column is operating at 1 atm to produce a product of ethanol and water which leaves the top plate at

78.41°C. The bottom product is to contain 1 mole per cent ethanol. The feed contains 17 mole per cent ethanol and is introduced at its boiling point. The feed rate is 44 moles per hr. Reflux is returned to the top plate at a rate of 31 moles per hr and at the top-plate temperature.

a. If plate efficiency is 60 per cent, calculate the number of actual plates.

b. Calculate the rates of heat transfer in reboiler and condenser.

c. Find the feed-plate location.

2.04 An absorption tower packed with ½-in. Berl saddles is to be used for scrubbing a very small amount of ammonia out of air at 70°F and about 1 atm pressure, with water at 70°F as the scrubbing liquid. The tower is 12 in. in internal diameter and has a packed height of 7 ft. The water rate is 5 gal per min. Experiment has shown that, below the loading point, the resistance offered by the wetted packing at this water rate is 1.5 times that of dry packing of similar size and shape and at the same rate of flow of gas. The tower is to be operated with a gas velocity of 1.5 ft per sec, based on the empty tower; this is below the loading point.

What would be the expected drop in pressure through the tower in inches of water at 70°F?

2.05 It is desired to strip ammonia from a water solution which is 20 per cent by weight of ammonia. Eight thousand cu ft per hr of air-ammonia mixture which is 10 per cent ammonia by volume (dry basis) is to be produced. The entering air contains no ammonia and the exhausted solution contains 2 per cent ammonia by weight. The gas and liquor rates are such that K_ga is 7 lb-moles/(hr) (cu ft) (atm). What volume of packing is required if the operation is isothermal at 20°C? If K_ga varies as $G^{0.8}$, what relative height of packing would be required if the gas rate and the liquor rate were decreased by 25 per cent?

2.06 A multipass cooler for a continuous ethyl alcohol still consists of a copper tube 1³⁄₁₆ in. inside diameter with walls ¹⁄₁₆ in. thick and 24 ft long, surrounded by a standard 2-in. steel pipe. The hot alcohol flows through the inner tube, and the cooling water flows through the outer pipe counter-current to the alcohol. The cooler consists of a number of these double pipes in series. If the alcohol is to be cooled from 172°F to 70°F, using cooling water entering at 50°F and leaving at 80°F, how many pipes in series will be needed to handle 200 gal alcohol per hour?

2.07 A 50-mole per cent solution of methanol in water is to be rectified to give a distillate containing 95 mole per cent methanol and a residue containing 95 mole per cent water. The feed enters the column at 20°C. A reflux ratio 40 per cent greater than the minimum is to be used.

a. What is the minimum reflux ratio?

b. How many perfect plates are needed for the desired separation under the above conditions?

c. If the feed is 2,000 lb per hr, calculate the pounds of product and residue per hour.

d. How much steam, at 5 psig, is required per hour?

2.08 The heats of combustion ($-\Delta H$) of crystalline succinic acid and succinic anhydride are 356.2 and 369.4 kg-cal per gram-mole respectively, and the entropy of the acid is 42.0 entropy units at 25°C. The entropy of the anhydride is estimated to be 35.0 units at 25°C. Calculate the partial pressure of water in the equilibrium system

$$\underset{\text{solid}}{C_4H_6O_4} \rightarrow \underset{\text{solid}}{C_4H_4O_3} + \underset{\text{gas}}{H_2O}$$

at 500 and 700°K. On the basis of these calculations, does the straight thermal dehydration of the acid to the anhydride appear to be commercially feasible or would it be necessary to use powerful desiccating agents? Assume the molal heat capacity of the acid is equal to that of the anhydride.

2.09 An experimental run made in a pilot-plant flow reactor, having an internal volume of 5 cu ft, converted 50 per cent of material A according to the homogeneous gas reaction $2A \rightarrow R$. The conditions were atmospheric pressure, 500°C, and a feed rate of 1 lb-mole per hr, gas at standard conditions.

For design purposes it is desired to find the volume of reactor required to treat 10,000 cu ft per hr of feed gases at 5 atm and 300°C with 25 per cent conversion.

Assume the gases behave as perfect gases, isothermal conditions for the reactor, and an activation energy of 30,000 cal per gram-mole for the homogeneous reaction.

2.10 A storage tank at 100°F is part full of a liquid mixture which contains 50 mole per cent *n*-butane and 50 mole per cent *n*-pentane. The vapor space contains only butane and pentane vapors. What is the pressure in the vapor space, and what is the composition of the vapors? At 100°F, pure *n*-butane has a vapor pressure of 3.0 atm; at 100°F pure *n*-pentane has a vapor pressure of 0.9 atm.

2.11 What effect does chemical equilibrium between SO_2 and SO_3 have on operating conditions used and yields obtained in sulfuric acid manufacture?

2.12 The autoclave process for hydrolyzing monochlorbenzene to phenol at 1,500 psia and 350°C in the presence of NaOH and CuCl is apparently a unimolecular reaction with a velocity constant of 0.0098 min^{-1}. What reaction time is required to obtain a conversion of 99 per cent using a batch of 1,000 lb monochlorbenzene?

2.13 Give examples of the following classes of organic chemicals which are in large-scale production and use: (1) hydrocarbon, (2) alcohol, (3) ketone, (4) ester, and (5) metallo-organic compounds. For each example, indicate (*a*) commercial method of production, (*b*) raw materials, and (*c*) use.

2.14 Outline the safety rules and practices for the protection of life, health, and property that should be observed in a plant producing toxic and highly flammable chemicals.

2.15 *a.* Describe how glycerin is usually obtained from fats.

b. Account for the presence of sodium chloride in the raw glycerin.

2.16 What weight of steel containing 0.020 per cent manganese should be taken so that the final solution will contain 10 ppm manganese?

2.17 What are the products of the following reactions?

a. Oxidation of formaldehyde

b. Hydrolysis of an ether

c. Hydrolysis of the CN group

d. Saponification of a fat

e. Inversion of sucrose

2.18 A plate-and-frame filter press with frames 1 in. thick is filtering a noncompressible slurry under constant pressure. The cake is washed with three successive portions of wash water of about the same viscosity as the filtrate; the pressure drop through the press during washing is the same as that during filtration. The time required for filtration only, to form a cake that fills the frame completely, is 2 hr. The time required for washing is 30 min. The time required for dumping, cleaning, and reassembling the press is 30 min. The resistance offered by the press and the cloth may be considered negligible in comparison with the resistance offered by the cake. By what percentage and in which direction would the substitution of frames 1½ in. thick change the average output from the press, in gallons of filtrate per hour of total operating time? Assume that the composition of the sludge, the filtration pressure, and the cleaning time are the same in both cases, and that the volume of wash water used is proportional to the volume of filtrate.

2.19 A mixture of the following composition is to be distilled in a continuous still:

Benzene	60 per cent
Toluene	25 per cent
Xylene	15 per cent

The overhead product is to be substantially pure benzene. The bottoms product is to be substantially pure xylene. From some plate in the column a side stream is to be taken off to a smaller stripper still that delivers substantially pure toluene as a bottoms product.

a. Draw a neat diagram showing, at least qualitatively, the concentrations of the several components on the plate of the main still as ordinates, and as abscissas the plate numbers in the main still. Indicate the position of the feed plate and the plate from which the side stream is taken.

b. Draw a neat diagram showing the main still with feed line, side-stream drawoff, and overhead and waste lines; and the stripper column with feed line, overhead lines, and drawoff line. Where would the overhead from the stripper still be sent?

2.20 Discuss the use and treatment of water in industrial chemical operations including particularly the compounds causing hardness, advantages and disadvantages of various methods of softening (including equations) and treating, and the reasons for these equations.

2.21 Mention uses and explain operation of the following in chemical process control:

Polarimeter	Spectrophotocolorimeter
Potentiometer	Calorimeter
Refractometer	

2.22 What are the differences between a rod mill, tube mill, and ball mill? What special advantages do each of these types of grinder have?

2.23 What are the raw materials used in the Fischer-Tropsch process for motor-fuel manufacture? What main reaction is involved? What by-products result?

2.24 Name or describe the specific types of equipment you would select to do the following jobs:

a. Concentrate a solution of material whose solubility decreases with increase in temperature.

b. Crystallize a material whose solubility increases greatly with temperature.

c. Crystallize a material whose solubility is independent of temperature.

d. Pump a liquid near its boiling point.

e. Dry a heat-sensitive solid product.

f. Transfer heat to and/or cool a highly viscous fluid.

g. Distill a liquid subject to heat polymerization.

h. Dry a material that "case hardens" easily.

2.25 The sulfur-burning process in a sulfuric acid plant comprises the following operations:

a. Sulfur is conveyed from storage pile to melting tank.

b. Sulfur is melted by means of steam coils.

c. Sulfur is burned in a spray-type burner with dry air.

Indicate the equipment needed for adequate automatic control of the process.

2.26 Fully discuss the following problems relating to phosphate utilization:

a. The use of CO_2 as an oxidizing agent to oxidize $P_{4(gas)}$ to the oxide for preparation of phosphoric acid.

b. The use of steam and silica for defluorinating phosphate for animal nutritional purposes.

c. The use of $Na_3PO_4 \cdot 12H_2O$ in boiler waters.

2.27 A paper plant requires $CaCO_3$ essentially free of all soluble impurities. Powdered $CaCO_3$ is available containing 1 per cent NaOH. A two-step, continuous-countercurrent washing system with 24,000 gal per day of pure water is to be used for removing the NaOH when feeding 10 tons per day of powdered $CaCO_3$ with the slurry discharge containing 0.091 tons of water per ton of $CaCO_3$ is removed in underflow. What is the caustic content of the washed and dried $CaCO_3$?

2.28 *a.* Name the two principal methods of manufacturing rayon.

b. Describe both methods named in *a* with respect to raw materials, preparation of solution, production of filaments, and any subsequent chemical treatment.

c. How does rayon differ from nylon with respect to composition and properties?

2.29 Draw the flow sheet for an alkali-chlorine plant producing liquid caustic, liquid chlorine, and bleaching powder from brine. Designate the quantity of each product expected to be produced from 1 ton of salt.

2.30 Draw a neat flow sheet showing the process for the manufacture of smokeless powder (for an 8-in. gun) from cotton linters.

2.31 A dilute mixture of ethyl acetate in air is the product of a certain drying operation. Outline possible methods of recovery of the ethyl acetate for reuse as a solvent.

2.32 The use of oxygen-enriched air in iron blast-furnace operation has been proposed. What modifications of present practice and equipment would this entail?

2.33 Discuss the chemistry of synthetic-rubber manufacture. What advantages and disadvantages does synthetic-rubber manufacture have compared to natural-rubber manufacture from an economic standpoint?

2.34 *a.* Give the three laws of thermodynamics and illustrate their significance.

b. What can thermodynamics tell you concerning a chemical reaction?

c. What is meant by

1. Reduced pressure?
2. Free energy?
3. Fugacity?
4. Reduced temperature?
5. Compressibility factors?

2.35 A gas system has two parallel lines 50 miles long, one 20 in. and the other 22 in. in diameter. Gas at 555 psig and 40°F is fed to the system amounting to 6 MM per hr measured at 30 in. and 60°F. Its specific gravity is 0.65. The viscosity at 500 psi and 40°F is 2.5×10^{-7} lb-sec per sq ft. The deviation from Boyle's law is $+0.00022P$ for the weight of a cubic foot at P psi. The 20-in. line has an efficiency of 92 per cent and the other, 88 per cent. What is the outlet pressure?

2.36 Two similar vertical-tube evaporators have been arranged as a double effect in the evaporation of a caustic soda liquor from 10 to 16 per cent, the first effect being operated as the high pressure one and the second at 28 in. Hg vacuum. The steam to the first effect is at 5 psi and the feed liquor is at 70°F. Operation is continuous. Given an adequate supply of steam (5 psi) and cooling water, and having available some old heat exchangers, an old water-tube condenser of small capacity, pumps, pipes, fittings, etc., how would you adapt the equipment for a 10 per cent increase in production? If you had to adapt the equipment to handle a temporary 50 per cent overload, how would you do it? Substantiate your proposed setup.

2.37 An evaporator (single effect) is removing 500 lb per hr of water from a colloidal suspension which deposits scale on the steam chest. During one 8-hr shift each week it is cleaned, which increases the over-all heat-transfer coefficient from 50 to 225. Assuming that the scale is deposited uniformly throughout the week and none flakes off, calculate:

a. The mean heat-transfer coefficient for the week.

b. How often the evaporator should be cleaned for maximum capacity.

2.38 Specify the type of operation and type of slurry for which each of the following filters would be adapted:

a. Plate and frame
b. Rotary continuous
c. Sweetland
d. Moore

2.39 Give a brief discussion of the processes of age hardening and precipitation hardening.

2.40 Describe briefly the main types of instruments used for checking the efficiency of combustion of the flue gases. State what you consider to be their relative advantages or disadvantages.

2.41 Give a discussion of "temperature measurement" indicating the range of application of instruments of different types, the accuracy obtainable, and the precautions necessary in practice to ensure accurate results.

2.42 Give at least four different methods of removing dust particles from a gas and compare their engineering requirements. Given a gas of 50,000-cfm flow with 50 lb per min of a hygroscopic dust, averaging 10 microns size, at a temperature of 95°C and a dew point of 70°C, what method would you recommend and why?

2.43 It is desired to recover ethanol from an air-ethanol mixture, that is 5 per cent by volume of ethanol and 95 per cent by volume of air at 90°F, by compressing the mixture to 100 psig and then cooling the gas at constant pressure to 78.8°F. Estimate the per cent recovery of the ethanol.

2.44 6,000 lb of a material goes through a crusher and grinder per hour in succession (on the same power drive). Screen analysis from the crusher shows a surface area of product of 500 sq ft per lb. Screen analysis of the grinder product indicates a surface area of 4,200 sq ft per lb. The Rittinger number of the material processed is 163 sq in. per ft-lb. The efficiency of the crusher is estimated to be 25 per cent while that of the grinder is 30 per cent. Estimate the total power to be delivered to the equipment.

2.45 Tank storage is to be provided for the following chemicals and solutions: (*a*) concentrated nitric acid, (*b*) 15 per cent sodium chloride solution, (*c*) benzol, (*d*) 50 per cent caustic soda solution, and (*e*) 90 per cent mixed acid. Specify the material of construction for each tank.

2.46 A leaf filter press is operating at constant pressure, building up a 1-in. noncompressible cake in 5 hr and is delivering 3.8 cu ft of filtrate per sq ft of filtering surface. Cleaning requires 30 min. If it is required to wash the cake with a volume of water equal to one-half the volume of the filtrate, what will be the maximum capacity of the press obtainable by varying the cake thickness? The nature of the sludge and the pressure remain unchanged.

2.47 A solid granular product is to be dried in recirculating air. The moist air bled off from the recirculating stream is at 120°F and has a dew point of 110°F. The air admitted to the dryer has a dry-bulb temperature of 100°F, and a wet-bulb temperature of 75°F.

Assuming that there is no loss of heat from the dryer, how much heat must be supplied for each pound of water removed from the cake? (Neglect heat of wetting of the solid.)

2.48 *a.* Discuss the manufacturing of synthetic methanol under the following headings:

1. Source, preparation, and purification of the reacting gases
2. The catalyst used
3. Pressures and temperatures employed

b. Draw a flow sheet.

2.49 In the case of absorption-tower design give or explain:

a. The data required to determine the packed volume.

b. The procedure to be followed to determine the packed volume.

c. The way in which the design of a stripping tower differs from that of an absorption tower.

d. The advantages and disadvantages of using the height-of-transfer-unit method instead of the method of operating lines.

e. For the case of a stripping tower followed by a rectifying tower, the economic factors that must be considered and the optimum value that must be determined.

2.50 As an engineer, you are asked to design the evaporating system to concentrate 50,000 lb per day of caustic solutions from 8 to 50 per cent. Briefly outline the procedure to be followed, including the data required, the method of determining the best setup, and materials of construction.

SECTION THREE

3.01–3.50

CIVIL ENGINEERING

3.01 *a.* What formula is well known for calculating the safe load on piles?

b. Give the formula.

c. If a drop hammer weighing 500 lb is used in a rig permitting a drop of 20 ft to drive some wooden piles, what is the allowable load per pile if the average penetration, after a number of blows, is 1 in.? Piles are being driven in clay.

d. If the piles are to support a column footing with a 40-ton total load (column load plus weight of footing), sketch the layout of piles, the location of the column with regard to them, the pile spacing and outside dimensions of the footing.

3.02 Write a clause in a set of specifications for "earth excavation" and "rock excavation" so that there will be a minimum of disputes between the engineer and the contractor as to the classification of materials for payment.

3.03 Name and describe four soil tests and tell what each is a measure of.

3.04 Answer or define briefly:

a. How would you place concrete under water?

b. By a schematic diagram explain the operation of a pneumatic caisson.

c. How are heads of timber piles protected during driving?

d. How are the heads of concrete piles protected during driving?

e. What kind of a pump would you use for raising a continuous but moderate flow of water from a sump in which the water level will rise 40 to 50 ft during the construction operations?

f. What is meant by pointing?

g. What are wales?

h. Why are cast-iron lintels supporting masonry over doorways or windows made in the form of an inverted T? Explain how this uses the material to the best advantage.

i. What are the purposes of stiffeners on plate girders?

j. What precautions must be taken when placing concrete in (1) hot, dry weather, and (2) in freezing weather?

3.05 *a.* Interlocking steel-sheet piling is to be driven to form a cellular cofferdam. In driving this sheeting what qualities of construction should be particularly insisted upon?

b. What advantages are possessed by deep arch web steel-sheet piling over shallower sections?

c. What effect does treating timber with preservatives have upon the structural strength of the timber?

d. What is "uncoursed masonry"?

e. In freezing weather, what precautions should be taken in preparing concrete aggregates and in protecting freshly poured concrete?

f. What is the distinction between a cofferdam and a caisson?

g. What is the generally accepted maximum pressure under which men may work in pneumatic caisson construction?

3.06 *a.* Under what soil conditions would you use each of the following types of sheeting in trenches for public-utility lines?

1. Vertical sheeting
2. Skeleton sheeting
3. Stay bracing
4. Box sheeting
5. Poling boards
6. Plywood panels

b. Under what conditions would you leave such sheeting in place?

c. Recently, cement-dispersing agents have been added to the cement used on many construction jobs. What benefits accrue through the dispersal of the cement particles through the concrete instead of allowing flocculation of the cement to occur?

3.07 *a.* When fresh concrete is exposed to rapid-drying conditions, what precautions shall be taken to keep the concrete moist and for how long a period?

b. In freezing weather, what precautions shall be taken to prepare the materials for making concrete and with what care and for what length of time shall the concrete be protected after pouring?

c. Give an approximate time limit in days before you would remove forms and supports from

1. Arch centers	4. Walls
2. Centering underbeams	5. Columns
3. Floor slabs	6. Sides of beams and other parts

d. What limit of time would you recommend from the time water is first added to the concrete mix until it reaches its final position in the forms?

e. Certain concrete columns are 40 ft high and 40 in. in diameter. Explain how you would go about filling the forms with concrete to insure an "A" grade of concrete.

3.08 Answer the following briefly:

a. In order that interlocking steel-sheet piling may be in a position to be closed when encircling a cofferdam frame, what essential must be considered in driving the sheeting?

b. When bridge floors are made of steel stringers supporting concrete slabs, what advantage would result from using shear adapters?

c. Where and how far apart should cross bridging be placed in a deck beam or girder bridge?

d. What effect does treating timber with preservatives have upon the structural strength of the timber?

e. How much and under what conditions should the working stress in untreated timber be reduced as a factor of safety against weathering?

f. What is meant by a voussoir? a skewback?

g. What is the difference between a "stringer" and a "floor beam"?

h. What is the difference between a bay and a bent?

3.09 Answer briefly:

a. How would you take care of a minor leak in the sides of a single-wall interlocking steel-sheet cofferdam?

b. What precautions would you take prior to unwatering the above cofferdam?

c. If the lunch whistle blew at a time when a pile-driving crew had only partly driven a pile would you permit the crew to stop for lunch? Why?

d. If you were ordering stone to riprap a stream bank near a bridge, what size stone would you try to get?

e. What is the advantage of prefabricating timber that is to be pressure creosoted? How would you treat the exposed timber in holes to be bored in the creosoted timbers?

3.10 Answer the following briefly:

a. In digging a trench for a sewer in hardpan and in the dry would it be necessary to use sheeting and bracing? Would this apply to any depth trench?

b. How would you protect steel from rusting if welding is to be done upon it at a later date?

c. Is "oiling the forms" harmful or beneficial to the concrete?

d. What is meant by "gunite" and how is it applied?

e. In structural welding, what advantage is there to the use of an alternating-current machine over a direct-current machine?

3.11 You are making a survey for relocation of a highway (or railway). Outline briefly the data you would secure in the field for the design and preparation of plans and specifications.

3.12 In reinforced concrete:

a. What is meant by balanced design?

b. What is meant by "the transformed section"?

c. What locates the neutral axis

1. In a new design?
2. In an investigation of an existing beam?

d. What assumption is made as to the variation of intensity of fiber stress in a beam?

e. In column design how much additional concrete coverage of outermost steel is usually specified for fireproofing?

f. In a T beam, what part of the cross-sectional area carries the shear?

g. What function are the stirrups called upon to play?

h. Why are stirrups not needed in slabs?

i. Distinguish between beam shear and punching shear.

j. How far above the ground should you place the reinforcement in a footing?

3.13 In recent years stabilization of existing highways and shoulders has been greatly advanced. Describe in detail what is meant by stabilization, what admixtures are used, how they are introduced into the soil, and what equipment is generally needed for a complete stabilization job. Include description of any necessary soil analyses as part of this process.

3.14 It is planned to construct a portland-cement reinforced-concrete pavement in two lanes each 10 ft wide. The pavement is to be laid on a subgrade which has a large amount of clay in it.

a. Explain in detail the work which should be done to prevent frost heave and to provide adequate drainage of the subgrade.

b. What factors will have an effect on the strength of the concrete? What steps should be taken to insure adequate strength. What mix would you recommend?

c. What is the purpose of placing reinforcing steel in concrete pavements? Where should it be placed within the slab? Why? Explain how you would design the reinforcing steel for a concrete pavement.

d. What are the advantages and disadvantages of using vibration in placing concrete for a pavement. What is the essential reason for vibrating concrete?

e. Describe four methods of curing concrete pavements. How is each method supposed to insure adequate curing? Which method do you consider to be the best? Why?

3.15 A badly cracked portland-cement concrete pavement is to be surfaced with bituminous concrete. The existing pavement is to be used as a base for the new surface.

Describe in detail:

a. The steps you would take to insure no further failure of the base.

b. The preparation of the base to receive the bituminous concrete surface.

c. The preparation (including mix recommended) and laying of the wearing course.

Sketch a cross section of the finished road.

3.16 At both approaches to a bridge it is necessary to construct fills of a maximum height of 20 ft and a base width of 49 ft with side slopes of 2:1.

a. Describe at least three methods of compacting fills and discuss the advantages and disadvantages of each.

b. What is meant by the term shrinkage, when used in connection with earthwork? What determines the amount of shrinkage? Why is it generally necessary to use a shrinkage factor in balancing cuts and fills? How is this factor used?

c. A temporary pavement is to be laid on the approaches. Describe in detail the construction of the type of pavement you would use. Upon what does the strength and durability of your pavement depend? Why would you recommend constructing this type of pavement in preference to some others which might have been used?

3.17 It is planned to construct a bituminous macadam road.

a. Outline the procedure which should be followed in constructing a bituminous macadam road.

b. Upon what does the strength and durability of a bituminous macadam road depend?

c. What are the principal maintenance problems of this type of road? What provisions should be made for handling these problems?

3.18 In the two lists given below, are various kinds of tests and short statements about the value of each test. For each test in List 1, select a statement from List 2 that is most appropriate.

List 1

1. Tension tests
2. Compression tests
3. Transverse tests
4. Impact tests
5. Shear tests
6. Torsion tests

List 2

a. With brittle materials a criterion of strength, called the modulus of rupture, together with the flexibility and toughness may be determined.

b. With ductile materials the strength, ductility, toughness, and modulus of elasticity may be determined. These tests are most valuable of all mechanical tests for ductile materials.

c. A valuable measure of shock resistance for brittle and ductile materials.

d. These tests afford an imperfect measure due to the existence of bending stresses.

e. This test is of great value in determining the strength of such materials as wood, concrete, cast iron, and brick.

f. The only test wherein the shearing modulus of elasticity may be determined for ductile materials.

3.19 In connection with design of railroad bridges, define and explain the following terms: (*a*) centrifugal force, (*b*) dead load, (*c*) Cooper's standard loading, (*d*) live load, and (*e*) impact.

3.20 Answer or define briefly:

In plate girders:

a. What is meant by a sole plate and what should be its minimum thickness?

b. State three limiting conditions for the spacing of stiffener angles.

c. Where must stiffener angles have milled ends?

d. How much of the web area may be used for flange area?

e. Anchor bolts are usually of what minimum diameter and embedded to what minimum length?

In truss design:

f. What is meant by "combined stresses"?

g. What is meant by "alternate stresses"?

h. What is a gusset plate?

i. What is a filler plate?

j. What are stay plates?

3.21 A town having a present population of 10,000 is planning to construct a rapid-sand-filtration plant. From the following data calculate (1) the size of the filter units, (2) the pounds of alum required per day, and (3) the size of the distribution reservoir required for fire protection.

a. Estimated future population is 14,000.

b. Consumption per capita is 100 gal per day.

c. Maximum rate of consumption is 225 per cent of average rate.

d. Filters to operate at a rate of 125,000,000 gal per day per acre.

e. Wash water equals 4 per cent of total water filtered.

f. Average hours of filter operation between washings equals 7½.

g. Time required to wash filter and restore it to satisfactory operating condition equals ½ hr.

h. Average alum dosage is 4½ grains per gal.

i. Fire protection to meet requirements of National Board of Fire Underwriters.

3.22 A grit chamber installation is to be provided for a city with an average dry-weather flow of 1,000,000 gal per day and a storm flow of 3,000,000 gal per day. What values would you choose for the following: (*a*) minimum detention period; (*b*) maximum velocity of flow; (*c*) length of units; (*d*) top width of units; (*e*) maximum depth of units; (*f*) number of units; (*g*) grit storage capacity; (*h*) method of cleaning; (*i*) average interval between cleanings. Give the reasons for your choice.

3.23 A sewage has a suspended solids content of 250 ppm. A sedimentation tank with a retention period of 1.5 hr is planned.

a. What will be the reduction in suspended solids?

b. If the average sewage flow is 500,000 gal per day, what must be the capacity of the tank in gallons?

c. What dimensions would you use if the tank is to be rectangular in plan?

d. If a hopper-bottom tank is to be used and the sludge is to be removed once daily, what should be the capacity of the sludge hoppers, assuming the water content of the sludge to be 95 per cent?

3.24 In designing sewerage systems:

a. What maximum spacing may be used between manholes? What factor controls this spacing?

b. What period of design should be used for sewers? For treatment works? Why should there be a difference?

c. What per capita flow of sanitary sewage should be provided for?

d. What minimum velocity of flow should be used for sanitary sewers? For storm drains?

e. What minimum size of pipe should be used for sanitary sewers? For storm drains? Why?

f. What method is best adapted for the determination of the size of a storm drain? Explain briefly.

g. Under what conditions should catch basins be used instead of inlets?

h. An 8-in. line and a 15-in. sewer come into a manhole. A 24-in. pipe leaves it. What should be the relative elevations of the three inverts?

3.25 You are called upon to design the storm-water drains for a subdivision. The rational method of design is to be employed. State clearly and in logical order the information which you would gather, the use to which you would put this data, and each successive step in design from the upper inlet to the lower end of the line where the drain discharges into a stream.

3.26 Prepare an outline showing each successive step in gathering the data for and preparing a design of the sanitary sewers for a small subdivision.

3.27 *a*. What is an Imhoff tank? Describe. For what is it used?

b. What is a rapid sand filter? Describe. For what is it used?

c. What is an Imhoff cone? Describe. For what is it used?

d. What is a sludge bed? Describe. For what is it used?

3.28 Discuss the various methods used in the secondary treatment of sewage effluents, giving the advantages and disadvantages of each.

3.29 Describe the activated-sludge process of sewage treatment. Include a statement of the principal biologic phenomena that occur.

3.30 *a*. Describe the separate sludge-digestion process used for sewage treatment.

b. Name two methods of dewatering sludge. Give advantages of each.

3.31 In each of the following select one, and only one, correct answer.

a. In the active-sludge process of sewage treatment, it is essential to have: (1) a dosing tank; (2) an adequate supply of air; (3) an Imhoff tank; (4) flocculation; (5) an acid sludge.

b. For protection of aquatic life in a fresh-water stream, sewage effluent should never lower the dissolved-oxygen content lower than: (1) 1 ppm; (2) 5 ppm; (3) 10 ppm; (4) 15 ppm; (5) 20 ppm.

c. The biochemical treatment of sewage effluents is essentially a process of (1) reduction; (2) dehydration; (3) polymerization; (4) oxidation; (5) alkalinization.

d. The process of lagooning is primarily a means of: (1) increasing the capacity of storage reservoirs; (2) increasing flow of sewage through Imhoff tanks; (3) reducing the excessive flow in sewers; (4) disposing of sludge; (5) rendering sludge suitable for fertilizing purposes.

e. In treating turbid waters a popular coagulant is: (1) calcium sulfate; (2) chlorine; (3) iodine; (4) ferric sulfate; (5) pulverized coke.

f. In most well-designed sewer systems: (1) manholes are generally equipped with regulators; (2) sewers never flow full; (3) sewage ejectors are used to accelerate flow and prevent deposition at low-flow periods; (4) catch basins are not usually essential; (5) manholes are always placed over the center lines of the sewer below.

g. Chlorine is used in the treatment of sewage to: (1) cause bulking of activated sludge; (2) help grease separation; (3) aid flocculation; (4) increase the biochemical oxygen demand; (5) reduce the production of ecologies.

h. The quantity of grit in sewage depends largely on: (1) the extent to which the sewered area is built up; (2) the number of industrial plants in the area; (3) the chemicals used in the precipitation process; (4) the strength of the sewage; (5) the period of detention.

i. Septic tanks are primarily used for: (1) the aerobic decomposition of deposited sewage solids; (2) separation of deposited solids; (3) separation of oil and grease scums; (4) anaerobic decomposition of deposited solids; (5) the nitrification of raw sewage.

j. The gas from Imhoff tanks is mainly composed of: (1) carbon dioxide; (2) methane; (3) nitrogen; (4) ethane; (5) hydrogen sulfide.

3.32 Show by sketch the plan and sections for a septic tank and subsurface irrigation system (nitrification field) for a country home housing 10 people—soil is fairly porous. Give dimensions and data for design.

3.33 Describe how malaria is transmitted. If appointed sanitary engineer to a county health unit, describe just what steps you would take to reduce the number of cases of malaria in your county.

3.34 *a.* A state has a population of 2,000,000. For the year 1943 the physicians of the state reported 2,891 cases of tuberculosis with 1,304 deaths from this disease. Compute: (1) case rate; (2) death rate; (3) fatality rate.

b. Define morbidity as used in vital statistics.

3.35 *a.* What diseases are prevented by protecting the dairy herd and what measures are applied in such protection?

b. What are the protective measures applied to the "milk line"?

c. Name a disease thus prevented.

d. What is the principal danger of dirty milk and what specific measures can be taken to eliminate this danger?

e. Name two methods of milk pasteurization that require the use of recording thermometers. Why is one method used more commonly than the other?

3.36 Give the method of transmission of

a. Bubonic plague
b. Murine typhus fever
c. Malaria
d. Dengue fever
e. Smallpox
f. Undulant fever
g. Tularemia
h. Yellow fever
i. Rocky Mountain spotted fever

3.37 In investigating a typhoid fever outbreak in a county of 10,000 population, what steps would you take and what data would you collect in determining the sources of the infection?

3.38 Name two methods of municipal sanitary garbage disposal applicable to a city or town. Compare the two methods giving the application of each with advantages and disadvantages. *Note:* Open refuse dumps and feeding of garbage to hogs not to be considered.

3.39 Explain how to calculate (*a*) the yield of a watershed for power or water-supply purposes, and (*b*) the necessary storage capacity to provide a given rate of delivery.

3.40 Discuss (*a*) the importance of leakage and waste in a water-supply distribution system, (*b*) the most satisfactory methods to reduce such water loss, and (*c*) the effectiveness of these methods or the percentage of waste reduction that may be realized from them.

3.41 Describe the general features of a rapid sand water filtration plant.

3.42 *a*. Explain the chemical reactions that take place in a zeolite softener.

b. What is the effect of hydrogen sulfide in water that is to be chlorinated?

c. Explain the lime-soda method of softening water and write the chemical equations to show just what chemical reactions take place.

3.43 For what purpose is each of the following chemicals used in the process of water treatment?

a. Chloramine
b. Sodium hexametaphosphate
c. Sodium bisulfite
d. Sulfur dioxide
e. Activated carbon
f. Aluminum sulfate
g. Hydrated lime
h. Sodium chloride
i. Sodium carbonate

3.44 *a*. What do the following terms mean when applied to pumps: (1) single stage, (2) centrifugal, (3) multistage, (4) positive displacement, (5) reciprocating, (6) double acting, (7) rotary.

b. For what service conditions would you recommend the use of a single-stage centrifugal pump?

c. State the service conditions for which you would recommend a two-stage pump instead of a single stage.

3.45 *a*. A report on a proposed municipal water supply shows the presence of *B. coli*, *coli-aerogenes*, or gives a colon index. What is the significance of these terms?

b. Under what conditions do anaerobic bacteria thrive? Under what conditions do aerobic bacteria thrive?

c. The report on a prospective water supply shows carbonate hardness—100 ppm. What is the significance of this information? Will softening be necessary for municipal use?

3.46 In carrying out a triangulation network for the horizontal control of an extended survey there are several factors which will influence the accuracy with which the distances between stations can be computed in addition to the precision with which the angles in the scheme are measured. State what these factors are and the manner in which each affects the determination of the lengths.

3.47 Describe the method which you would use to carry an important traverse along a concrete highway. The traverse is to connect a survey of valuable property with a pair of Geodetic Control Survey stations about one-half mile away so that the coordinates of the property corners may be determined. It is desired to have the linear measurements correct to 1 in 20,000. List the equipment and personnel which you would use to carry out this work with the required accuracy and with safety. List the corrections which it would be necessary to apply to the tape measurements as actually made.

3.48 Compare the advantages and disadvantages of surveys by transit and tape, transit and stadia, plane-table, and aerial photography, and indicate clearly under what conditions and to what types of work each is applicable.

3.49 Explain the methods which you would use to get line and grade from the surface into a deep, straight tunnel through a 20-ft diameter shaft and project the line through the tunnel to the next shaft some miles away. Because of water-bearing seams it is anticipated that a portion of the rock tunnel will have to be driven under air.

3.50 Show by means of suitable ruled sketches and full explanation the procedure you would use in laying out a control survey system for a bridge of four spans across a wide river. Both banks are unobstructed. Piers are to be constructed within rectangular cofferdams. Suitable range flags must be located from which the piles for the cofferdams can be driven on proper lines in both directions. The control must be adequate to permit the location of finished work within the cofferdams with the necessary precision for steel arch construction.

SECTION FOUR

4.01–4.50

ELECTRICAL ENGINEERING

4.01 Design a lighting layout for a parking lot in a downtown area. This lot measures 200 by 300 ft. The projectors may be mounted on 25-ft poles located around the outer edge of the lot.

4.02 Two 500-watt, bare incandescent lamps, each having symmetrical downward intensity of 800 candlepower, are mounted outdoors 10 ft above a rectangular table. The table measures 6 by 16 ft and the lamps are located directly above the long centerline and 4 ft in from each end. Determine the horizontal illumination at (*a*) the center of the table, (*b*) the center of each end, and (*c*) each corner.

4.03 A retail store maintains a 20 ft-c illumination at counter height. The luminaires use 750-watt P. S. Mazda lamps. What per cent of power cost could be saved if the existing luminaires were replaced with fluorescent units and the level raised to 30 ft-c? (Take fluorescent lumens per watt as 42.)

4.04 Specify the lighting installation, including the foot-candle intensity, wattage of lamps, type reflectors, and the wiring, for a drafting room 20 by 30 by 12 ft? The drafting tables are 4 by 3 ft and are raised 3 ft from the floor.

4.05 A manufacturer of engines is erecting a machining and assembly plant which has a work floor 40 by 250 ft with a ceiling height of 18 ft. There are columns spaced 20 ft apart which support beams 18 in. deep and 10 in. wide extending from side to side. The floor is occupied by lathes, grinders, drills, etc., to a height of 5 ft 6 in. Three-phase power is available at 120/208 volts 60 cycles.

a. What illumination in foot-candles is required?

b. What general type of lighting and kind of fixtures would be suitable?

c. Specify lamp size and arrangement of fixtures.

d. What circuit arrangement would be suitable?

e. What conditioning of walls and ceilings should be recommended?

4.06 Would you permit two type T #6 wires and one bare #6 wire to be run in a ¾-in. conduit as service conductors? Length of run is 90 ft and the equivalent of three right-angle bends are included.

4.07 What defects would justify an inspector in ordering the wiring torn out of a new residence and reinstalled?

4.08 A 250-volt 10-kw d-c generator is separately excited. It has an effective armature circuit resistance of 0.5 ohm and inductance of 0.1 henry when it is supplying rated current. Suddenly the terminals beyond its protective circuit breaker are short-circuited with a short-circuit resistance of 0.2 ohm. The breaker operates 0.02 sec after the fault occurs. Neglecting saturation of the magnetic circuit, determine the maximum current to which the generator is subjected.

4.09 The field of a 120-volt d-c generator draws 8.4 amp. What resistance is required of a field discharge resistor such that the induced voltage, upon disconnecting the field from the 120-volt line, will be limited to one-third of the standard high-potential test voltage?

4.10 A symmetrical three-conductor cable is enclosed in a grounded metal sheath. The capacitance between the three conductors connected together and the sheath is 0.5 μf. The capacitance between one conductor and the other two connected together and also connected to the sheath is 0.6 μf. Calculate the charging current per conductor when a 60-cycle three-phase 25-kv voltage between conductors is applied to the cable.

4.11 A 60-cycle 2,300/230-volt transformer is to have a density in the core of 62,000 lines per sq in. Calculate the area of the core, assuming that the effective area of iron is 0.9 of gross area of the core. Assume that there are 1,500 turns on the high-tension winding.

4.12 A 60-cycle 200-kva three-winding transformer is rated at 2,400 volts primary voltage, and there are two secondary windings, one rated at 600 volts and the other at 240 volts. There are 200 primary turns. The rating of each secondary winding is 100 kva, one-half that of the transformer. Determine (*a*) turns in each secondary winding; (*b*) rated primary current at unity power factor; (*c*) rated primary current at 0.8 pf, lagging current; (*d*) rated current of the 600- and 240-volt secondary windings; (*e*) primary current when the rated current, pf = 1, flows in the 240-volt winding and the rated current, pf = 0.7 lagging, flows in the 600-volt winding.

4.13 A 15-kva 2,300/230-volt transformer is given a short-circuit test by impressing 65 volts on the high-tension side with the 230-volt side short-circuited. The power input for rated current is 350 watts. If the core loss is 245 watts,

Find:

a. Per cent voltage regulation at full load and unity power factor, and

b. The maximum efficiency that could be expected from this transformer at full load.

4.14 Two transformers, each rated at 100 kva, 2,200/220 volts, and 60 cycles, operate in parallel to supply a 200-kva load at a lagging power factor of 0.80. The short-circuit tests on these transformers show that, with power supplied to the 2,200-volt windings, there is rated current in each transformer under the following conditions:

Transformer *A*—1,000 watts at 72 volts
Transformer *B*—1,100 watts at 75 volts

Calculate the current in the 220-volt coils of each transformer under the above conditions, in percentage of the total. Neglect the exciting currents.

4.15 Explain how to obtain balanced three-phase voltages from two-phase and from three-phase circuits by means of two transformers of appropriate voltages.

4.16 A turbine-driven a-c generator is to deliver power to an electric furnace located 10 miles from the turbine. The turbine generator is 60-cycle three-phase star-connected, with 11,000 volts between terminals. The electric furnace is three-phase, operates at 200 volts between electrodes, and takes 3,000 kva at 80 per cent lagging power factor. Specify the number, size, type, and location of the transformers required; and the voltage, size, and spacing of conductors of the high-tension line, the loss of which is not to exceed 5 per cent of the delivered power. (Draw diagram and show all essential calculations.)

4.17 A load of 25,000 kw at 85 per cent pf is located 25 miles from a large substation at which 60-cps power is available at 12.5, 66, and 115 kv. Choose voltage of transmission line and size of conductor you would recommend and give reasons for your choice. Voltage regulation and power loss are not to exceed 8 and 6 per cent respectively.

4.18 Draw a one-line diagram of essential electrical circuits and apparatus for a generating station consisting of two 50,000-kw generators, with direct-connected exciters, two step-up transformers, one high-voltage bus, no low-voltage bus, and two outgoing transmission lines which connect to a system having other generating stations. Indicate location of current and potential transformers and name instruments and relays connected to their secondaries. Instrument and relay circuits are not to be shown.

4.19 An industrial plant is supplied from a three-phase transmission line having a capacity of 10,000 kva. The present plant load is 5,000 kw, balanced, three phase, and at a lagging power factor such that the transmission line is loaded to capacity. The plant must increase its load and this will be done with 30 induction motors which run at 80 per cent pf. In order to make use of the line to its full capacity in active power a synchronous condenser having losses of 300 kw (at the load at which it will operate) will be installed in the plant.

a. Determine the maximum kva in new induction motors that can be added without overloading the line.

b. What is the kva rating of the synchronous condenser required for this service?

c. Draw a power vector diagram.

4.20 An industrial load consists of:

One 50-hp induction motor; load, 30 hp; efficiency, 0.86; and pf, 0.70.

One 100-hp induction motor; load, 75 hp; efficiency, 0.89; and pf, 0.80.

Two 15-hp induction motors; load, 15 hp; efficiency, 0.92; and pf, 0.85.

One 300-hp induction motor; load, 310 hp; efficiency, 0.92; pf, 0.85.

Lighting load, 33 kw.

Synchronous motor (to be added): 500 hp, 0.80 pf, leading current; load, 300 hp; and efficiency, 0.925, exclusive of field loss.

Determine for load, over-all, (*a*) kilowatts; (*b*) kva; (*c*) kilovars; (*d*) power factor.

4.21 In a given plant the following sources of power are available: 2,300-volt three-phase, 440-volt three-phase, 220/110-volt single-phase three wire. The frequency is 60 cycles. The following applications are to be taken care of. In each case state the type of motor and control and the current characteristics, considering the three sources named above, which you consider best suited for each application, giving your reasons.

a. A 100-kw d-c generator to be driven by a direct-connected motor.

b. A slow-speed (600 rpm) compressor to be driven by a direct-connected motor. The compressor is equipped with an unloader to facilitate starting. The horsepower required is 200.

c. A number of machine tools driven by individual motors of from 2 to 15 hp operating at constant speed.

d. A blower to have three speeds—1,200, 900, and 600 rpm approximately; and requiring 15 hp at the highest speed. The blower is to be direct-connected to the motor.

e. A crusher requiring considerable adjustment of speed and rather heaving starting torque. The maximum horsepower is 50.

f. A number of small ventilating fans requiring approximately ⅙ hp each at constant speed.

4.22 A telephone line consisting of two #12 standard copper wires spaced 1 ft apart has the following parameters: $r = 10.44$ ohms per loop mile; $l = 0.00366$ henry per loop mile; $c = 0.00838 \times 10^{-6}$ f per loop mile and $g = 0.300 \times 10^{-6}$ mho per loop mile.

Determine: (*a*) the wavelength in miles; (*b*) the phase velocity as a percentage of the speed of light; (*c*) the loss in decibels per loop mile; and (*d*) the inductive loading per loop mile required for producing distortionless transmission.

4.23 An ideal transmission line 15.25 wavelengths long connects a generator, with an internal impedance of $100 + j0$ ohms, to a load of $200 + j200$ ohms. The load is matched to the line by means of a stub line bridged across the load. The frequency of operation is 600 mc. The line and the stub are to have the same characteristic impedance. Calculate the characteristic impedance of the line and the location and the minimum length of the stub for a proper termination of the line.

4.24 It is desired to transmit over a single-phase line 10 miles long, a load of 1,200 kw 0.85 pf lagging current, the loss not exceeding 7.5 per cent of the power delivered. The conductors are spaced 18 in. on center. The voltage at the load is 11,000 volts 50 cycles. (*a*) Draw a vector diagram. Determine: (*b*) the smallest size AWG solid-copper conductor, (*c*) the resistance per wire, (*d*) the reactance per wire, (*e*) the sending-end voltage, (*f*) the line regulation, and (*g*) the efficiency.

4.25 A 60-cycle three-phase 100-mile transmission line with a resistance and reactance of 0.35 and 0.8 ohm respectively per mile of wire, draws a charging current of 0.5 amp per mile when the line is tested at 100,000 volts to neutral. Calculate the efficiency when this line delivers 50,000 kw at 132,000 volts and when the power factor is 0.80 lagging.

4.26 A Y-connected generator rated at 220 volts has 0.2 ohm resistance and 2.0 ohms reactance per phase. The generator is connected by lines each having an impedance of $2.06\underline{/29.05^\circ}$ ohms to a Y-Y transformer bank. Each transformer has a total equivalent impedance referred to the high side of $100\underline{/60^\circ}$ ohms, and the transformer bank is connected through lines each of which has a resistance of 50 ohms and an inductive reactance of 100 ohms. If the ratio of transformation is 6 and the low-voltage side is connected to the generator lines, calculate the actual fault current for a three-phase symmetrical short circuit at the load.

4.27 The data for a 335-hp 2,000-volt three-phase six-pole 50-cycle Y-connected induction motor are as follows: ohmic resistance per phase of stator, 0.165 ohm; rotor, 0.0127 ohm; and ratio of transformation, 4:1. No-load test: line voltage, 2,000 volts; line current, 15.3 amp; and power, 10,100 watts. The friction and windage of the motor are 2,000 watts. Blocked test: line voltage, 440 volts; line current, 170 amp; power, 40,500 watts. When the slip is 0.015, determine (*a*) the current in stator and rotor, (*b*) motor output, (*c*) speed, (*d*) torque developed by rotor and torque at pulley, (*e*) power factor, and (*f*) efficiency.

4.28 A shunt-wound generator rated at 35 kw 125 volts is to be converted into a series generator to produce the same terminal voltage at rated load. The machine has six poles and each field spool has 480 turns and carries 11 amp. Calculate the number of turns on each spool of the series winding, neglecting drop in series field.

4.29 A 2,500-kva three-phase 60-cycle 6,600-volt alternator has a field resistance of 0.43 ohm and an armature resistance of 0.072 between each terminal and the neutral. The windings are Y-connected. The field current at full-load unity power factor is 200 amp, and at full-load 0.80 pf lagging it is 240 amp. The friction loss is 35 kw and the core loss, 47.5 kw. Assume friction and core loss constant at either unity power factor or 0.80 pf lagging.

a. Calculate the full-load efficiency at unity power factor.
b. Calculate the full-load efficiency at 0.80 pf.

4.30 A generator having 100 commutator segments is operating at 1,200 rpm. Each brush covers two commutator segments. If the current in the coil being commutated is 100 amp and its inductance is 0.10 millihenry, what is the emf of voltage of self-induction during commutation?

4.31 A 10-hp 550-volt 60-cps three-phase induction motor has a starting torque of 160 per cent of full-load torque and a starting current of 425 per cent full-load current.

a. What voltage is required to limit the starting current to full-load value?

b. If the motor is used on a 440-volt 60-cps system, what is the starting torque and starting current expressed in per cent of full-load values?

4.32 A 120-volt d-c motor rated at 5 hp has a field resistance of 50 ohms and an armature circuit resistance of 0.8 ohm. Approximately what starter resistance will be required to limit the armature current at starting to 200 per cent of rated armature current?

4.33 A 208-volt 60-cycle four-wire three-phase source of power supplies a 208-volt balanced motor load of 28.8 kw with a lagging power factor of 80 per cent. In addition, it supplies three 120-volt 60-amp resistive loads to neutral. If the circuit breaker should disconnect the phase load from one line to neutral, what would be the total currents in the four lines?

4.34 Oil circuit breakers have the following four ratings: (1) voltage, (2) continuous current, (3) short-time currents, and (4) interrupting current.

a. What is the relative magnitude of the last two, compared with the Continuous current?

b. State what parts of a breaker determine the values which may be assigned to each of these ratings.

c. State the parts of the system to which a breaker is connected. Determine, for each rating, the value which the breaker actually carries in operation.

4.35 The input to a 600-volt 100-hp synchronous motor is measured by the two-wattmeter method. One wattmeter reads plus 62.5 kw, and the other reads plus 30.5 kw. The motor is known to be taking a leading current. Determine the line current and the output if the efficiency of the motor at this load is 0.90 exclusive of the d-c field loss.

4.36 Two three-phase alternators are operating in parallel to supply a 4,000-kw unity power-factor load at 6,600 volts. The current delivered by alternator No. 1 is 200 amp at 0.85 pf leading. Find the power, power factor, and current for alternator No. 2.

4.37 Two alternators are to be operated in parallel. Explain what conditions must be met before closing the switch placing them in parallel. Explain what characteristics are required if the two machines are to share all leads in proportion to their respective ratings. How may the load be shifted from one machine to another? What factors determine the power factors of alternators supplying a definite load in parallel?

4.38 *a.* Name and describe in some detail three commercial methods of starting single-phase induction motors.

b. To how large a rating are single-phase induction motors available?

c. How would you reverse the direction of rotation of a repulsion-starting single-phase induction motor?

d. How does the universal motor differ from a d-c series motor?

4.39 A permanent-magnet loudspeaker is equipped with a 10-ohm 10-turn voice coil wound on a tube 1 in. in diameter. The flux density in the air gap is 10,000 lines per sq in. If the impedance of the voice coil is a pure resistance, what will be the maximum thrust delivered to the cone if the impressed signal is 20 db above 0.005 watt?

4.40 A power triode with fixed values of excitation and plate voltage, is working into a resistance load as a power converter. If the maximum power output occurs with a load resistance of 2,000 ohms, what is the approximate plate resistance of the tube?

4.41 Plate characteristic curves for a 2A3 tube (E_f = 2.5 volts direct current) accompany this question. Design a transformer-coupled audio amplifier to operate class *A*, without drawing grid current, from a 250-volt d-c plate supply voltage. It is to feed an 8-ohm nonreactive voice coil from a transformer (which may be assumed ideal) that is to present the tube with an effective load resistance having the recommended value of 2,500 ohms. The average tube dissipation under quiescent conditions is to be 15 watts. The shift in operating point with grid excitation may be neglected. Determine: (*a*) the turn ratio of the transformer; (*b*) the operating point; (*c*) the maximum rms sinusoidal signal voltage; and (*d*) the power output and current, second-harmonic distortion. Also, (*e*) draw a complete circuit diagram, giving all operating voltages.

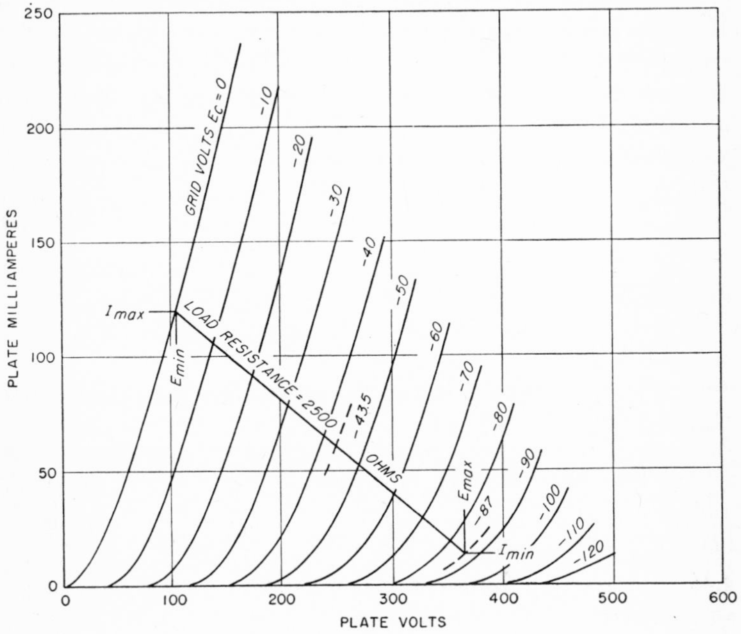

FIG. 4.41

4.42 A stack of selenium rectifier disks is rated at 2 amp average and 20 volts inverse peak per disk. A rectifier to operate from a 208 volt three-phase four-wire without transformers is desired.

Specify the number of disks per stack, and the number of single stacks required, together with the voltage and current capacity assuming 15 per cent voltage regulation from no load to full load, for the following cases:

a. The rectifier that will give the largest output without using stacks in parallel.

b. The rectifier that gives the smallest voltage ripples.

c. The rectifier that requires the smallest number of disks and still draws a balanced load. How does the ripple in this case compare with that of *b*?

4.43 A single-phase condenser motor, operating at rated load, takes 2.50 amp from a 220-volt line; the current in the 6.75-μf condenser is 1.30 amp, and the current in the main winding of the motor is 1.45 amp. The total power input is 550 watts.

a. What is the apparent impedance of the two windings of the motor?

b. What is the power delivered to each winding of the motor?

4.44 A vacuum tube draws a plate current of 6 ma when operating at 200 volts (plate) and −6 volts (grid). If the grid voltage is reduced to −4 volts (with the same plate voltage), the plate current is doubled. In order to bring the plate current back to its original value, the plate voltage had to be reduced to 150 volts. Find:

a. Amplification factor
b. Mutual conductance
c. Plate resistance

4.45 Show a diagram of internal connections for an assembly of gas diodes that will take power from a 208/120 four-wire three-phase 60-cycle system and supply 10 kw of direct current at 240/120 volts and three wires. Specify the rating of the tubes and any auxiliary equipment required. What can be done to make the output voltage independent of the load?

4.46 A wave trap for use in blocking carrier current frequencies as furnished by the manufacturer consists of an air core coil and a variable capacitor pack connected in parallel. The inductance of the coil is 260 microhenrys.

Calculate the capacitance in microfarads required to tune the trap for 60 kc.

4.47 A type 6L6 pentode is operated as an audio amplifier at 250 volts on the plate and 250 volts on the screen grid. It is transformer-coupled to an 8-ohm voice coil through a transformer with an impedance ratio of 312.5 to 1 and operated with a grid bias of −15 volts. Assume that the transformer is ideal and the grid signal is 10 volts rms. Using the curves for an RCA 6L6, compute approximately: (*a*) the dynamic operating point, corrected for effects of rectification with large signal; (*b*) the fundamental component of plate signal current; and (*c*) the percentage of second-harmonic distortion.

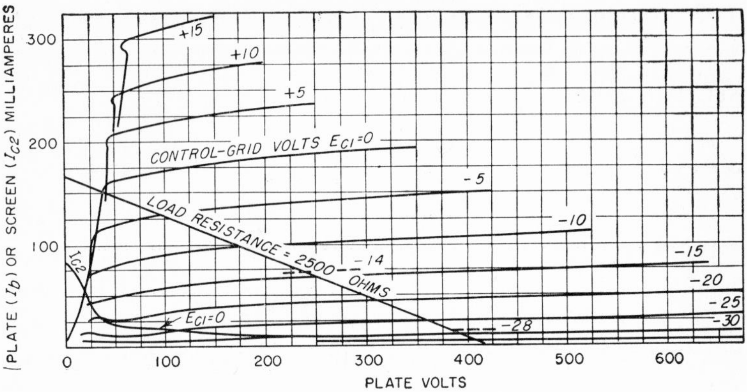

FIG. 4.47

4.48 A three-phase 230-volt wound rotor induction motor had been in operation for several years when minor trouble developed and, in checking, it was found that the line was connected to the rotor and that the stator terminals were connected to the controller and grids. Explain under what conditions of motor design this is possible.

4.49 A two-element 115-volt 5-amp polyphase watt-hour meter, having a basic watt-hour constant of $K_H = 2/3$, is connected to a three-phase three-wire circuit through 100/5-amp current transformers and 2,300/115-volt potential transformers. A stop-watch check shows that the meter disk is making 15 revolutions in 50 sec. What is the kilowatt load on the circuit?

4.50 Explain what means are generally employed to protect a transmission line against lightning and switching disturbance.

SECTION FIVE

5.01–5.25

ENGINEERING ECONOMICS AND BUSINESS RELATIONS

5.01 In production control, the following items are considered:

a. Standardization of equipment
b. Various raw materials used
c. Speed at which operations are performed
d. Sequence of operations
e. Preparation of work orders

Explain why each of these items is necessary.

5.02 Modern factory production in all its variety and complexity has been developed and brought to its present mechanical perfection principally through the application of the laws of specialization. State the four laws of specialization as applied to the job, the individual, the machine, and the product.

5.03 Give a definition of the following phrases in connection with company-union labor agreements:

a. Craft union
b. Industrial union
c. Open shop
d. Closed shop
e. Union shop
f. Industry-wide bargaining
g. Down-time pay
h. Maintenance of membership
i. Check-off
j. Seniority

5.04 What is meant by the following phrases in connection with company-union labor agreements?

a. Plant-wide seniority
b. Departmental seniority
c. Superseniority and synthetic seniority
d. Probationary employees
e. Grievance
f. Arbitration of grievances
g. Call-in pay
h. Portal-to-portal pay
i. Featherbedding
j. Boycotts

5.05 What are standard costs? How are they established and used?

5.06 Explain the law of diminishing returns using the variation in the height of a proposed office building as an example.

5.07 In what ways is safety related to plant layout?

5.08 What is meant by "preventive maintenance"? Outline briefly a procedure of operation for such a maintenance program in a particular industrial plant of your choice.

5.09 A small manufacturer with a maximum factory output of 1,200 machines per year prepared the following estimate of manufacturing expenses at various outputs:

Output	Direct labor and material	Indirect factory costs	Selling and administrative costs	Total cost	Unit cost
0	0	$28,000	$26,000	$ 54,000	
200	$16,000	30,000	27,000	73,000	$365.00
400	32,000	32,000	28,000	92,000	230.00
600	48,000	34,000	29,000	111,000	185.00
800	64,000	36,000	30,000	130,000	162.50
1,000	80,000	38,000	31,000	149,000	149.00
1,200	96,000	40,000	32,000	168,000	140.00

At the start of the year, after obtaining contrasts with reliable buyers for 600 machines at $160 each, it becomes evident that due to business conditions it will not be possible to sell any more machines in the domestic market for the remainder of the year regardless of price.

A reliable foreign purchaser offers to buy 600 machines at $100 each.

Disregarding all questions of long-run policy with respect to foreign sales, should the offer be accepted? Why?

5.10 A shoe manufacturer produces a pair of shoes at a labor cost of 90 cents a pair and a material cost of 80 cents a pair. The fixed charges on the business are $90,000 a month and the variable costs are 40 cents a pair. If the shoes sell for $3 a pair, how many pairs must be produced each month for the manufacturer to break even?

5.11 Define depreciation rate and give the general formula for determining it by (*a*) the straight-line method, and (*b*) the sinking-fund method. The Interstate Commerce Commission prescribes the former in maintaining the accounts of public utilities, while engineers customarily use the latter in determining the economic propriety of major undertakings. Explain why, although there is a radical difference in the rates developed by the two formulas, both of these choices are appropriate and adequate for their respective purposes.

5.12 *a.* To what extent are general partners liable for debts of the firm?

b. In what way would the formation of a limited partnership change the liability status of those who enter the firm as limited partners?

c. What is the purpose of providing for cumulative voting at stockholders' meetings instead of following the more usual method of giving one vote for each share?

5.13 Explain or discuss the differences of the following terms:

a. Partnership and corporation
b. Stock watering
c. Certified check
d. Corporation bond
e. Letter of credit
f. Bill of lading
g. Promissory note
h. Liquidated damages and unliquidated damages
i. Money and barter

5.14 What are the essential elements of a contract?

5.15 What conditions may render a contract illegal?

5.16 *a.* When may contracts be terminated before execution?

b. Under what conditions may a contract be taken out of the hands of a contractor?

5.17 State five rules of ethical behavior for a professional engineer.

5.18 Is it proper or improper for a professional engineer (*a*) to participate in competitive bidding against his colleagues to secure a professional engagement that is to go to the lowest bidder, or (*b*) to accept an engagement to review the work of another professional engineer without his knowledge? Give reasons for your answers.

5.19 An old, light-capacity highway bridge may be strengthened at a cost of $9,000 or it may be replaced by a modern bridge of sufficient capacity at a cost of $55,000. The present net salvage value of the old bridge is $13,000. It is estimated that the reinforced bridge will last for five years after which replacement will be necessary. At the end of the five years, the net salvage value of the reinforced bridge will be $10,000 and the net salvage value of the new bridge will be $15,000 after 30 years. The additional cost of maintenance and inspection of the old bridge will be $300 per year. Assuming interest at 6 per cent and depreciation on a straight line basis, state whether it is more economical to reinforce the old bridge or to replace it. Show the calculations on which you base your reply.

5.20 Which is the more economical: (*a*) a building costing $20,000 which will have to have an addition built 15 years from now at an additional cost of $10,000, or (*b*) a complete building constructed now at a cost of $25,000? Interest at 6 per cent. Assume life of the building is so long that depreciation may be neglected.

5.21 Two proposed types of bridges are to be compared as to capitalized cost at 6 per cent interest in perpetuity. Bridge *A* has a life of 30 years; initial cost and cost of renewal is $10,000; annual maintenance is $50; repairs every five years are $200; no salvage value. Bridge *B* has a life of 45 years; initial cost and cost of renewal is $15,000; no annual maintenance cost; repairs every five years are $100; salvage value is $3,000. Determine the capitalized cost of each.

5.22 A debt of $1,000 is to be paid off in five equal yearly payments, each payment combining an amortization installment and interest at 4 per cent on the previously unpaid balance of the debt. What should be the amount of each payment?

5.23 A syndicate wishes to purchase an oil well which, estimates indicate, will produce a net income of $200,000 per year for 30 years. What should the syndicate pay for the well if, out of this net income, a return of 10 per cent on the investment is desired and a sinking fund will be established at 3 per cent interest to recover the investment?

5.24 Two methods, *A* and *B*, of conveying water are being studied. Method *A* requires a tunnel, first cost $150,000; life perpetual, annual operation, and upkeep are $2,000. Method *B* requires a ditch plus a flume. First cost of ditch is $50,000; life perpetual, annual operation, and upkeep are $2,000. First cost of the flume is $30,000, life, 10 years; salvage value is $5,000; annual operation and upkeep are $4,000. Compare the two methods for perpetual service, assuming an interest rate of 5 per cent.

5.25 A $1,000,000 issue of 3 per cent 15-year bonds was sold at 95. If miscellaneous initial expenses of the financing were $20,000 and a yearly expense of $2,000 is incurred, what is the true cost to the nearest 0.5 per cent that the company is paying for the money it borrowed?

SECTION SIX

6.01–6.50

MECHANICAL ENGINEERING

6.01 At 5 cents per kwhr, how much will it cost to maintain a temperature of 96°F for 24 hr in a box 2 ft sq on each side if the outside temperature is 72°F and the over-all heat-transfer coefficient for the box is 0.1 Btu/(hr)(sq ft)(deg) difference in temperature?

6.02 A building located in Newark, N.J., is to be heated to 70°F during the hours from 8:00 A.M. to 5:00 P.M. and 50°F the rest of the day. The heat loss is 650,000 Btu per hr, based on a design temperature of −10°F. Coal with a calorific value of 13,500 Btu per lb is used with an efficiency of 65 per cent. How much coal will be required for a normal heating season? Degree-days for Newark are 5,210.

6.03 Find the season fuel cost of heating a building whose heat loss calculated on the basis of 70° and 0° is 240,000 Btu per hr, for a season of 7,000 degree-days.

a. Using coal at $4.50 per ton and 12,000 Btu per lb, with an efficiency burning of 60 per cent.

b. Using oil at 6 cents per gal and 142,000 Btu per gal, burned with an efficiency of 75 per cent.

c. Using gas at 80 cents per 1,000 cu ft and 550 Btu per cu ft, burned with an efficiency of 70 per cent.

6.04 Calculate the heat loss in Btu per sq ft per hr through a wall construction of 8-in. cinder block with 2 in. of cork and

½ in. of plaster on one side, and ½ in. of plaster on the other side. Assume still air on both sides having a temperature difference of 40°F.

6.05 The cross section of a wall of a cold storage room consists of 16 in. of brick ($K = 3.6$), and air space equivalent to the resistance of about 8 in. of brick, 8 more in. of brick, 4 in. of corkboard ($K = 0.3$) and 1.5 in. of cement plaster ($K = 2.3$).

Find the quantity of heat transmitted through the wall by conduction per day per square foot of wall surface when the temperatures of the inner and outer wall surfaces are 30 and 70°F, respectively.

6.06 Air passes through a duct at the rate of 1,800 cu ft per min, the dry-bulb temperature being 70°F and the relative humidity 40 per cent. It is proposed to raise the humidity of the air to 75 per cent by blowing into it (*a*) water spray at 50°F or (*b*) saturated steam at atmospheric pressure. How many pounds of water or steam will be required and what will be the final dry- and wet-bulb temperatures in each case? Assume adiabatic conditions and thorough mixing so as to produce uniform conditions.

6.07 Water enters a cooling tower at 126°F and leaves at 80°F. Air enters at 85°F and relative humidity 47 per cent and leaves in a saturated condition at 115°F. Determine:

a. Weight and volume of air needed per pound of water cooled.

b. Amount of water that can be cooled with 2,000 cfm of free air.

6.08 An auditorium seating 1,800 people is to be maintained at 78°F dry-bulb and 67° wet-bulb temperature when outdoor air is at 90°F dry-bulb and 75° wet-bulb. Solar heat load is 120,000 Btu per hr. Determine:

a. Cubic feet per minute of outdoor air required for ventilation.

b. Volume (in cfm) of conditioned air at 65°F dry-bulb that must be circulated to carry the total sensible heat load.

c. Wet-bulb temperature of the conditioned air to absorb the moisture load.

6.09 An auditorium seats 5,000 persons. The heat losses from the building are 1,250,000 Btu per hr. Assume each person to give off 220 Btu per hr sensible heat and 180 Btu per hr latent heat. Assume that 1,800 cu ft of ventilating air at outside air conditions is supplied per person per hour. The temperature of the air outdoors is 0°F and it is assumed to be dry.

$$\text{Barometer} = 14.5 \text{ psia}$$

There is no air recirculation. Vitiated air leaves the building at 70°F.

For air: $C_p = 0.241, \quad C_v = 0.171, \quad R = 53.34$

Determine:

a. Temperature at which ventilating air must enter auditorium.

b. The Btu that must be supplied by the heating coils per hour to the ventilating air.

6.10 In an auditorium maintained at a temperature not to exceed 75°F and a relative humidity not to exceed 60 per cent, a sensible heat load of 450,000 Btu per hour, and 1,200,000 grains of moisture per hour must be removed. Air is supplied to the auditorium at 65°F.

a. How many pounds of air per hour must be supplied?

b. What is the dew-point temperature and the relative humidity of the entering air?

c. How much latent heat load is picked up in the auditorium?

6.11 A fan whose static efficiency is 40 per cent has a capacity of 60,000 cu ft per hr at 60°F and a barometer of 30 in. Hg, and gives a static pressure of 2 in. of water column on full delivery. What size electric motor should be used to drive this fan?

6.12 A fan discharged 9,300 cfm of air through a duct 3 ft in diameter against a static pressure of 0.85 in. of water. The gage fluid density was 62.1 lb per cu ft, the air temperature 85°F and the barometric pressure 28.75 in. Hg. If the power input to the fan is measured as 3.55 hp, what is the over-all mechanical efficiency of the fan? What is the static efficiency of the fan?

6.13 What horsepower is supplied to air moving at 20 ft per min through a 2 by 3 ft duct under a pressure of 3 in. water gage?

6.14 A fan whose efficiency is 40 per cent has a capacity of 60,000 cu ft per hr at 60°, a barometer of 30 in., and gives a pressure of 2 in. of water column on full delivery. What size electric motor should be used to drive this fan? Give computations.

6.15 A refrigeration plant is rated at 20-ton capacity.

a. How many pounds of air per hour will it cool from 90 to 70°F at constant pressure?

b. What is the approximate engine horsepower required to operate the plant?

6.16 A single-acting twin-cylinder 12 by 12 in. compressor receives saturated ammonia vapor at 31.16 psia and discharges it at 180 psia. Saturated liquid enters the expansion valve. The water to be frozen is at 80°F and the manufactured ice is at 16°F. The speed of the compressor is 150 rpm and volumetric efficiency is 82 per cent. The ratio of the ideal to brake work of the compressor is 80 per cent. Assume specific heat of ice is 0.5 Btu per lb. Determine:

a. Capacity

b. Tons of ice per 24 hr, neglecting radiation losses

c. The brake horsepower of the compressor

6.17 In the two-speed planetary reduction gear shown schematically, either gear *A* or internal gear *C* can be clutched-in at will directly to a shaft rotating at constant speed, the other gear meanwhile being held stationary by means of a brake. (The clutch and brake mechanisms are not shown.) The gears are of 12 diametral pitch. Gear *A* has a pitch diameter of 3 in., and planet gears *BB* each have 18 teeth. Find the ratio between the high and low speeds of the follower shaft *D*.

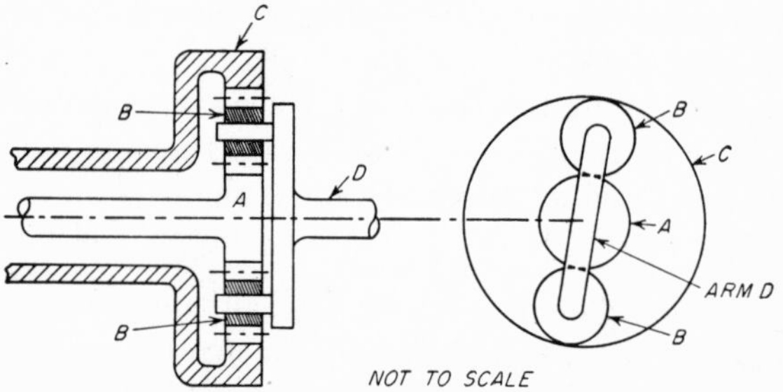

Fig. 6.17

6.18 An ideal refrigeration cycle using ammonia as the refrigerant compresses isentropically from saturated vapor at 20 to 190 psi. The temperature at the high-pressure side of the expansion valve is 80°F. Draw the *TS* diagram. Considering 1 lb, find (*a*) the net work, (*b*) the heat rejected to the condenser water, (*c*) the refrigeration, (*d*) the coefficient of performance, and (*e*) the pounds of NH_3 circulating per ton of refrigeration.

6.19 An airplane engine having 14 cylinders and a 5⅜-in. bore by 6-in. stroke develops a torque of 2,100 ft-lb at 2,500 rpm, peak power. The clearance volume of each cylinder is 23.4 cu in. Total engine weight is 1,450 lb. Calculate (*a*) the compression ratio, (*b*) the bmep at peak power, and (*c*) the bhp per lb.

6.20 *a*. A shaft made of SAE 1045 steel (ultimate = 97,000 psi and yield point = 58,000 psi) is subjected to a torque varying from 20,000 in-lb clockwise to 6,000 in-lb counterclockwise. What would be the diameter of the shaft if the factor of safety is 2 based on the yield point and the endurance strength in shear?

b. Find the diameter of the shaft when it transmits a constant torque of 20,000 in-lb and the factor of safety is 2, as in *a*.

c. Explain the reason for the difference in diameters obtained in *a* and *b*.

6.21 A metal transport plane has a wing spread of 88 ft. What difference of potential exists between the extremities of the wings when the airplane moves in a horizontal plane with a speed of 150 mph? The value of the vertical component of the earth's magnetic field is 0.65 gauss at the airplane.

6.22 *a*. Define a boiler horsepower.

b. What is the relationship between a boiler horsepower and a mechanical horsepower?

c. Calculate the horsepower of a boiler generating 4,000 lb of dry steam per hr, with a factor of evaporation of 1.06. The latent heat of steam at 212°F is 970 Btu per lb.

6.23 A steam boiler on a test generates 885,000 lb of steam in a 4-hr period. The average steam pressure is 400 psia, the average steam temperature is 700°F, and the average temperature of the feedwater supplied to the boiler is 280°F. If the boiler efficiency for the period is 82.5 per cent, and if the coal has a heating value of 13,850 Btu per lb as fired, find the average amount of coal burned in short tons per hour.

6.24 A test of an oil-fired boiler indicated 12.77 lb of water evaporated per lb of oil. The boiler pressure was 200 psia, superheat was 87°F., feedwater temperature 93°F and boiler and furnace efficiency 82.8 per cent. What was the calorific value of the oil?

6.25 Assume you are called upon to make a heat balance test of a 500-sq-ft coal-fired steam boiler when operating at 100 per cent of rating. Steam is generated at a pressure of about 100 psig and is returned as condensate without loss at a temperature of about 150°F.

No testing equipment whatever is available at the plant but it may be assumed that facilities exist for the attachment of necessary testing apparatus.

a. What performance data or results would you present in your report? Be specific and complete but do not include irrelevant material.

b. What testing equipment would you select to make the test? Where possible, indicate the size, range, or capacity of the equipment you specify.

c. Make a line diagram indicating the test setup you would use, locating pertinent test apparatus.

d. Indicate the formulas or expressions you would use to determine *a* above and define all symbols in these expressions.

6.26 A stoker-fired boiler plant having dutch-oven-type furnaces was operated for a year with an average flue-gas analysis of 13 per cent CO_2, 0 per cent CO, and 6.25 per cent O_2, and combustible matter to ash pit 10 per cent. The second year an effort was made to raise the efficiency and an average flue-gas analysis of 15 per cent CO_2, 0.1 per cent CO, and 3.9 per cent O_2 was maintained with 16 per cent combustible matter to ash pit. A high grade of Pennsylvania bituminous slack coal was burned both years, having 7 per cent ash and 14.200 Btu bone dry. At the end of the second year it was found that the efficiency was the same as for the first year of operation yet the cost per 1,000 lb of steam had increased 2 per cent. Explain.

6.27 As chief engineer of a large industrial plant you are asked by company executives to study the possibilities connected with a proposal of a nearby steam plant to sell you steam for all your requirements. Assuming your boilers to be serviceable and in no immediate need of extensive repairs, how much (cents per 1,000 lb of steam delivered) would you be willing to pay for such service, if the following were the conditions at your plant:

a. Four boilers with annual average efficiency of 70 per cent.

b. Personnel for boiler operation and maintenance—12 men.

c. Fuel—coal burned on underfed stokers—12,000 Btu per lb, $4.50 per ton.

d. Feedwater—60 per cent return from system—the balance, city water at 7 cents per 1,000 gal—lime soda softeners.

e. Lubricants, miscellaneous supplies—$2,000 per year.

6.28 A multistage impulse turbine running at 3,600 rpm and delivering 1,000 hp, receives steam at 180 psia and 600°F, and the exhaust is at 16 psia. It is desired to limit the peripheral velocity of the turbine blading to approximately 625 ft per sec. The stage efficiency is 75 per cent, all stages are of the same diameter, and the reheat factor may be initially assumed at 1.06. Making suitable allowances for various losses, determine the proper number of stages, the actual engine efficiency and the ideal and actual steam rates.

6.29 A Corliss engine 28 in. diameter by 54 in. stroke, driving a three-roller cane mill through double-reduction machine-cut spur-gearing runs at 60 rpm, receives live steam at the throttle at 150 psi saturated steam and exhausts against 15 psi pressure. Valve gear is set for $\frac{3}{8}$ cutoff. Piston rod is 5 in. diameter. Engine does not have tail rod. Assuming a transmission loss of 10 per cent in each gear reduction and an additional loss of 15 per cent for misalignments in the mill coupling and crownwheels, determine:

a. Mean effective pressures at head and crank ends

b. Horsepower delivered by engine at crankshaft

c. Horsepower delivered to mill

6.30 A steam-electric generating station has four 10,000-kw turbogenerators. Steam is supplied at 250 psia and 600°F. Exhaust is at 2 in. Hg abs. Daily load factor is 75 per cent. Assuming average steam rates and efficiencies, determine:

a. Tons of coal required per day

b. Condenser cooling water in gallons per minute

6.31 A car engine rated at 12 hp gives a maximum torque of 6,516 in-lb. The clutch is of a single-plate type, and both sides of the plate are effective. The coefficient of friction is 0.3, the axial pressure is limited to 12 psi, and the external radius of friction surface is 1.25 times the internal radius. Find the dimensions of the plate and the total axial pressure which must be exerted by the springs.

6.32 A four-cylinder engine is equipped with a flywheel which may be considered to have an effective weight of 50 lb concentrated in the rim at a mean radius of 7 in. The excess energy delivered to the flywheel, which increases its speed from minimum to maximum, is estimated to be 20 per cent of the indicated work per revolution. At an output of 20 hp, the mean speed is 1,800 rpm and the mechanical efficiency of the engine is 80 per cent. Find the total speed variation.

6.33 A single-stage impulse turbine receives steam having an available energy of 100 Btu per lb. Five per cent of the maximum theoretical nozzle exit velocity is lost through nozzle friction; 10 per cent of the entering relative velocity is lost by the steam in passing through the blading. The nozzle makes an angle of 20° with the plane of the wheel. The blading is symmetrical, i.e., equal entrance and exit angles. Blade speed is 900 ft per sec. Assume nozzle inlet velocity negligible. Calculate:

a. Steam velocity leaving nozzle.

b. Relative velocity entering blade.

c. Relative velocity leaving blade.

d. Absolute exit velocity.

e. Blade entrance angle.

f. Force exerted on blade by each pound of steam flowing per second.

g. Blade horsepower if 1,800 lb of steam flow per hr.

h. Shaft horsepower. Friction between the steam and the wheel absorbs 6 hp. Bearing and governors take 2 hp. Assume this 2 hp does not go into the steam.

i. Steam entering the turbine has an enthalpy of 1,200 Btu per lb. Neglecting radiation losses from the turbine, what should be the enthalpy of the steam leaving the turbine if the energy due to residual velocity goes to increasing the enthalpy of the steam.

6.34 Heat-transfer equipment with a variable steam load up to 20,000 lb per hr requires 200 equivalent ft of pipe-line connection to a source of steam supply at 125 psig pressure. The maximum safe working steam pressure in the equipment is 25 psig pressure. Determine the size of the pipe for the connecting line, and make a rough sketch showing the arrangement of the essential valves in this line.

6.35 A tubular-type air heater has 31,154 sq ft of heating surface and heats 357,000 lb per hr of air from 80 to 479°F. Flue gas enters at 725°F. and leaves at 405°F. What is the heat-transfer rate, in Btu/(sq ft)(hr)(deg) mean temperature, difference? What is the weight of flue gas passing through?

6.36 Exhaust steam at 1 psig pressure and containing 12 per cent moisture is fed into an open-type feed-water heater. How many pounds of this steam are required to raise the temperature of 1,000 lb of water from 60 to 200°F? The barometric pressure is 30 in. Hg.

6.37 Diesel fuel, $C_{12}H_{26}$, when injected into compressed air burns at a 30 to 1 air fuel ratio by weight. If the engine exhausts at 600°F into a heating system where the room temperature is 75°F what per cent of the fuel supplied is available to the heating system? From the combustion equation, the gas leaving the engine is made up of: $12CO_2$, $13H_2O$, $69.56N_2$, and 88.06 air.

6.38 A test on a 1-cylinder Otto 4-cycle (typical gasoline engine) internal-combustion engine yielded the following data: torque, 700 ft-lb; mean effective pressure, 110 psi; bore, 11 in.; stroke, 12 in.; speed, 300 rpm; fuel consumption, 24 lb per hr; and lower heating value of fuel, 18,000 Btu per lb. Find:

a. The thermal efficiency of the engine.

b. The mechanical efficiency.

c. The fuel cost of horsepower per hour with fuel at 10 cents per gallon.

6.39 *a.* An automobile motor has a torque of 230 ft-lb, driving the rear axles through a differential having a ratio of 4.11, and an efficiency of 97 per cent. Calculate the tractive effort at the rear wheels, their diameters being 30 in.

b. What rear-wheel horsepower is developed when the speed is 40 mph?

6.40 Calculate the bore and stroke of a 6-cylinder automobile motor to deliver 30 bhp at 1,800 rpm, the ratio of stroke to bore being 1.4. Assume the mean effective pressure in the cylinder to be 90 psi and the mechanical efficiency 85 per cent.

6.41 *a.* What width of single leather belt is required to deliver 10 hp when running on a pulley 6 in. in diameter at 1,700 rpm? State the rule used.

b. How does a crown hold a belt on the center of a pulley?

6.42 A screw press, having two screws of ½ in. pitch and exerting a pressure of 50 tons, is to be driven by an electric motor running at 1,700 rpm and connected to the screws by a suitable train of gears, the successive ratios of which are not to exceed 6 to 1. The pressure head is moved at the rate of 1 in. per min. The over-all efficiency is assumed to be 40 per cent. Sketch a suitable gear train and calculate the horsepower delivered by the motor when the press is operating at 50 tons pressure.

6.43 Find suitable pitch and width of face for a pair of 14½° involute spur gears to transmit 8 hp. The velocity ratio is to be 2 to 3 and the distance between centers is 10 in. The pinion is to be of mild steel and is to run at 150 rpm. The gear is to be bronze.

6.44 Two three-speed pulleys are to be connected by a crossed belt. The driving shaft runs at a constant speed of 200 rpm and the driven shaft at 50, 150, and 500 rpm. Calculate the diameters of the steps on both pulleys, assuming the diameter of the smallest step on the driven pulley to be 6 in.

6.45 Sketch a form of mechanism producing the following types of motion: (*a*) slow advance and quick return, (*b*) rotary into straight-line harmonic, (*c*) parallel straight line, (*d*) intermittent rotary from continuous rotary, and (*e*) rotary rocking from continuous rotary.

6.46 *a.* Sketch three common types of power screw threads and note the advantage and/or disadvantage of each.

b. Prove that the length of a nut should equal the diameter of the bolt if the shearing stress is one-half the tensile stress.

6.47 What weight can be lifted by a screw jack that has an efficiency of 80 per cent, if it is operated by a 50-lb force at the end of a 30-in. lever and the pitch of the screw is ½ in.?

6.48 A hoist consists of a drum 24 in. in diameter fastened to a gear wheel with 80 teeth. The gear wheel is turned by a double-threaded worm. If the hoist can raise a 4,000-lb weight on a ⅞-in. rope at the rate of 100 fpm, what torque and horsepower are being supplied at the shaft of the worm gear? Assume a mechanical efficiency of 60 per cent.

6.49 A safety valve spring having 9½ coils has the ends squared and ground. The outside diameter of the coil is 4½ in. and the wire diameter is ½ in. It has a free length of 8 in. Determine the length to which this spring must be initially compressed to hold a boiler pressure of 205 psig on a 1¼-in. diameter valve seat.

Determine the stress if the spring is compressed to its solid length.

$$E_s = 11.5 \times 10^6 \text{ psi}$$

Calculations and formula must be shown.

6.50 Construct the outline of a disk cam to give uniform acceleration and deceleration to a pointed follower which rises 3 in. while the cam turns through 180°, dwells for 60° cam rotation, falls with uniform velocity while the cam turns through 60°, and dwells the remaining 60°.

SECTION SEVEN

7.01–7.75

STRUCTURAL ENGINEERING

7.01 A steel hanger consists of a plate 5 by ¼ in. held at the top by four ¾-in. rivets in single shear. The rivets are arranged in diamond form so that the first net section has one hole and the second net section has two holes. In which way is the joint most likely to fail? What is the efficiency of the joint? Use unit stresses of 16,000 psi for tension, 12,000 psi for shear, and 24,000 psi for bearing.

7.02 A tension member is made up of ⅜-in. thick steel plates 9 in. wide and spliced by a lap joint made with three rows of ¾-in. bolts snug fit in drilled holes and arranged in the pattern shown. The permissible stresses in the bolts and the plates are: 20,000 psi for tension in the net section, 16,000 psi for shear, and 32,000 psi for bearing. (*a*) What is the maximum permissible tension in the plates in pounds? (*b*) What is the efficiency of the joint in per cent?

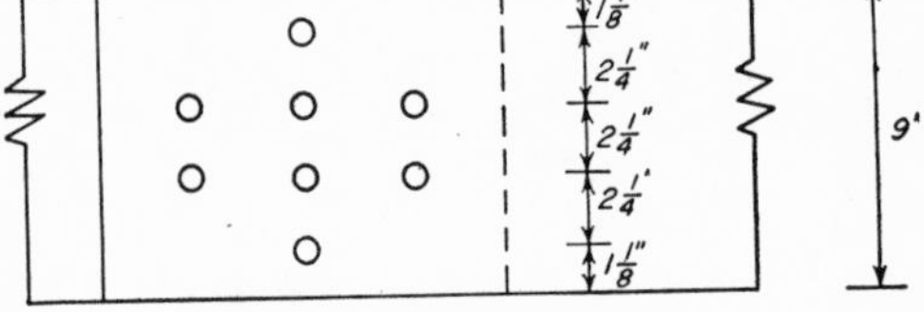

Fig. 7.02

7.03 A double-covered riveted butt seam has main plates ½ in. thick and 5⁄16-in. cover plates. The rivets are ¾ in. in diameter (the holes 13⁄16 in.) and are arranged in four rows, two on each side of the seam. The pitch in the rows next to the seam is three rivet diameters, and in the outer rows six rivet diameters. Find the allowable load per inch of seam and the working efficiency. The permissible working stresses in the rivets and plates are: 16,000 psi for tension, 10,000 psi for shear, and 20,000 psi for bearing.

7.04 Two plates ¾ in. thick are to be spliced for tension by 7/16-in. plates. Rivets are ⅞ in. diameter and holes 15/16 in. Permissible working stresses in rivets and plates are: tension, 16,000 psi; shear, 12,000 psi; and bearing, 24,000 psi. With the rivet layout as follows, what would be the pitch to the nearest inch for high efficiency? What is the efficiency?

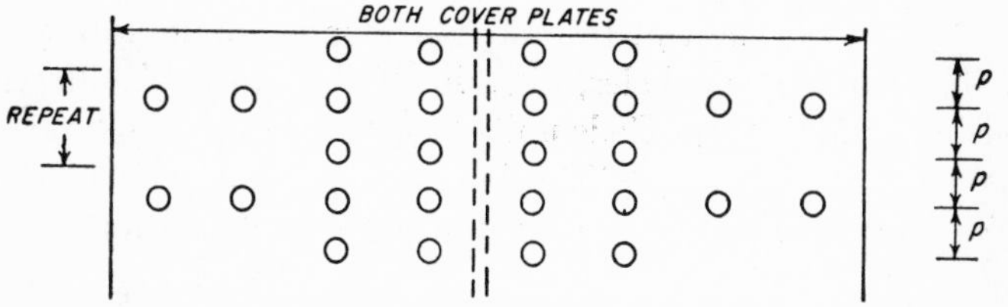

FIG. 7.04

7.05 A 5-ft diameter tank is to be designed to withstand an internal working pressure of 500 psi. All rivets are to be the same size for both the transverse and longitudinal double cover-plated butt joints. Rivet holes are drilled 1/16 in. larger diameter than the rivets. Working stresses for plates and rivets are: tension, 20,000 psi; shear, 15,000 psi; and bearing, 24,000 s.s., 30,000 d.s. If the longitudinal rivet pattern is as shown, what is the rivet pitch to the nearest inch, the efficiency of the joint, and the thickness of the main plate and cover plates?

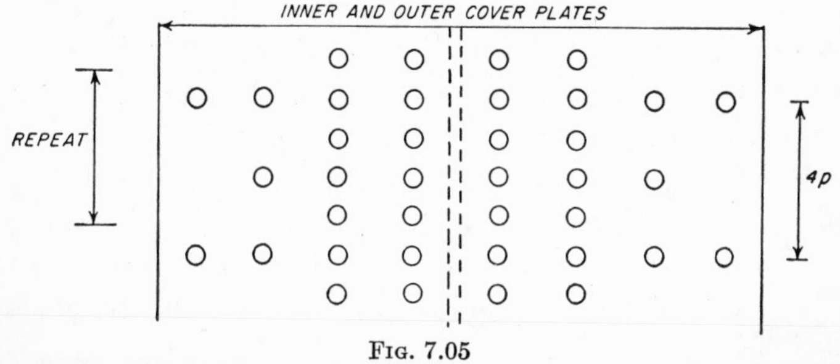

FIG. 7.05

7.06 What will be the rivet pitch and cover-plate thickness for the transverse plate splice of question 7.05 for the rivet pattern shown?

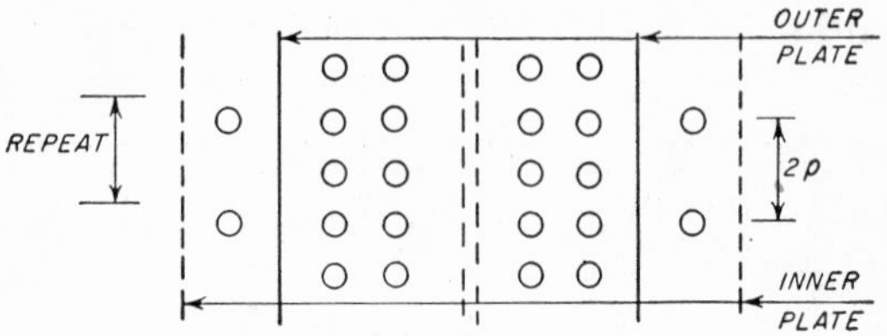

FIG. 7.06

7.07 The longitudinal quadruple-riveted butt joint shown has ¾-in. thick main plates and ½ in. splice plates. Rivets are 1⅛ in. diameter and holes, 1³⁄₁₆ in. If this splice was designed by using ASME Boiler Code unit stresses of 11,000 psi in tension, 8,800 psi in shear, and 19,000 psi in bearing, what is the efficiency of the splice and in what way is the splice likely to fail?

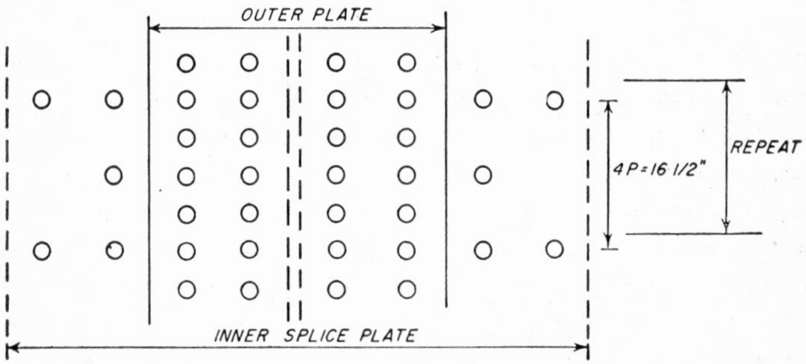

FIG. 7.07

7.08 Design a longitudinal lap joint for a tank 72 in. in diameter carrying 125 psi internal pressure. The allowable working stresses are: 16,000 psi in tension, 12,000 psi in shear, and 24,000 psi in bearing.

7.09 Design a welded joint as shown to develop the full strength of the angle in tension. The allowable stress in the throat of the fillet welds is 15,000 psi and the tensile stress in the angle is 20,000 psi.

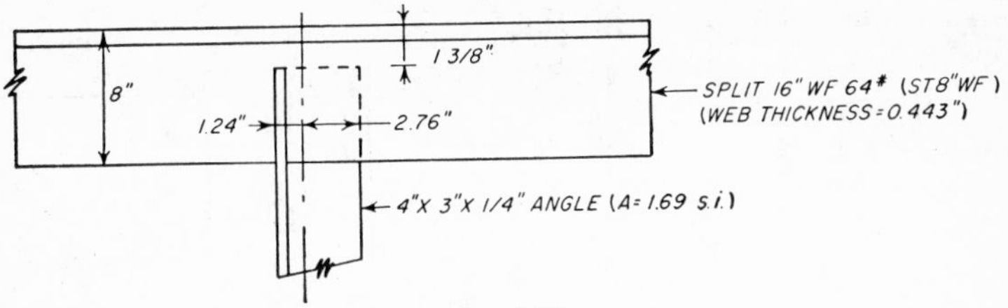

FIG. 7.09

7.10 Design a welded joint to develop the full strength of the T in tension. The allowable stresses in fillet welds are: 2,000 lb per in. for ¼-in. fillet weld; 2,500 lb per in. for 5⁄16 in.; 3,000 lb per in. for ⅜ in.; and 3,500 lb per in. for 7⁄16 in. Tensile stress in the T is 20,000 psi.

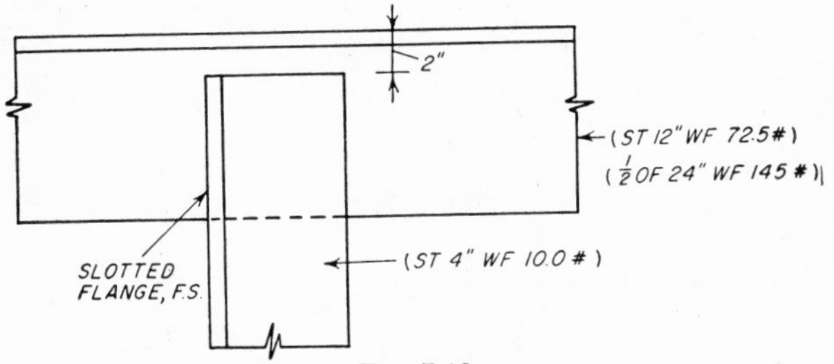

FIG. 7.10

7.11 A single plate 9 by 26 in. is fastened to the flange of a column with six bolts snug fit in drilled holes and arranged as shown. The working stresses in the bolts and the plate may be: 16,000 psi in shear, 32,000 psi in bearing, and 20,000 psi in tension. What diameter of bolts and thickness of plate should be used and what is the size of the load P if the maximum load on a corner rivet shall not exceed 9,500 lb?

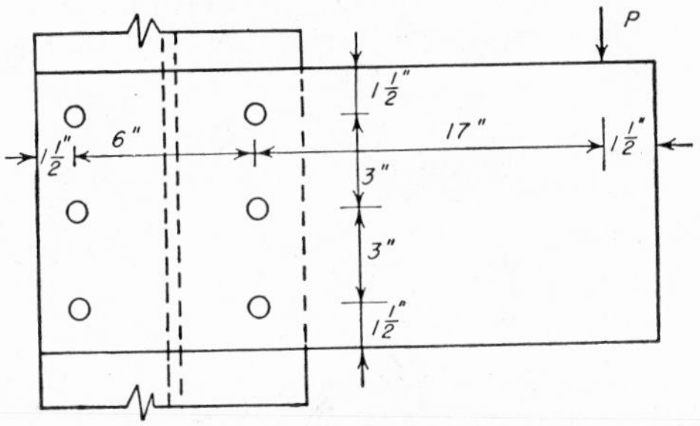

FIG. 7.11

7.12 Find the force in the outermost rivet under combined shear and torsion of the bracket shown.

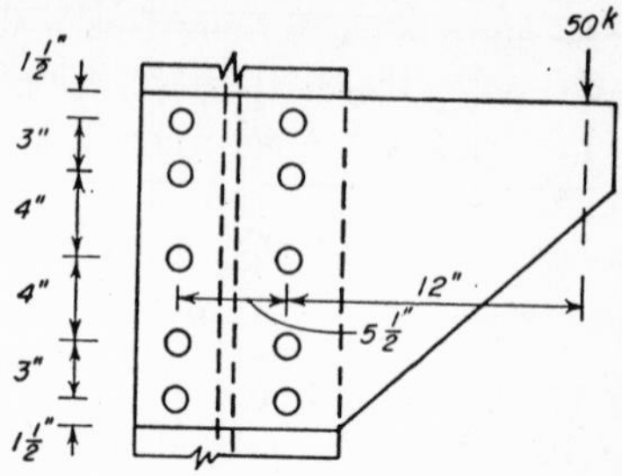

Fig. 7.12. Two ½-in. plates, one on each flange of column. All rivets are ⅞ in. diameter.

7.13 Find the force per inch in the outermost inch of fillet weld under combined shear and torsion of the following bracket of one plate and 32 in. of ¼-in. fillet weld.

Is this a good arrangement of welds?

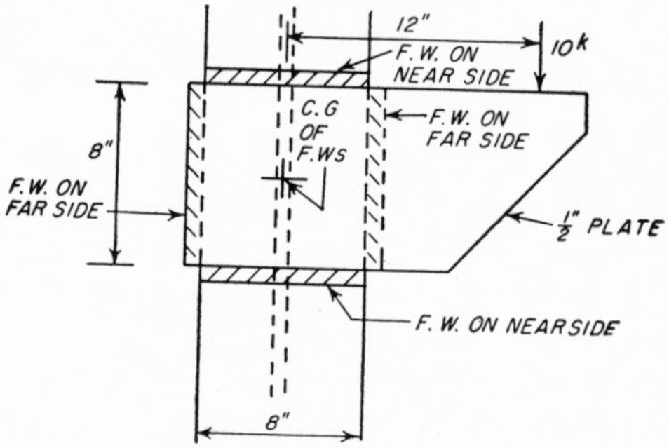

Fig. 7.13

7.14 An A4 standard beam connection is made up of two angles 4 by 3½ by ⅜ in. with 4-in. legs outstanding. Rivets are ⅞ in. diameter. What is the tension in the top rivet under a maximum shear loading?

7.15 An A10 standard beam connection is made up of two angles 4 by 3½ by 7/16 in. with 4-in. legs outstanding. Rivets are ⅞ in. diameter. What is the tension in the top rivet under a maximum shear loading?

7.16 A bracket in the form of a plate 12 by ⅝ in. by 1 ft 6 in. is to be welded to the 12-by 1-in. flange of a WF column section.

The plate is to be placed with the 18-in. side horizontal and symmetrically located with respect to the center line of the flange. The bracket is to support a pair of vertical forces of 100,000 lb each spaced 16 in. apart and symmetrically located with respect to the flange. Design the weld for this connection if the allowable shearing stress through the throat of the weld is 13,000 psi.

7.17 The main material of a plate girder consists of a web plate 42 by ⅜ in., four angles 6 by 4 by ⅝ in. placed 42½ in. back to back of 6-in. legs, and two cover plates 14 by ½ in. What total uniform load may be placed on this girder if the span is 30 ft? What is the maximum permissible spacing of ¾-in. rivets in the vertical legs of the flange angles at a point where the total shear is 75,000 lb?

7.18 A simply supported 50-ft-long plate girder of 36½ in. depth back to back of angles and without cover plates is to be designed for a single moving concentrated load of 70 kips (including impact). The top flange is considered to be laterally supported. The web plate has already been selected at 36 by ⅜ in. Select proper flange angles and compute the maximum end of girder flange to web rivet pitch for ¾-in. rivets. The fiber stress should not exceed 18,000 psi and shear in rivets 15,000 psi.

7.19 A plate girder having a simple span of 60 ft carries a total uniform load of 5,000 lb per lin ft. Design a section to take the maximum moment.

7.20 A channel and a WF beam form a T beam of 30 ft simple span. What concentrated load P may be supported at the center of the T beam if the shear in the rivets is not to exceed 15,000 psi, the fiber stress in the WF is not to exceed 20,000 psi in tension, the fiber stress in the channel is not to exceed 17,050 psi, and the deflection for the concentrated load is not to exceed $1/360$ of the span? Channel: weight = 33.9 lb, d = 15 in., a = 9.90 in.², I = 312.6 and 8.2 in.⁴, x = 0.79 in., web t = 0.400 in. WF section: d = 18.16 in., a = 28.22 in.², I = 1,674.7 and 206.8 in.² Rivets: diameter = ⅝ in., spacing 6-in. centers longitudinally.

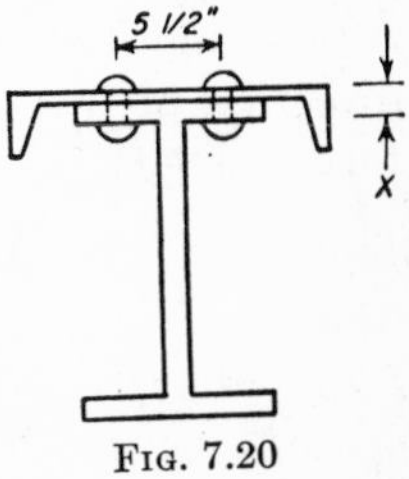

FIG. 7.20

7.21 A crane-runway girder of 21 ft span is simply supported at the ends. The girder carries a pair of moving wheel loads with axles 11 ft 4 in. on centers. Each wheel load carries 38,500 lb. Determine the maximum bending stress in the girder if the section is made up of a 24 WF 80 on top of which is fastened a 12-in. by 20.7-lb channel with the flanges turned down, and indicate the reasonableness of the bending stresses. Also compute the maximum permissible pitch for the two rows of ¾-in. diameter rivets, one on each side of the top beam flange, holding the two sections together.

Allowable rivet shearing stress = 15,000 psi, and bearing stress = 32,000 psi. WF section: depth = 24 in., area = 23.54 in.^{2}, I = 2,230 and 82.4 in.^{4}, flange thickness = 0.727 in., and web thickness = 0.455 in. Channel: d = 12 in., a = 6.03 in.^{2}, I = 128.1 and 3.9 in.^{4}, x = 0.70 in., flange t = 0.501 in., and web t = 0.280 in.

7.22 A steel beam 24 ft long carrying a total uniformly distributed load of 10,000 lb per ft is supported at the two ends and at the center. Compute the change in bending moment at the center of the span when the center reaction settles ½ in. I of the beam = 1,373 in.^{4}, and E of the beam = 30,000,000 psi.

7.23 What would be the sizes required for the three WF steel beams of the horizontal frame in question 1.618, considering only the tank loads? What AISC standard end connections are needed? Neglect deflection considerations.

7.24 Find the amount and direction of the deflection (in terms of EI) at the $4P$ load.

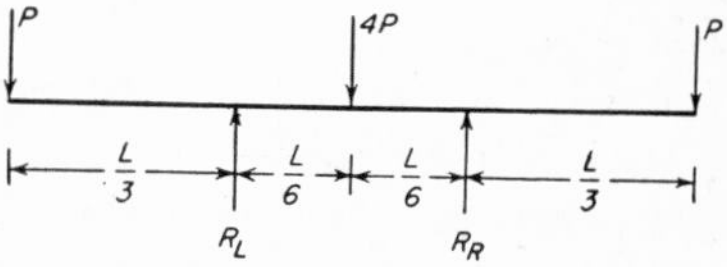

FIG. 7.24

7.25 Find the location and amount of the maximum deflection (in terms of EI) for this beam.

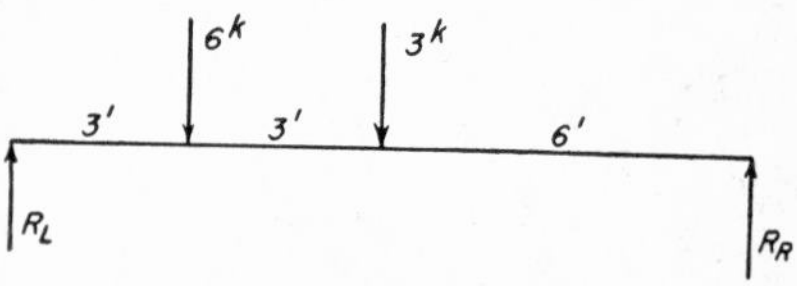

FIG. 7.25

7.26 A 20-ft beam of I moment of inertia has top and bottom cover plates over the center 10 ft of the beam giving a moment of inertia of $2I$ for the built-up section. The beam carries a uniform load of 1 kip per ft over the full length of the beam and 10 kips of load concentrated at the center. Find the deflection at the center in terms of EI.

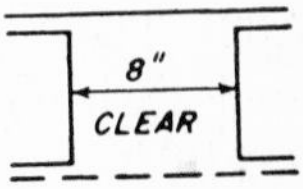

FIG. 7.27

7.27 An elevated water tank has legs consisting of two channels, one cover plate, and one open side adequately latticed. These legs are continuous for a height of 100 ft, but they are fixed at their ends and braced both ways at each 20-ft interval. What is the maximum capacity of one leg if the allowable unit stress is given by $f_s = 17{,}000 - 0.485(L/r)^2$?

One plate 13 by ⅜ in.

Two 8-in. channels at 11.5 lb each.

Properties of one channel are: $A = 3.36$ in.², $I_{x\text{-}x} = 32.3$ in.⁴, $I_{y\text{-}y} = 1.3$ in.⁴, $x = 0.58$ in.

7.28 A top chord member of a bridge truss is made up of two 15-in. 50 lb channels (placed 12 in. clear distance with flanges turned out), with one 22 by ¾-in. cover plate, and with one open side adequately latticed. The member is supported in either a horizontal or a vertical plane by members or bracing at panel points that are 25 ft on centers, and the chord may be considered fixed at these points. What is the safe axial load, applied at the center of gravity of the cross section, that the chord may carry (neglecting deflection), if the unit stress is governed by the formula $15{,}000 - L^2/4r^2$?

7.29 A 15-ft H column is made up of four angles 4 by 3 by ⅜ in. and a web plate 8 by ⅜ in. The angles are 8½ in. back to back with long legs outstanding. What is the permissible concentric load according to a standard column formula?

7.30 A steel column unbraced for a length of 20 ft is made up of a 14 WF 287 and two cover plates 22 by 2 in. Will this column carry a concentrated load of 1,250 kips placed on the axis of the web of the WF but acting as on the inner face of one of the cover plates? Use AISC column formula and method of design. For the 14 WF 287, $A = 84.37$ in.², $d = 16.81$ in., $I_{1\text{-}1} = 3{,}912$ in.⁴, $I_{2\text{-}2} = 1{,}466.5$ in.⁴.

7.31 A column with an unsupported length of 20 ft carries a centrally applied load of 210,000 lb and an eccentric load of 40,000 lb applied at a distance of 24 in. from the center line. What is the size of column required?

7.32 The bottom chord of a roof truss is to be made of two steel angles with vertical legs ½ in. clear back to back. The angles are 10 ft long center to center of truss panel points and carry a load of 65,000 lb in tension. The angles are connected to a ½-in. thick gusset plate at each end by a single row of ⅞-in. rivets passing through the vertical legs. What size angles will be required, taking into consideration both the eccentricity of the connection and bending due to the weight of the angles, if the maximum tensile stress is not to exceed 22,500 psi?

7.33 The bottom chord of a bridge truss is to be made of two channels with flanges outstanding and with webs vertical and 12 in. clear distance apart. If the tensile stress is not to exceed 18,000 psi and shear and bearing of rivets is not to exceed 15,000 psi and 32,000 psi respectively, what size channels will be required (if they are adequately laced one to the other) to carry a tension of 350,000 lb and bending due to their own weight? The length of the chord is 25 ft center to center of panel points.

7.34 The top chord of a roof truss, having a very slight slope, is to be made of a structural T (ST) section and is continuous over panel points 8 ft on centers. Purlins bring 4,000-lb concentrations of load to the roof truss at the panel points and halfway between these points. This is to be a welded truss with center of gravity of members matching the joint-line diagram of the truss. Design the chord member, by AISC standards, to carry an axial compressive load of 60,000 lb.

7.35 If the top chord in question 7.34 had carried a compressive load of 75,000 lb and been made up of an angle and plate set symmetrically on each side of ½-in. gusset plates and fastened with ⅞-in. rivets, what would be a satisfactory cross section for the chord?

7.36 The top chord of a roof truss has a slope of 1 vertical to 2 horizontal. What size standard I-beam purlin is required to satisfy the following conditions if the combined bending stress is not to exceed 18,000 psi?

Span of purlin is 20 ft. Purlin is simply supported at its ends with the bottom flange resting on top chord of roof truss.

The purlin is supported in the plane of the top chord of the roof truss by sag rods at the third points of the purlins running to the ridge purlins. There is a load normal to the top flange of the purlin of 90 lb per ft of purlin, and a vertical load of 160 lb per ft including the weight of the purlin.

7.37 What diameter bolt is required if the bolt is subjected to a tension of 20,000 lb and a torque (for tightening) of 6,000 in-lb and the maximum normal stress is not to exceed 25,000 psi?

7.38 A 4- by 6-in. timber beam has a 4- by ½-in. steel plate connected to the lower surface. Find the neutral axis of the combination. What is the maximum fiber stress in the steel when that in the wood is 600 psi? E_S = 30,000,000 psi, and E_W = 1,500,000 psi. Use nominal sizes for the timber.

7.39 24 WF 160 stringers are spaced 5 ft on centers and have a 7-in. concrete slab bonded to the top flange of the steel stringers by means of Z-bar shear adapters. The top of the concrete is 5½ in. above the top of the WF. If the stringers make 40-ft simple spans and carry the full dead weight, what static concentrated load at the center of each stringer may the composite section carry if the stress in the steel is not to exceed 18,000 psi and the stress in the concrete 1,350 psi?

7.40 In a composite beam of question 7.39, if the end shear were 33,000 lb, what would be the spacing of the Z-bar shear adapters at the end of the beam if they are fastened to the top flange of the WF stringer with two ⅞-in. rivets?

7.41 A vertical retaining wall made of reinforced concrete is 18 ft high and is rigidly supported at the base. The wall is loaded by earth pressure which varies from 0 at the top to 540 psf at the base. For a 1-ft wall length, determine the wall thickness at the base and design the steel needed at the base. Use $f'_c = 2{,}500$ psi and $f_s = 18{,}000$ psi and 1951 ACI specifications.

7.42 A reinforced concrete slab is simply supported on two parallel supports 10 ft center to center and carries a uniform live load of 400 psf. Design the slab by 1951 ACI specifications if the ultimate strength of the concrete is not to be less than 3,000 psi.

7.43 A pit, walled with concrete, is rectangular in shape. A reinforced concrete slab is to be designed to frame on top of the four walls, with a small amount of continuity. The center-to-center distance between wall bearings is 12 ft for the short span and 30 ft for the long span. Design the slab by the 1951 ACI specifications to carry a uniform live load of 300 psf if f'_c is to be 3,000 psi minimum and f_s is to be 18,000 psi.

7.44 A concrete beam as shown has a simple span of 15 ft. It was designed according to 1951 ACI specifications with $f'_c = 3{,}000$ psi and $f_s = 18{,}000$ psi. Assuming that the web reinforcement is satisfactory, what concentrated live load may be carried at the center of the span if the deflection due to this load is not to exceed 1/800 of the span?

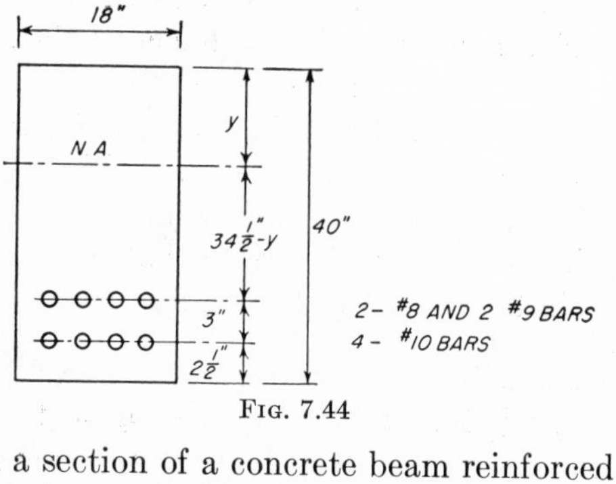

FIG. 7.44

7.45 Design a section of a concrete beam reinforced for tension only. The beam is simply supported on a span of 20 ft and carries a total load of 1,500 lb per ft. What stirrups will be required? Use the 1951 ACI specifications with $f'_c = 2{,}500$ psi and $f_s = 18{,}000$ psi. Make $b = \frac{1}{2}d$ (about).

7.46 Design the steel and the required section for a concrete beam reinforced for tension only. The beam, carrying a total uniform load of 1,500 lb per ft, is continuous across three spans of 20 ft each and rests upon its supports. Use the 1951 ACI specifications with $f'_c = 2{,}500$ psi and $f_s = 18{,}000$ psi. Make $b = \frac{1}{2}d$ (about).

7.47 This double-reinforced concrete beam is now to carry a maximum bending moment of 50,000 ft-lb. The concrete tested better than 3,000 psi. Steel may be stressed to 18,000 psi. Assume adequate web reinforcement. Is this bending moment permissible?

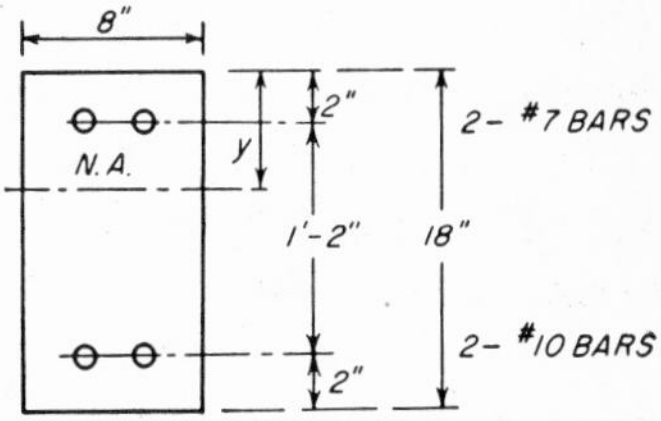

FIG. 7.47

7.48 A concrete beam of 24 in. width and 34 in. over-all depth is to carry a total moment of 650 ft-kips. Using $f'_c = 3{,}750$ psi and $f_s = 20{,}000$ psi, design the required steel reinforcement.

7.49 The dimensions for the concrete beam designed in question 7.45 must be retained but the beam must now carry an additional load of 500 lb per ft. What will the new schedule of reinforcing steel be?

7.50 This illustrated concrete T beam is loaded with a total uniform load producing a moment of 200,000 ft-lb and a shear of 40,000 lb. Assume $n = 10$.

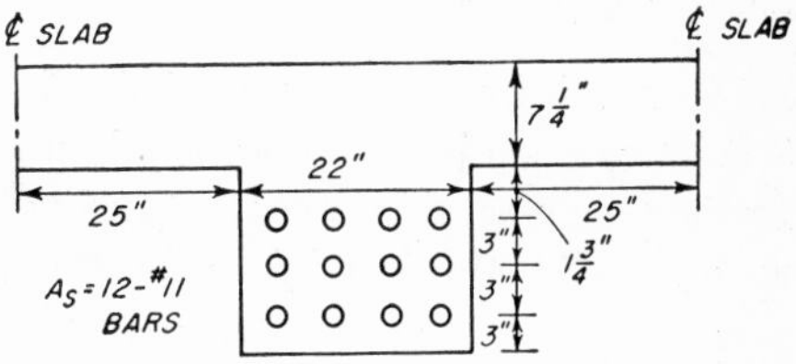

FIG. 7.50

a. Locate the neutral axis and find the moment of inertia of the beam.

b. Find the maximum unit tensile and compressive stresses.

c. Design a suitable stirrup arrangement.

7.51 A T beam has a 40-ft span and is simply supported. The slab has a thickness of 6 in. and the T beam stem is 24 in. wide. The stems of the T beams are 6 ft 0 in. on centers. The live loading is a truck which runs with one front wheel and one rear wheel on the longitudinal axis of the T beam, and produces a moment at the midpoint of the T beam of 172 ft-kips. Impact adds moment of 52 ft-kips. If d is 24 in. from top of slab to bottom of stem, design the necessary steel, in tension and/or compression, to carry the live + impact + dead moment and in the web to carry the shear (live + impact is 22 kips). Check design by using $f = Mc/I$. Use $f'_c = 3{,}000$ psi and $f_s = 20{,}000$ psi.

7.52 A floor is composed of T beams, 8 ft on centers, of 16-ft span center-to-center bearings, with a partial restraint at the ends equal to 20 per cent of the simple T beam moment. The live loading is 1,000 psf. If the slab is 4.5 in. of total thickness, design the T beam, showing sizes of all steel required work out a suitable stirrup spacing. Use $f'_c = 3{,}750$ psi and $f_s = 20{,}000$ psi.

7.53 A 15-ft long spirally reinforced concrete column 22 in. in diameter has reinforcing consisting of twelve #11 bars centered on a 16-in. diameter circle. If $f'_c = 2{,}500$ psi and $f_s = 16{,}000$ psi what axial load may this column carry by the 1951 ACI specifications? What is the size and pitch of the spiral reinforcement if $f'_s = 60{,}000$ psi?

7.54 Design a 14-ft long spirally reinforced concrete column to carry an axial load of 300,000 lb. Use the 1951 ACI specifications with $f'_c = 2{,}500$ psi and $f_s = 20{,}000$ psi. Use cold drawn wire with $f'_s = 60{,}000$ psi.

7.55 A reinforced concrete tied column, 10 in. in diameter and 8 ft long, is subjected to an axial compressive load of 100,000 lb. Design the steel reinforcement, using the 1951 ACI specifications with $f'_c = 3{,}000$ psi and $f_s = 20{,}000$ psi.

7.56 A short 28-in. square tied column is to carry an axial load of 700,000 lb. Design the steel reinforcement, using the 1951 ACI specifications with $f'_c = 3{,}000$ psi and $f_s = 16{,}000$ psi.

7.57 A composite column is to carry an axial load of 900,000 lb. What would be a satisfactory section by the 1951 ACI Specifications if $f'_c = 3{,}000$ psi, $f_s = 16{,}000$ psi, and $f'_s = 60{,}000$ psi?

7.58 A steel *H* column is encased in concrete and is unsupported for its 20 ft of height. It carries an axial load of 300,000 lb. Design this column by the 1951 ACI Specifications.

7.59 A pipe column is filled with concrete and is unsupported for its 20 ft of height. It carries an axial load of 240,000 lb. Design this column by the 1951 ACI Specifications.

7.60 A tied column is 14 by 14 in. in cross section and 16 ft high. It is reinforced with twelve #7 bars and is adequately tied. What axial load may this column carry according to the 1951 ACI Specifications if $f'_c = 3{,}000$ psi and the vertical reinforcement is rail steel?

7.61 A reinforced concrete tied column has a normal load, N, of 170,000 lb applied 2.5 in. eccentrically along one axis. If $f'_c = 2{,}500$ psi and $f_s = 20{,}000$ psi, find the fiber stresses in the concrete by recognized theory for uncracked sections and check by the 1951 ACI Specifications for combined axial and bending stresses.

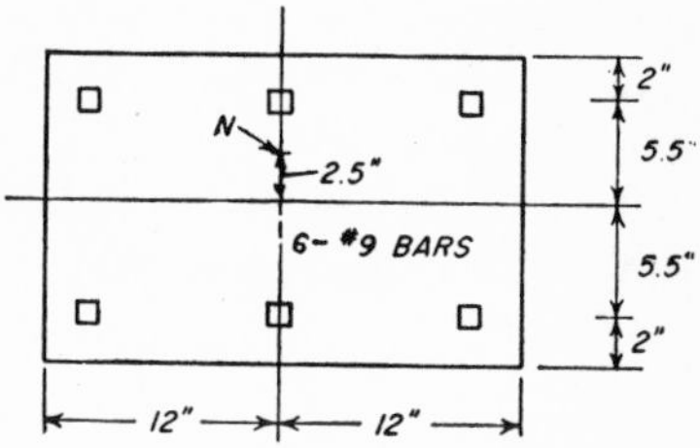

FIG. 7.61

7.62 If the reinforced concrete tied column in the preceding question was subjected to a load, N, of 30,000 lb applied 18 in. eccentrically instead of the 2.5 in. as shown, would the column be safe? Use recognized theory for cracked sections, and check the fiber stress found by comparing it to that which is allowed under the 1951 ACI Specifications.

7.63 Design a square concrete spread footing for a centrally placed column load of 700,000 lb. The column is 28 by 28 in. in cross section. $f'_c = 3{,}000$ psi and $f_s = 16{,}000$ psi. Soil bearing = 3 tons per sq ft.

7.64 Design a rectangular concrete spread footing for a centrally placed column load of 700,000 lb, where the short dimension of the footing is 9 ft. The column is 28 by 28 in. in cross section. $f'_c = 3{,}000$ psi and $f_s = 16{,}000$ psi. Soil bearing = 3 tons per sq ft.

7.65 A 12 by 12-in. concrete column carrying a load of 75,000 lb and a 15 by 15-in. concrete column carrying a load of 120,000 lb are 12 ft center to center. If $f'_c = 3{,}000$ psi and $f_s = 18{,}000$ psi, design a combined footing to support these loads if the soil bearing = 2 tons per sq ft.

7.66 If the timbers are short-leaf southern pine with working stresses of $P = 1{,}200$ psi compression parallel to the grain, $Q = 380$ psi compression perpendicular to the grain, and N psi compression at an angle θ with the grain, is this joint satisfactory when $N = \dfrac{PQ}{P \sin^2 \theta + Q \cos^2 \theta}$?

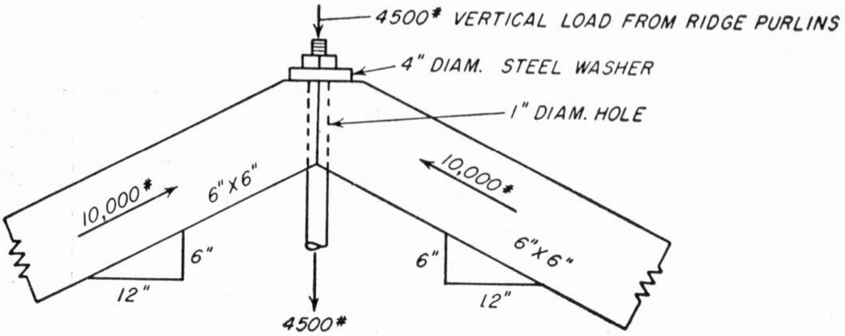

FIG. 7.66

7.67 A 4 by 6-in. timber diagonal of a timber roof truss is cut square ended and notched into a 6 by 6-in. bottom chord timber. If the unit stresses are the same as in the preceding question is this notch satisfactory in bearing?

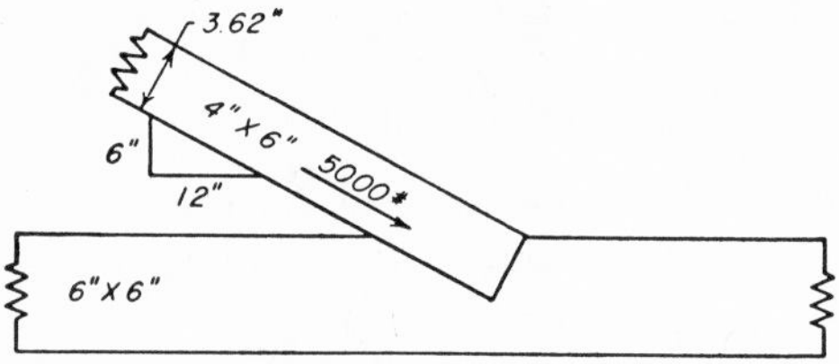

FIG. 7.67

7.68 Timber joists of 3 by 12 in. nominal dimension are on 16-in. centers and their ends rest upon steel beams of 6-in. flange width and on 14-ft centers. Including the weight of the joist and floor, what is the maximum allowable working load per square foot of floor if dressed timbers are used and the following stresses are not to be exceeded: shear at 120 psi; bending at 1,600 psi; bearing at 380 psi; and deflection not to exceed $\frac{1}{360}$ span with $E = 1{,}600{,}000$ psi?

7.69 A wood floor with a 14-ft span is to carry 250 psf including its weight. An opening 5 ft square is to be left in the center of the floor Sketch a plan showing how the floor joists should be placed and specify the size of the floor joists if the stress conditions in the preceding question are not to be exceeded.

7.70 How should four 2- by 8-in. dressed planks be framed to give the maximum stiffness as a beam?

7.71 How should four 2- by 8-in. dressed planks be framed to carry the maximum bending shear?

7.72 The top chord of a wooden roof truss is continuous, supported, and braced at 6-ft centers. The chord carries a maximum axial load of 60,000 lb and purlins bring loads to the truss only at panel points. What 6-in. dressed section of dense southern yellow pine is required?

7.73 A timber column 12 ft long carries a compressive axial load of 27,500 lb and is to be of one piece. What size dressed dense southern yellow pine is required?

7.74 A timber column 12 ft long carries a compressive axial load of 75,000 lb. The column is to be a hollow box made of four 2-in. planks. What size dressed planks of dense southern yellow pine will be required?

7.75 Two 2- by 4-in. and one 4- by 8-in. dressed dense southern yellow pine timbers are nailed together to form an approximate 8- by 8-in. cross (in cross section). If all three timbers are 10 ft long, what safe axial load may this composite column carry?

LAND SURVEYING

8.01 Complete the differential level notes shown below. Show the usual arithmetic check.

Point	B.S.	H.I.	F.S.	Elevation—ft
B.M. 49	1.37			284.69
T.P. 1	4.58		6.93	
T.P. 2	8.72		8.38	
T.P. 3	11.47		2.16	
T.P. 4	10.97		1.83	
T.P. 5	7.69		0.41	
T.P. 6	5.41		3.84	
T.P. 7	8.48		11.92	
B.M. 50			9.15	

8.02 From the following notes determine (*a*) the length and (*b*) the bearing of the line *PQ*.

Course	Length	Bearing
PA	300.0	N45°E
AB	200.0	S70°E
BC	250.0	Due east
CQ	163.4	N60°E

8.03 Compute the missing dimensions of Lots 1, 3, 7, and 8 of block *A* from the information shown in the sketch below:

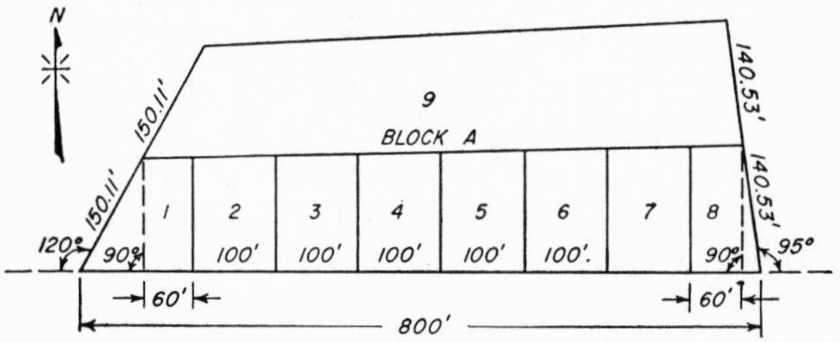

Fig. 8.03

8.04 Write a metes and bounds deed description for the house and lot where you live, assuming courses and distances where necessary. Draw a sketch map of the property and buildings, showing all information which should appear on a plan to be filed with the deed description at the registry of deeds.

8.05 In addition to the usual information shown on an ordinary property-survey plan, what pertinent information or data should appear on a plan of survey of property abutting on tidal waters or on an inland river where a riparian grant or lease is involved.

8.06 A slope distance was measured with a 300-ft steel tape and read as 292.59 ft. Temperature was 95°F. The vertical angle of the slope was +4°58′. The coefficient of expansion of the steel tape was 0.0000064 per 1°F. The applied tension was 30 lb. The tape weighed 6 lb. The tape was supported at the ends only on the slope. The tape was of standard length under a 30-lb tension when fully supported, at a temperature of 68°F. Compute the corrected horizontal length of the line.

8.07 What precaution should be taken to eliminate errors of instrument adjustment, when

a. Projecting a line forward from a backsight?

b. Turning an angle between two points whose difference in angular elevation is 45° or more?

c. Setting a point in a deep canyon on line with a foresight on top of a high peak?

d. Leveling between two points from one setup?

8.08 One side of a piece of property is defined in a deed in the following forms: "Beginning at a point in the northerly line of First Street in the town of London, N.J., at a drill hole in a stone monument sunk in the ground at the southeast corner of land now or formerly belonging to Joe Doe, and running N2°10′E a distance of 156.74 ft to a chisel cut in a traprock ledge . . . all bearings being true . . . ." In resurveying this property you find without any reasonable doubt both the drill hole and the chisel cut. The distance measures 144.74 ft and the true bearing is found to be N1°20′E. Is the owner of the property entitled to 144.74 ft or to 156.74 ft along this line? Explain your answer. How should the distance and bearing be shown on a map which you are to prepare for the owner?

8.09 A curved street, 60 ft between property lines, is to be laid out with a center-line radius of 400 ft. The intersection angle of the two tangents is 40°00′. Compute the deflection angles and chords necessary to lay out stakes on the inner property line with the transit at the point of curvature, the arc distance between all stakes except the last pair to be 25.00 ft.

8.10 Given: the following cross sections for a roadbed of 20 ft.

Station 4 + 00	$\frac{-4.0}{16.0}$	$\frac{-6.0}{0}$	$\frac{-12.0}{28.0}$
Station 5 + 00	$\frac{-2.0}{13.0}$	$\frac{-3.0}{0}$	$\frac{-8.0}{22.0}$

Find: the volume in cubic yards by (*a*) average end area method, and (*b*) prismoidal formula.

8.11 Plot the cross sections shown in the following notes:

Station	Surface elevation	Grade elevation	Cross section
2 + 87	100.6	102.87	$\frac{13.3}{-4.2}$ -2.3 $\frac{7.0}{0.0}$
2 + 76	102.8	102.76	$\frac{10.3}{-2.2}$ 0.0 $\frac{11.9}{+1.9}$
2 + 64	103.7	102.64	$\frac{10.0}{0.0}$ $+1.1$ $\frac{13.2}{+3.2}$
2 + 50	106.4	102.50	$\frac{13.4}{+3.4}$ $+3.9$ $\frac{17.1}{+7.1}$
2	115.1	102.00	$\frac{16.7}{+6.7}$ $+13.1$ $\frac{26.7}{+16.7}$
1	117.7	101.00	$\frac{22.7}{+12.7}$ $\frac{10.0}{+17.2}$ $+16.7$ $\frac{10.00}{+13.1}$ $\frac{22.2}{+12.2}$
0	109.2	100.00	$\frac{18.0}{+8.0}$ $\frac{9.0}{+10.1}$ $+9.2$ $\frac{8.5}{+7.8}$ $\frac{18.4}{+14.7}$ $\frac{24.6}{+14.6}$

In cut, base = 20.0 ft Side slope = 1.0 to 1.0
In fill, top = 14.0 ft Side slope = 1.5 (horizontal) to 1.0 (vertical)

\+ = cut − = fill

8.12 Compute the area (in acres) enclosed by the following compass and chain traverse by the *DMD* method.

Point	Bearing	Distance (chains) (1 chain = 66 ft)
1	N09°15′W	6.22
2	N66 30 E	4.88
3	S88 30 E	4.32
4	S61 30 E	3.72
5	S12 30 W	4.34
6	S79 15 W	10.30

8.13 List five or more methods of describing a parcel of land for conveyance by deed.

8.14 Plat the boundaries of a parcel of land on a scale of 1 in. to 200 ft, the parcel to be approximately 600 ft wide by 1,000 ft long; show on the plat the following items:

a. A line bearing N45°E.

b. A line having a length of 4.25 chains.

c. Two curves, reverse to each other, with radii of 200 ft and 500 ft, respectively.

d. Lines tangent to the curves in *c.*

e. A boundary street having an angle which is an angle of the parcel boundary also.

f. A side tie of 175 ft being measured on the prolongation of the north line of lot *A*.

g. Any additional item you wish to add to produce a closed figure.

h. Show all dimensions you deem necessary for a surveyor to make a ground location, in addition to those required above.

8.15 Write a proper legal description of the parcel you have platted in the above question; omit the caption of county, tract, and place of record. The description must be sufficiently detailed to enable a surveyor to stake the boundaries without other information.

8.16 Compute the horizontal distances and the elevations in the following stadia notes: F/i = 100, $(F + c)$ = 1 ft, instrument at Sta. M (elev. 372.9) H.I. = 5.0 ft. (See next page.)

Point	Rod reading	Vertical angle
1	8.65	+3°54′
2	7.93	−1 25 on 3 ft
3	5.43	−3 57
4	10.36	+0 48 on 2 ft

8.17 Compute the latitudes and departures for the closed field bounded by the following bearings and distances. Balance, compute the closure error, and compute the area of the enclosed field in square feet by coordinates.

Line	Bearing	Distance (ft)
AB	N30°E	420
BC	S20°E	610
CD	S46½°W	535
DA	N3°W	578

8.18 Indicate whether you would add or subtract the following tape corrections, in applying them to actual tape measurements in (1) measuring an unknown distance of about 100 ft; and (2) in laying out one point exactly 100.00 ft from another point:

a. A slope correction of 0.03 ft.

b. A temperature correction of 0.01 ft, temperature above that of standardization.

c. A sag correction of 0.04 ft.

d. A standardization correction of 0.008 ft (tape too long).

8.19 An angle is to be measured with a 10-in. transit with as great accuracy as the instrument is capable of giving. State the complete procedure which you would use to measure this angle, eliminating such instrumental and personal errors as possible. Indicate which steps will eliminate each type of instrumental or personal error. How closely would you estimate the angle could be measured with this instrument in 1 hr devoted to fieldwork?

8.20 A series of perpendicular offsets are taken from a transit line to a curved boundary line. These offsets were taken 25 ft apart and were taken in the following order: 0, 4.6, 8.9, 15.3,

10.4, 13.2, 18.5, 23.4, 17.6, 9.3, 3.2, 0. Find the area included between the transit line and the curved line by Simpson's one-third rule and check by the trapezoidal rule.

8.21 In testing a dumpy level for adjustment by the peg method the following rod readings were taken. Instrument at *A*: B.S. on *A*, 3.148 ft; F.S. on *B*, 3.398 ft. Instrument at *B*: B.S. on *B*, 4.465 ft; F.S. on *A*, 4.035 ft. Compute the true difference in elevation between *A* and *B*. Determine if the cross hair should be moved up or down and the rod reading on *A* to give a level sight with the instrument 4.465 ft above *B*.

8.22 You have been retained by a client to survey a city lot, with the buildings on it, which he contemplates purchasing. In the course of the survey you discover that the principle building, constructed in 1900, projects 0.2 ft beyond the street line. What information would you show on your plan of the lot? How would you advise your client in this matter? On what reasoning would your advice be based?

8.23 In running differential levels, what are the reasons for insisting that the aggregate of the backsight *distances* should very nearly equal the aggregate of the foresight *distances?* If the sums of these distances are equal, is it essential that each backsight distance should equal that of the corresponding foresight? Explain.

8.24 *a.* A line is described in a deed as running a definite distance to a definite known object of certain position. Will the line be construed as running to that object or the prescribed distance if the two do not agree?

b. What is the term "northerly" construed to mean in the absence of other information? With other information?

c. A piece of land described by "metes and bounds" and also by area is sold. Which description will stand if the two do not agree?

8.25 *a.* List five or more methods of describing a parcel of land for conveyance by deed.

b. What are the necessary elements that should be shown upon a completed survey plan of a piece of property?

c. The precedence of certain types of evidence of original boundary locations is known as the order of calls. List these in their order of precedence.

d. Define the term party wall. Explain the significance of a party wall to a surveyor.

See also some questions 1.401 to 1.425.

PART THREE

Answers to Questions from Professional Engineer's Examinations

SECTION ONE

1.101–1.725

BASIC FUNDAMENTALS

CHEMISTRY, SCIENCE, AND MATERIALS

1.101 A liter of hydrochloric acid (density 1.201) contains $1{,}000 \times 1.201 \times 0.4009 =$ **481.5** grams HCl.

Molecular weights:
$$HCl = 1.008 + 35.46 = 36.47$$
$$NaCl = 23 + 35.46 = 58.46$$
$$H_2SO_4 = 2 \times 1.008 + 32 + 4 \times 16 = 98.02$$
$$Na_2SO_4 = 2 \times 23 + 32 + 4 \times 16 = 142.00$$

Check equation:
$$2 \times 58.46 + 98.02 = 214.92 = 142.00 + 2 \times 36.47$$

Weight of NaCl required $= 481.5 \times 58.46/36.47 =$ **771.7** grams

Weight of (100 per cent) H_2SO_4 required

$$= \frac{481.5}{36.47} \times \frac{98.02}{2} = \mathbf{646.8} \text{ grams}$$

Basis: 1 mole NaCl $\rightarrow$ 1 mole HCl

$\frac{1}{2}$ mole $H_2SO_4 \rightarrow$ 1 mole HCl

1.102 *a.* Oxidation and reduction occur simultaneously in a chemical reaction. In the process of oxidation, one or more electrons are lost by an atom or an ion, while in reduction one or more electrons are gained by an atom or an ion. The oxidizing agent is reduced by the gain of electrons and the reducing agent is oxidized by the loss of electrons.

b. The observations of Newlands, Lotharmeyer, and Mendeleev indicated to Mendeleev that when the elements were arranged in the order of increasing atomic weights, they could be divided on the basis of chemical behavior into series or periods, not all of which, however, contained the same number of elements. The properties of the elements were thought to be a periodic function of their atomic weights. Later investigations have shown that most of the physical and chemical properties of the elements are periodic functions of their atomic numbers.

c. Radioactivity has been defined as the spontaneous disintegration of atoms accompanied by the emission of "rays." In the case of radium, the rays have been identified as alpha (helium with a double positive charge), beta (high-velocity electrons), and gamma (X-rays with wavelengths from 10^{-9} to 10^{-8} cm).

d. Acidity is customarily considered to be a function of the concentration of the hydrogen ion (H^+) or oxonium ion (H_3O^+). The more general definition of an acid, however, is that the ion or molecule may act as a proton donor.

The hydrogen-ion concentration in any solution is a function of the nature of the acid under consideration and of the nature of the solvent used.

In aqueous solutions, the greater the concentration of hydrogen ion (H^+)—more recent concept, oxonium ion (H_3O^+)—the greater the acidity of the solution.

The concentration of the hydrogen ion is usually expressed as pH, where $pH = 1/H^+$ per liter. That is, $pH = 1$ when $H^+ = 10^{-1}$ moles per liter.

1.103 One ton ore that shows 60 per cent copper contains 1,200 lb copper per ton ore. One pound CuS contains 0.666 lb copper. Therefore, 1 ton ore contains $1{,}200/0.666 - 1{,}200$, or 600 lb sulfur.

Sulfur available for H_2SO_4 production equals $600 - 60$, or 540 lb. Atomic weight of $H_2SO_4 = 2 \times 1 + 32 + 4 \times 16 = 98$. One pound 93 per cent H_2SO_4 contains $0.93 \times 32/98$ or 0.304 lb sulfur. Therefore, 1 ton ore will produce $540/0.304 = 1{,}775$ lb 93 per cent H_2SO_4.

1.104 The production of sodium hydroxide (caustic soda) from soda ash (Na_2CO_3) is known as the lime-soda process. Caustic soda prepared from soda ash as manufactured by the Solvay process is characterized by its low chlorine content.

The reaction depends on the low solubility product of calcium carbonate.

$$Na_2CO_3 + Ca(OH)_2 \rightleftarrows 2NaOH + CaCO_3\downarrow$$

The degree of conversion is a function of the initial concentration of soda ash, a 12 per cent solution giving approximately 95 per cent conversion and a 15 per cent solution giving only 90 per cent conversion.

The reaction equilibrium is insensitive to temperature changes, but the reaction rate and rate of settling of $CaCO_3$ are favored

Step	Equipment	Engineering problems
1. Preparation of soda-ash solution	Tanks with agitation	Economic consideration of cost of processing dilute solutions with high degree of conversion as compared to cost of processing more concentrated solution with a lower degree of conversion
2. Blending of soda solution with reburned and make-up lime	Classifier shaker	Feed rates, screen size, etc.
3. Soda solution causticized with slight excess of lime	Tanks with agitation	Corrosion, agitation, retention time, temperature of reaction
4. Separation of liquids and solids in first of two thickeners	Dorr thickener sludge pump	Settling rates, retention time, etc.
5. Overflow from 4 containing 10 to 11% NaOH is fed to evaporator	Evaporator and auxiliary equipment	Materials of construction, heat transfer, economic operating conditions
6. Underflow from 4 pumped to second thickener. Filtrate from 7 and water is added	Same as 4	Same as 4
7. Underflow from 6 filtered on continuous filter	Continuous filter	Optimum operating conditions; that is, vacuum, filter media, etc.
8. Overflow from 6 used as weak liquor in 1		
9. Filter cake from 7 returned to lime kiln		

by increased temperatures. The commercial process may be carried out as a batch or as a continuous operation. The process, equipment, and engineering problems are shown in the table on page 127.

1.105 Equal numbers of molecules of different (nonvolatile and nonelectrolyte) solutes dissolved in equal weights of the same solvent normally depress the vapor pressure, raise the boiling point, and lower the freezing point by constant amounts.

When 1 gram molecular weight nonvolatile nonelectrolyte is dissolved in 1,000 grams benzene, the freezing point of benzene is lowered 5.12°C.

Twenty grams unknown substance in 1,000 grams benzene lowers the freezing point (5.49 − 4.82) or 0.67°C.

Therefore, (5.12/0.67) × 20, or 152.8, grams would be required to lower the freezing point by 5.12°C. The experimental value of the molecular weight is 152.8.

$$M = \frac{1{,}000 \times K_f \times W}{W_0 \times \Delta T}$$

where M = the molecular weight
K_f = the molal lowering of freezing point
W = weight of the unknown substance
W_0 = weight of solvent used
ΔT = the experimental freezing point lowering

1.106 The freezing point-solubility curve of binary systems (H_2O–Na_2SO_4 in this instance) should be studied carefully in problems of this type. The transition temperature between Na_2SO_4 and H_2O lies at 32.38°C. At temperatures above this point, the decahydrate becomes unstable with respect to the anhydrous salt. In this problem, the solution was saturated at 32°C so that only the decahydrate need be considered. Analysis of solubility data indicates that Na_2SO_4 is soluble to the extent of 46.25 grams per 100 grams water when equilibrium is attained with the decahydrate as the solid phase.

Basis of solution: 46.25 grams Na_2SO_4 and 100 grams H_2O at 32°C

Molecular weight: $Na_2SO_4 = 142$
$H_2O = 18$
$Na_2SO_4 + 10H_2O = 142 + 180 = 322$

Total weight of solution = 146.25 gram
Weight to be removed = $146.25 \times 0.6 = 87.75$ gram
Weight of solution crystallized per gram $Na_2SO_4 = 322/142 = 2.27$

Weight of Na_2SO_4 crystallized = $87.75/2.27 = 38.6$
Weight of H_2O removed from solution = $38.6 \times 180/142 = 49.0$
Concentration of liquor

$$= \frac{\text{grams } Na_2SO_4}{100 \text{ grams } H_2O} \times (46.25 - 38.6) \times \frac{100}{(100 - 49)} = \frac{15 \text{ grams } Na_2SO_4}{100 \text{ grams } H_2O}$$

Inspection of solubility curve indicates a temperature of 16.6°C.

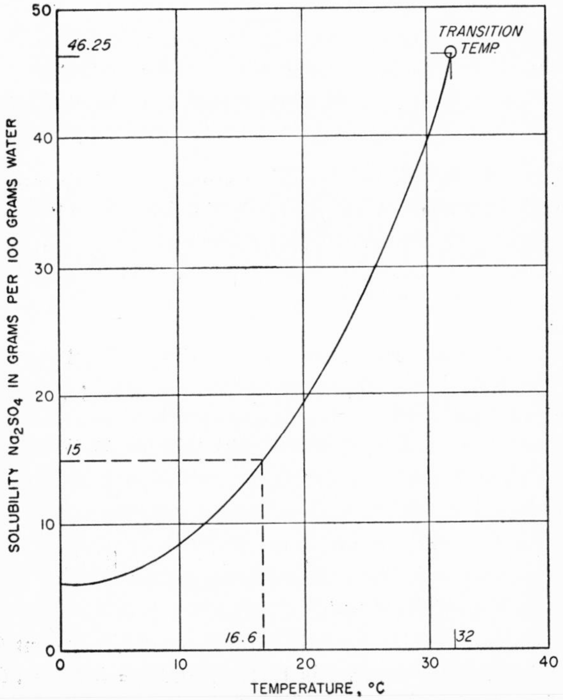

FIG. 1.106

1.107 1 barrel = 4 sacks cement = 4 cu ft
1 gal water = 0.134 cu ft

1 sack cement	= (1 − 0.513)	= 0.487 cu ft
1½ cu ft sand	= 1.5(1 − 0.360)	= 0.960 cu ft
3 cu ft stone	= 3(1 − 0.330)	= 2.010 cu ft
5 gal water	= 5 × 0.134	= 0.670 cu ft
		4.127 cu ft

One barrel cement will produce 16.51 cu ft of 1:1½:3 concrete with 20 gal water.

1.108

$$Fe_3O_4 + CO \rightarrow 3FeO + CO_2$$
$$3FeO + 3CO \rightarrow 3Fe + 3CO_2$$

Each lb-mole Fe_3O_4 requires 4 lb-moles CO for the reduction of Fe_3O_4 to Fe.

Atomic weight $Fe_3O_4 = 3 \times 55.84 + 4 \times 16 = 231.52$

$$3FeO = 215.5 \text{ and } CO = 28$$
$$2{,}000/231.52 = 8.63 \text{ lb-moles in 1 ton } Fe_3O_4$$
$$8.63 \times 0.84 = 7.25 \text{ lb-moles } Fe_3O_4 \text{ in 1 ton ore}$$
$$n = 7.25 \times 4 = 29.00 \text{ lb-moles CO required to reduce } Fe_3O_4 \text{ in 1 ton ore}$$

Using the perfect-gas law, which states that 1 lb-mole perfect gas occupies 359 cu ft at atmospheric pressure (14.7 psi) and 492°R (Rankin or absolute temperature) which are standard conditions and correcting for temperature and pressure by

$$VP = nRT$$
$$V(\text{vol}) = \frac{29.00 \times 10.71 \times (460 + 85)}{(100 + 14.7)} = \frac{1472 \text{ cu ft CO}}{1 \text{ ton ore}}$$

where $R = 10.71$ = the gas constant or unit conversion factor $\dfrac{(14.7 \times 359)}{1 \times 492}$

[To change from $\dfrac{\text{psi} \times \text{cu ft}}{°R}$ to $\dfrac{\text{psf} \times \text{cu ft}}{°R}$ multiply $R(10.71)$ by 144, and the new $R = 1{,}544$.]

Since the gas used in the reduction is only 28 per cent CO, the total volume of gas required is 1,472 ÷ 0.28 = 5,230 cu ft gas at 85°F and 100 psi.

1.109
$$\begin{aligned} Al &= 27,\ 2Al \text{ or } Al_2 = 54 \\ Fe &= 56,\ 2Fe \text{ or } Fe_2 = 112 \\ SO_4 &= 32 + 4 \times 16 = 96,\ (SO_4)_3 = 288 \end{aligned}$$

$$?Al + ?Fe_2(SO_4)_3 \rightarrow Al_2(SO_4)_3 + ?FeSO_4$$
$$2Al + 3Fe_2(SO_4)_3 \rightarrow Al_2(SO_4)_3 + 6FeSO_4$$
$$2 \times 27 + 3 \times (112 + 288) \rightarrow (54 + 288) + 6 \times (56 + 96)$$
$$54 + 1{,}200 \rightarrow 342 + 912$$

Valences: $Al = 0,\ Fe_2(SO_4)_3 = (+3) \times 2,\ (-2) \times 3$
$Al_2(SO_4)_3 = (+3) \times 2,\ (-2) \times 3$
$FeSO_4 = (+2)(-2)$

Valence change: $Al + 0 \rightarrow +3$ = loss of 3 electrons
$Fe + 3 \rightarrow +2$ = gain of 1 electron

Therefore: 2Al loses 6 electrons when $1Al_2(SO_4)_3$ is formed.
$3Fe_2(SO_4)_3$ gains 6 electrons when $6FeSO_4$ is formed.

1.110 3. Lime

1.111 5. Methane (approximately 60 to 75 per cent)

1.112 1. 0 to 25

1.113 3. Relative stability

1.114 2. Saprophytic

1.115 5. The maximum velocity of flow is 1 ft per sec.

1.116 4. The sludge and raw sewage are not mixed.

1.117 2. 0.1 per cent

1.118 3. Oxidize putrescible matter

1.119 5. A leaping weir

1.120 7.5 gal water (per cu ft) weighs 62.4 lb, sp gr = 1. One bag cement (1 cu ft) weighs 94 lb.

Material	Weight (in lb)	Divided by sp gr × wt (1 cu ft water)	Absolute vol (in cu ft)
Cement	94	3.10 × 62.4	= 0.49
Sand	200	2.65 × 62.4	= 1.21
Gravel	350	2.65 × 62.4	= 2.11
5 gal water	41.6	1 × 62.4	= 0.67

a. Total weight concrete = 685.6 lb; total volume = 4.48 cu ft
b. One cu ft concrete weighs 685.6/4.48 or 153 lb
c. 27 ÷ 4.48 = 6.026 (of the above) batches per cu yd
Weight of materials per cu yd of concrete:

Cement:	$94 \times 6.026 =$	567 lb
Sand:	$200 \times 6.026 =$	1,205 lb
Gravel:	$350 \times 6.026 =$	2,109 lb
Water:	$41.6 \times 6.026 =$	250 lb
Weight 1 cu yd concrete =	153×27	= 4,131 lb

1.121 *a*. Dissolve 1 gram chemically pure *o*-tolidine in 1 liter (1:10) HCl.

b. Add 15 grams $CuSO_4 \cdot 5H_2O$ to distilled water containing 10 cc concentrated H_2SO_4 and dilute to 1 liter.

c. Dissolve 0.25 grams $K_2Cr_2O_7$ in distilled water containing 1 cc concentrated H_2SO_4 and dilute to 1 liter.

Solutions *b* and *c* are the colorimeter standards. 0.5 cc *o*-tolidine reagent *a* is mixed with 50 cc water to be tested. After 5 min the water sample is placed in a tube of the same dimensions as the standard and is compared in a colorimeter. The amount of chlorine (in parts per million) can be read from a calibration curve after the density of color is determined.

1.122 The treatment of raw water for municipal use may include aeration to oxidize ferrous iron and remove gases which cause a bad odor and unpalatable taste. The water may then be treated with aluminum sulfate, hydrated lime, and activated carbon along with softening agents and chlorine.

Aluminum sulfate is the most commonly used coagulant. The hydrated lime is used in order to insure the proper degree of completion of the reaction.

$$Al_2(SO_4)_3 + 3Ca(OH)_2 \rightarrow 2Al(OH)_3 + 3CaSO_4$$

The activated carbon absorbs materials which cause bad odor and poor taste.

The mechanical devices used include softeners, clarifiers, where the coagulant and sludge from the water treatment are removed, and sand filters.

1.123 Hardness, alkalinity, and acidity are ppm (parts per million) of equivalent (eq) $CaCO_3$. This figure may be found by multiplying the equivalents per million of the substance under consideration by 50, the equivalent weight of $CaCO_3$.

That is: 1 eq Na_2CO_3 = mol wt/2 Na_2CO_3 (½ mol wt Na_2CO_3)
1 eq $CaCO_3$ = mol wt/2 $CaCO_3$
1 eq HCl = mol wt HCl

Hardness in water is usually classified as "carbonate" and "noncarbonate" hardness. The principle sources of carbonate hardness are the bicarbonates of calcium and magnesium. The bicarbonates form carbonates on heating, as

$$Ca(HCO_3)_2 + \Delta(\text{heat}) \rightarrow \underset{\text{(precipitate)}}{CaCO_3\downarrow} + \overset{\text{(volatile gas)}}{CO_2\uparrow} + H_2O$$

Noncarbonate hardness usually is produced by the sulfates of calcium and magnesium. These salts usually form scale on the hottest part of any heating equipment, since the solubility of the salts decreases with temperature.

The analysis of a water sample for noncarbonate hardness will be used as an example. Standard works on water analysis should be consulted for complete analytical procedures.

Test for sulfate hardness: A known volume of water to be analyzed is boiled for 15 min to remove bicarbonates, a known volume of soda reagent (an excess is necessary) is now added and the solution is boiled for 10 min more. The resulting solution is brought up to volume with distilled water. After cooling, a known volume of the treated water is filtered, and the filtered solution is titrated with $N/50$ (2 per cent normal) solution of H_2SO_4.

A blank (or reference solution) using distilled water and the same amount of soda reagent is now run. The difference between the amount of $N/50$ H_2SO_4 required for the blank and that required for the sample is a measure of the sulfate hardness.

$$CaSO_4 + Na_2CO_3 \rightarrow CaCO_3\downarrow + Na_2SO_4$$
$$MgSO_4 + NaOH \rightarrow Mg(OH)_2 + Na_2SO_4$$
$$Na_2CO_3 + H_2SO_4 \rightarrow Na_2SO_4 + H_2O + CO_2\uparrow$$
$$2NaOH + H_2SO_4 \rightarrow Na_2SO_4 + H_2O$$

One eq $CaCO_3$(produced) = 1 eq Na_2CO_3(used) = 1 eq H_2SO_4 (difference between sample and blank)

Alkalinity may be caused by carbonates or bicarbonates in natural waters or by hydroxides in industrial waste. Alkalinity is determined by titration with standard acid (as $N/50$ H_2SO_4) with a proper indicator. Alkalinity may be reported in terms of ppm or equivalent $CaCO_3$. That is, 1 eq $Ca(HCO_3)$ = 1 eq $CaCO_3$ = 1 eq Na_2CO_3.

Alkalinity and acidity may be reported in terms of pH where $pH = \log 1/[H^+]$. Water whose pH value lies between 1 and 7 would be acid and water whose pH lies between 7 and 14 would be alkaline. Standard works on water analysis should be consulted for analytical procedures.

Turbidity is determined by comparing the sample under consideration with a standard prepared from 1 gram of reference material (i.e., fuller's earth) in 1 liter water. This turbidity is rated 1,000. Suitable dilutions of the standard solution are prepared for comparisons. Comparisons may be made by means of the platinum wire method or the turbidimeter.

Color in natural water may be due to colloidal solutions of organic material, iron salts, manganese salts, and in the case of streams polluted with industrial waste the color may be caused by any number of inorganic or organic compounds. The color of the water is compared with standards which represent ppm of platinum. Potassium platinic chloride and cobaltous chloride are used in the standard solution.

1.124 A 1:2:3 mix of concrete with 6 gal water per bag cement.

	Cubic feet	Pounds per cu ft	Weight in lb	Divide by sp gr × wt of cu ft water	Cubic feet
Cement	1	94	94	3.1 × 62.4	0.49
Sand	2	105	210	2.7 × 62.4	1.23
Gravel	3	100	300	2.7 × 62.4	1.78
Water	6/7.5	62.4	50	1 × 62.4	0.80
Total wt and vol concrete =			654 lb		4.30 cu ft

1 cu ft concrete weighs 654/4.30 or 152 lb

27/4.30 = 6.29 = no. of above batches per cu yd

Weight of materials per cu yd concrete:

Cement:	$94 \times 6.29 =$	590 lb
Sand:	$210 \times 6.29 =$	1,320 lb
Gravel:	$300 \times 6.29 =$	1,880 lb
Water:	$50 \times 6.29 =$	314 lb
Weight 1 cu yd concrete =	$152 \times 27 =$	4,104 lb

1.125 In designing a concrete mix the ultimate strength (in psi at 28 days), the workability (slump), and the degree of exposure (from protected concrete to extreme exposure of temperature, weather, and type of water) all affect the choice of the water-cement ratio. The greater the ultimate strength and the greater the degree of exposure, the lower the water-cement ratio should be. A high slump, indicating a high water-cement ratio, will give greater workability, although workability may be increased by vibrating the concrete, by using air-entrained cement, or by adding fly ash to the cement and thus reducing the actual amount of cement to be used. The degree of the sharpness of the sand and its size (fine, medium, or coarse and the proportional variation) as well as the size of the large aggregate (stone) and its hardness and sharpness of cleavage, all have a bearing on the proportions. The cement fills the voids in the sand and the sand fills the voids in the larger aggregate.

ELECTRICITY

1.201

$$5 \text{ mph} = \frac{5 \times 5{,}280}{3{,}600} = 7.33 \text{ fps}$$

$$\text{Horsepower} = \frac{200 \times 7.33}{550} = 2.67 \text{ hp}$$

$$\text{Current} = \frac{2.67 \times 746}{0.70 \times 110} = \mathbf{25.8} \text{ amp}$$

1.202 12 and 20 ohms in parallel.

$$\frac{1}{R_1} = \frac{1}{12} + \frac{1}{20} = \frac{32}{240} = \frac{1}{7.5}$$

$$R_1 = 7.5$$

Resistance A to B = 16 ohms = R_{AB}

$$\frac{1}{R_{AB}} = \frac{1}{16} = \frac{1}{(R_2 + 7.5)} + \frac{1}{30} = \frac{(30 + R_2 + 7.5)}{30(R_2 + 7.5)}$$

$$1.87R_2 + 14.08 = R_2 + 37.5$$

$$0.87R_2 = 23.42,\ R_2 = \mathbf{26.8}\ \text{ohms}$$

1.203 Three resistors in parallel: $\frac{1}{R_1} = \frac{1}{5} + \frac{1}{2} + \frac{1}{10} = \frac{8}{10}$

$R_1 = 1.25$

Two resistors in parallel: $\frac{1}{R_2} = \frac{1}{4} + \frac{1}{4} = \frac{2}{4}$

$R_2 = 2.00$

Two lines of resistors: Line 1. $6.75 + 1.25 = 8$ ohms
Line 2. $2.00 + 6.00 = 8$ ohms

$$\frac{1}{R_3} = \frac{1}{8} + \frac{1}{8} = \frac{2}{8}$$

$R_3 = 4$ ohms

$$\text{Current} = \frac{V}{R} = \frac{12}{(4 + 1)} = \mathbf{2.4}\ \text{amp from battery}$$

1.204 Two resistors in parallel: $\frac{1}{R} = \frac{1}{5} + \frac{1}{17} = \frac{22}{85}$

$R = 3.86$

$$\text{Current} = \frac{V}{R} = \frac{6}{3.86} = 1.553\ \text{amp}$$

Each coil has 6 volts.

Coil *1* takes $6/5 = 1.2$ amp
Coil *2* takes $6/17 = 0.353$ amp
$\Sigma = 1.553$ amp (check)

1.205 Increase in cathode weight = 300 − 15 = 285 lb. At 382.52 amp-hr per lb this requires 285 × 382.52 = **109,000** amp-hr.

$$\text{Current} = \frac{109{,}000}{15 \times 24} = \mathbf{303}\ \text{amp}$$

$$\text{Plate area} = \frac{40 \times 36}{144} = 10\ \text{sq ft}$$

Current density = 303/10 = **30.3** amp per sq ft
Reference: "Standard Handbook for Electrical Engineers."

1.206 Fifty kva at 90 per cent pf = 0.9 × 50 = 45 kw

$$\text{Input} = 45 + \frac{400 + 600}{1{,}000} = 46 \text{ kw}$$

$$\text{Efficiency} = 45/46 = \mathbf{97.83} \text{ per cent}$$

Maximum efficiency occurs when copper loss is equal to core loss. To reduce the full-load copper loss to equal the core loss requires that the load be reduced to

$$\sqrt[2]{400/600} = \sqrt[2]{0.667} = 0.816 \text{ or } \mathbf{81.6} \text{ per cent of full load}$$

1.207 The equivalent resistance of similar lamps in parallel varies inversely as the number of lamps in the group. The voltage across groups in series varies directly as the equivalent resistance, by Ohm's law. Therefore, the voltage across each group will vary inversely as the number of lamps in the group.

$$\text{Voltage across 25-lamp group} = 220 \times \frac{15}{(15 + 25)} = \mathbf{82.5} \text{ volts}$$

$$\text{Voltage across 15-lamp group} = 220 \times \frac{25}{(15 + 25)} = \mathbf{137.5} \text{ volts}$$

Assuming constant resistance, the current through each lamp varies directly as the voltage.

Current through each lamp in 25 group = (82.5/110) × 0.9 = **0.675** amp
Current through each lamp in 15 group = (137.5/110) × 0.9 = **1.12** amp

1.208 Wire tables in handbook show that copper wire of 0.204-in. diameter has a resistance of 0.253 ohms per 1,000 ft at 25°C. The two wires from the generator to the load 500 ft away will then have a resistance of 0.253 ohms. The load requires a current of 10,000/120 = 83.3 amp. Generator voltage must be greater than the load voltage by the IR drop in the line:

$$V_g = 120 + 83.3 \times 0.253 = 120 + 21.1 = 141.1 \text{ volts}$$

The power loss in the line will be I^2R, or

$$P_L = (83.3)^2 \times 0.253 = \mathbf{1{,}755} \text{ watts}$$

1.209 Charge is the product of capacitance and voltage, or $Q = CE$. The voltage across capacitors in series varies inversely as the capacitance:

$$\text{Voltage across 8 } \mu\text{f} = 120 \frac{12}{(8+12)} = \mathbf{72} \text{ volts}$$

$$\text{Voltage across 2 } \mu\text{f and 10 } \mu\text{f} = 120 \frac{8}{(8+20)} = \mathbf{48} \text{ volts}$$

The charge of the 8 μf $= 8 \times 10^{-6} \times 72 = \mathbf{576 \times 10^{-6}}$ coulombs

The charge of the 2 μf $= 2 \times 10^{-6} \times 48 = \mathbf{96 \times 10^{-6}}$ coulombs

The charge of the 10 μf $= 10 \times 10^{-6} \times 48 = \mathbf{480 \times 10^{-6}}$ coulombs

Energy stored $= \frac{1}{2}$ charge $\times$ voltage

Total energy $= \frac{1}{2} \times 576 \times 10^{-6} \times 72 + \frac{1}{2} \times (96 + 480)10^{-6} \times 48 = 0.0207 + 0.0138 = \mathbf{0.0345}$ joule

1.210 *a.* By Ohm's law and Kirchhoff's law:

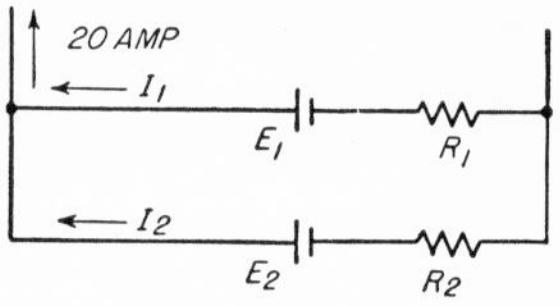

FIG. 1.210

$$E_1 - I_1R_1 = E_2 - I_2R_2 \qquad (1)$$
$$I_1 + I_2 = 20 \qquad (2)$$

Substituting (2) in (1)

$$E_1 - I_1R_1 = E_2 - (20 - I_1)R_2$$

$$I_1 = \frac{E_1 - E_2 + 20R_2}{R_1 + R_2} = \frac{(2.1 - 2.0 + 20 \times 0.05)}{(0.05 + 0.05)} = \frac{1.10}{0.10} = \mathbf{11} \text{ amp}$$

$$I_2 = 20 - I_1 = 20 - 11 = \mathbf{9} \text{ amp}$$

b. As a lead storage cell discharges, the following reaction takes place:

$$PbO_2 + 2H_2SO_4 + Pb \rightarrow PbSO_4 + PbSO_4 + 2H_2O$$

(positive plate) (negative plate) (positive plate) (negative plate)

The sulfuric acid combines with the lead peroxide of the positive plate and the lead of the negative plate to form lead sulfate and water. The specific gravity of the sulfuric acid electrolyte therefore decreases as this reaction takes place.

1.211 The equation for emf of a d-c generator may be found in any handbook: $E = \dfrac{ZPNBA}{60a10^8}$ volts

where Z = number of armature conductors
P = number of poles
N = speed in rpm
B = average flux density under the poles in lines per sq in.
A = area of each pole face in sq in.
a = number of parallel paths through the armature

Substituting the values given:

$$E = \frac{360 \times 4 \times 1200 \times 40{,}000 \times (6 \times 6)}{60 \times 4 \times 10^8} = \mathbf{103.7} \text{ volts}$$

1.212 By Ohm's law and Kirchhoff's law:

$$IR = 15 - 2I_2 = 10 - 1I_1 \qquad (1)$$
$$I_1 + I_2 = I \qquad (2)$$

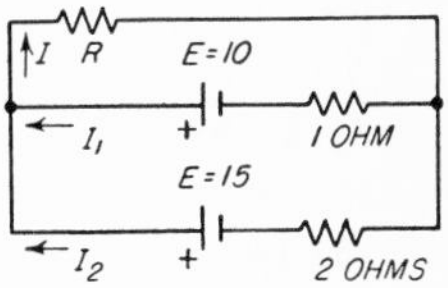

FIG. 1.212

If $I_1 = I_2$, then $I_1 = \dfrac{I}{2}$ and $I_2 = \dfrac{I}{2}$ [from (2)]

Substituting in (1)

$$IR = 15 - 2\frac{I}{2} \qquad \text{or } I(1 + R) = 15 \qquad (3)$$

and

$$IR = 10 - \frac{I}{2} \qquad \text{or } I(0.5 + R) = 10 \qquad (4)$$

Dividing (3) by (4)

$$\frac{(1 + R)}{(0.5 + R)} = \frac{15}{10} \qquad \text{and } 10 + 10R = 7.5 + 15R$$
$$5R = 2.5 \qquad \text{and } R = \mathbf{0.5} \text{ ohm}$$

1.213 The 60-watt lamp could be connected in series with the parallel combination of the two 30-watt lamps across 240 volts for normal operation as shown. Since resistance

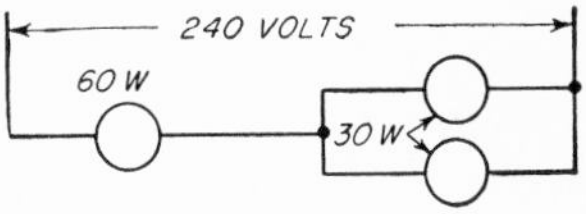

FIG. 1.213

= (volts)²/watts, the resistance of two 30-watt 120-volt lamps in parallel would be equal to the resistance of the 60-watt 120-volt lamp and the voltage across each lamp would be normal.

1.214 Total equivalent resistance:

$$R = 15 + \frac{7 \times 11}{7 + 11} = 15 + 4.28 = 19.28 \text{ ohms}$$

The total current, by Ohm's law of $I = V/R$:

$$I = 110/19.28 = \mathbf{5.7} \text{ amp}$$

This is the current through the 15-ohm resistance. The total current divides inversely as the resistances through each branch of the parallel combination:

$$\text{Current through the 7-ohm branch} = 5.7 \times \frac{11}{7 + 11} = \mathbf{3.48} \text{ amp}$$

$$\text{Current through the 11-ohm branch} = 5.7 \times \frac{7}{7 + 11} = \mathbf{2.22} \text{ amp}$$

1.215 $$I = \frac{\text{hp} \times 746}{V \times \text{efficiency}} = \frac{5 \times 746}{220 \times 0.85} = 19.9 \text{ amp}$$

IR permitted $= 0.05 \times 220 = 11$ volts
R for 300 ft $= 11/19.9 = 0.523$ ohm
$R/1{,}000$ ft $= 1{,}000/300 \times 0.523 = 1.74$ ohms
Size wire = **#12** AWG
Current capacity check—25 amp

1.216 $$P = V \times I = 115 \times 15 = 1{,}725 \text{ watts}$$

Therefore, **17** 100-watt lamps can be used

1.217 $$V_2 = \frac{20{,}000}{16{,}000} V_1 = 1.25 \times 60 = 75 \text{ volts}$$

$$V = V_1 + V_2 = 60 + 75 = \mathbf{135} \text{ volts}$$

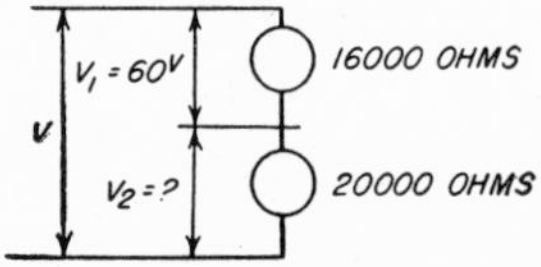

Fig. 1.217

1.218 $$R_{\text{total}} = 1 + 7 + \frac{3 \times 6}{3 + 6} = 10 \text{ ohms}$$

$$I_{\text{total}} = {}^{30}\!/_{10} = 3.0 \text{ amp}$$

a. Voltage across 7-ohm device $= 3 \times 7 = 21$ volts

b. Voltage across 3-ohm device and voltage across 6-ohm device $= 3 \times 2 = 6$ volts

Power expended on 3-ohm device $= I^2R = 6 \times {}^6\!/_3 = 12$ watts

c. Current in 6-ohm device $= \dfrac{V}{R} = \dfrac{6}{6} = 1.0$ amp

1.219 $$I_{\text{line}} = \frac{\text{hp} \times 746}{V \times \text{efficiency}} = \frac{10 \times 746}{220 \times 0.83} = 40.8 \text{ amp}$$

$$I_{\text{starting}} = 2 \times 40.8 = 81.6 \text{ amp}$$

$$I_a = 81.6 - {}^{220}\!/_{100} = 79.4 \text{ amp}$$

$$I_a = \frac{V}{R_1 + Ra} = 79.4 = \frac{220}{R_1 + 0.25}$$

$$R_1 + 0.25 = 2.77, \quad R_1 = \mathbf{2.5} \text{ ohms}$$

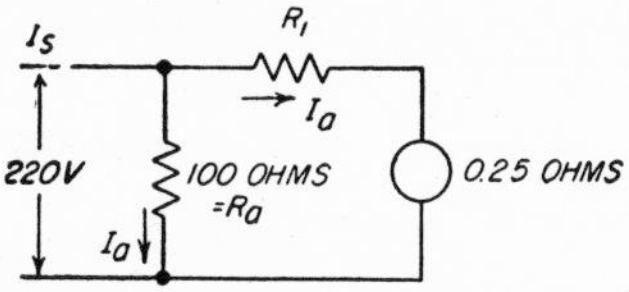

FIG. 1.219

1.220 $$I = \frac{V}{Z} \text{ and } Z = R + jX_L - jX_c$$

$$Z = 63 + j377 \times 0.15 - j\frac{10^6}{377 \times 15}$$

$$= 63 + j56.6 - j177$$

$$= 63 - j120 = 135\underline{/-62.2^\circ}$$

$$I = {}^{110}\!/_{135\underline{/-62.2}} = \mathbf{0.815\underline{/62.2^\circ}} \text{ amp}$$

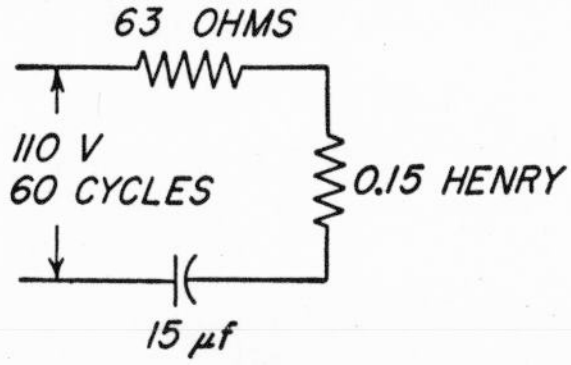

FIG. 1.220

1.221 Power input $= \frac{\text{hp} \times 746}{\text{efficiency}} = \frac{8 \times 746}{0.82} = 7{,}280$ watts

The apparent power = power divided by power factor and $\text{va}_{\text{input}} = 7{,}280/0.70 = 10{,}400$ va. As the motor is a three-phase balanced load, one-third or 3,460 va is applied to each phase. The three phases are Y connected with a line-to-line voltage of 220 volts. Hence each phase voltage is $220/\sqrt{3} = 127$ volts. Since the apparent power per phase is 3,460 va and the phase voltage is 127 volts, $I\varphi = 3{,}460/127 = 27.3$ amp current per phase and also per line in a Y connection.

1.222 The plate characteristic curves, commonly found in tube manuals, are a family of graphs, each drawn for a constant value of control grid bias voltage, E_c, in which the vertical axis is plate current, I_p, and the horizontal axis is plate voltage, E_p. Suppose the wish is to find r_p, g_m, and μ for a 6J5 triode at the point $E_c = -9$ volts, $I_p = 5.5$ ma, and $E_p = 240$ volts. To find r_p, find the change in E_p for a small change in I_p, with E_c held constant at -9 volts. Find that at $E_c = -9$ and $I_p = 6$, $E_p = 246$, and that at $E_c = -9$ and $I_p = 5$, $E_p = 236$. Hence:

$$r_p = \frac{\Delta E_p}{\Delta I_p} = \frac{(246 - 236)}{(6 - 5)10^{-3}} = \textbf{10,000 ohms}$$

To find g_m, find the change in I_p, occasioned by a small change in E_c with E_p held constant at 240 volts. Find that at $E_p = 240$ and $E_c = -10$, $I_p = 3.5$, and that at $E_p = 240$ and $E_c = -8$, $I_p = 7.5$. Hence:

$$g_m = \frac{\Delta I_p}{\Delta E_c} = \frac{(7.5 - 3.5)10^{-3}}{-8 - (-10)} = 2 \times 10^{-3} \text{ or } \textbf{2,000 micromhos}$$

To compute μ, find the change in E_p caused by a small change in E_c with I_p held constant at 5.5 ma. Find that at $I_p = 5.5$ and $E_c = -8$, $E_p = 222$, and that at $I_p = 5.5$ and $E_c = -10$, $E_p = 262$. Hence:

$$\mu = -\frac{\Delta E_p}{\Delta E_c} = -\frac{(262 - 222)}{-10 - (-8)} = \textbf{20}$$

As a check, $\mu = g_m \times r_p = 2 \times 10^{-3} \times 10^4 = 20$

1.223 The internal resistance of the cell on short circuit is found from Ohm's law.

$$R_i = \frac{E_i}{I_{\text{short-circuit}}} = \frac{1.5}{25} = \mathbf{0.06} \text{ ohms}$$

When connected to an external resistance, R_e, and using Ohm's law again

$$I = \frac{E_i}{R_i + R_e} = \frac{1.5}{0.06 + 1.00} = 1.414 \text{ amp}$$

The voltage across the battery terminals when connected to the 1-ohm load will be the internal voltage minus the IR drop,

$$E_t = E_i - IR_i = 1.5 - 1.414 \times 0.06 = \mathbf{1.414} \text{ volts}$$

This voltage is also that across the 1-ohm load,

$$E_t = IR_e = 1.414 \times 1 = \mathbf{1.414} \text{ volts (check)}$$

1.224 *a.* The period of any oscillation is the time required per cycle. Hence the period

$$T = \frac{1}{f} = \frac{1}{5} = \mathbf{0.2} \text{ sec}$$

b. In the absence of resistance, the natural undamped frequency of transient oscillations is the same as the a-c resonant frequency; that is, the angular frequency is

$$\omega_0 = \frac{1}{\sqrt{LC}}, \text{ whence } C = \frac{1}{\omega_0^2 L} = \frac{1}{(5 \times 2\pi)^2 \times 100}$$

$$C = 10.1 \times 10^{-6} \text{ f or } \mathbf{10.1}\ \mu\text{f}$$

1.225 *a.* The differential equation for a series L-C-R circuit during discharge is, by Kirchhoff's voltage law,

$$R \times i + L\frac{di}{dt} + \frac{1}{C}\int_0^t i\,dt = 0$$

In this problem the initial charge Q is the value of the last term at $t = 0$. This fact may be more conveniently observed if the substitution of q is made for $\int_0^t i\,dt$.

The equation then becomes $R\frac{dq}{dt} + L\frac{d^2q}{dt^2} + \frac{1}{C}q = 0$

b. In the equation as first written, each term represents a voltage drop. Thus $R \times i$ is the instantaneous resistance drop and $L\,di/dt$ is the instantaneous inductive voltage drop. The voltage drop across the capacitance, because of the voltage due to the initial charge, is

$$e_c = \frac{1}{C}\int_0^t i\,dt - \frac{Q}{C}$$

HYDRAULICS

1.301 Depth cylinder = 60 ft
Diameter cylinder = 40 ft
Weight water = 62.5 lb per cu ft
Intensity water pressure at base = 60 × 62.5 = 3,750 psf
Total pressure on base = $\pi\,(20)^2 \times 3{,}750 = 4{,}710{,}000$ lb
Total pressure on side = $\pi \times 40 \times 60 \times 3{,}750/2$
= 14,130,000 lb
Total normal pressure on base and sides = **18,840,000** lb

1.302

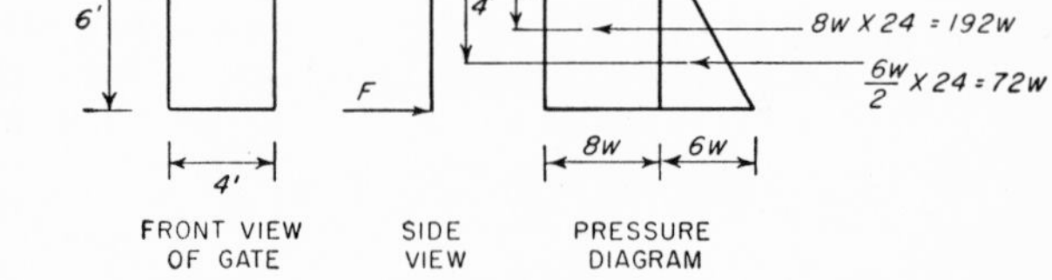

FIG. 1.302

Sum of moments of forces about hinge = 0

$$+3 \times 192w + 4 \times 72w - 6F = 0$$

$$F = 96w + 48w = 144 \times 62.5 = \mathbf{9{,}000}\text{ lb}$$

1.303 $x_c - x_0 =$

$$\frac{l_1^2}{12x_0} \text{ or } \frac{1}{12} = \frac{9}{12x_0}$$

$$x_0 = \mathbf{9}\text{ ft}$$

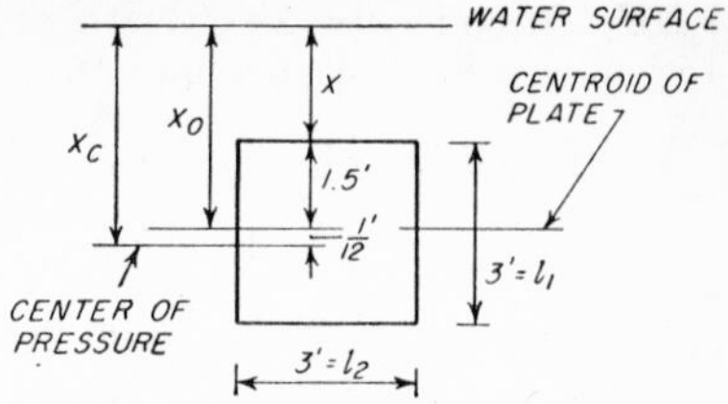

FIG. 1.303

$x = 9$ ft $- 1.5$ ft $=$ **7.5** $=$ distance top edge of plate is below water surface.

1.304 Assume negligible prestress in the flat bands and that wood staves will swell when wet and fit tight, one to the other.

$$T = \frac{pd}{2} = \frac{fA}{x}$$

where T = tension in pipe per linear inch,
p = water pressure in psi
d = diameter of pipe in inches
f = allowable tension in band in psi
A = cross-sectional area of band in square inches
x = spacing of bands in inches

$$\frac{150 \times 48}{2} = \frac{15{,}000 \times 4 \times 0.75}{x}, \quad x = \mathbf{12.5}\text{ in.}$$

1.305 Weight water displaced when caisson is floating $= 62.5 \times 20 \times 50 \times d = 75 \times 2{,}000 = 150{,}000$ lb

d = distance water surface to bottom of caisson = 2.4 ft
Weight in tons needed to sink caisson through water to bottom $= W \times 2{,}000 = 62.5 \times 20 \times 50 \times 17.6, \quad W = \mathbf{550}T$

1.306 Width barge = 20 ft
Weight water displaced = weight barge = $250T$
d = draft in feet

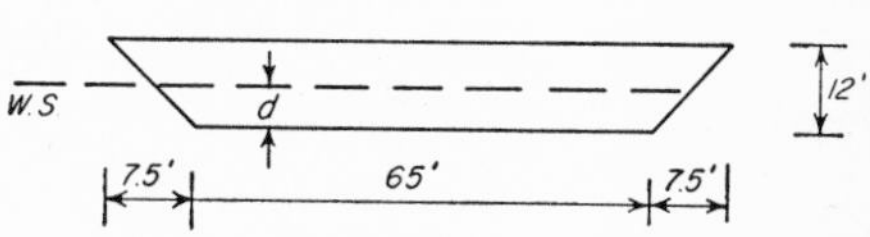

FIG. 1.306

$$\frac{250 \times 2000}{62.4} = \left(65 + \frac{7.5d}{12}\right) d \times 20$$

$$d^2 + 104d = 640, \quad d = \mathbf{5.8}\text{ ft}$$

1.307 Wood cube 2 × 2 × 2 ft will displace 2 × 2 × 1 ft or 4 cu ft of water.

Water will rise in tank h ft.

$$h \times 4 \times 4 = 4, \qquad h = 0.25 \text{ ft.}$$

Original water pressure on one side of tank $= 4 \times 9 \times \frac{1}{2}(0 + 62.5 \times 9) = 10{,}100$ lb

New water pressure =

$4 \times 9.25 \times \frac{1}{2}(0 + 62.5 \times 9.25) = 10{,}675$ lb

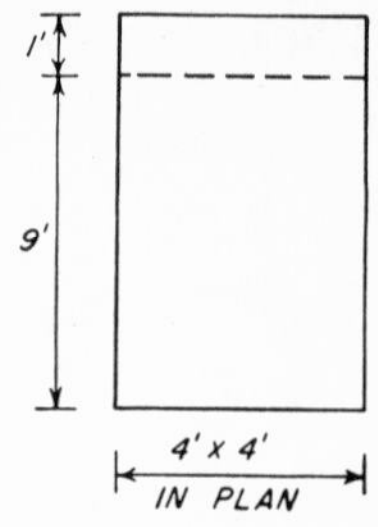

Fig. 1.307

Increase in water pressure per side = **575** lb

1.308 Pressure head + velocity head + elevation + lost head (if any) = constant = energy equation. All heads and elevations are in feet.

$$Q = v \times a, \quad 49.5 \text{ cfs} = v \text{ fps} \times 7.07 \text{ sq ft}$$

$$v = 7 \text{ fps and } \frac{v^2}{2g} = \frac{49}{64.4} = 0.7 \text{ ft}$$

P_R = pressure head at summit = 2.31 × 30 = 69.3 ft

Total head of pump = 69.3 + 0.7 + 300 + 10 = 380 ft

$$\text{Energy of pump} = \frac{380 \text{ ft} \times 49.5 \text{ cfs} \times 62.4 \text{ lb/cu ft}}{550 \text{ fps}} = \mathbf{2{,}130} \text{ hp}$$

1.309 $$V_A = \frac{\text{discharge}}{A \text{ of 12-in. pipe}} = \frac{2}{0.785} = 2.55 \text{ fps}$$

$$V_D = \frac{2}{0.196} = 10.2 \text{ fps}$$

Equate energy of points A and B.

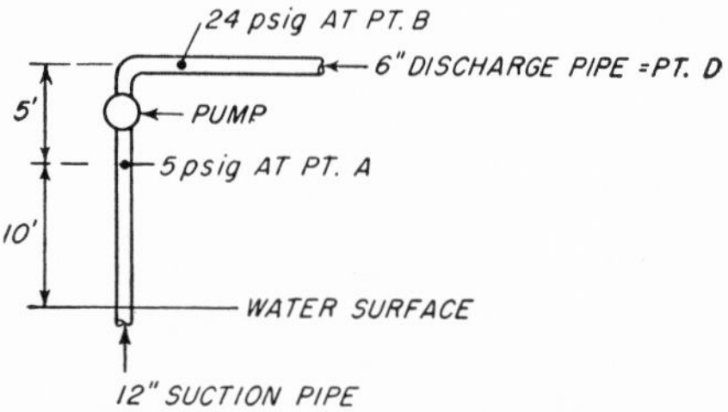

Fig. 1.309

$$-5 \times 2.31 + \frac{2.55 \times 2.55}{2 \times 32.2} + 0 + \text{pump head}$$

$$= +24 \times 2.31 + \frac{10.2 \times 10.2}{64.4} + 5$$

$$\text{Pump head} = +55.4 + 11.6 + 1.60 - 0.10 + 5 = 73.5 \text{ ft}$$

Horsepower output of pump $= 73.5 \times 2 \times 62.4 \div 550$
$= \mathbf{16.7}$ hp

1.310 This is the case of water passing through an orifice under constant head. The barge sinks as fast as the water rises within the barge.

$$v = \sqrt{2gh} = \sqrt{64.4 \times 4} = 16.06 \text{ fps}$$

The rate water enters the barge $= 0.60 \times 0.196 \times 16.06$
$= 1.88$ cfs

$$\text{Time needed to sink barge} = \frac{20 \times 10 \times 2}{1.88} = \mathbf{213} \text{ sec}$$

1.311 Francis's formula for a contracted weir with no velocity of approach is given by

$$Q = 3.33(b - 2H/10)H^{3/2} \text{ with } b = 10 \text{ ft and } H = 0.875 \text{ ft}$$

$$Q(\text{discharge of cfs}) = 3.33\left(10 - \frac{2 \times 0.875}{10}\right)\sqrt{0.875^3}$$

$$Q = 3.33(10 - 0.175)\sqrt{0.67} = 3.33 \times 9.825 \times 0.819 =$$
26.8 cfs

1.312 Francis's formula for a suppressed weir with no velocity of approach is given by

$$Q = 3.33 \times bH^{3/2} = 3.33 \times 7 \times 0.819 = \mathbf{18.8} \text{ cfs}$$

1.313 Use energy equation (all items in feet).
Elevation = entrance loss + discharge loss + friction loss

$$100 = 0.5\frac{v^2}{2g} + \frac{v^2}{2g} + f\frac{l}{d}\frac{v^2}{2g}$$

f for clear smooth pipe and an assumed velocity of 5 to 6 fps from tables = 0.0182

$$l = 12{,}000 \text{ ft}, \ d(\text{diameter of pipe in feet}) = 1 \text{ ft}$$

$$100 = \left(0.5 + 1.0 + \frac{0.0182 \times 12{,}000}{1}\right) \times \frac{v^2}{64.4}$$

$$v^2 = \frac{6{,}440}{220} = 29.2, \ v = 5.41 \text{ fps}$$

$$Q = \text{average} = 0.785 \times 5.41 = \mathbf{4.25} \text{ cfs}$$

1.314 $7{,}500 \text{ gal per min} = \dfrac{7{,}500}{7.5 \times 60} = 16.7 \text{ cfs}$

$$Q = \text{average}, \ v = \frac{16.7}{1.77} = 9.45 \text{ fps}$$

Elevation = entrance loss + velocity loss + pipe loss + pressure head

$$180 = \left(0.5 + 1.0 + 0.0160 \times \frac{4{,}000}{1.5}\right) \frac{v^2}{2g} + h(\text{pressure})$$

$$h(\text{pressure}) = 180 - 44.2 \times \frac{9.45 \times 9.45}{64.4} = 180 - 61.3$$

$$= 118.7 \text{ ft}$$

$$\text{Pressure in pipe} = \frac{118.7}{231} = \mathbf{51.4} \text{ psi}$$

1.315 Pressure head (pump) = total elevation pumped + total pipe losses.

$$Q = \text{average}, \quad v = \frac{2}{0.196} = 10.2 \text{ fps}$$

$$h(\text{pump}) = 1{,}250 - 1{,}000 + \frac{0.0225 \times 8{,}000}{0.5} \times \frac{v^2}{2g} + \frac{1.5v^2}{2g}$$

$$= 250 + 361.5 \times \frac{10.2 \times 10.2}{64.4} = 833 \text{ ft}$$

$$833 = 1{,}100 - 1{,}000 + \frac{0.0225 \times 3{,}200}{0.5} \times \frac{10.2 \times 10.2}{64.4} + \text{pressure head}_{3,200}$$

Pressure head at 3,200 = 833 − 100 − 233 = 500 ft

Pressure at 3,200 = 500/2.31 = **216** psi

1.316 Equate energy between A and B and between A and M.
(A and B):

$$h(\text{pump}) = 900 - 800 + 0.02 \times \frac{4{,}000}{1} \times \frac{v^2}{2g} + \frac{1.5v^2}{2g}$$

$$= \left(100 + 81.5\frac{v^2}{2g}\right)$$

(A and M):

$$\left(100 + 81.5\frac{v^2}{2g}\right) + 100 = 100 \times 2.31 + 0.02 \times \frac{2{,}000}{1}\frac{v^2}{2g}$$

$$41.5\frac{v^2}{2g} = 31,\ v^2 = \frac{31 \times 64.4}{41.5} = 48,\ v = 6.92 \text{ fps}$$

Q = average = 0.785×6.92 = **5.43** cfs

Pump horsepower output

$$= \frac{5.43 \times 62.4}{550}\left(100 + 81.5 \times \frac{31}{41.5}\right)$$

$$= 0.615(100 + 61) = \mathbf{99} \text{ hp}$$

1.317 Write energy relationship between points A, B, C, and Y. Hydraulic gradient at point Y will be called Y.

1. (A and Y): $1{,}000 - Y = \dfrac{0.02 \times 3{,}000}{0.67}\dfrac{V_a^2}{2g} = 90\dfrac{V_a^2}{2g}$

2. (Y and B): $Y - 850 = \dfrac{0.02 \times 2{,}000}{0.5}\dfrac{V_b^2}{2g} = 80\dfrac{V_b^2}{2g}$

3. (Y and C): $Y - 875 = \dfrac{0.02 \times 1{,}000}{0.5}\dfrac{V_c^2}{2g} = 40\dfrac{V_c^2}{2g}$

a. (1) + (2): $150 = 90\dfrac{V_a^2}{2g} + 80\dfrac{V_b^2}{2g}$

b. (1) + (3): $125 = 90\dfrac{V_a^2}{2g} + 40\dfrac{V_c^2}{2g}$

c. $Q(\text{pipe } A) = Q(\text{pipe } B) + Q(\text{pipe } C)$
$0.349V_a = 0.196V_b + 0.196V_c$

Equations a, b, c can best be solved by assuming values of V_a, and then V_b and V_c can be found from equations a and b. If these values satisfy equation c, the assumed value of V_a was good. Thus, if V_a is taken as 8.03 fps, then $V_b = 6.9$ fps and $V_c = 7.4$ fps.

$$Q_a = 2.80 \text{ cfs} = Q_b + Q_c = \mathbf{1.35} \text{ cfs} + \mathbf{1.45} \text{ cfs}$$

1.318 $Q_R = aV_R$, $7 = 1.767V_R$, $V_R = 3.96$ fps, $\dfrac{V_R^2}{2g} = 0.244$

Let elevation of hydraulic gradient at Y be Y. Equate energy between R and Y, Y and A, Y and B.

1. $400 - Y = 0.02 \times (2{,}000/1.5) \times 0.244 = 6.5$
   $Y = 393.5$

2. $393.5 - 250 = 143.5 = 0.02 \times \dfrac{13{,}000}{1} \times \dfrac{V_a^2}{2g} = 4.04V_a^2$

$$V_a^2 = 35.6, \quad V_a = 5.96 \text{ fps}$$

$$Q_R - Q_A = Q_B = 7 - 0.785 \times 5.96 = 2.32 = \frac{\pi d^2}{4} \times V_b$$

$$d^2 = 2.95 \div V_b$$

3. $393.5 - 50 = 343.5 = 0.02 \times \dfrac{4{,}000}{2g} \times \dfrac{V_b^2}{d}$

$$\frac{V_b^2}{d} = 276, \quad \frac{V_b^4}{d^2} = 76{,}200$$

$$V_b^5 = 2.95 \times 76{,}200 = 225{,}000$$

by trial: $11^5 = 161{,}000$, $12^5 = 248{,}500$

$$11.9^5 = 239{,}000, \quad 11.8^5 = 228{,}500, \quad 11.75^5 = 224{,}000$$

Now $$d^2 = \frac{2.95}{11.75} = 0.251$$

$$d = 0.5 \text{ ft} = \mathbf{6} \text{ in.}$$

1.319 The loss in head between points A and B in either the 36- or the 24-in. pipe must be the same.

$$0.022 \times \frac{2{,}000}{3} \times \frac{V_3^2}{2g} = 0.023 \times \frac{6{,}000}{2} \times \frac{V_2^2}{2g}$$

$$\frac{44}{3} V_3^2 = 69V_2^2, \quad V_3 = V_2\sqrt{\frac{3 \times 69}{44}} = 2.17V_2$$

$$Q_4 = Q_2 + Q_3$$
$$75.4 = 3.14V_2 + 7.07V_3 = 3.14V_2 + 7.07 \times 2.17V_2$$
$$V_2 = \frac{75.4}{3.14 + 15.33} = 4.08 \text{ fps}$$

Now $V_3 = 8.85$ fps

$$Q_2 = 3.14 \times 4.08 = 12.9 \text{ cfs}$$
$$Q_3 = 7.07 \times 8.85 = 62.5 \text{ cfs}$$
$$\Sigma = Q_4 = 75.4 \text{ cfs}$$

1.320 Let p stand for pipe and n for nozzle.

$$A_p \times V_p = 8 \times A_n \times V_n$$
$$19.63 \times V_p = 8 \times 0.049 \times V_n = 0.392V_n$$
$$V_n = 50V_p$$

Equate energy of reservoir and nozzles.

$$600 = 0.017 \times \frac{25{,}000 \times V_p^2}{5 \times 2g} + \left(\frac{1}{(0.95)^2} - 1\right) \times \frac{2{,}500V_p^2}{2g}$$
$$38{,}600 = 85V_p^2 + 2{,}700V_p^2 = 2{,}785V_p^2$$
$$V_p^2 = 13.8,\ V_p = 3.72 \text{ fps},\ V_n = 186.0 \text{ fps}$$
$$Q_p = 3.72 \times 19.63 = 73.0 \text{ cfs}$$

$$\text{Horsepower of eight jets} = \frac{73.0 \times 62.4}{550} \times \frac{186.0 \times 186.0}{64.4} = 4{,}450 \text{ hp}$$

1.321 Let t = throat and p = pipe.

$$\frac{A_t}{A_p} = \frac{1}{9} \qquad \frac{d_t}{d_p} = \frac{1}{3} = \frac{8 \text{ in.}}{24 \text{ in.}}$$

h_t and h_p = recorded pressure heads in feet.

$$Q = \frac{C \times A_t}{\sqrt{1 - (d_t/d_p)^4}} \sqrt{2g(h_t - h_p)}$$
$$= \frac{0.99 \times 0.349 \sqrt{64.4(36 - 9)}}{\sqrt{1 - 1/81}} = \frac{0.346 \times 8.03 \times \sqrt{27}}{\sqrt{80/9}}$$
$$= \frac{9 \times 2.78 \times 5.2}{8.94} = 14.53 \text{ cfs}$$

1.322 Area $= \frac{2 \times 4 \times 12}{2} + 4 \times 30 = 168$ sq ft

Wetted perimeter $= 30 + 2\sqrt{16 + 144}$

$= 30 + 2 \times 12.65 = 55.3$ ft

Hydraulic radius $= R = \frac{A}{P} = \frac{168}{55.3} = 3.04, \quad R^{1/2} = 1.743$

$S =$ slope of 1 in 1,000 $= 0.001$

$n = 0.02, \frac{n}{R^{1/2}} = 0.01145$

$$\text{Kutter's } C = \frac{41.65 + 0.00281/S + 1.811/n}{1 + (41.65 + 0.00281/S) \times \frac{n}{R^{1/2}}}$$

$$= \frac{41.65 + 2.81 + 90.55}{1 + 44.46 \times 0.01145} = \frac{135.01}{1.51}$$

$$= 89.4$$

$v = C \times R^{1/2} \times S^{1/2} = 89.4 \times 1.743 \times 0.0316 = 4.92$ fps

$Q = 168 \times 4.92 =$ **826** cfs

1.323 $R = \frac{A}{P} = \frac{\pi d^2/8}{\pi d/2} = \frac{d}{4} = \frac{5}{4} = 1.25$ ft

$$\sqrt{R} = 1.118, \quad \sqrt[3]{1.118} = 1.038 = R^{1/6}$$

$$C(\text{by Manning formula}) = \frac{1.486 \times R^{1/6}}{n}$$

$$C = \frac{1.486 \times 1.038}{0.015} = 102.5$$

$Q =$ average $= a \times C \times R^{1/2} \times S^{1/2}$

$= 9.82 \times 102.5 \times 1.118 \times 0.0316$

$Q = 35.5$ cfs

1.324 The Manning formula may be written

$$Q = a \times K \times R^{2/3} \text{ or } K = \frac{Q}{aR^{2/3}}$$

$$R = \frac{a}{P} = \frac{10 \times 5}{20} = 2.5,\ R^2 = 6.25,$$

$$R^{2/3} = 1.84 \text{ (rectangular flume)}$$

$$K = \frac{200}{50 \times 1.84} = 2.17$$

The new shape will be one-half of a hexagon.

$$P = 20, \text{ one side } = 20/3 = 6.67 \text{ ft},$$
$$\text{depth} = 6.67 \times 0.866 = 5.77 \text{ ft}$$
$$A = (6.67 + 6.67/2) \times 5.77 = 57.7$$
$$R = 57.7/20 = 2.885,\ R^2 = 8.33,\quad R^{2/3} = 2.03$$

$$Q = 57.7 \times 2.17 \times 2.03 = \mathbf{254 \text{ cfs}}$$

1.325 The common value for $n = 0.013$
Area 10-in. circle = 0.545 sq ft
Angle subtended by open segment

$$= 2 \times \text{angle whose cosine} = 2.5/5 = 0.500$$
$$= 2 \times 60° = 120°$$

Area of cross section of flow:

$$A_f = \frac{360 - 120}{360} \times 0.545 + \frac{2.5 \times (5 \times 0.866)}{144}$$

$$A_f = 0.364 + 0.075 = 0.439 \text{ sq ft}$$

$$P = \frac{2}{3} \times \frac{\pi \times 10}{12} = 1.757 \text{ ft}$$

$$R = \frac{A_f}{P} = \frac{0.439}{1.757} = 0.25,\ R^2 = 0.0625,\ R^{2/3} = 0.397$$

$$S = 0.01,\ S^{1/2} = 0.10$$

Using Manning formula

$$Q = a \times (1.486/n) \times R^{2/3} \times S^{1/2}$$
$$= 0.439 \times (1.486/0.013) \times 0.397 \times 0.10 = \mathbf{2.00 \text{ cfs}}$$

MATHEMATICS AND MEASUREMENTS

1.401 By law of sines

$$\frac{BC}{AB} = \frac{\sin 30°}{\sin 10°}$$

$$BC = 50 \times 0.5000/0.1737 = 143.97 \text{ ft}$$

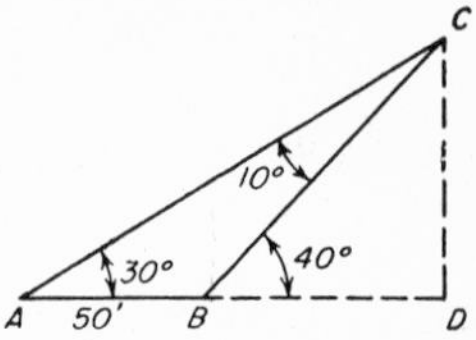

FIG. 1.401

$$CD = 143.97 \times \sin 40°$$
$$= 143.97 \times 0.6428 = 92.54 \text{ ft.}$$

$$BD = 143.97 \times \cos 40° = 143.97 \times 0.7660 = 110.29 \text{ ft}$$

$$\tan 30° = \frac{CD}{AB + BD}$$

$$CD = 160.29 \times 0.5774 = \mathbf{92.54} \text{ ft (check)}$$

1.402 Equation of line is in the form of $y = mx + b$
when $x = 0$, $mx = 0$ and $y = b = 1$

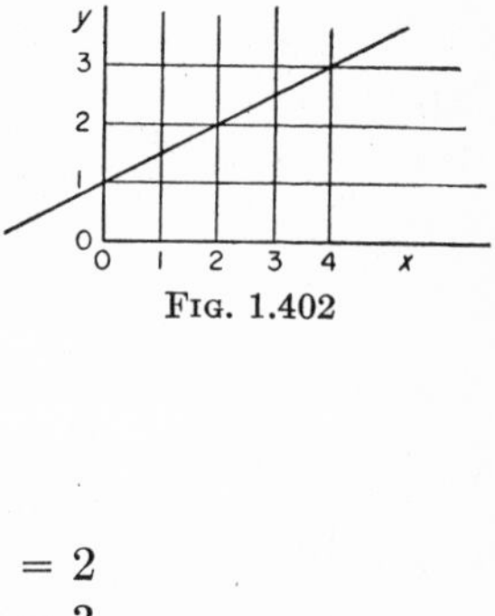

FIG. 1.402

$$m = \text{slope of line} = \frac{y_2 - y_1}{x_2 - x_1}$$

$$= \frac{3-2}{4-2} = \frac{1}{2} = 0.5$$

$$y = \mathbf{0.5}x + 1$$

Check: When $x = 2$, $y = 0.5 \times 2 + 1 = 2$
When $x = 4$, $y = 0.5 \times 4 + 1 = 3$

1.403 (1) $x^2 + y^2 = 5z$
(2) $x^2 - y^2 = 3z$
(1) + (2) $2x^2 = 8z$ and if $z = w^2$
$x^2 = 4z = 4w^2$
$x = 2w$ and $y = w$ or $x = 2y$

If $z = 1^2$ then $x = 2$ and $y = 1$
$z = 2^2$ then $x = 4$ and $y = 2$
$z = 3^2$ then $x = 6$ and $y = 3$
$z = n^2$ then $x = 2n$ and $y = n$

There are an infinite number of values that will satisfy.

1.404 *a.* $A = 89.42 = \pi d^2/4 = 0.785d^2$, $d =$ **10.67** in.
b. Circumference $= \pi d = 3.14 \times 10.67 = 33.52$ in.
c. Length of side of a regular inscribed hexagon $= d/2$
$=$ **5.335** in.

1.405

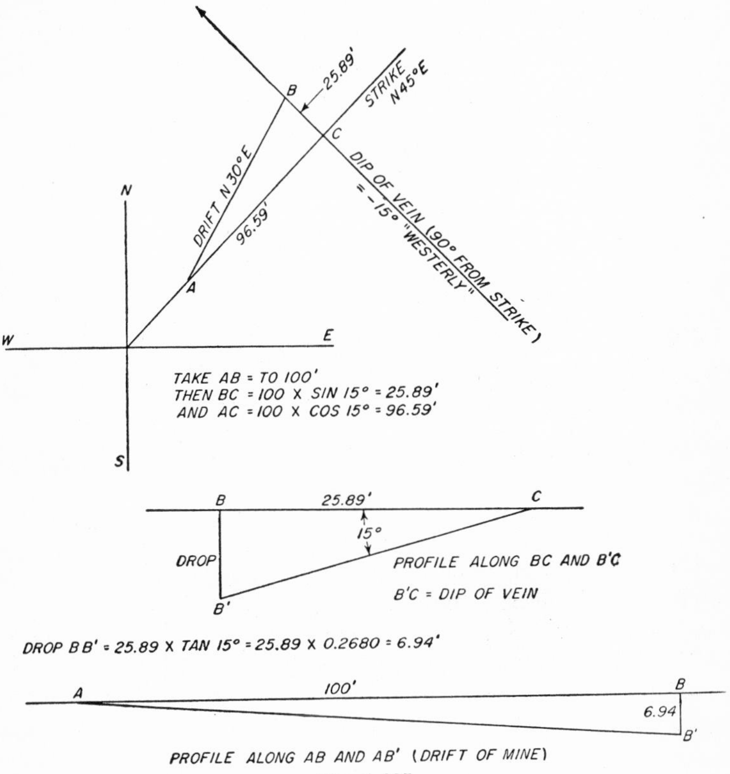

Fig. 1.405

Grade (per cent) $AB' = -6.94 \times 100/100 =$ **−6.94** per cent

1.406 Tape was used 9.17 times. If the tape is short, the distance measured is too long.

Total correction $= -0.10 \times 9.17 = -0.92$ ft
Corrected or true distance taped $= 916.58 - 0.92 =$ **915.66** ft

1.407 $$4 + \frac{(x+3)}{(x-3)} - \frac{4x^2}{(x^2-9)} = \frac{(x+9)}{(x+3)}$$

To clear of fractions, multiply by $(x^2 - 9)$

$$4x^2 - 36 + x^2 + 6x + 9 - 4x^2 = x^2 + 6x - 27$$

Combining terms,

$$-27 = -27, \text{ or } 0 = 0$$

Since this is an identity, there are an infinite number of + or − values for x.

A special case is for $x = \pm 3$

$$x = +3, \quad +4 + \frac{6}{0} - \frac{36}{0} = \frac{12}{6}$$

or

$$+4 + \infty_1 - \infty_2 = 2$$

$$x = -3, \quad +4 - \frac{0}{-6} - \frac{36}{0} = +\frac{6}{0}$$

or

$$+4 - 0 - \infty_2 = \infty_1$$

If we approach ± 3 as a limit from 2 or 4 and use sufficient significant figures, the two very large values, here called infinity, will differ by enough to show that the equation is an identity.

1.408 The center of gravity of a circle is at its center and that of a triangle is one-third of the height above the base (or side).

Find center of gravity of 24-in. diameter circle with 9 by 12 triangular hole.

Above OX, take moments of areas about OX.

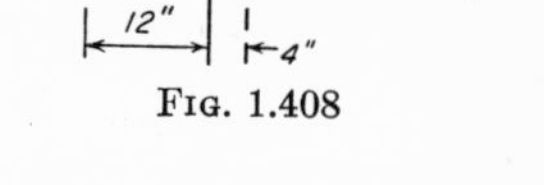

FIG. 1.408

Part	Area	×	Arm	=	Moment
Circle	452.4 sq in.	×	12 in.	=	+5,428.8 cu in.
Triangle	− 54.0	×	15	=	− 810.0
Net area	398.4 sq in.	×	(11.59 in.)	=	+4,618.8 cu in.

To right of OY take moments of areas about OY.

Circle	+452.4	× 12	= +5,428.8
Triangle	− 54.0	× 16	= − 864.0
Net area	398.4 sq in.	× (11.46 in.)	= +4,564.8 cu in.

1.409 The center of gravity of this area lies on the Y-Y axis. To find X, take moment of areas (of right half only because of symmetry) about top of figure.

Area no.	Area	× Arm	= Moment
1	2 × 6 = 12 sq in.	× 1 in.	= 12.00
2	1 × 10 = 10	× 7	= 70.00
3	½ × 1 × 10 = 5	× 5.33	= 26.67
Total	27	× (4.02 in.)	= 108.67

The moment of inertia of an area about an axis other than that through its center of gravity = I about center of gravity plus area times distance between center-of-gravity axis and new axis squared.

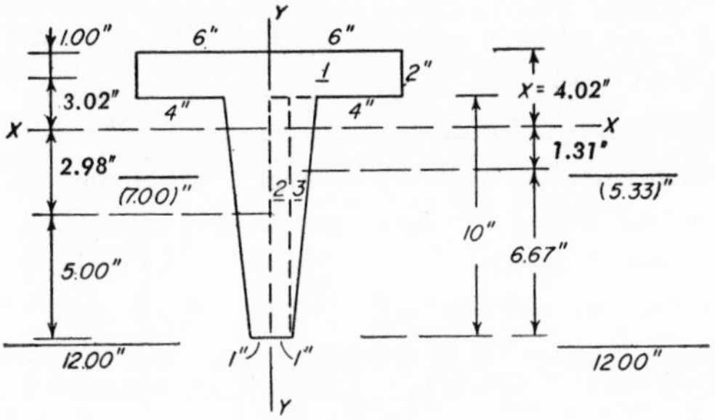

FIG. 1.409

$$I_{x\text{-}x} = 644.0 \text{ in.}^4$$

Double area	I_{cg}	+ Area × d^2	= New I
1	$\frac{1}{12}$ × 12 × 2 × 2 × 2	+ 12 × 2 × 3.02 × 3.02	= 8.0 + 218.9
2	$\frac{1}{12}$ × 2 × 10 × 10 × 10	+ 2 × 10 × 2.98 × 2.98	= 166.7 + 177.6
3	$\frac{1}{36}$ × 2 × 10 × 10 × 10	+ ½ × 2 × 10 × 1.31 × 1.31	= 55.6 + 17.2
Total		644.0 in.⁴	= 230.3 + 413.7

$$I_{y\text{-}y} = 313.0 \text{ in.}^4$$

Double area	I_{cg} + Area × d^2	= New I
1	$\frac{1}{12} \times 2 \times 12 \times 12 \times 12 \quad + 0$	= 288.00
2	$\frac{1}{12} \times 10 \times 2 \times 2 \times 2 \quad + 0$	= 6.67
3	$2 \times \frac{1}{36} \times 10 \times 1 \times 1 \times 1 + 2 \times \frac{1}{2} \times 1 \times 10 \times 1.33 \times 1.33$	= 0.55
		17.78
Total		313.00 in.^{4}

1.410 X distance to center of gravity = 2.14 in. to right. Moments about Y-Y axis:

Area no.	Area	× Arm	= Moment
1	16 sq in.	× 1 in.	= 16 cu in.
2	8	× 4 in.	= 32
3	4	× 3 in.	= 12
Total	28 sq in.	× (2.143 in.)	= 60 cu in.

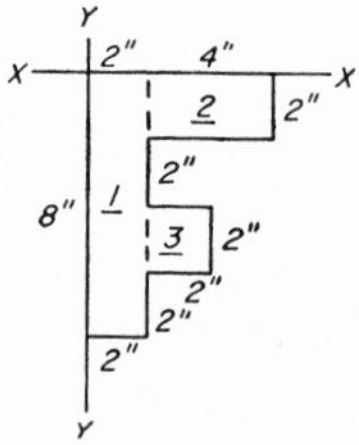

FIG. 1.410

Y distance to center of-gravity = 3.29 in. down from x-x. Moments about x-x:

Area no.	Area	× Arm	= Moment
1	16 sq in.	× 4 in.	= 64 cu in.
2	8	× 1	= 8
3	4	× 5	= 20
Total	28 sq in.	× (3.286) in.	= 92 cu in.

$$I_{x\text{-}x} = 453.3 \text{ in.}^4$$

Area	I_{cg} + $A \times d^2$	= New I
1	$\frac{1}{12} \times 2 \times 8 \times 8 \times 8 + 16 \times 4 \times 4$	= 85.3 + 256
2	$\frac{1}{12} \times 4 \times 2 \times 2 \times 2 + 8 \times 1 \times 1$	= 2.7 + 8
3	$\frac{1}{12} \times 2 \times 2 \times 2 \times 2 + 4 \times 5 \times 5$	= 1.3 + 100
	453.3 in.^{4}	= 89.3 + 364

$$I_{y\text{-}y} = 197.3 \text{ in.}^4$$

Area	I_{cg} + $A \times d^2$ = New I
1	$\frac{1}{12} \times 8 \times 2 \times 2 \times 2 + 16 \times 1 \times 1 = 5.3 + 16$
2	$\frac{1}{12} \times 2 \times 4 \times 4 \times 4 + 8 \times 4 \times 4 = 10.7 + 128$
3	$\frac{1}{12} \times 2 \times 2 \times 2 \times 2 + 4 \times 3 \times 3 = 1.3 + 36$
	$197.3 \text{ in.}^4 = 17.3 + 180$

1.411 Let x = rate (mph) of plane B and $x + 90$ = rate (mph) of plane A.

$$\frac{900}{(x + 90)} + 2.25 = \frac{900}{x}, \quad \text{(hours + hours = hours)}$$

Multiply through by $x(x + 90)$ to clear of fractions

$$900x + 2.25(x^2 + 90) = 900x + 81{,}000$$
$$x^2 + 90x = 36{,}000$$

Complete square

$$x^2 + 90x + 45 \times 45 = (x + 45)^2 = 36{,}000 + 2{,}025$$
$$x + 45 = 195, \ x = 150, \ x + 90 = 240$$

Check $\quad 900/240 + 2.25 = 6.00 \text{ hr} = 900/150$

1.412 Let A be one number and B the other. Given

$$A^2 + B^2 = 100 \text{ and } 2(A + B) = 28$$

This suggests a 3-4-5 triangle where

$$A = 6, \ B = 8, \text{ and } C = 10$$

Thus $\quad 36 + 64 = 100 \text{ and } 2(6 + 8) = 28$
$\quad$ and $AB = 48$

By direct solution

$$A + B = 14 \text{ and } A^2 + 2AB + B^2 = 196$$

But $A^2 + B^2 = 100$ so $2AB + 100 = 196$ and $AB = 48$
For a check, solve for A and B.

$$A = 14 - B \text{ and } A^2 = 196 - 28B + B^2$$
$$196 - 28B + B^2 + B^2 = 100 \text{ and } B^2 - 14B + 48 = 0$$

By quadratic equation

$$B = \frac{-(-14) \pm \sqrt{+196 - 192}}{2} = \frac{+14 \pm 2}{2}$$

$$= +8 \text{ or } +6 \text{ and } A = +6 \text{ or } +8$$

1.413 Area of field $= xy$

$$(1) \qquad +xy + 2{,}500 = (x + 100)(y - 25)$$
$$(2) \qquad +xy - 5{,}000 = (x - 100)(y + 50)$$
$$xy + 2{,}500 = xy + 100y - 25x - 2{,}500$$
$$(a) \quad +100y - 25x = +5{,}000$$
$$xy - 5{,}000 = xy - 100y + 50x - 5{,}000$$
$$(b) \quad -100y + 50x = 0$$
$$(a) \quad +100y - 25x = +5{,}000$$
$$(a) + (b) \qquad +25x = +5{,}000$$
$$x = +200$$
$$y = +100$$

Check: $xy = 20{,}000$
$xy + 2{,}500 =$
$22{,}500 = 300 \times 75$
$xy - 5{,}000 =$
$15{,}000 = 100 \times 150$

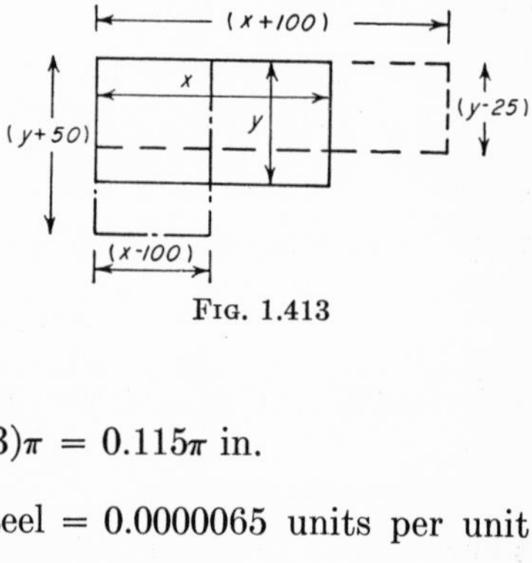

Fig. 1.413

1.414 Tire must be expanded

$$(62.378 - 62.263)\pi = 0.115\pi \text{ in.}$$

Coefficient of expansion of steel = 0.0000065 units per unit per degree F.

t = degrees above 65°F that tire must be heated. Inside circumference of tire = 62.263π

$$0.115\pi = 62.263\pi \times 0.0000065 \times t$$

$$t = \frac{0.115}{0.405 \times 1/1{,}000} = 284°\text{F}$$

Temperature of tire must be raised to 284 + 65 = **349**°F or above.

1.415 A $-60°F$ change in temperature will shorten a 90.000-ft length of steel tape by $90 \times 60 \times 0.0000065 = 0.035$ ft.

90.035 ft must be read on the tape to lay out a 90.000-ft distance on the ground.

1.416 Ten men can dig $^{10}/_{8} \times 150 = 187.5$ ft of trench in 7 hr.
Ten men can dig 200 ft of trench in $(7 \times 200)/187.5 = 7.467$ hr.
Three men can backfill 200 ft of trench in 8 hr.
Ten men can backfill 200 ft of trench in $^{3}/_{10} \times 8 = 2.4$ hr.
Ten men can dig and backfill 200 ft of trench in 9.867 hr = **9** hr **52** min

1.417 (1) $$x^2 + y^2 = +15{,}025$$
(2) $$2x + 4y = +530 \text{ or } x = +265 - 2y$$

$$x^2 = +70{,}225 - 1{,}060y + 4y^2$$

(1) $$y^2 + 4y^2 - 1{,}060y + 70{,}225 = +15{,}025$$
$$y^2 - 212y + 11{,}040 = 0$$

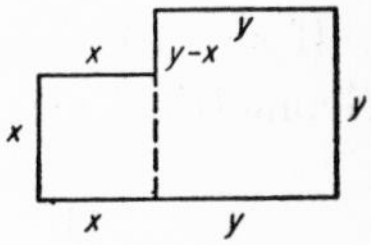

FIG. 1.417

By quadratic equation

$$y = \frac{-(-212) \pm \sqrt{212 \times 212 - 44{,}160}}{2}$$

$$y = \frac{+212 \pm \sqrt{784}}{2} = \frac{+212 \pm 28}{2} = +106 \pm 14 = 120 \text{ or } 92$$

When $y = 120$, $x = 25$ and $14{,}400 + 625 = 15{,}025$
When $y = 92$, $x = 81$ and $8{,}464 + 6{,}561 = 15{,}025$

Both solutions satisfy.

1.418 (a) $y^3 = x^3$ and $y = \sqrt[3]{x^3} = x$ or a straight line
Area $= \frac{1}{2} \times 4 \times 4 =$ **8**

(b) $$\text{Area} = \int_1^3 (x^3 + 3x^2)dx = \left.\frac{x^4}{4} + \frac{3x^3}{3}\right]_1^3$$
$$= 81/4 + 27 - 1/4 - 1 = 20 + 26 = \mathbf{46}$$

(c) $$\frac{d}{dx}(4x^2 + 17x) = \mathbf{8x + 17}$$

Also $$\frac{d}{dx}(ax^2 + b^{1/2}) = \mathbf{2ax}$$

(*d*) $$\int (7x^3 + 4x^2)dx = \frac{7x^4}{4} + \frac{4x^3}{3} + c_1$$

Also $$\int x \cos (2x^2 + 7)dx = \frac{\sin}{4}(2x^2 + 7) + c_1$$

1.419 The increase in length of 100-ft tape from 10°C to 30°C = 100 × (30 − 10) × 0.000011 = 0.022 ft. The tape at 30°C = 100.042 + 0.022 = 100.064 ft. The measurement of 1,256.271 ft is short because it was made with a long tape.

The correction at +0.064 ft per 100 ft = 12.563 × 0.064 = +0.804 ft.

True length of line = 1,256.271 + 0.804 = 1,257.075 ft.

1.420 Arithmetical progression:

$$x + (x + a) + (x + 2a) = 45$$
$$3x + 3a = 45, \quad x + a = 15, \text{ and } a = 15 - x$$

If $x = 10$, then $a = 5$ and the three numbers are 10, 15, and 20.
Geometrical progression:

$$\begin{aligned} 10 + 2 &= 12 = b &&= 12 \text{ and } r = 1.5 \\ 15 + 3 &= 18 = br &&= 12 \times 1.5 \\ 20 + 7 &= 27 = br^2 &&= 12 \times 1.5 \times 1.5 \end{aligned}$$

By direct solution:

(1) $x + a = +15$ or $a = +15 - b + 2 = 17 - b$
(2) $x + 2 = b$ or $x = b - 2$

(3) $x + a + 3 = br$ or $18 = br$ and $r = \dfrac{18}{b}$

(4) $x + 2a + 7 = br^2$ or $(b - 2) + 2(17 - b) + 7 = 18 \times \dfrac{18}{b}$

(4) becomes

$$b^2 - 39b + 324 = 0, \quad b = \frac{-(-39) \pm \sqrt{1{,}521 - 1{,}296}}{2}$$

$$b = \frac{+39 \pm 15}{2} = 12, \quad \text{and } x = 10, \quad a = 5, \quad r = 1.5$$

1.421 (*a*) (1) $+4x^2 + 7y^2 = +32$, or $+12x^2 + 21y^2 = +96$

(2) $-3x^2 + 11y^2 = +41$, or $-12x^2 + 44y^2 = +164$

(1′) + (2′). $+65y^2 = +260$

$$y^2 = 4, \quad y = +2, \quad x = \pm 1, \quad \text{and } y = -2, \quad x = \pm 1$$

(*b*)

$$\begin{aligned} (1)\quad & +x + 2y - z = +6 \\ 2 \times (2)\quad & +4x - 2y + 6z = -26 \\ (3)\quad & +3x - 2y + 3z = -16 \end{aligned}$$

$(a) = (1) + 2 \times (2)$, $+5x + 5z = -20$, or $+x + z = -4$

$(b) = (1) + (3)$ $\quad +4x + 2z = -10$, or $+x + 0.5z = -2.5$

$(a') - (b') =$ $\quad +0.5z = -1.5$

From (a'), $x = -1$; and from (1), $y = +2$ $\quad z = -3$

Check using (2) and (3).

1.422 (*a*) $\cos 2A = 2\cos^2 A - 1$

$$2\cos^2 75° - 1 = \cos 150° = -\cos 30°$$

$$\cos 30° = \frac{\sqrt{3}}{2} = \frac{1.732}{2} = 0.866$$

$$\cos^2 75° = \frac{1 - 0.866}{2} = \frac{+0.133}{2} = 0.0666$$

$$\cos 75° = \sqrt{0.0666} = 0.258$$

(*b*) Angle $A = 75° = AoX$ (first quadrant)

$\sin A = Aa$

$\cos A = oa$

$\tan A = \dfrac{Aa}{oa}$

Angle $B = BoX = 105°$ (second quadrant)

$\cos B = bo = -oa$

$\sin B = Bb = Aa$

$\tan B = \dfrac{Bb}{bo} = -\dfrac{Aa}{oa}$

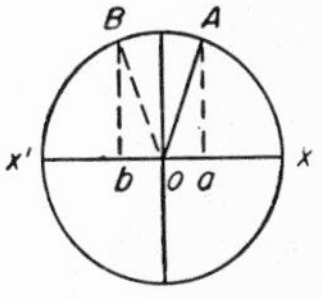

(*b*)

FIG. 1.422*b*

1.423 Volume $= x(20 - 2x)^2$

$$= 400x - 80x^2 + 4x^3$$

$$\text{(for } V \text{ max)} \quad \frac{dV}{dx} = 0$$

$$= +400 - 160x + 12x^2$$

or $\quad +3x^2 - 40x + 100 = 0$

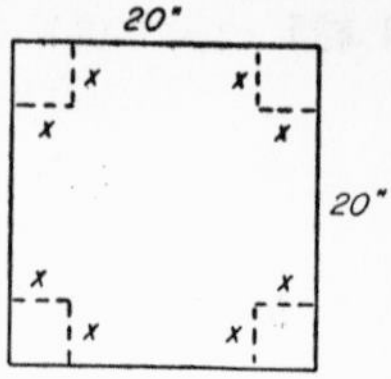

FIG. 1.423

Using quadratic equation

$$x = \frac{-(-40) \pm \sqrt{1{,}600 - 1{,}200}}{6} = \frac{+40 \pm 20}{6} = +10 \text{ or } 3.33$$

V min (0) when $x = 10$, so use $x = 3.33$

$V = \mathbf{13.33 \times 13.33 \times 3.33} = \mathbf{592.59}$ cu in.

x may be found by trial (carry volume to $\frac{1}{100}$ s).

1. Try values of $x = 1, 2, 3,$ and 4.
2. Try values of $x = 3.1$ to 3.5.
3. Try values of $x = 3.31$ to 3.35.

1.424 $s = \frac{1}{2}(a + b + c) = \frac{1}{2}(9 + 12 + 10) = 15.5$

$$r = \sqrt{\frac{(s-a)(s-b)(s-c)}{s}} = \sqrt{\frac{6.5 \times 3.5 \times 5.5}{15.5}}$$

$$r = \sqrt{8.07} = 2.84$$

$$\tan\frac{1}{2}A = \frac{r}{(s-a)} = \frac{2.84}{6.5} = 0.437, \quad \frac{1}{2}A = 23.6°, \quad A = 47.2°$$

$$\tan\frac{1}{2}B = \frac{r}{(s-b)} = \frac{2.84}{3.5} = 0.812, \quad \frac{1}{2}B = 39.05°, \quad B = 78.1°$$

$$\tan\frac{1}{2}C = \frac{r}{(s-c)} = \frac{2.84}{5.5} = 0.517, \quad \frac{1}{2}C = 27.35°, \quad C = 54.7°$$

Check: 180.0°

Area $ABC = \frac{1}{2} \times 12 \times 10 \times \sin 47.2° = 60 \times 0.7337 = 44.0 \text{ ft}^2$

$$\text{Volume prism} = \frac{(h_a + h_b + h_c)}{3} \times 44.0$$

$$= \frac{(8.6 + 7.1 + 5.5)}{3} \times 44.0$$

$$= \frac{21.2}{3} \times 44.0 = 311 \text{ ft}^3$$

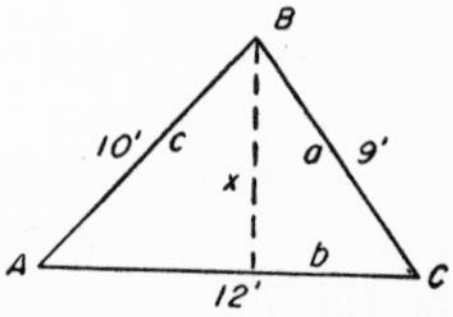

FIG. 1.424

1.425

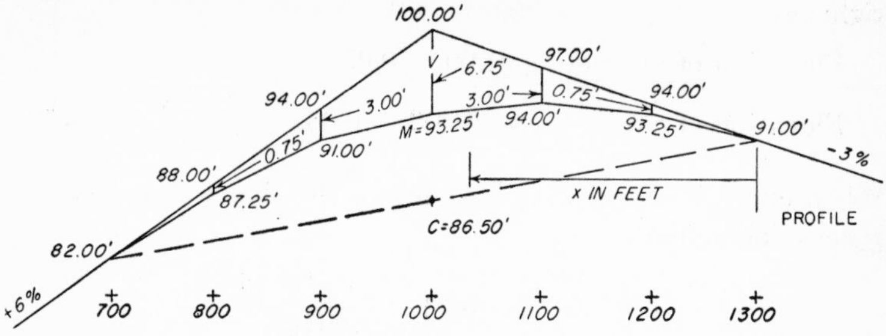

FIG. 1.425. Profile of curve.

Elevations along Grade Tangents and Parabola

Station	Vertex Elevation	−	Drop to tangent	=	Elevation of tangent	−	Drop to parabola	=	Elevation of parabola
7 + 00	100.00	−	3 × 6	=	82.00	−	0.00	=	82.00
8 + 00	100.00	−	2 × 6	=	88.00	−	0.75	=	87.25
9 + 00	100.00	−	1 × 6	=	94.00	−	3.00	=	91.00
10 + 00				=	100.00	−	6.75	=	93.25
11 + 00	100.00	−	1 × 3	=	97.00	−	3.00	=	94.00
12 + 00	100.00	−	2 × 3	=	94.00	−	0.75	=	93.25
13 + 00	100.00	−	3 × 3	=	91.00	−	0.00	=	91.00

Point C has an elevation the mean of that at 7 + 00 and 13 + 00.

Point M has an elevation the mean of 100.00 and C. V = 6.75 ft. Distance down (in feet) from tangent to parabola

$$= \left(\frac{x}{\tfrac{1}{2}\text{ length of parabola}}\right)^2 \times 6.75 = \left(\frac{x}{300}\right)^2 \times 6.75$$

For stations 8 + 00 and 12 + 00, drop $= (^{100}/_{300})^2 \times 6.75 = 0.75$ ft

For stations 9 + 00 and 11 + 00, drop $= (^{200}/_{300})^2 \times 6.75 = 3.00$ ft

From the table above it is fairly obvious that the high point of the parabola is at station 11 + 00. In other cases not so obvious, it is usually a matter of observation on which side of V

the high point lies. In this case, knowing the high point is to the right of V

$$\text{Elevation of tangent} = 91.00 + 0.03x$$

$$\text{Elevation of curve} = y = 91.00 + 0.03x - \left(\frac{x}{300}\right)^2 \times 6.75$$

When curve is at maximum elevation, the slope of the tangent is zero. Therefore

$$\frac{dy}{dx} = 0 = +0.03 - \frac{2x \times 6.75}{90{,}000}$$

$$13.5x = 2{,}700, \quad x = 200$$

or high point is at station $13 + 00 - 2 + 00 = 11 + 00$

The above work may be done by cut and try with more work and perhaps less accuracy.

MECHANICS (KINETICS)

1.501 Velocity = acceleration × time, or $v = at$

$$v = 16 \text{ ft per sec} = a \times 4, \quad a = 4 \text{ ft per sec}^2$$

$$\text{Tension in cable} = Ma = \frac{W}{g}(g + a)$$

$$T = (2{,}000/32.2)(32.2 + 4) = \mathbf{2{,}250} \text{ lb}$$

1.502 Final velocity squared = initial velocity squared plus twice acceleration times distance body moves.

$$v^2 = 0 = 16 \times 16 + 2 \times a \times 5, \quad a = -25.6 \text{ ft per sec}^2$$

$$\text{Tension in cable} = Ma = \frac{W}{g}(g + a)$$

$$= (2{,}000/32.2)(32.2 - 25.6) = \mathbf{410} \text{ lb}$$

1.503 Force normal to plane = 40×0.866
= 34.67 lb

Force parallel to plane = 40×0.500
= 20.00 lb

Friction force = $34.67 \times 0.3 = 10.40$ lb

Resultant force parallel to plane
= $20.00 - 10.40 = 9.60$ lb

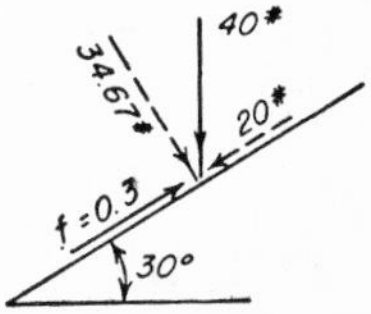

FIG. 1.503

Force = mass × acceleration or $9.60 = \dfrac{40}{32.2} \times a$

$$a = \mathbf{7.73} \text{ ft per sec}^2$$

Distance weight moves = ½ × acceleration × time squared

$$D = \tfrac{1}{2}at^2 \text{ and } 60 = \tfrac{1}{2} \times 7.73t^2$$
$$t = \mathbf{3.94} \text{ sec}$$

Distance weight moves during third second

$$= (7.73/2)(3^2 - 2^2) = \mathbf{19.33} \text{ ft}$$

1.504 Initial velocity $= \dfrac{30 \times 5{,}280}{60 \times 60} = 44$ ft per sec

Final velocity = initial velocity minus the acceleration × time

$$0 = 44 - a \times 5, \quad a = 8.8 \text{ ft per sec}^2$$

Force = mass × acceleration, $F = (6{,}000/32.2) \times 8.8 = 1{,}640$ lb
Taking moments about bottom of rear wheel

$$\Sigma M_{W_R} = 0 = +10 \times 2 \times W_F - 6{,}000 \times 5 - 1{,}640 \times 2$$
$$W_F = 1{,}500 + 164 = 1{,}664 \text{ lb}$$

Normal pressure on each front wheel = 1,664 lb
Normal pressure on each rear wheel = 1,336 lb

1.505 The weight × distance of free fall + the weight × displacement of spring = work of spring = average force of spring × displacement of spring squared.

$$1{,}000 \times 6 + 1{,}000 \times d_s = (2000/2) \times d_s^2$$
$$d_s^2 - d_s - 6 = 0 = (d_s - 3)(d_s + 2)$$
$$d_s = \mathbf{+3} \text{ in.}$$

(The spring does not elongate, hence $d_s = -2$ is meaningless.)

1.506 Work of spring = kinetic energy of car
Let R = resistance of spring in pound per inch.

$$\frac{R}{2} \times d_s^2 = \frac{1}{2} Mv^2$$

$$\frac{R}{2} \times 2.5 \times 2.5 = \frac{1}{2} \times \frac{100{,}000}{32.2} \times 2 \times 2 \times 12$$
$$R = \mathbf{23{,}850} \text{ lb per in.}$$

1.507 Block M has a 50-lb component parallel to the 30° plane and an 86.67-lb component normal to the 30° plane.

Friction force block $M = 86.67 \times 0.2 = 17.33$ lb

Block N has an 86.67-lb component parallel to the 60° plane and a 50-lb component normal to the 60° plane.

Friction force block $N = 50 \times 0.2 = 10$ lb

Net force block $M = 50 + 17.33 = 67.33$ lb

Net force block $N = 86.67 - 10 = 76.67$ lb

Resultant force $= 76.67 - 67.33 = 9.33$ lb down 60° plane

$$\text{Force} = \text{mass} \times \text{acceleration}, \ 9.33 = \frac{(100 + 100)}{32.2} \times a$$

$$a = \mathbf{1.505} \text{ ft per sec}^2$$

Distance weights move $= \frac{1}{2} \times$ acceleration $\times$ time squared

$$15 = \tfrac{1}{2} \times 1.505 \times t^2, \quad t = \mathbf{4.47} \text{ sec}$$

Tension in the connecting cord $= T$

(On weight M side) $T = 67.33 + (100/32.2) \times 1.505 = 72.00$ lb

(On weight N side) $T = 76.67 - (100/32.2) \times 1.505 = 72.00$ lb

1.508 $T_x = T_y$ and $T_x + T_y = T_z = 2T_x = 2T_y$ (where $T =$ tension in cords carrying weights)

Weights y and z will fall, weight x will rise.

Say weight x rose 10 ft and weight y fell 8 ft, then the pulley carrying their joint cord must rise one-half the difference or 1 ft in order for the cord to remain taut. That gives $d_z = \dfrac{d_x - d_y}{2}$

$$\therefore (1) \quad a_z = \frac{a_x - a_y}{2} = 0.5(a_x - a_y)$$

$$(2) \quad T_x = \frac{10g}{g} + \frac{10}{g} a_x = +10 + 0.31a_x$$

$$(3) \quad T_y = \frac{20g}{g} - \frac{20}{g} a_y = +20 - 0.62a_y$$

$$(4) \quad T_z = \frac{30g}{g} - \frac{30}{g} a_z = +30 - 0.93a_z$$

$$(2') \quad T_z = +20 + 0.62a_x$$

$$(3') \quad T_z = +40 - 1.24a_y$$

$$(5) = (3') - (2'), \quad 0 = +20 - 0.62a_x - 1.24a_y$$

$$(6) = (3') - (4), \quad 0 = +10 - 1.24a_y + 0.93a_z$$

but $(1') = 0.93 \times (1) + 0.93a_z = +0.465a_x - 0.465a_y$

(6′) Substituting (1′) in (6)

$$-0.465a_x + 0.465a_y + 1.24a_y = +10$$

(7) = $\frac{4}{3} \times (6')$

$$-0.62a_x + 2.27a_y = +13.33$$

(5) $\quad +0.62a_x + 1.24a_y = +20.00$

(8) = (5) + (7) $\quad 3.51a_y = +33.33$

(8′) $\quad a_y = +\ 9.5$ ft per sec^2

From (5) $\quad a_x = +13.3$ ft per sec^2

From (1) $\quad a_z = +\ 1.9$ ft per sec^2

Now $d = \frac{1}{2}at^2$ and $v = at$

At the end of 1 sec $d_x = 6.70$ ft up, $\quad v_x = 13.3$ fps

$d_y = 4.75$ ft down, $v_y = 9.5$ fps

$d_z = 0.85$ ft down, $v_z = 1.9$ fps

1.509 Positive work − negative work = final kinetic energy.

Positive work = foot-pounds of drop

$$= \frac{1 \times 100 \text{ ft}}{100} \times 120{,}000 \text{ lb} = 120{,}000 \text{ ft-lb}$$

Negative work = friction loss

$$= 10 \text{ lb per ton} \times 60^T \times 100 = \underline{-60{,}000 \text{ ft-lb}}$$

$$\text{Final kinetic energy} = \frac{1}{2} \times \frac{120{,}000}{32.2} \times v^2 = 60{,}000 \text{ ft-lb}$$

$$v^2 = 32.2$$

Striking velocity = **5.67** fps

$$\text{Final kinetic energy} = 60{,}000 \times 12 = \frac{100{,}000}{2} \times d_s^2$$

Spring will shorten **3.795** in.

1.510 Initial kinetic energy = uphill work + friction

$$30 \text{ mph} = \frac{30 \times 5{,}280}{60 \times 60} = 44 \text{ fps}$$

(1)

$$\frac{1}{2} \times \frac{80{,}000}{32.2} \times (44)^2 = \frac{80{,}000}{2{,}000} \times 10 \times d_1 + \frac{2 \times d_1}{100} \times 80{,}000$$

divide (1) by 800

$$3{,}010 = 0.5d_1 + 2d_1 = 2.5d_1 \text{ or } d_1 = \mathbf{1{,}204} \text{ ft on slope}$$

Downhill work − friction = kinetic energy

$$+\frac{2 \times 1{,}204}{100} \times 80{,}000 - 10 \times 1{,}204 \times \frac{80{,}000}{2{,}000} = \frac{80{,}000 \times v^2}{64.4}$$

$$+24.08 - 6.02 = 18.06 = \frac{v^2}{64.4}, \quad v = 34 \text{ fps}$$

Kinetic energy = friction

$$80{,}000 \times \frac{v^2}{64.4} = \frac{80{,}000}{2{,}000} \times 10 \times d_2$$

$$18.06 = \frac{d_2}{200}$$

$$d_2 = \mathbf{3{,}612} \text{ ft on level track}$$

1.511 $$\frac{50}{r} = \sin 5° = 0.0872, \ r = 574 \text{ ft}$$

$$45 \text{ mph} = 45 \times 5{,}280/3{,}600 = 66 \text{ fps}$$

Gage of a standard railroad track = 4 ft 8½ in. or 4.9 ft center-to-center rails.

a. Superelevation for equal wheel pressures

$$= \frac{G \times v^2}{g \times r} = \frac{4.9 \times 66 \times 66}{32.2 \times 574} = \mathbf{1.15} \text{ ft}$$

b. Horizontal force 5 ft. above rail for 60 mph speed =

$$\frac{Wv^2}{g \times r} = \frac{100{,}000 \times 88 \times 88}{32.2 \times 574} = 41{,}950 \text{ lb}$$

Superelevation = 8 in. in 4.9 ft or 0.67/4.9, and position of vertical force (weight) off center at top of rails =

$$x = 5 \times 0.67/4.9 = 0.683 \text{ ft}$$

Distant vertical force from center inner rail =

$$4.9/2 - 0.683 = 1.767 \text{ ft}$$

$\Sigma M_{\text{inner rail}}$

$$0 = +5 \times 41{,}950 + 1.767 \times 100{,}000 - 4.9 \times R_{\text{outer}}$$

Normal pressure outer rail $= R_{\text{outer}} =$

$$42{,}750 + 36{,}000 = \mathbf{78{,}750}\ \text{lb}$$

1.512 $$60 \text{ mph} = 88 \text{ fps}$$

a. $$\tan A = 0.15$$
$$A = 8.53° = \text{angle of superelevation}$$

b. Now

$$\tan(A + B) = \frac{88 \times 88}{32.2 \times 500} = 0.482$$
$$A + B = 25.73°$$
$$A = \mathbf{8.53°} \text{ (angle of superelevation)}$$
$$B = 17.20° \text{ and } \tan B = 0.310$$

Skidding will impend if f is below **0.310**

1.513 Vertical is shorter than 100 ft by $\frac{5 \times 5}{200} = 0.125 \text{ ft} = h$

$$\text{Tension in cable} = \frac{100}{99.875} \times 20{,}000 = \mathbf{20{,}025}\ \text{lb}$$

$$\text{Horizontal pull} = \frac{5}{99.875} \times 20{,}000 = \mathbf{1{,}001}\ \text{lb}$$

$$v^2 = 2gh = 2 \times 32.2 \times 0.125 \text{ or } 0.25g$$

Tension of cable when swinging through vertical position

$$= 20{,}000 + \frac{20{,}000 \times 0.25g}{g \times 100} = \mathbf{20{,}050}\ \text{lb}$$

1.514 $$\sin 45° = \cos 45° = 0.707$$

The vertical velocity at the high point of path = 0 = initial velocity × sin 45° − gt

$$300 \times 0.707 = 32.2 \times t \text{ and } t = 6.6 \text{ sec}$$

Maximum height projectile will reach

$$= 300 \times t \times \sin 45° - \tfrac{1}{2}gt^2$$
$$= 300 \times 6.6 \times 0.707 - \tfrac{1}{2} \times 32.2 \times 6.6 \times 6.6$$
$$= 1{,}400 - 700 = \mathbf{700}\ \text{ft}$$

For 45° angle, h_{max} = initial velocity squared divided by $4g$ or

$$\frac{300 \times 300}{4g} = 700 \text{ ft}$$

Range = twice the initial velocity $\times \cos 45° \times t$

$$= 2 \times 300 \times 0.707 \times 6.6 = \mathbf{2{,}800} \text{ ft}$$

$$\left(\text{Also max range} = \frac{v^2}{g} = \frac{300 \times 300}{g} = 2{,}800 \text{ ft}\right)$$

1.515 (See the special formulas in answer 1.514.)

Maximum range $= 40 \times 5280 = \dfrac{v^2}{32.2}$ or $v^2 = 6{,}800{,}000$ and $v = \mathbf{2{,}600}$ fps

Maximum height $= \dfrac{v^2}{4g} = \frac{1}{4} \times$ max range $= {}^{40}\!/_{4} = \mathbf{10}$ miles

1.516 18 in. = 1.5 ft

$\sin 60° = 0.866 \times 1.50 = 1.30$ ft (radius)
$\cos 60° = 0.500 \times 1.50 = 0.75$ ft (center ball below top end of rod)

$$\tan 60° = 1.732 = \frac{v^2}{gr}, \quad v^2 = 1.732 \times 32.2 \times 1.30$$

$$v = \mathbf{8.52} \text{ fps} = \mathbf{62.6} \text{ rpm}$$

Weight of 3-in. cast-iron ball $= \frac{1}{6} \times \pi \times (\frac{1}{4})^3 \times 450 =$ 3.68 lb

Moment (about point where arm connects to vertical shaft) of horizontal effective force and weight (vertical)

$$\Sigma M = 0 = -0.75 \times \left(\frac{3.68 \times v^2}{gr}\right) + 1.30 \times (3.68)$$

Check: $0.75 \times 1.732 = 1.30$

$$\text{Tension in arm} = 3.68 \sqrt{(1)^2 + (1.732)^2} = \mathbf{7.36} \text{ lb}$$

1.517 60 mph = 88 fps

Radius = 1,000 ft, very nearly.
Let A = the angle the cord makes with the vertical

$$\tan A = \frac{v^2}{gr} = \frac{88 \times 88}{32.2 \times 1000} = 0.2735, \quad A = \mathbf{15.3°}$$

The horizontal displacement of the weight =

$$6 \times \sin 15.3° = 6 \times 0.264 = \mathbf{1.58} \text{ ft}$$

The tension in the cord $= 25\sqrt{(1)^2 + (0.274)^2}$
$= 25 \times 1.036 = \mathbf{25.9}$ lb

1.518 Distance projectile must travel

$$= \text{initial velocity squared} \times \frac{\sin 2A}{g} = \left[2(v\cos A)\left(\frac{v \sin A}{g}\right)\right]$$

$$10 \times 5{,}280 = \frac{1{,}500 \times 1{,}500}{32.2} \times \sin 2A$$

$$\sin 2A = \frac{322 \times 0.528}{225} = 0.756, \quad 2A = \mathbf{49.1°}$$

$$A = \mathbf{24°\ 33'}$$

1.519 $I = \frac{1}{2}Mr^2$ for a solid cylinder about geometric axis

M(for 24-in. diameter cylinder)

$$= \pi \times \left(\frac{12}{12}\right)^2 \times \frac{4}{3} \times \frac{450}{32.2} = 58.5$$

M(for 22-in. diameter cylinder)

$$= \pi \times \left(\frac{11}{12}\right)^2 \times \frac{4}{3} \times \frac{450}{32.2} = 49.2$$

I(24-in. cylinder) $= \frac{1}{2} \times 58.5 \times 1^2 = 29.3$
I(22-in. cylinder) $= \frac{1}{2} \times 49.2 \times (11/12)^2 = 20.6$
I(net) (lb × ft × sec²) $= \mathbf{8.7}$

1.520 $M = (490/32.2) \times \pi \times r^2 \times L = 47.8 \times r^2 \times L$
$I = \frac{1}{2}Mr^2 = 23.9 \times r^4 \times L$
I(about axis of 40-in. disk) $= I_{cg} + M \times d^2$
where d is the distance between axes
I (40 in.) $= 23.9 \times \frac{1}{3} \times (20/12)^4 = +61.50$
I (10 in.) $= 7.97 \times (5/12)^4 = -\ 0.24$
I (12 in.) $= 7.97 \times (6/12)^4 + 15.93 \times (6/12)^2 \times (12/12)^2$
$= -0.50 - 3.98 = -4.48$

I(net) $= +61.50 - 4.72 = \mathbf{56.78}$ lb × ft × sec²

1.521 Angular velocity $= 1{,}500$ rpm $= 1{,}500 \times \dfrac{2\pi}{60}$

$= 157$ radians per sec

$157 = \alpha t = \alpha 60, \quad \alpha =$ **2.617** radians per sec^2

Number of revolutions until wheel stops

$=$ mean angular velocity $\times$ time

$= \dfrac{1{,}500 + 0}{2} \times 1(\text{minute}) =$ **750** revolutions

Angular velocity at end of 40 sec $= 157 - 2.617 \times 40$
$=$ **52.3** radians per sec $=$ **500** rpm

1.522 Angular velocity $= 60$ mph $= 88$ fps at rim

$$88 \text{ fps} = \frac{88}{3\pi} \text{ rps} = \left(\frac{88}{3\pi}\right) \times 2\pi = 58.7 \text{ radians per sec}$$

Number of revolutions to stop wheel $= \dfrac{500}{3\pi}$ or $\left(\dfrac{500}{3\pi}\right) 2\pi$

$=$ **333** radians

Angular velocity squared = twice the total number of revolutions to stop times the angular acceleration.

$(58.7)^2 = 2 \times 333 \times \alpha, \ \alpha =$ **5.17** radians per sec^2

1.523 $M(\text{hemisphere}) = \dfrac{490}{32.2} \times \dfrac{1}{6} \times \pi \times \left(\dfrac{6}{12}\right)^3 \times \dfrac{1}{2}$

$= 0.498$ lb $\times$ sec^2 per ft

Center of gravity hemisphere $= \frac{3}{8}r = \frac{3}{8} \times 3 = 1.125$ in. above diametral plane

Angular velocity $= 300$ rpm $= 31.4$ radians per sec

Outward (horizontal) force = mass $\times$ radius distance (axis to center of gravity of weight) $\times$ angular velocity squared

$$\text{ohf} = 0.498 \times \tfrac{12}{12} \times 31.4 \times 31.4 = 493 \text{ lb}$$

Moment in rod $= \dfrac{(1.125 - 0.500)}{12} \times 493 =$ **25.6** ft-lb

For zero moment in rod, place rod at center of gravity of weight or 1.125 in. above diametral plane.

1.524

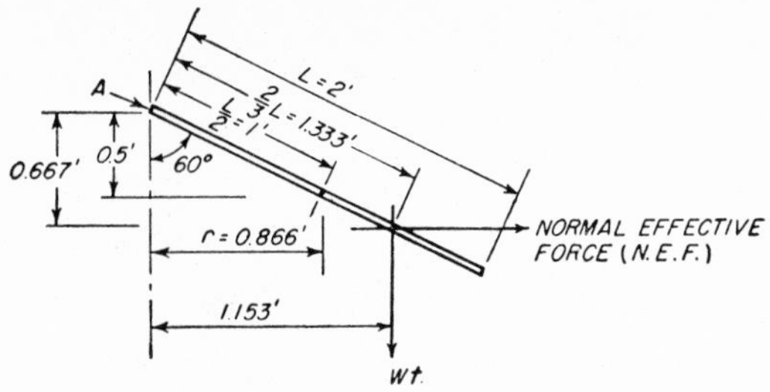

Fig. 1.524

$$\Sigma M_A = 0 = -0.667 \times \text{nef} + 1.153 \times \text{weight}$$
$$0 = -0.667 \times M \times 1.153 \times V_a^2 + 1.153 \times 32.2M$$
$$V_a^2 = \frac{32.2}{0.667} = 47.6$$

V_a (angular velocity) = **6.9** radians per sec = **66** rpm

1.525 Angular velocity = V_a = 240 rpm = 25.1 radians per sec

$$2T = \frac{M}{2} r_{c.g} \times V_a^2 \text{ where } r_{c.g} = \frac{2}{\pi} \times \text{(mean radius of rim)}$$
$$\frac{M}{2} = \frac{1}{2} \times \frac{450}{32.2} \times \frac{18}{12} \times \pi \left[\left(\frac{72}{12}\right)^2 - \left(\frac{68}{12}\right)^2\right] = 125$$
$$T = \frac{125}{2} \times \frac{2}{\pi}\left(\frac{72+68}{2 \times 12}\right) \times 25.1 \times 25.1 = \mathbf{146{,}000} \text{ lb}$$
$$\text{Tension in rim} = \frac{146{,}000}{4 \times 18} = \mathbf{2{,}032} \text{ psi}$$

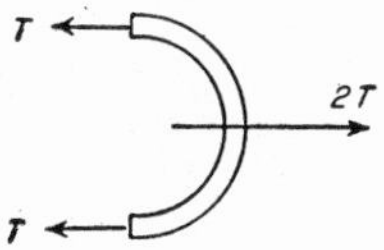

Fig. 1.525

MECHANICS (STATICS)

1.601 $\Sigma V = +10 - 10 - 10 + 10 = 0$

$$\Sigma M(\text{about } F_1) = +5 \times 10 + 9 \times 10 - 12 \times 10$$
$$= +20 \text{ ft-lb (clockwise)}$$

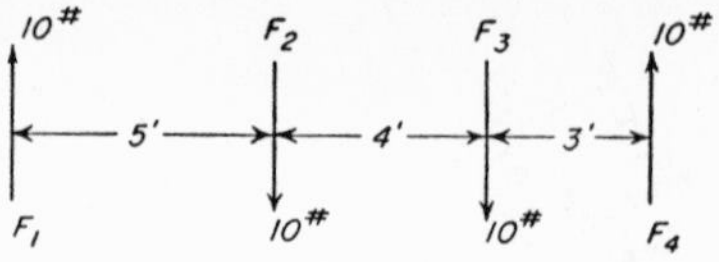

FIG. 1.601

The resultant is equal to a clockwise couple of **20** ft-lb. Had the right hand force (F_4) acted downward, then

$$\Sigma V = +10 - 10 - 10 - 10 = -20 \text{ lb acting downward}$$

and $\Sigma M(F_1) = +5 \times 10 + 9 \times 10 + 12 \times 10 = +260 \text{ ft-lb}$

The resultant would be a 20-lb force acting downward and $^{260}/_{20} = 13$ ft to right of F_1.

1.602 Find center of gravity of pile group.

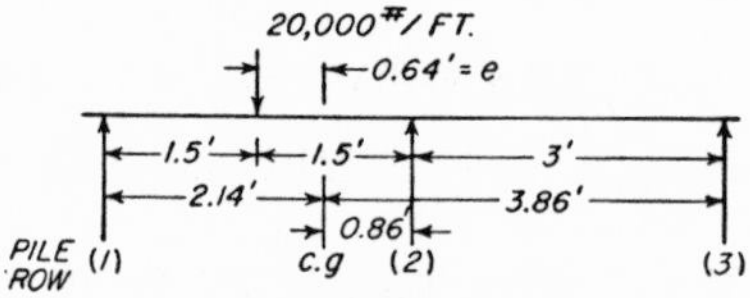

FIG. 1.602

M about Pile Row 1

Pile row	Pile spacing center to center	Area piles per ft	Distance from row 1.	Area × distance	x = distance center of gravity pile group to pile	I = area × x^2
1.	2.5 ft	0.400 sq ft	0	0	+2.14 ft	1.835
2.	4.0 ft	0.250	3 ft	0.750	−0.86	0.185
3.	6.0 ft	0.167	6 ft	1.000	−3.86	2.485
Sum		0.817	(2.14) ft	1.750		4.505

Center of gravity of pile group lies 1.750/0.817 or 2.14 ft to right of row 1. The 20,000 lb per ft load P is 0.64 ft eccentric e to center of gravity of piles.

$$\text{Load on any piles} = \frac{P}{A} + \frac{Pex}{I} \quad \text{and} \quad \frac{P}{A} = \frac{20{,}000}{0.817} = 24{,}500 \text{ lb}$$

$$\frac{Pex}{I} = \frac{20{,}000(0.64)x}{4.505} = 2840x$$

Pile row	$\frac{P}{A}$	$\frac{Pex}{I}$	Stress in pile
1.	+24,500	+ 6,080	= 30,580 lb per pile
2.	+24,500	− 2,440	= 22,060 lb per pile
3.	+24,500	−10,960	= 13,540 lb per pile

Check: (1) $30{,}580 \div 2.5 = 12{,}210$ lb per ft
(2) $22{,}060 \div 4.0 = 5{,}515$ lb per ft
(3) $13{,}540 \div 6.0 = 2{,}258$ lb per ft
19,983 lb per ft (say OK)

1.603 $\Sigma M_{R_L} = 0 = +4 \times 1{,}000 \times 2 + 10{,}000 - 12R_R,$

$$R_R = +1{,}500 \text{ lb}$$

$$\Sigma M_{R_R} = 0 = +12R_L + 10{,}000 - 4 \times 1{,}000 \times 10,$$

$$R_L = +2{,}500 \text{ lb}$$

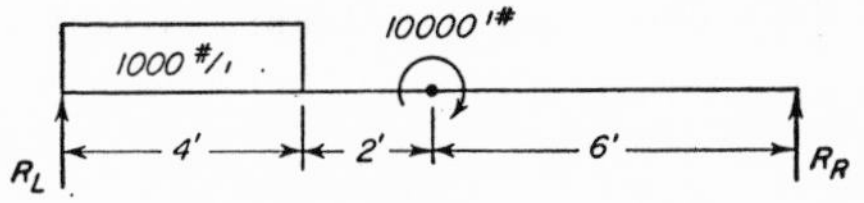

Fig. 1.603. Forces.

Check:

$$V = 0 = +R_L + R_R - 4 \times 1{,}000 = +2{,}500 + 1{,}500 - 4{,}000$$

Fig. 1.603. Shear and moment.

M at point 2.5 ft to right of R_L

$$= +2{,}500 \times 2.5 - 1{,}000 \times 2.5 \times 2.5/2 = +3{,}125 \text{ ft-lb}$$

M at point 4.0 ft to right of R_L

$$= +2{,}500 \times 4 - 1{,}000 \times 4 \times 2 = +2{,}000 \text{ ft-lb}$$

M at point 5.0 ft to right of R_L

$$= +2{,}500 \times 5 - 1{,}000 \times 4 \times 3 = +500 \text{ ft-lb}$$

M at point 6.0 ft to right of R_L but to left of couple

$$= +2{,}500 \times 6 - 1{,}000 \times 4 \times 4 = -1{,}000 \text{ ft-lb}$$

M at point 6.0 ft to right of R_L but to right of couple = 9,000 ft-lb

1.604 $\Sigma M_{R_L} = 0$

$$= +5 \times 2{,}000 + 10 \times 4{,}000 + 15 \times 6{,}000 + 20 \times 1{,}000 \times 10 - 20R_R$$

$$R_R = 17{,}000 \text{ lb}$$

$\Sigma M_{R_R} = 0$

$$= -5 \times 6{,}000 - 10 \times 4{,}000 - 15 \times 2{,}000 - 20 \times 1{,}000 \times 10 + 20R_L$$

$$R_L = 15{,}000 \text{ lb}$$

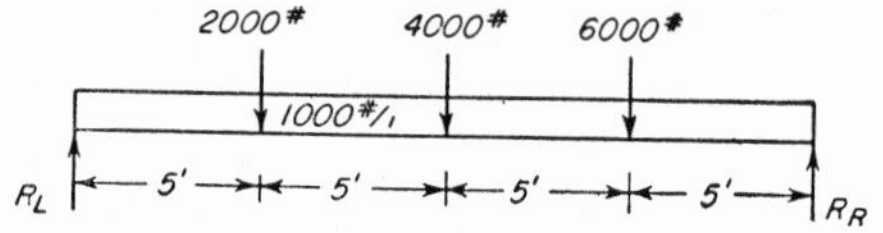

FIG. 1.604. Forces.

Check: $\Sigma V = 0$

$$= +15{,}000 - 2{,}000 - 4{,}000 - 6{,}000 - 20{,}000 + 17{,}000$$

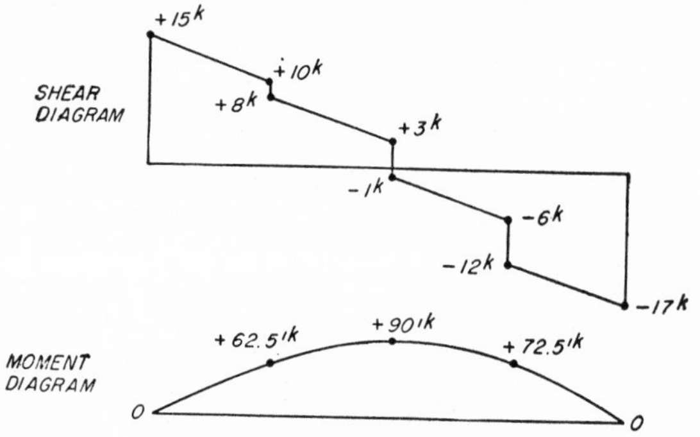

FIG. 1.604. Shear and moment.

Forces to left point of moments:

M at left quarter point

$$= +15 \times 5 - 1 \times 5 \times 5/2 = 62.5 \text{ ft-kips}$$

M at center line

$$= +15 \times 10 - 2 \times 5 - 1 \times 10 \times 10/2 = 90 \text{ ft-kips}$$

M at right quarter point

$$= +15 \times 15 - 2 \times 10 - 4 \times 5 - 1 \times \frac{15 \times 15}{2} = 72.5 \text{ ft-kips}$$

Check: M at right quarter point, forces to right of point of moments $= +17 \times 5 - 1 \times 5 \times 5/2 = +72.5$ ft-kips

1.605 ΣM_{R_L}

$$0 = +2 \times 20 \times 6 - 14R_R, \quad R_R = 17.14 \text{ kips}$$

ΣM_{R_R}

$$0 = -2 \times 20 \times 8 + 14R_L, \quad \underline{R_L = 22.86 \text{ kips}}$$

Check: $\Sigma V = 0 = +40.00 \text{ kips} - 2 \times 20$

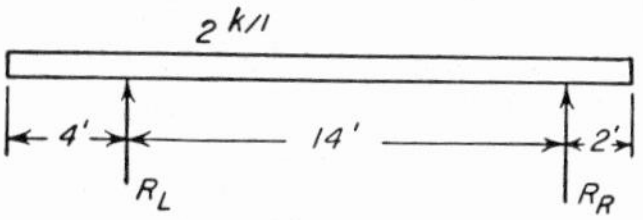

Fig. 1.605. Forces.

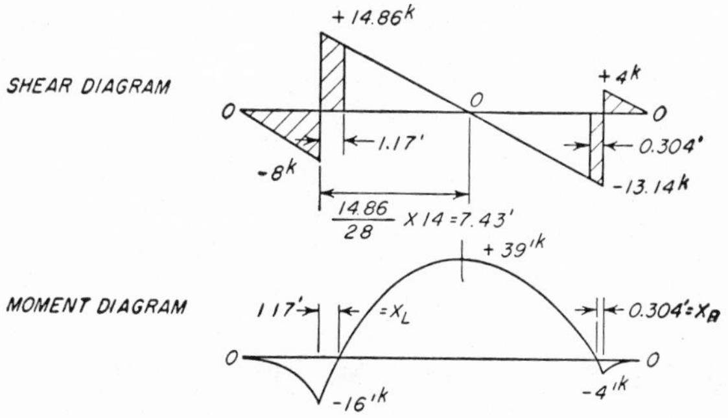

Fig. 1.605. Shear and moment.

$$M \text{ at } R_L = -2 \times 4 \times 2 = -16 \text{ ft-kips}$$
$$M \text{ at } R_R = -2 \times 2 \times 1 = -\ \ 4 \text{ ft-kips}$$

$$M \text{ at } 11.43 \text{ ft } (M \text{ max}) = -2 \times 11.43 \times \frac{11.43}{2} + 22.86 \times 7.43$$
$$= +39 \text{ ft-kips}$$

$$M = 0 \text{ when } x_L = 1.17, \text{ and } \frac{4 \times 8}{2} = 16 = 14.86x - \frac{2x^2}{2}.$$

Similarly $M = 0$ when $x_R = 0.304$ ft

1.606

$$\Sigma M_{R_L} = 0 = +1 \times 24 \times 6 + 15 \times 9 - 18R_R, \quad R_R = 15.5 \text{ kips}$$
$$\Sigma M_{R_R} = 0 = -1 \times 24 \times 12 - 15 \times 9 + 18R_L, \quad \underline{R_L = 23.5 \text{ kips}}$$

Check: $\Sigma V = 0 = -15 - 24 + 39.0 \text{ kips}$

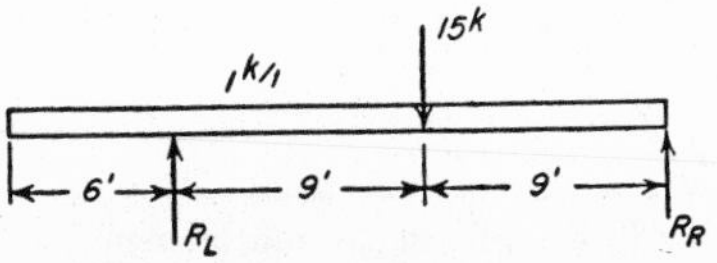

Fig. 1.606. Forces.

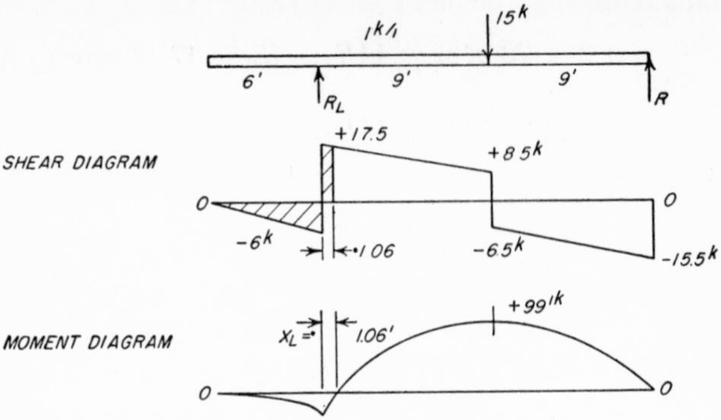

FIG. 1.606. Shear and moment.

M at $R_L = -1 \times 6 \times 3 = -18$ ft-kips

$M_{\max}$ at 15 kips load $= -1 \times 15 \times 15/2 + 23.5 \times 9 = 99$ ft-kips

$M = 0$ when $x_L = 1.06$ ft, and $18 = 17.5x - \dfrac{x^2}{2}$

1.607 ΣM_{R_L}

$0 = +4 \times 15 \times 15/2 + 30 \times 20 - 30 \times R_R, \quad R_R = +35$ kips

ΣM_{R_R}

$0 = +30R_L - 4 \times 15 \times 22.5 - 30 \times 10, \quad \underline{R_L = +55 \text{ kips}}$

Check: $\Sigma V = 0 = -60 - 30 + 90$ kips

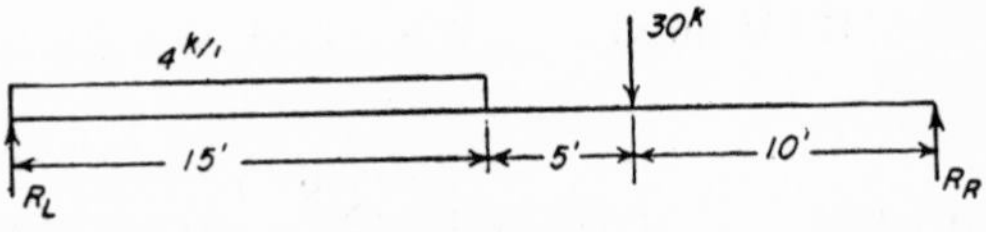

FIG. 1.607. Forces.

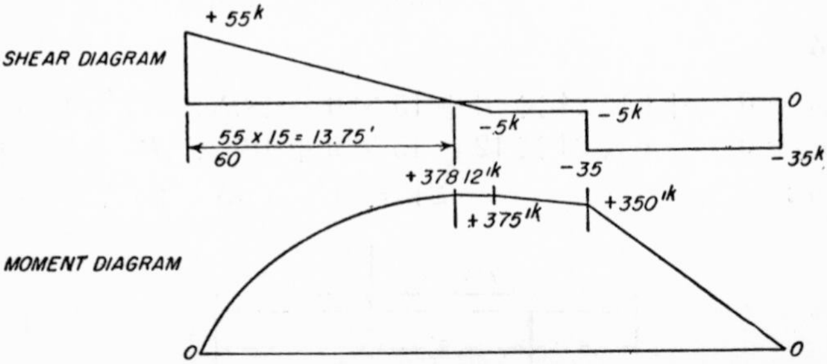

FIG. 1.607. Shear and moment.

Maximum moment at point 13.75 ft to right of R_L

$$= +55 \times 13.75 - 4 \times \frac{13.75^2}{2} = 378.12 \text{ ft-kips}$$

$$M \text{ at 15-ft point} = +55 \times 15 - 4 \times \frac{15^2}{2} = +375 \text{ ft-kips}$$

$$M \text{ at 20-ft point} = +35 \times 10 = 350 \text{ ft-kips}$$

1.608 ΣM_{R_L}

$$0 = +0.4 \times 14 \times 7 + 3 \times 4 - 10R_R, \quad R_R = +5.12 \text{ kips}$$

ΣM_{R_R}

$$0 = -0.4 \times 14 \times 3 - 3 \times 6 + 10R_L, \quad R_L = +3.48 \text{ kips}$$

Check: $\Sigma V = 0 = -3 - 0.4 \times 14 + 8.60 \text{ kips}$

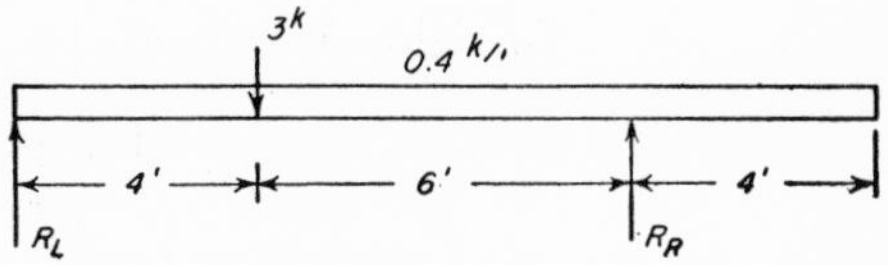

FIG. 1.608. Forces.

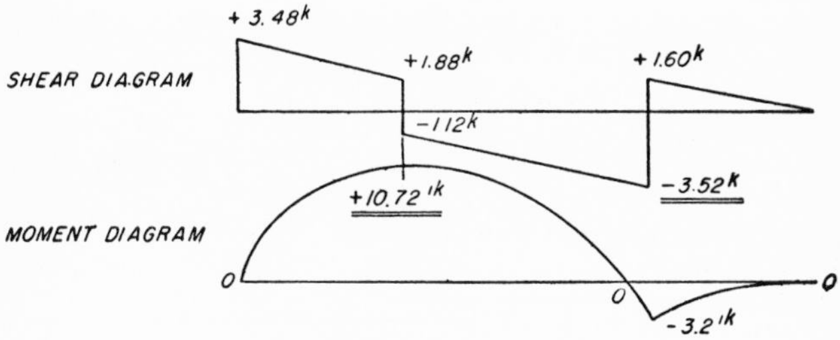

FIG. 1.608. Shear and moment.

$$M \text{ at 4-ft pt} = +3.48 \times 4 - 0.4 \times 4 \times 2$$
$$M \text{ at } R_R = -0.4 \times 4 \times 2$$

$$\text{Section modulus} = \frac{bh^2}{6} = \frac{h^3}{12} = \frac{M}{f} = \frac{10{,}720 \times 12}{1{,}750} = 73.5,$$

$$h = 9.6 \text{ in.}$$

$$\text{Area} = bh = \frac{h^2}{2} = \frac{3V}{2v} = \frac{3 \times 3{,}520}{2 \times 128} = 41.3, \ h = 9.1 \text{ in.}$$

Use a **6** by **12** (5.5 by 11.5 in. dressed). $A = 63.3$ sq in., $S = 121 \text{ in}^3$.

If no requirements were set for the ratio of b to h, a 4 by 12 (3.62 by 11.5) or a 6 by 10 (5.5 by 9.5) would satisfy.

1.609 *Using moment distribution:*

Fixed end moments (clockwise ↷ = +, counterclockwise ↶ = −)

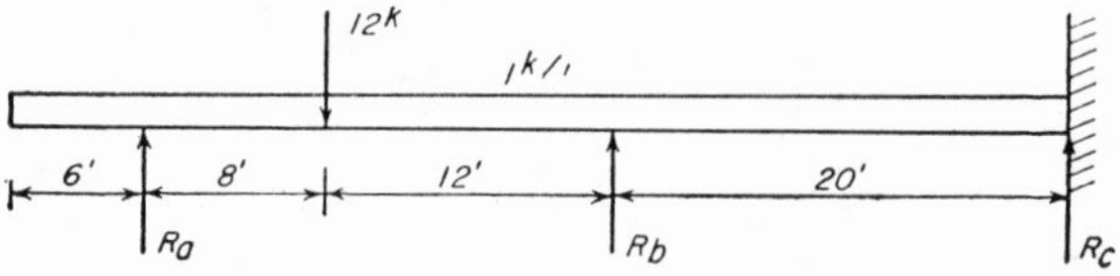

FIG. 1.609

Uniform load: To left of $R_a = 1 \times 6 \times 3 = +18$ ft-kips

To right of R_a (and elsewhere) $= \frac{wl^2}{2} = \frac{1 \times \overline{20}^2}{12} = \pm 33.33$ ft-kips

Concentrated load: To right of $R_a = \frac{Pab^2}{l^2} = \frac{12 \times 8 \times 12 \times 12}{20 \times 20} = -34.56$ ft-kips

To left of $R_b = \frac{Pa^2b}{l^2} = \frac{12 \times 8 \times 8 \times 12}{20 \times 20} = +23.04$ ft-kips

Distribution factors		0		0.5	0.5		1.0
Fixed end moments	+18	−34.56		+23.04			
		−33.33		+33.33	−33.33		+33.33
Net fixed end M	+18	−67.89		+56.37	−33.33		+33.33
		+49.89	→	+24.94			
		−11.99	←	−23.99	−23.99	→	−11.99
		+11.99	→	+ 6.00			
		− 1.50	←	− 3.00	− 3.00	→	− 1.50
		+ 1.50	→	+ 0.75			
		− 0.19	←	− 0.38	− 0.38	→	− 0.19
		+ 0.19	→	+ 0.10			
				− 0.05	− 0.05	→	− 0.02
Final moment	+18 ↷	−18 ft-kips ↶		+60.75 ↷	−60.75 ft-kips ↶		+19.63 ft-kips ↷

(To left) M at R_b

$$0 = -1 \times 26 \times 13 - 12 \times 12 + 20R_a + 60.75,$$
$$R_a = +21.06 \text{ kips}$$

(Left and right) M at R_b

$$0 = -1 \times 46 \times 3 - 12 \times 12 + 20 \times 21.06 + 19.63 - 20R_c,$$
$$R_c = +\ 7.94 \text{ kips}$$

M at R_c

$$0 = -1 \times 46 \times 23 - 12 \times 32 + 40 \times 21.06 + 20R_b + 19.63,$$
$$R_b = +29.00 \text{ kips}$$

Check: $\Sigma V = 0 = +21.06 + 29.00 + 7.94 - 46 - 12$

M at 12 kips load $= -1 \times 14 \times 7 + 21.06 \times 8 = 70.48$ ft-kips

Using three moment equations (signs follow fiber stress convention):

$$M_1l_1 + 2M_2(l_1 + l_2) + M_3l_2 = -\tfrac{1}{4}w_1l_1^3 - \tfrac{1}{4}w_2l_2^3 - P_1l_1^2(k_1 - k_1^3)$$

1. Take two spans, R_a to R_c and $k_1 = 8/20 = 0.4$

$$-18 \times 20 + 2M_b(20 + 20) + M_c \times 20 = -\frac{1 \times 20^3}{4} - \frac{1 \times 20^3}{4} - 12 \times (20^2)(0.4 - 0.064).$$

$$-360 + 80M_b + 20M_c = -2{,}000 - 2{,}000 - 1{,}614.4 = -5{,}254.4$$

$$(a) \quad +4M_b + M_c = -262.70$$

2. Take two spans R_b to R_d where $R_d = 0$ ft to right of R_c

$$M_b(20) + 2M_c(20 + 0) + M_d(0) = -2{,}000$$
$$(b) \quad M_b + 2M_c = -100$$
$$(b') \quad 4M_b + 8M_c = -400$$

subtracting (a) from (b') $+7M_c = -137.28$

$$M_c = -19.61 \text{ ft-kips}$$

and the minus sign indicates tension in top fiber over R_c.

Substituting in (b), $M_b = -100 + 39.22 = -60.78$ ft-kips. Reactions are found as before.

1.610 The first step is to cut pulley ropes and place rope forces at axles of pulleys or on beam.

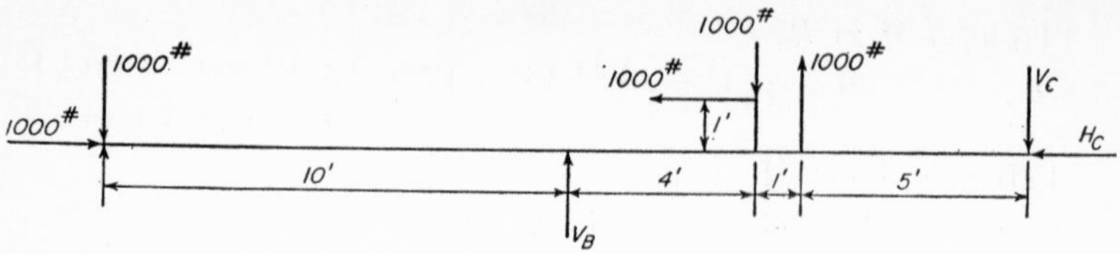

Fig. 1.610. Forces.

$$\Sigma H = 0 = +1{,}000 - 1{,}000 - H_c, \quad H_c = 0$$

$$M_B = 0$$

$$= -10 \times 1{,}000 - 1 \times 1{,}000 - 5 \times 1{,}000 + 4 \times 1{,}000 + 10V_c$$

$$V_c = 1{,}200 \text{ lb}\downarrow$$

$$M_C = 0$$

$$= -20 \times 1{,}000 - 1 \times 1{,}000 - 6 \times 1{,}000 + 5 \times 1{,}000 + 10V_B$$

$$V_B = 2{,}200 \text{ lb}\uparrow$$

Check: $\Sigma V = 0 = -1{,}000 + 2{,}200 - 1{,}000 + 1{,}000 - 1{,}200$

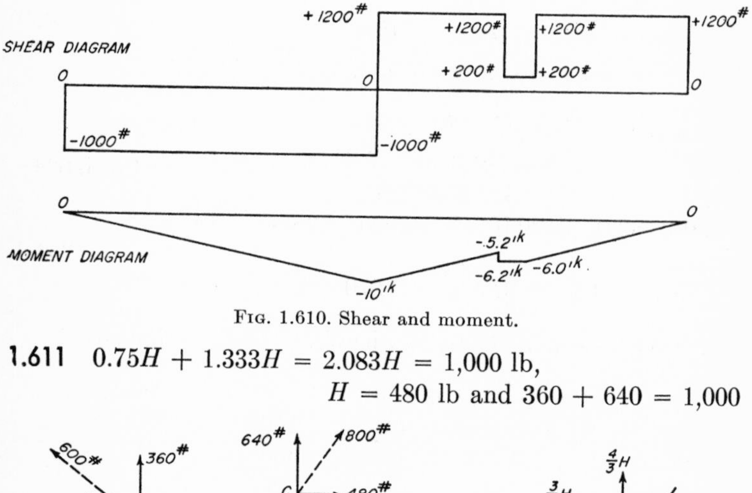

Fig. 1.610. Shear and moment.

1.611 $0.75H + 1.333H = 2.083H = 1{,}000$ lb,

$H = 480$ lb and $360 + 640 = 1{,}000$

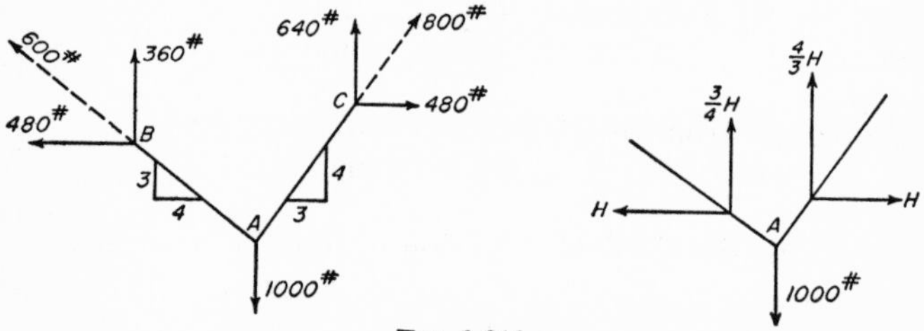

Fig. 1.611

Check: $\Sigma M_B = 0 = +4 \times 1{,}000 + 1 \times 480 - 7 \times 640$

$$= +4{,}480 - 4{,}480$$

1.612 $\Sigma M(\text{left rope}) = 0 = -200x + 150(10 - x)$

$$x = \mathbf{4.29}\text{ ft}, \quad \text{and} \quad 10 - x = 5.71\text{ ft}$$

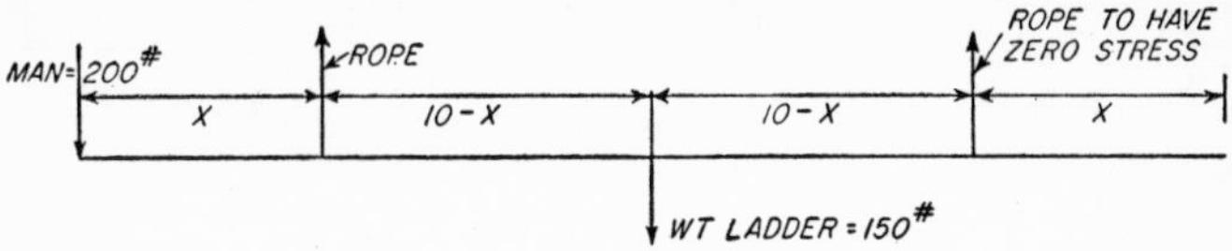

Fig. 1.612

Check: $\Sigma_M(\text{right rope})$

$$0 = -200 \times 15.71 - 150 \times 5.71 + \text{rope}_L \times 11.42$$

$$\text{Rope}_L = 350\text{ lb.} \quad \Sigma V = 0 = +350 - 200 - 150$$

1.613

$$h = \sqrt{400 - 64} = 18.32\text{ ft}$$

$$\Sigma M_a = 0 = +4 \times 150 - 18.32H$$

$$H = \mathbf{32.75}\text{ lb}$$

Frictional force at A must at least $=$ H.

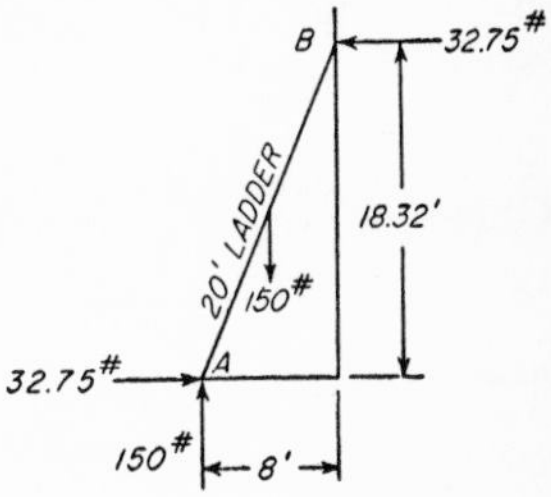

Fig. 1.613

1.614

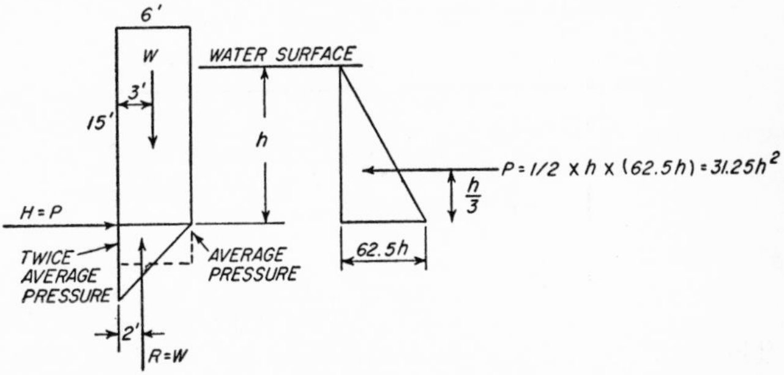

Fig. 1.614

Length is 1 ft perpendicular to the cross section.

$W = 1 \times 6 \times 15 \times 150 = 13{,}500$ lb

$$\text{Overturning couple} = P \times \frac{h}{3} = 10.417h^3$$

$$\text{Righting couple} = W \times 1 = 13{,}500\text{ lb-ft}$$

$$h^3 = \frac{13{,}500}{10.417} = 1{,}296, \quad h = \mathbf{10.9}\text{ ft}$$

1.615 Length is 1 ft along wall.

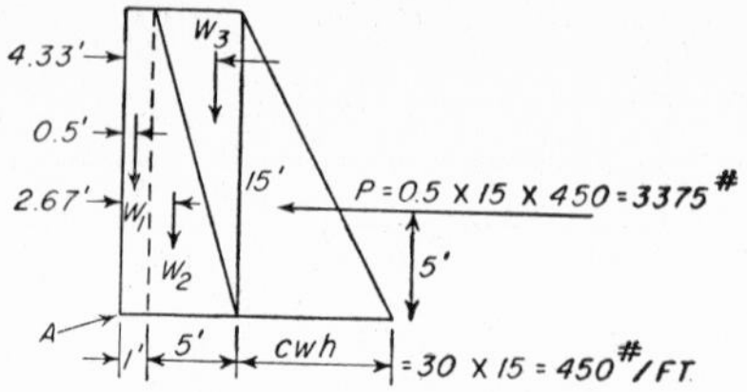

FIG. 1.615. Vertical and horizontal forces.

$$W_1 = 1 \times 1 \times 15 \times 150 = 2{,}250 \text{ lb}$$
$$W_2 = 1 \times 5/2 \times 15 \times 150 = 5{,}625 \text{ lb}$$
$$W_3 = 1 \times 5/2 \times 15 \times 100 = 3{,}750 \text{ lb}$$
$$\Sigma W = R = 11{,}625 \text{ lb}$$

At the moment of overturning, R would act at A.

For M(about A)

F	$\times$ a	$=$ M
W_1 = 2,250 lb	$\times$ 0.5 ft	= + 1,125 ft-lb
W_2 = 5,625	$\times$ 2.67	= +15,000
W_3 = 3,750	$\times$ 4.33	= +16,250
(P = 3,375)	$\times$ 5.00	= −16,875
$R = \Sigma W$ = 11,625	$\times$ (1.33)	= +15,500

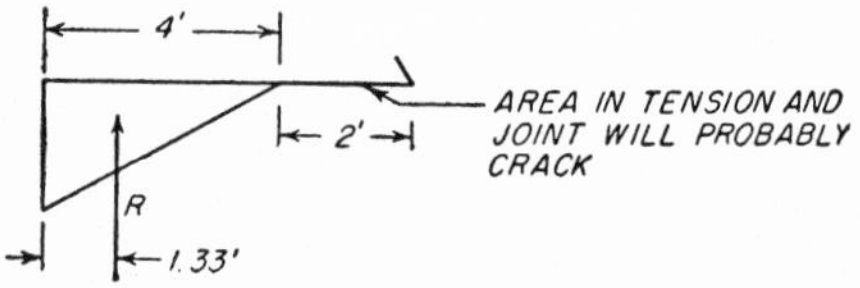

FIG. 1.615. Force on base.

The wall is safe against overturning.

$$\Sigma W \times f = 3{,}375, \quad f = \frac{3{,}375}{11{,}625} = 0.29$$

The wall is probably safe against sliding.

1.616

To locate R between front and rear axles.

$$\Sigma M(\text{16-ton axle}) = 0 = +20 \times d - 14 \times 4$$

$$d = 2.8 \text{ ft}, \quad \frac{d}{2} = 1.4 \text{ ft}$$

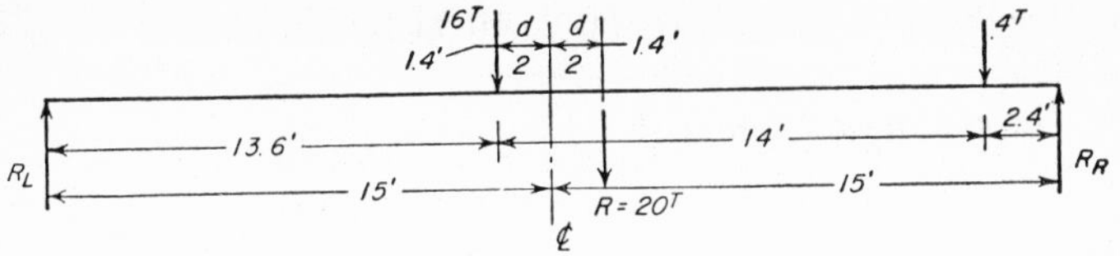

FIG. 1.616

To place a truck on a span so as to produce maximum moment, the rear axle is placed as far to one side of the center line as the resultant of the front and rear axles lays on the other side of the center line. If the span is too short to get both front and rear axles on the span, place rear axle at the center line.

$$R_L = \frac{13.6}{30} \times 20 = 9.067 \text{ tons}, \quad R_R = \frac{16.8}{30} \times 20 = 10.933 \text{ tons}$$

Maximum moment (about 16-ton axle) $= 9.067 \times 13.6$
$= \mathbf{123.3}$ **ft-tons**

If 16-ton axle is placed at the center line of the span

$$R_L = \frac{12.2}{30} \times 20 = 8.133 \text{ tons and } M = 8.133 \times 15 = \mathbf{122} \text{ ft-tons}$$

Maximum shear occurs when the 16-ton axle is just to the right of $R_L = \frac{27.2}{30} \times 20 = \mathbf{18.13}$ tons

1.617 First, read the answer to 1.616. Then locate the resultant of the tractor and semitrailer axle loads by taking moments about the 8-kip axle.

$$14 \times 32 + 28 \times 32 = x(8 + 32 + 32), \; x = \frac{42 \times 32}{72} = 18.67 \text{ ft}$$

$$d = 18.67 - 14 = 4.67 \text{ ft}, \; \frac{d}{2} = 2.33 \text{ ft}$$

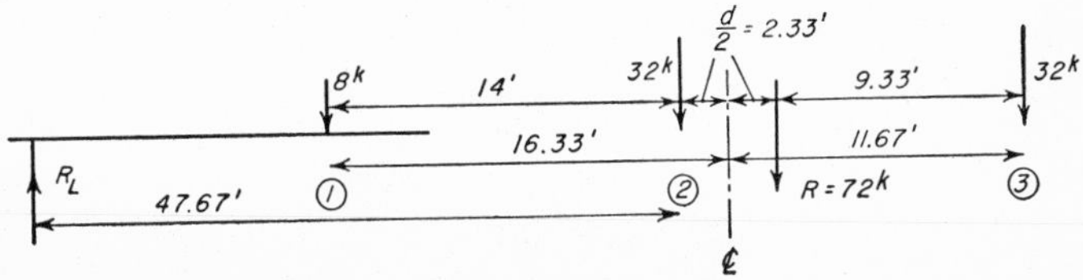

FIG. 1.617

a. The 8-kip axle (①) is (50 − 16.33 ft) or **33.67** ft to right of R_L.

b. The maximum moment (about axle ②)

$$R_L \times 47.67 - 8 \times 14 = 0$$

$$R_L = \frac{47.67}{100} \times 72 = 34.4 \text{ kips}$$

$$\therefore \text{ Maximum } M = 34.4 \times 47.67 - 112$$
$$= 1{,}640 - 112 = \mathbf{1{,}528} \text{ ft-kips}$$

c. The maximum shear is R_R with truck and trailer backed up so that axle ③ is at R_R.

$$R_R = \frac{(100 - 9.33)}{100} \times 72 = \mathbf{65.3} \text{ kips} = Ma \times \text{shear}$$

1.618 M(about line TR)

$$0 = 100 \times 7.07 - V_s \times 17.07, \qquad V_s = 41.4 \text{ kips}$$

M (about line ESF)

$$0 = -100 \times 10 + 2V_T \times 17.07, \qquad V_T = 29.3 \text{ kips}$$

$$V_R = 29.3 \text{ kips}$$

$$100.0 \text{ kips}$$

Check: $\Sigma V = 0 = -100 + V_R + V_s + V_T$

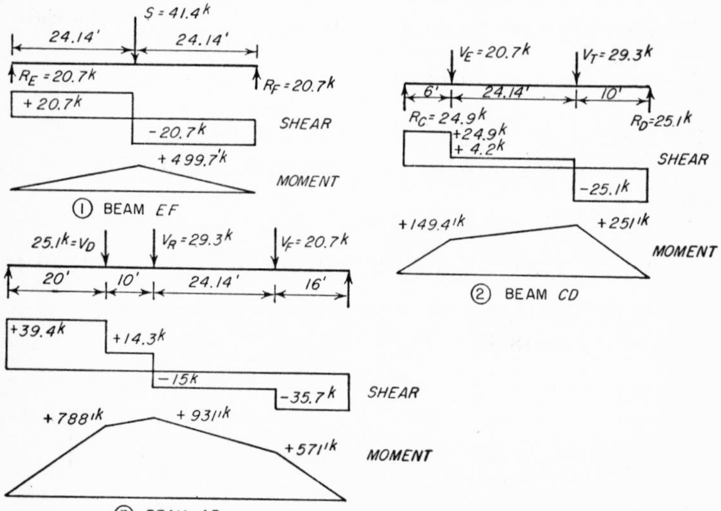

Fig. 1.618

1.619 By symmetry and inspection, $R_L = R_R = 5{,}000$ lb.

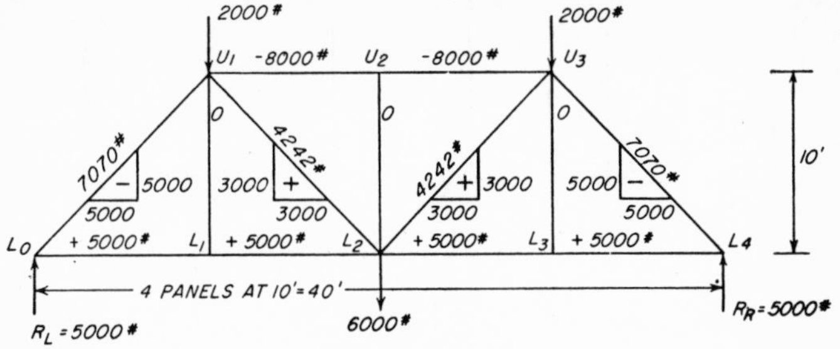

FIG. 1.619. Truss.

By analyzing joints L_1, U_2, and L_3, the stress in the verticals U_1L_1, U_2L_2, and U_3L_3 must be zero, as ΣV must equal zero and there is no outside vertical force or other vertical member or member having a vertical component to counteract any stress in these three members.

Use the "method of joints" ($\Sigma H = 0$ and $\Sigma V = 0$ for all stresses or components of stresses of all members meeting at a joint), letting + indicate tension and − indicate compression, but noting that for any joint the sum of the forces acting in one direction must equal the sum of the forces acting in a 180° direction regardless of signs.

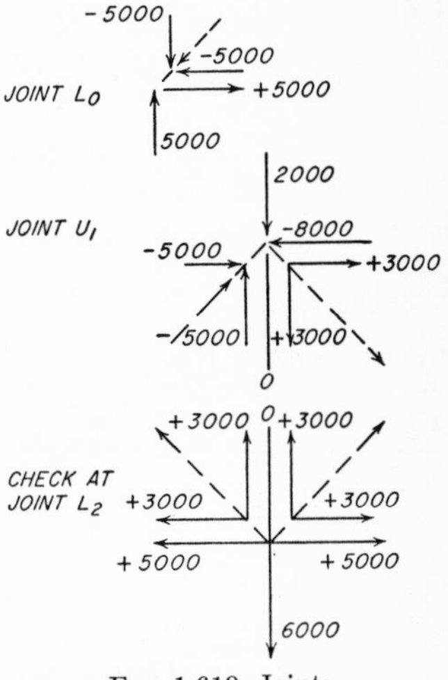

FIG. 1.619. Joints.

Also note that no joint can be analyzed if the stresses in more than two members meeting at that joint are unknown.

1.620 To solve for the stress in L_0L_1, pass the section 1-1, cutting members L_0U_1 and L_0L_1. Take moments about L_0U_1 extended to U_1. Assume stress of L_0L_1 acts out of L_0.

$$\Sigma M_{U_1} = 0 = +(4{,}000 - 1{,}000) \times 10 - 5 \times S_{L_0L_1}$$
$$S_{L_0L_1} = +6{,}000 \text{ lb (tension)}$$

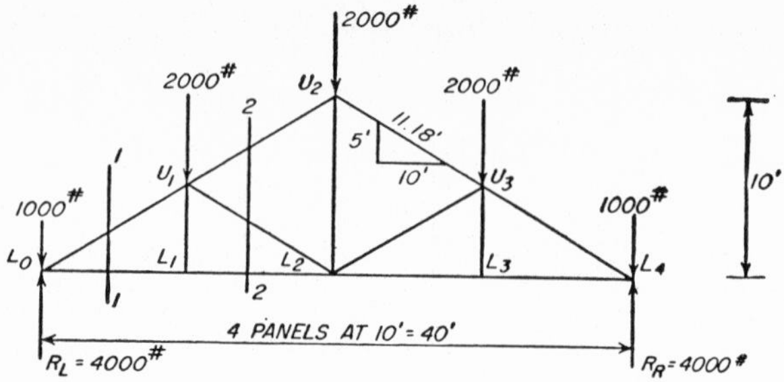

FIG. 1.620. Forces on truss.

To solve for the stress in U_1U_2 and U_1L_2, pass the section 2-2, cutting members U_1U_2, U_1L_2, and L_1L_2.

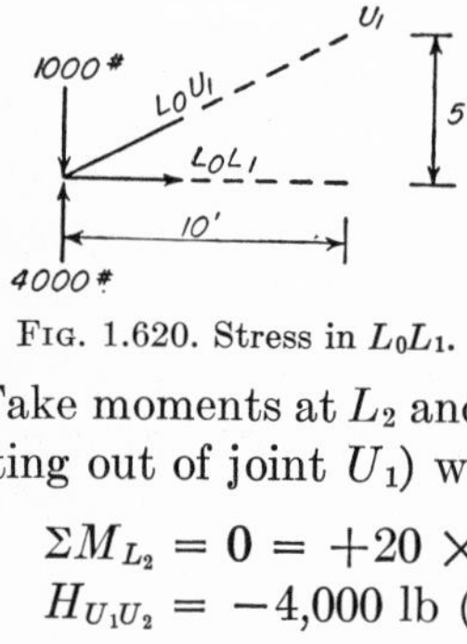

FIG. 1.620. Stress in L_0L_1.

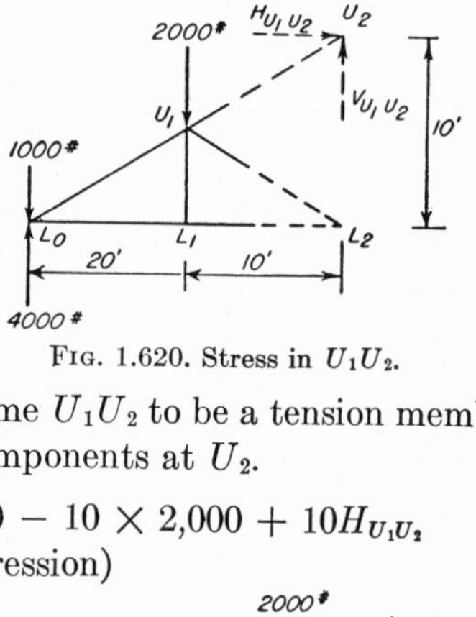

FIG. 1.620. Stress in U_1U_2.

Take moments at L_2 and assume U_1U_2 to be a tension member (acting out of joint U_1) with components at U_2.

$$\Sigma M_{L_2} = 0 = +20 \times 3{,}000 - 10 \times 2{,}000 + 10H_{U_1U_2}$$
$$H_{U_1U_2} = -4{,}000 \text{ lb (compression)}$$

($-$ sign indicates compression)

and $$S_{U_1U_2} = \frac{11.18}{10} \times (-4{,}000)$$
$$= \mathbf{-4{,}472} \text{ lb (compression)}$$

Now take moments at L_0 and assume U_1L_2 to be taken with components acting at L_2. Forces U_1U_2 and L_1L_2 and $H_{U_1}L_2$ or their lines of action pass through L_0.

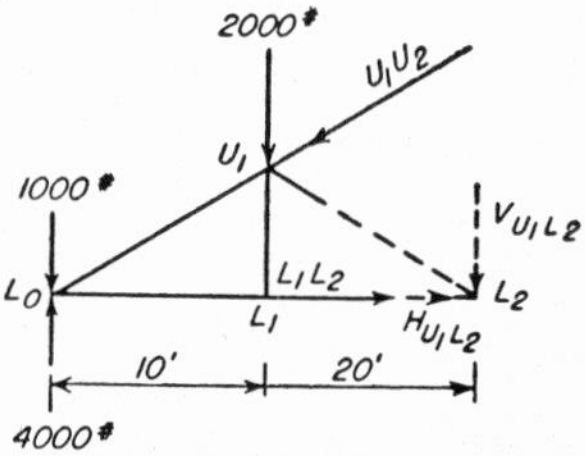

FIG. 1.620. Stress in U_1L_2.

$$\Sigma M_{L_0} = 0 = +10 \times 2{,}000 + 20 \times V_{U_1L_2}$$
$$V_{U_1L_2} = -1{,}000 \text{ lb (compression)}$$
$$S_{U_1L_2} = \frac{11.18}{5} \times 1{,}000 = \mathbf{-2{,}236} \text{ lb (compression)}$$

1.621

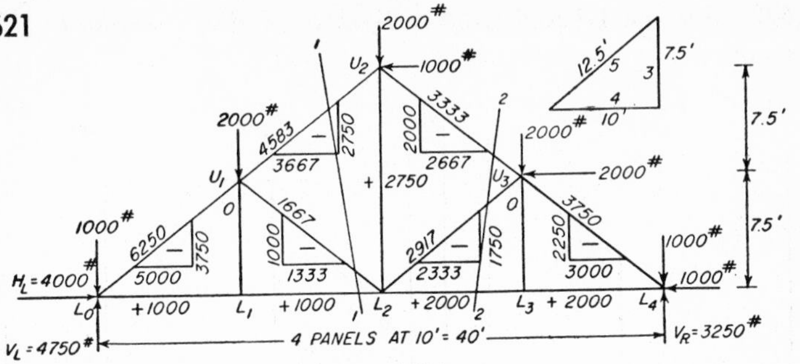

FIG. 1.621

$$\Sigma M_{L_0} = 0 = +10 \times 2{,}000 + 20 \times 2{,}000 + 30 \times 2{,}000 + 40 \times 1{,}000 - 7.5 \times 2{,}000 - 15 \times 1{,}000 - 40V_R$$

$$V_R = 3{,}250 \text{ lb}$$

$$\Sigma M_{L_4} = 0 = -10 \times 2{,}000 - 20 \times 2{,}000 - 30 \times 2{,}000 - 40 \times 1{,}000 - 7.5 \times 2{,}000 - 15 \times 1{,}000 + 40V_L$$

$$V_L = 4{,}750 \text{ lb}$$

Check: $\Sigma V = 0 = -1{,}000 - 2{,}000 - 2{,}000 - 2{,}000 - 1{,}000 + 8{,}000$ lb

Pass vertical sections through second and third panels and find $H_{U_1U_2}$, $V_{U_1L_2}$, $H_{U_2U_3}$, and $V_{L_2U_3}$ as in the answer to 1.620.

Section 1-1:

$$\Sigma M_{L_2} = 0 = +(4{,}750 - 1{,}000) \times 20 - 2{,}000 \times 10 + H_{U_1U_2} \times 15$$

$$H_{U_1U_2} = -3{,}667 \text{ lb}$$

$$\Sigma M_{L_0} = 0 = +2{,}000 \times 10 + V_{U_1L_2} \times 20$$

$$V_{U_1L_2} = -1{,}000 \text{ lb}$$

Section 2-2:

$$\Sigma M_{L_4} = 0 = -2{,}000 \times 10 - 2{,}000 \times 7.5 - V_{L_2U_3} \times 20$$

$$V_{L_2U_3} = -1{,}750 \text{ lb}$$

$$\Sigma M_{L_2} = 0 = +2{,}000 \times 10 - 2{,}000 \times 7.5 - (3{,}250 - 1{,}000)20 - H_{U_2U_3} \times 15$$

$$H_{U_2U_3} = -2{,}667 \text{ lb}$$

Stresses or components of stress in other members and checks are obtained by applying $\Sigma H = 0$ and $\Sigma V = 0$ at each joint.

1.622 Section 1-1 and truss to right of section (assume U_2U_3 as tension):

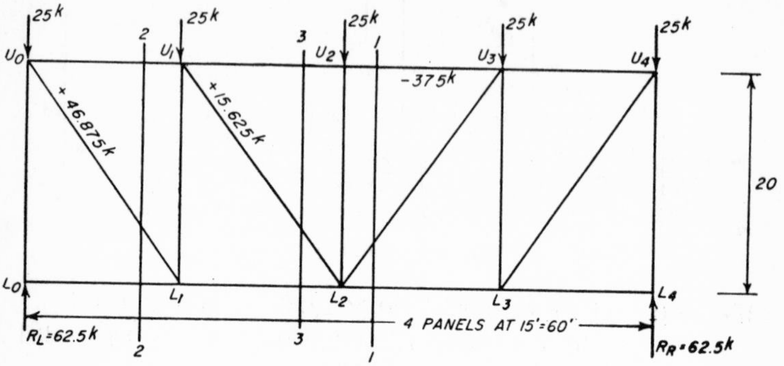

FIG. 1.622

$$\Sigma M_{L_2} = 0 = +15 \times 25 + 30 \times 25 - 30 \times 62.5 - 20S_{U_2U_3}$$
$$S_{U_2U_3} = -\mathbf{37.5} \text{ kips (compression)}$$

Section 2-2 and truss to left of section (assume U_0L_1 as tension):

$$\Sigma V = 0 = +62.5 - 25 - V_{U_0L_1}, \quad V_{U_0L_1} = +37.5 \text{ kips}$$
$$S_{U_0L_1} = +\mathbf{46.875} \text{ kips (tension)}$$

Section 3-3 and truss to left of section (assume U_1L_2 as tension):

$$\Sigma V = 0 = +62.5 - 25 - 25 - V_{U_1L_2}, \quad V_{U_1L_2} = +12.5 \text{ kips}$$
$$S_{U_1L_2} = +\mathbf{15.625} \text{ kips (tension)}$$

1.623

$$\Sigma M_{L_6} = 0$$
$$= -1 \times 48 - 2(40 + 32 + 24 + 16 + 8) - 6 \times 32 + 40H_{U_6}$$
$$H_{U_6} = +12 \text{ kips (to right)}$$
$$H_{L_6} = -12 \text{ kips (to left) and} \quad V_{L_6} = +12 \text{ kips (up)}$$
$$\Sigma V = 0 = -17 + 12 + V_{U_6}, \quad V_{U_6} = +\ 5 \text{ kips (up)}$$

a. Vertical section in second panel from left end and components of U_1U_2 acting at U_2

$$\Sigma M_{L_2} = 0 = -1 \times 16 - 2 \times 8 + 8H_{U_1U_2}$$
$$H_{U_1U_2} = +4 \text{ kips (tension)}$$

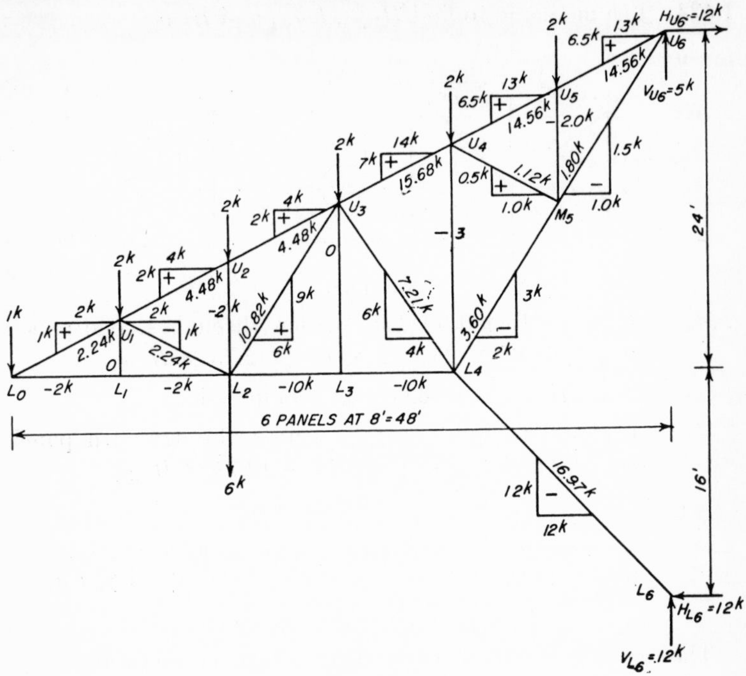

Fig. 1.623

b. Vertical section in fourth panel from left end and components of U_3U_4 acting at U_4

$$\Sigma M_{L_4} = 0 = -1 \times 32 - 2 \times 24 - 8 \times 16 - 2 \times 8 + 16H_{U_3U_4}$$

$$H_{U_3U_4} = +14 \text{ kips}$$

c. Vertical section in sixth panel from left end and components of U_5U_6 acting at U_4

$$\Sigma M_{L_4} = 0 = -1 \times 32 - 2 \times 24 - 8 \times 16 - 2 \times 8 + 2 \times 8 + 16H_{U_5U_6}$$

$$H_{U_5U_6} = +13 \text{ kips}$$

d. The remaining components and the necessary checks are easily obtained by applying $\Sigma H = 0$ and $\Sigma V = 0$ at each joint. Having one component of stress, the other component of stress and the actual stress in the members are found from simple proportion.

1.624 Use moments to find $H_{U_1U_2}$, L_2L_3, and $H_{U_4U_5}$

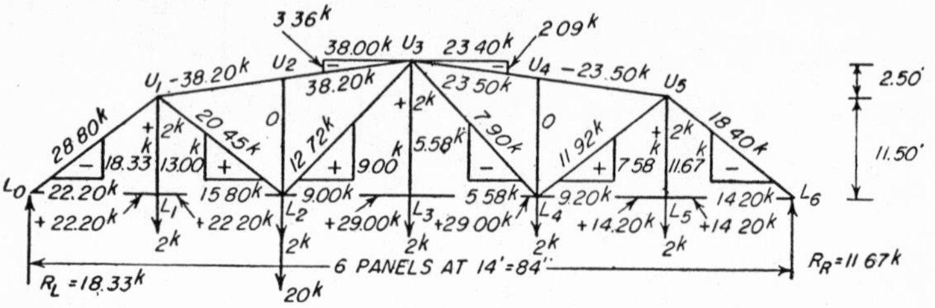

FIG. 1.624

$\Sigma M_{L_2} = 0$ (truss to left of L_2), section through second panel.

$$0 = +18.33 \times 28 - 2 \times 14 + 12.75 \times H_{U_1U_2}$$

$$H_{U_1U_2} = \mathbf{-38.00} \text{ kips (compression)}$$

$\Sigma M_{L_4} = 0$ (truss to right of L_4), section through fifth panel.

$$0 = -11.67 \times 28 + 2 \times 14 - 12.75 \times H_{U_4U_5}$$

$$H_{U_4U_5} = \mathbf{-23.40} \text{ kips}$$

$\Sigma M_{U_3} = 0$ (truss to right of U_3), section through fourth panel.

$$0 = -11.67 \times 42 + 2 \times 28 + 2 \times 14 + 14 \times L_3L_4$$

$$L_3L_4 = \mathbf{+29.0} \text{ kips (tension)}$$

The remaining components and the necessary check are easily obtained by applying $\Sigma H = 0$ and $\Sigma V = 0$ at each joint. Having one component of stress, the other component of stress and the actual stress in the members are found from simple proportion.

1.625 $\Sigma M_{(B-C)}$

$0 = +40 \times 2{,}400 + 30V_{AD}$

$V_{AD} = -3{,}200$ lb

$H_{AD} = -1{,}600$ lb

$S_{AD} = \mathbf{-3{,}580}$ lb (compression)

In both legs AB and AC there are horizontal components parallel to BC equal to $^{20}\!/_{10} \times 400 = 800$ lb. Thus each leg, AC and AB, has three components:

$x = 400$, $y = 800$, $V = 1{,}600$

Stress in AB and AC =

$400\sqrt{1^2 + 2^2 + 4^2} = 400\sqrt{21}$

$= \mathbf{+1{,}832}$ lb (tension)

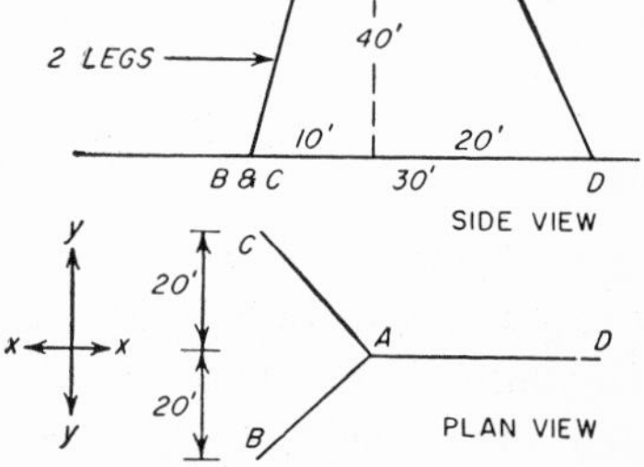

FIG. 1.625

THERMODYNAMICS

1.701 *a. Latent heat* (latent heat of evaporation): The quantity of heat required to evaporate 1 lb saturated liquid.

b. Specific heat: Amount of transferred heat required to change the temperature of one unit weight of a substance one degree unit of temperature.

c. Heat of fusion: The quantity of heat required to change the state of a substance from solid to liquid without change of temperature.

d. Btu: $\frac{1}{180}$ the quantity of heat required to raise the temperature of 1 lb pure water from 32 to 212°F under standard atmospheric pressure.

e. Absolute temperature: A measure of the ability to transfer heat to other bodies based on a reference temperature (absolute zero) where a body has given up all the thermal energy it possibly can. Absolute zero = −273.16°C = −459.69°F.

f. Calorie: The quantity of heat required to raise the temperature of 1 gram water from 14.5°C to 15.5°C.

g. Watt: Power expended when 1 amp flows between two points having a potential difference of 1 volt.

$$1 \text{ watt} = 1 \text{ joule per sec} = 10^7 \text{ ergs per sec} = 10^7 \text{ dyne-cm per sec}$$

1.702 T = final temperature (°F)

T_I = initial temperature of ice (°F)

T_w = initial temperature of water (°F)

W_I = weight of ice (lb)

W_W = weight of water (lb)

HF = heat of fusion = 144 Btu per lb

Heat lost by water = heat gained by ice

$$\begin{aligned} W_W(T_w - T) &= W_I(\text{HF}) + W_I(T - T_I) \\ 100(100 - T) &= 30(144) + 30(T - 32) \\ 10{,}000 - 100T &= 4{,}320 + 30T - 960 \\ 130T &= 6{,}640 \\ T &= 51°\text{F} \end{aligned}$$

1.703 Initial temperature of cold water $= T_C$ (°F)
Initial temperature of hot water $= T_H$ (°F)
Volume of cold water $= V_C$ (cu ft)
Volume of hot water $= V_H$ (cu ft)
Total volume $= V_T$ (cu ft)
Weight of cold water $= W_C$ (lb)
Weight of hot water $= W_H$ (lb)
Total weight $= W_T$ (lb)
Specific weight $= w$ (lb/cu ft)
Heat lost by hot water = heat gained by cold water

$$W_H(T_H - T) = W_C(T - T_C)$$
$$V_H(w)(T_H - T) = V_C(w)(T - T_C)$$
$$V_H(62.5)(160 - 70) = V_C(62.5)(70 - 40)$$
$$90V_H = 30V_C \text{ and } V_C = 3V_H$$
$$V_C + V_H = V_T = (25)(75)(5) = 9375 = 3V_H + V_H = 4V_H$$
$$V_H = 2{,}344 \text{ cu ft}$$

$$V_C = V_T - V_H = 9{,}375 - 2{,}344 = \mathbf{7{,}031} \text{ cu ft}$$

1.704 Weight of water $= W_w$ (lb)
Weight of ice $= W_I$ (lb)
Weight of steam $= W_s$ (lb)
HV = heat of vaporization = 970 Btu per lb
HF = heat of fusion = 144 Btu per lb
Heat lost by steam in condensing = (HV)(W_s) = $970W_s$ (Btu)
Heat lost by condensed steam $= (T_s - T)W_s$ $= (212 - 80)W_s = 132W_s$ (Btu)
Heat gained by ice in melting = (HF)$W_1 = 144 \times 100$ = 14,400 (Btu)
Heat gained by ice and cold water =

$$(T - T_w)(W_I + W_w) = (80 - 32)(100 + 300) = 19{,}200 \text{ (Btu)}$$

Heat lost by steam = heat gained by ice and water

$$970W_s + 132W_s = 1{,}102W_s = 14{,}400 + 19{,}200 = 33{,}600$$
$$W_s = \frac{33{,}600}{1{,}102} = \mathbf{30.5} \text{ lb}$$

1.705 V_1 = initial volume, p_1 = initial pressure
V_2 = final volume, p_2 = final pressure
T_1 = initial temperature
T_2 = final temperature
$V_1 = 12V_2$, $K = 1.4$ for air

For adiabatic process $\dfrac{p_2}{p_1} = \left(\dfrac{V_1}{V_2}\right)^k$ and $\dfrac{p_2}{13} = \left(\dfrac{12V_2}{V_2}\right)^{1.4}$

$$p_2 = 13(12)^{1.4} = 13 \times 32.4 = \mathbf{421} \text{ psi}$$

$$\frac{T_2}{T_1} = \left(\frac{V_1}{V_2}\right)^{k-1} \text{ and } \frac{T_2}{580} = \left(\frac{12V_2}{V_2}\right)^{1.4-1} = (12)^{0.4}$$

$$(°R = 120°F + 460° = 580°R)$$

$$T_2 = 580(12)^{0.4} = 580 \times 2.71 = \mathbf{1570°R} = \mathbf{1110°F}$$

1.706 $\dfrac{p_2}{p_1} = \dfrac{T_2}{T_1}$ (constant-volume process)

$$p_1 = 32 + 14.7 = 46.7 \text{ psia}$$
$$T_2 = 75 + 460 = 535°R$$
$$T_1 = 50 + 460 = 510°R$$
$$p_2 = 46.7 \times 535/510 = 49.1 \text{ psia}$$
$$= 49.1 - 14.7 = \mathbf{34.4} \text{ psig}$$

1.707 $R = \dfrac{pv}{T} = \dfrac{p_1V_1}{WT_1} = \dfrac{p_2V_2}{WT_2}$ where $v = \dfrac{V}{W}$

v = specific volume, R = gas constant,
V = total volume, W = total weight

$$0°F = 460°R \text{ and } 200°F = 660°R$$

$$V_1 = 100V_2, \quad \frac{14.7 \times 100V_2}{460} = \frac{p_2V_2}{660}$$

$$p_2 = 660/460 \times 14.7 \times 100 = \mathbf{2{,}110} \text{ psia}$$

1.708 *a.* The heating value of a fuel is the amount of heat that must be removed from the products of complete combustion of a unit amount of fuel to cool the products down to the temperature of the original air-fuel mixture. Most common fuels contain hydrogen, which when burned forms water vapor or steam. The higher heating value is obtained when all the water vapor of combustion condenses, thus giving up its latent heat of evaporation. The lower heating value will be obtained when sufficient excess air is used to prevent any condensation of water vapor.

b. If the final volume of the products of a constant-pressure combustion exceeds the original volume, part of the fuel energy must be used to push the atmosphere out of the way. In this case, the heating value at constant pressure is less than that at constant volume by a quantity equal to the work done in pushing the atmosphere out of the way. If the final volume of the products is less than the original volume, the constant-pressure heating value exceeds the constant-volume value by a quantity equal to the work done on the gas by the atmosphere during the volume contraction.

1.709 When a gas or a gaseous mixture remains in contact with a liquid surface, it will acquire vapor from the liquid until the partial pressure due to the water vapor in the air is equal to the saturated vapor pressure of the water at the existing temperature. When the vapor concentration reaches the equilibrium value, the gas is said to be saturated with vapor. It is not possible for the gas to contain a greater concentration of vapor, for as soon as the vapor pressure of the liquid is exceeded by the partial pressure of the vapor, condensation takes place.

Vapor pressure of the pond water at 70°F = 0.363 psia. Partial pressure of air at 90°F dry bulb and 65°F wet bulb = 0.170 psia.

Since 0.363 is greater than 0.170, water will be evaporated into the air stream.

1.710 *a.* Near the floor. Since the specific weight of the hot air is less than that of the cold air, the warm air will rise, thus setting up convection currents.

b. e = emissivity factor, expressing the degree to which the source surface approaches an "ideal black body." An "ideal black body" is one which could absorb (or emit) all the radiant energy that falls on it.

Most nonmetallic substances regardless of color have e equal to or greater than 0.8.

Aluminum paint has an e = 0.3 to 0.5. Therefore, to heat a room most efficiently, the radiators should be painted with black rather than aluminum paint.

1.711

$$1 \text{ kw} = 3{,}413 \text{ Btu per hr}$$
$$50{,}000 \text{ kw} = 170{,}650{,}000 \text{ Btu per hr}$$
$$\frac{\text{Btu per hr}}{\text{lb per hr}} = \frac{\text{Btu}}{\text{lb}} = \frac{170{,}650{,}000}{569{,}000}$$
$$= h_1 - h_2' = 300 \text{ Btu per lb}$$
$$\eta_e = \text{engine efficiency}$$
$$h_1 - h_2 = \frac{h_1 - h_2'}{\eta_e} = \frac{300}{0.75} = 400 \text{ Btu per lb}$$
$$h_1 = 950 + 300 = 1{,}250 \text{ Btu per lb}$$
$$h_2 = 1{,}250 - 400 = 850 \text{ Btu per lb}$$

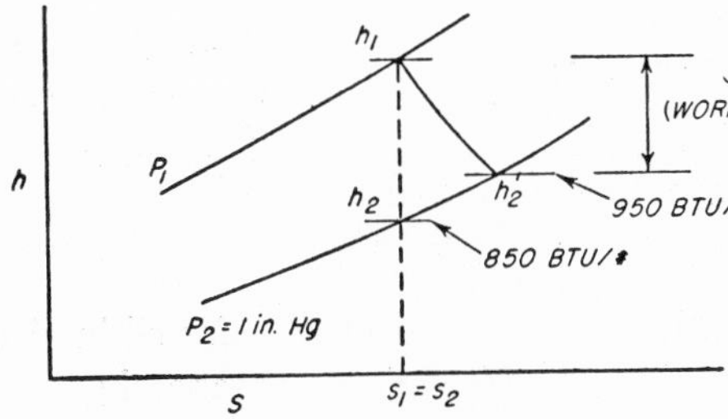

FIG. 1.711

Using a Mollier chart, find s_2 by following constant pressure line (1 in. Hg) down to h_2 = 850 Btu per lb and then project vertically up to h_1 = 1,250 Btu per lb.

Condition at h_1 = T_1 = 476°F, P_1 = 243 psia

1.712 Total weight of snow = volume × specific weight

$$= (10 \times 50 \times \tfrac{1}{2}) \times 10 = 2{,}500 \text{ lb}$$

$$\text{Btu necessary to melt snow} = \frac{\text{weight} \times (\text{heat of fusion})}{\text{efficiency}}$$
$$= \frac{2{,}500 \times 144}{0.50} = 720{,}000 \text{ Btu}$$

$$3{,}415 \text{ Btu} = 1 \text{ kwhr and kwhr needed} = \frac{720{,}000}{3{,}415} = 211$$

$$\text{Cost} = 0.02 \times 211 = \$4.22$$

1.713 W_{bo} = lb steam per hr = 885,000 ÷ 4 = 221,250 lb per hr

h_1 = enthalpy of water (280°F at 400 psia) reaching boiler = 248.4 Btu per lb (see steam tables)

h_2 = enthalpy of steam delivered by boiler (700°F at 400 psia) = 1,362.7 Btu per lb

Boiler output per hr $= W_{bo} \times (h_2 - h_1)$

$= 221{,}250\ (1{,}362.7 - 248.4) = 247 \times 10^6$ Btu per hr

Pounds coal necessary per hr

$$= \frac{\text{Btu per hr output}}{\text{(heating value per lb)(efficiency)}}$$

$$= \frac{247 \times 10^6}{13{,}850 \times 0.825} = 21{,}600 \text{ lb per hr}$$

$$\text{Coal burned per hour} = \frac{21{,}600}{2{,}000} = \textbf{10.8} \text{ tons per hr}$$

1.714

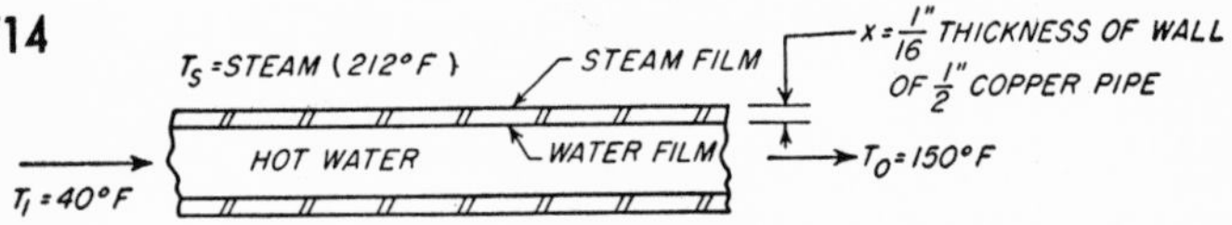

Fig. 1.714

$Q = UA\Delta t_m$ where Q = heat transferred in Btu per hr

U = Transmittance in Btu/(sq ft) (°F)(hr)

Δt_m = logarithmic mean temperature difference per °F

$$\text{Surface area} = \pi \left(\frac{D}{12}\right) \times L = \pi \left(\frac{0.5}{12}\right) \times 20 = 2.62 \text{ sq ft}$$

$$\Delta t_m = \frac{\Delta t_a - \Delta t_B}{\log_e (\Delta t_a / \Delta t_B)}$$

where $\Delta t_a = T_s - T_1 = 212 - 40 = 172°F$

$\Delta t_B = T_s - T_0 = 212 - 150 = 62°F$

$$\Delta t_m = \frac{172 - 62}{\log_e (172/62)} = \frac{110}{\log_e 2.77} = \frac{110}{1.02} = 108°F$$

$$\frac{1}{U} = \frac{1}{h_w} + \frac{x}{K} + \frac{1}{h_s}$$

where K = thermal conductivity of copper in

$$\frac{\text{(Btu per in. of thickness)}}{\text{hr/(sq ft)(°F)}}$$

h_w = surface coefficient of heat transfer (water film) in Btu/(hr)(sq ft)(°F)

h_s = surface coefficient of heat transfer (steam film) in Btu/(hr)(sq ft)(°F)

(Values of K, h_w, and h_s obtained from Kent's "Mechanical Engineers' Handbook," Power, Wiley, 1950.)

$$\frac{1}{U} = \frac{1}{600} + \frac{0.0625}{2,100} + \frac{1}{1,000}$$

$$= 0.00167 + 0.00003 + 0.001 = 0.00270$$

U = 370 Btu/(sq ft)(°F)(hr)

$Q = 370 \times 2.62 \times 108 = 105,000$ Btu per hr

w = weight of water (lb per hr)

c_p = mean specific heat coefficient = 1

$Q = Wc_p(T_0 - T_1)$

and $105,000 = W(1)(150 - 40) = W(110)$

$$W = \frac{105,000}{110} = \mathbf{956} \text{ lb per hr}$$

$$\frac{W}{500} = \frac{956}{500} = \mathbf{1.91} \text{ gal water per min}$$

1.715 Btu output per lb of coal = (heat of combustion per lb coal)(Eff.) = (14,000)(0.50) = 7,000 Btu/lb

h_2 = enthalpy of steam (212°F and 50 per cent quality)

$h_2 = (h_f + x_2 h_{fg})$ [from vapor tables]

$= 180 + 0.50 \times 970 = 665$ Btu/lb

h_{fg} = enthalpy of a fluid and vapor (gas).

h_1 = enthalpy of water (70°F) = 38 Btu/lb

Btu output per lb coal = $w_{bo}(h_2 - h_1)$

where w_{bo} = lb steam per lb coal

$7,000 = w_{bo}(665 - 38) = 627 w_{bo}$

$w_{bo} = 7,000 \div 627 =$ **11.2** lb steam per lb coal

1.716 Indicated horsepower $= I_{\text{hp}} = \dfrac{P_m LAN}{33,000}$

P_m = mean effective pressure, psia

L = stroke, ft

A = net area of piston, sq in.

N = power cycles per minute per cylinder end

D = piston diameter, in.
D_R = piston rod diameter, in.

$$\text{Area of head end of piston} = \frac{\pi D^2}{4} = \frac{\pi}{4} \times (6)^2 = 28.4 \text{ sq in.}$$

$$\text{Area of crank end of piston} = \frac{\pi}{4}(D^2 - D_R{}^2)$$

$$= \frac{\pi}{4}(36 - 1.56) = 27.0 \text{ sq in.}$$

I_{hp}, head end = 62 × 0.67 × 28.4 × 300 ÷ 33,000
= 10.65 hp

I_{hp}, crank end = 62 × 0.67 × 27 × 300 ÷ 33,000
= 10.15 hp

Total I_{hp} = 10.65 + 10.15 = 20.8 hp
Brake hp = (total I_{hp})(mean efficiency)
= 20.8 × 0.83 = 17.25 hp
1 hp = 0.746 kw

Generator output = (brake hp)(0.746)(generator efficiency)
= 17.25 × 0.746 × 0.92 = **11.85** kw

1.717 $I_{hp} = \dfrac{P_m LAN}{33{,}000}$ (see answer to 1.716)

$$\text{Work per revolution} = 2P_m LA = 2 \times 120 \times 1 \times \frac{\pi}{4}(10)^2$$

= **18,850** ft-lb

I_{hp} = 18,850 × 300 ÷ 33,000 = **171.5** hp

1.718 $\dfrac{P_1V_1}{T_1} = \dfrac{P_2V_2}{T_2}$ and $\dfrac{740 \times 400}{291} = \dfrac{760 \times V_2}{273}$

where T is in degrees absolute = °C + 273

$V_2 = {}^{273}\!/\!_{291} \times {}^{740}\!/\!_{760} \times 400 =$ **366** cc

1.719 1 liter water = 1,000 cc = 1,000 grams

$$Q = WC(T_2 - T_1)$$

where Q = heat added (calories)
W = weight of water (grams)
C = thermal capacity $\left(\dfrac{\text{calories}}{\text{°C per gram}}\right)$

$$500 = 2{,}000\,(1)(T_2 - 30)$$
$$T_2 - 30 = 0.25$$
$$T_2 = \mathbf{30.25°C}$$

1.720 For a Carnot cycle the $T - S$ diagram is a rectangle.

$$T_1 = 273 + 157 = 430°\text{K}$$
$$T_2 = 273 + 100 = 373°\text{K}$$

$$\text{Thermal efficiency} = \frac{(T_1 - T_2)}{T_1} \times 100$$
$$= \frac{(430 - 373)}{430} \times 100 = \mathbf{13.25}\text{ per cent}$$

1.721 1 watt = 5.689×10^{-2} Btu per min
Weight of 1 gal water = 62.5/7.5 = 8.33 lb
Btu per min effective in heating water
= (watts input)(efficiency)(5.689×10^{-2})
= (300)(0.75)(5.689)$(10)^{-2}$ = 12.8 Btu per min
Btu per gal necessary to heat water
= (weight of water in lb) × (temperature change in °F)
= 8.33(120 − 60) = 500 Btu per gal

$$\text{Time to heat 1 gal water} = \frac{\text{Btu per gal}}{\text{Btu per min}} = \frac{500}{12.8}$$

= **39.1** min per gal or 0.65 hr per gal

$$\text{Cost to heat 1 gal of water} = \frac{\text{cost}}{\text{kwhr}} \times \text{kw} \times \frac{\text{hr}}{\text{gal}}$$

= 0.05 × 0.300 × 0.65 = **$0.01** or **1** cent

1.722 Saving in Btu

$$= \left[\frac{(\text{Btu saved})}{(\text{hr})(°\text{F})(\text{area})}\right] \times (\text{hr})(\Delta T)(\text{area in sq ft})$$
$$= \frac{(0.40 - 0.18)}{1 \times °\text{F} \times 1} \times 5{,}000 \times 35 \times 10{,}000 = 385 \times 10^6\ \text{Btu}$$

$$\text{Pounds of coal saved} = \frac{\text{saving in Btu}}{(\text{Btu/lb coal}) \times \text{efficiency}}$$
$$= \frac{385 \times 10^6}{13 \times 10^3 \times 0.60} = 49{,}400\ \text{lb}$$

Saving in dollars = (cost/ton) (tons saved) = 15 × 49,400/2,000
= **$371**

1.723 psia = 14.7 + psig = 14.7 + 20 = 34.7

$h_2 = h_f + xh_{fg}$ and $h_1 = h_f$

where x = quality of the steam
h_1 = enthalpy of condensed water
h_2 = enthalpy of original mixture per lb
h_f = enthalpy of 1 lb water
h_{fg} = change of enthalpy during vaporization

$$\Delta(\text{Btu per lb}) = h_2 - h_1 = h_f + xh_{fg} - h_f = xh_{fg}$$

$$\text{Quality} = x = \frac{\Delta(\text{Btu per lb})}{h_{fg}} = \frac{475}{939.5} = 0.507 = \mathbf{50.7} \text{ per cent}$$

1.724 (See answer to 1.716 for symbols.)

$I_{\text{hp}} = P_m LAN/33{,}000$

$$\text{Area piston, head end} = \frac{\pi}{4} \times 144 = 113.1 \text{ sq in.}$$

$$\text{Area piston, crank end} = \frac{\pi}{4}(12^2 - 2^2) = 110.0 \text{ sq in.}$$

$$I_{\text{hp}} \text{ head end} = \frac{70 \times 1.5 \times 113.1 \times 350}{33{,}000} = 126.0$$

$$I_{\text{hp}} \text{ crank end} = \frac{70 \times 1.5 \times 110.0 \times 350}{33{,}000} = 122.5$$

$$I_{\text{hp(total)}} = 248.5 \text{ hp}$$

Brake hp = (I_{hp})(mechanical efficiency) = 248.5 × 0.92
= **228.5** hp

1.725 1 hp = 42.41 Btu per min

Btu per min dissipated as heat = 42.41 × hp
= 42.41 × 300 = 12,720

Btu per min necessary to heat water from 80°F to 180°F
= 12,720 = weight water per min × 100

Weight water per min = 127.2 lb per min

$$= \frac{127.2 \times 7.5}{62.5} \text{ or } \mathbf{15.3} \text{ gal per min}$$

SECTION TWO

2.01–2.50

CHEMICAL ENGINEERING

Reference will be made a number of times in this section to J. H. Perry, "Chemical Engineers' Handbook," 3d ed., McGraw-Hill, 1950, simply by stating "Perry, p.—."

2.01

Coal analysis (dry)	Refuse	Flue gas (volatile)
C = 75%	C = 0	CO_2 = 12.6%
Ash = 8%		CO = 1.0%
H_2, O_2 = 17%		O_2 = 6.2%
		N_2 = 80.2%
100%		= 100.0%

Basis will be 100 lb fuel.

100 lb fuel contains 75 lb carbon or $^{75}/_{12}$ (atomic weight)

$$= 6.25 \text{ lb-atoms}$$

1 lb-mole of flue gas contains 0.136 lb atoms of carbon, i.e.,

$$\begin{aligned} CO_2 &= 0.126 \text{ lb-mole} \\ CO &= \underline{0.010} \text{ lb-mole} \\ & \quad 0.136 \text{ lb-mole} \end{aligned}$$

$$\text{Therefore } \frac{6.25}{0.136} = \frac{46 \text{ lb-moles dry stack gas}}{100 \text{ lb fuel}}$$

The stack gas (dry) contains $\dfrac{0.062 \text{ lb-mole oxygen}}{\text{lb-mole stack gas}}$ and for each 100 lb fuel, there is $46 \times 0.062 = 2.86$ lb-moles of oxygen in the stack gas.

Since this oxygen came from the air (21 per cent oxygen and 79 per cent nitrogen) there is $2.86 \times \frac{0.79}{0.21}$ or 10.75 lb-moles of N_2 in stack gas from excess air.

The nitrogen in the stack gas that comes from the air supplied for combustion is

$$46 - (5.79 + 0.46 + 2.86 + 10.75) = 26 \text{ lb-moles } N_2$$

where $$\frac{0.126}{0.136} \times 6.25 = 5.79 \text{ lb-moles } CO_2$$

and $$\frac{0.010}{0.136} \times 6.25 = 0.46 \text{ lb-mole } CO$$

The oxygen supplied for combustion by the air is

$$26 \times \frac{0.21}{0.79} = 6.90 \text{ lb-moles}$$

Oxygen required for combustion of carbon is

$$C + O_2 \rightarrow CO_2 \text{ or } \frac{0.126}{0.136} \times 6.25 = 5.79 \text{ lb-moles}$$

$$C + \tfrac{1}{2} \times O_2 \rightarrow CO \text{ or } \tfrac{1}{2} \times \frac{0.010}{0.136} \times 6.25 = 0.23 \text{ lb-mole}$$

$$6.02 \text{ lb-moles}$$

Oxygen supplied by air for combustion of H in fuel is 6.90 − 6.02 = 0.88 lb-mole per 100 lb fuel

Available O_2 and H_2 in fuel per 100 lb fuel is

$H_2 + \frac{1}{2} \times O_2 \rightarrow H_2O$
$2X + (\frac{1}{2}X - 0.88)\ 32 = 17$ (from fuel analysis)
$X = 2.55$ lb-moles hydrogen or 5.10 lb per 100 lb fuel
$\frac{1}{2}X = 1.275$ lb-moles total oxygen required.
$(\frac{1}{2}X - 0.88) = 0.395$ lb-mole available oxygen in fuel
= 12.65 lb per 100 lb fuel

a. Per cent oxygen

lb-mole of O_2 for combustion of 100 lb fuel

CO_2 = 5.79 lb-moles
CO = 0.23 lb-mole
H_2 = 1.27 lb-moles (= ½X)
7.29 lb-moles

But there are 2.86 lb-moles oxygen in stack gas

$$\therefore \text{ per cent oxygen} = \frac{2.86}{(7.29 - 0.39)} \times 100 = 41.5 \text{ per cent}$$

b. Complete analysis of fuel

C = 75.0 per cent
ash = 8.0 per cent
H_2 = 5.1 per cent (X above)
O_2 = 11.9 per cent (17.0 − 5.1)

c. Cubic feet stack gas per pound fuel (at 680°F)

Basis—100 lb fuel

H_2O in air (80 per cent relative humidity and 36 mm vapor pressure) $= \dfrac{36 \times 0.80}{760 - 36 \times 0.80} = 0.0393$ mole H_2O per mole air

$\therefore \dfrac{46 \times 0.802}{0.79} = 46.75$ lb-mole air (dry) and $46.75 \times 0.0393 = 1.84$ lb-mole water vapor in air. H_2O from combustion of $H = 5.1/2 = 2.55$ lb-mole

Total lb-moles stack gas per 100 lb fuel
$= 46 + 1.84 + 2.55 = 50.39$ lb-moles

Total lb-moles stack gas per 1 lb fuel $= 0.504$ lb-mole $= n$

$$\therefore V = \frac{n \cdot RT}{P} = \frac{0.504 \times 10.71 \times (460 + 680)}{14.7} = \mathbf{418.0} \text{ cu ft}$$

d. Cubic feet of air per pound fuel (at 90°F)

$$n = 0.4675 + 0.0184 = 0.486 \text{ lb-mole per lb fuel}$$

$$V = \frac{0.486 \times 10.71 \times (460 + 90)}{14.7} = \mathbf{195.0} \text{ cu ft}$$

2.02 At top, 740 mm, 20°C, 0.13 per cent NH_3 by volume
At base, 745 mm, 40°C, 4.90 per cent NH_3 by volume
100 cfm gas
100 per cent − 4.90 per cent = 95.1 per cent = 0.951.
Air, cfm = 100 × 0.951 = 95.1

$(mV_1) = (mV_0) \times \frac{T_1}{T_0} \times \frac{P_0}{P_1}$ = mole-volume at other than standard condition

(mV_1) for air at 745 mm and 40°C

$$= 359 \times \frac{(273 + 40)}{273} \times \frac{760}{745} = 421 \text{ cu ft per mole}$$

$$\frac{95.1}{421.0} = 0.226 \text{ mole of air flowing per min}$$

$$\frac{\text{Mole } NH_3}{\text{Mole air}} \text{ at entrance} = \frac{0.049}{0.951} = 0.0515$$

$$\frac{\text{Mole } NH_3}{\text{Mole air}} \text{ at exit} = \frac{0.0013}{0.9987} = 0.0013$$

Mole ammonia absorbed per mole air flowing
= 0.0515 − 0.0013 = 0.0502

a. Rate of flow of gas at exit in cfm

$$V = 0.226 \times 359 \times \frac{(273 + 20)}{273} \times \frac{760}{740} = 89.5 \text{ cfm}$$

b. Weight of ammonia absorbed per min
= 0.226 × 0.0502 × 17 = 0.193 lb NH_3 per min
where atomic weight NH_3 = 17

2.03 1. Look up *x-y* data (Perry, p. 574).
2. Construct *x-y* diagram.
3. Locate top product and feed, and bottom product on *x-y* diagram. *x-y* data indicates that a top product boiling at 78.41°C would have a vapor composition of 0.7815 mole fraction of ethanol.
4. Material balance per 44 moles feed
a. $0.17F = 0.7815D + 0.01W$
or $17 \times 44 = 78.15\text{D} + W$
b. $44 = D + W$
$77.15D = 16 \times 44$
$D = 9.12$ moles per hr
$W = 34.88$ moles per hr

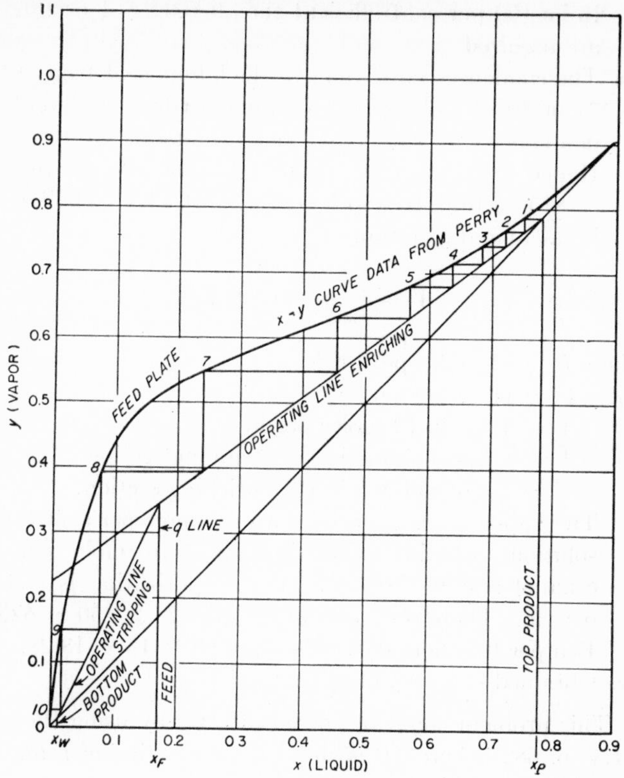

FIG. 2.03

5. Intercept of operating line $= \dfrac{9.12}{9.12 + 31} = 0.227.$
6. Construct operating line for enriching section.
7. Since the feed is a saturated liquid q (where $c_p\Delta t = 0$) $= \dfrac{c_p\Delta t + \lambda}{\lambda} = 1$ and the slope of the q line $= \dfrac{q}{q-1} = \dfrac{1}{1-1}$ $= \dfrac{1}{0} = \infty$. Construct q line.
8. Construct operating line in stripping section.
9. Construct McCabe-Thiele stepwise representation of theoretical plates.
   a. Ten theoretical plates are required. Therefore 10/0.60 or 17 actual plates are required. If reboiler is considered

to be 100 per cent efficient then 9/0.60 + 1 or 16 plates are required.

b. The condenser must remove the latent heat from 9.12 + 31 or 40.12 moles of top product per hr. The latent heat of a vapor (78.15 moles per cent ethanol) is 420 Btu per lb. Hence 40.12 × 39.84 × 420 = **672,000** Btu per hr where 0.7815 × 46 + 0.2185 × 18 = 39.84. The reboiler duty is calculated as follows:

$$\bar{V} = F\ (q - 1) + V$$

where F = 44 moles per hr
$(q - 1) = (1 - 1) = 0$
$\bar{V} = V$ = 40.12 moles per hr
$\bar{V}$ = vapor volume in the stripping section
V = vapor volume in the enriching section.

The vapor in equilibrium with a 1 mole per cent ethanol solution contains approximately 0.10 mole per cent ethanol and its latent heat of vaporization is 850 Btu per lb. Therefore q = 40.12 × 18.28 × 850 = **623,000** Btu per hr where 0.01 × 46 + 0.99 × 18 = 18.28.

c. Obtained from *x-y* diagram.

2.04 This problem could be solved directly by using the graph in Perry, p. 682, where ΔP is shown as a function of L and G/ϕ for a variety of packing material.

Solution: 5 gal water per min is equivalent to

$$\frac{5}{7.5} \times 62.5 \times 60 = 2{,}500 \text{ per hr}$$

$$L = 2{,}500 \div \frac{\pi}{4} \times 1 \times 1 = 3{,}180 \text{ lb/(hr)(sq ft)}$$

$$G/\phi = (1.5 \times 3{,}600) \times \left(\frac{\pi}{4} \times 1^2\right) \times \left(\frac{492}{530} \times 0.0807\right)$$
$$= 318 \text{ lb per hr}$$
$$= (\text{ft per sec} \times \text{sec per hr}) \times (\text{sq ft}) \times (\text{weight air in lb per cu ft at } 70°\text{F})$$

From graph, for ½-in. Berl saddles, Δp = 0.20 in. per ft

∴ 7 × 0.20 = 1.40 in. water = the drop of pressure through the tower

2.05 Perry, p. 674.

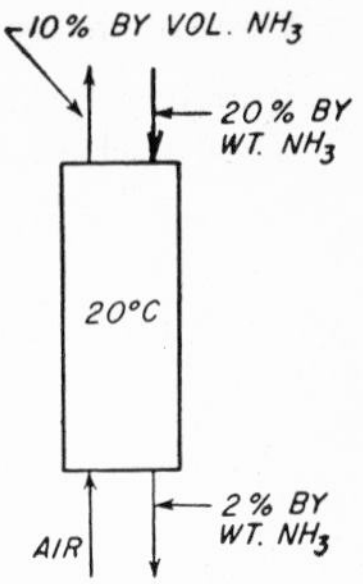

FIG. 2.05

1. For 25 gram of NH_3 per 100 gram of H_2O, the partial pressure of NH_3 = 227 mm.
2. For 2.04 gram of NH_3 per 100 gram of H_2O, the partial pressure of NH_3 = 12.2 mm.

Assume that the total pressure of the exit gas is 760 mm and that the gas leaves saturated with water at 20°C.

p (water) = 17.5 mm (from steam tables)
p (air + NH_3) = 760 − 17.5 = 742.5 mm
p (NH_3) = 0.10 × 742.5 = 74.25 mm
Top: $Pai - Pag = 227 - 74.2 = 152.8$ mm
Bottom: $Pai - Pag = 12.2 - 0 = 12.2$ mm

$$(\Delta p)_{lm} = \frac{152.8 - 12.2}{2.3 \times \log_{10}(152.8/12.2)} = 55.6 \text{ mm}$$
$$= 0.0732 \text{ atm}$$

N = lb-moles NH_3 stripper per hour = pV/RT

$$= \frac{74.25 \times 8{,}000}{760 \times 0.730 \times 293 \times 1.8} = 2.03$$

$$V = \frac{N}{K_g a(\Delta p)_{lm}} = \frac{2.03}{7 \times 0.0732} = \mathbf{3.96} \text{ cu ft}$$

When gas rate is decreased 25 per cent,

$$V_2 = (4/3)^{0.8} \times V_1 = 1.259 \times 3.96 = \mathbf{5.00} \text{ cu ft}$$

2.06 It is assumed that the alcohol to be cooled is 95 per cent alcohol. The arithmetic mean temperature of each fluid will be used in evaluating fluid properties:

$$T_{\text{alc.}} = \frac{172 + 70}{2} = 121°\text{F}$$

$$T_{\text{water}} = \frac{80 + 50}{2} = 65°\text{F}$$

The volume of alcohol to be handled is assumed to have been measured at room temperature. Hence

Alcohol, lb per hr = $200 \times 8.33 \times 0.804$ = 1,340 lb per hr
Specific heat of 95 per cent alcohol = 0.742
Heat to be transferred from alcohol to water = q
$= 1{,}340 \times 0.742 \times (172 - 70) = 101{,}400$ Btu per hr

Calculation of film coefficient, h_i, for alcohol:

$$\text{Mass velocity} = G = \frac{1{,}340 \times 4 \times (16)^2 \times (12)^2}{60 \times 60 \times \pi \times (19)^2}$$

$$= 48.4 \text{ lb per sec} \times \text{sq ft}$$

$$R_e = \frac{DG}{\mu} = \frac{(19)}{16 \times 12}(48.4)\frac{1}{(0.77)(0.000672)}$$

$$= 9{,}250 \text{ (no units)}$$

where μ = lb per sec × ft = centipoise × 0.000672
k = 0.087 Btu/(hr)(sq ft)(°F)

$$h_i = 0.0225\,\frac{k}{D}\,(R_e)^{0.8}\left[\frac{C\mu}{k}\right]^{0.3}$$

$$= 0.0225\,\frac{(0.087)(16)(12)}{19}\,(9{,}250)^{0.8}\left[\frac{0.742 \times 0.77 \times 2.42}{0.087}\right]^{0.3}$$

$$= 67.5 \text{ Btu/(hr)(sq ft)(°F)}$$

where 2.42 = 0.000672 × 3,600

Calculation of h_0 for water:

$$\text{Rate of flow} = \frac{101{,}400}{(80 - 50) \times 3{,}600} = 0.939 \text{ lb per sec}$$

$$\text{Area of annulus} = \frac{\pi}{4 \times 144}\left[(2.067)^2 - \left(\frac{21}{16}\right)^2\right] = 0.01395 \text{ sq ft}$$

$$\text{Mass velocity} = G = \frac{0.939}{0.01395} = 67.3 \text{ lb per sec} \times \text{sq ft}$$

$$\text{Equivalent diameter} = D_e = \frac{4 \times \text{area annulus}}{\text{area heating surface}}$$

$$D_e = \frac{4 \times 0.01395}{\pi \times 21/16 \times 1/12} = 0.162 \text{ ft}$$

$$R_e = \frac{D_e G}{\mu} = \frac{0.162 \times 67.3}{1.052 \times 0.000672} = 15{,}420 \text{ (no units)}$$

By McAdams equation (modified D and B equation).

$$h_0 = 160\,(1 + 0.01 \times 65)\left(\frac{67.3}{62.3}\right)^{0.8} \times \frac{1}{(0.162 \times 12)^{0.2}}$$

$$h_0 = 246 \text{ Btu/(hr)(sq ft)(°F)}$$

Over-all coefficient, V_0, based on outside surface of copper tube is given by:

$$\frac{1}{U_0} = \frac{1}{h_0} + \frac{LA_0}{KA_{av}} + \frac{A_0}{h_iA_i}$$

$$\frac{1}{U_0} = \frac{1}{246} + \frac{(1/16 \times 1/12)(21/16\pi \times 1)}{222 \times (20/16\pi \times 1)} + \frac{(21/16\pi \times 1)}{67.5 \times (19/16\pi \times 1)}$$

$\frac{1}{U_{0_c}} = 0.02047$ and $U_{0_c} = 48.9 =$ the clean heat-transfer coefficient.

Fouling resistances of at least 0.001 should be assumed on the inside and on the outside of the tubing.

$$\frac{1}{U_{0_D}} = 0.02047 + 0.002 = 0.02247$$

$U_{0_D} = 44.5 =$ the heat-transfer design coefficient

The logarithmic mean temperature difference from alcohol to water:

$$(\Delta t)_{lm} = [(172 - 80) - (70 - 50)] \div 2.3 \log_{10} \frac{(172 - 80)}{(70 - 50)} = 47.2°\text{F}$$

Required heat-transfer area:

$$A = \frac{q}{U_0(\Delta t)_{lm}} = \frac{101{,}400}{44.5 \times 47.2} = 48.3 \text{ sq ft}$$

Area per pass, based on outside surface of copper tube:

$$a = (\pi 21/16 \times 1/12) \times 24 = 8.25 \text{ sq ft}$$

Number of passes in series $= \frac{48.3}{8.25} = 5.8$

Therefore, use 6 passes.

2.07 X-Y data from Perry, p. 574

Boiling point of 50 mole per cent solution = 73.1°C

$\Delta t = 73.1 - 20 = 53.1°C$

c_p = specific heat of feed = 0.81

λ = latent heat of feed = 16,300 Btu per lb-mole

$$q = \frac{\lambda + c_p \times \Delta t}{\lambda} = \frac{16{,}300 + 0.81 \times 25 \times 53.1 \times 1.8}{16{,}300}$$

$$= 1.12$$

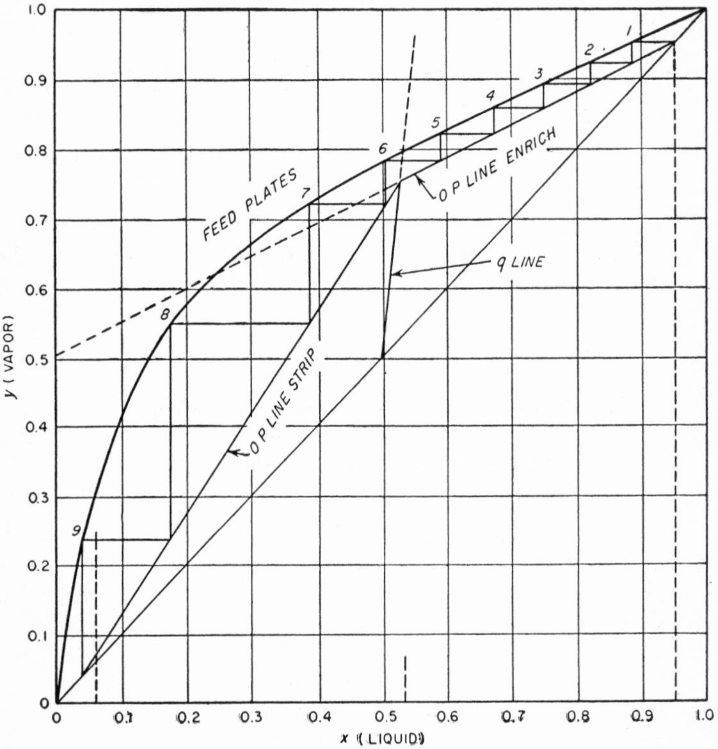

Fig. 2.07

where 25 = average mole weight of feed (lb per lb-mole)

Slope of q-line $= q/(q - 1) = 1.12/0.12 = 9.33$

a. $R_{\min} = (0.95 - 0.79)/(0.79 - 0.53) = 0.615$

b. $R = \left(\frac{100 + 40}{100}\right) \times 0.615 = 0.861$

$$Y\text{-intercept} = \frac{X_D}{R+1} = \frac{0.95}{1.861} = 0.51$$

From the diagram, number of perfect plates is 8.85. Therefore, use **9** plates.

c. 2,000 lb per hr feed = 80 lb-moles per hr.
Product = 40 lb-moles per hr
$= (0.95 \times 40 \times 32 + 0.05 \times 40 \times 18) = 1{,}252$ lb per hr
Residue = 40 lb-moles per hr
$= (0.95 \times 40 \times 18 + 0.05 \times 40 \times 32) = 748$ lb per hr
2,000 lb per hr

d. $V = RD = 0.861 \times 40 = 34.44$ lb-moles per hr
$\bar{V} = F(q-1) + V = 80(1.12 - 1) + 34.44$
$= 44.0$ lb-moles per hr

Pounds steam per hr $= {}^{970}\!/_{960} \times 18 \times 44.0 =$ **800**

2.08 Heat of this reaction *at* 25°C is:

$\Delta H = 369.4 - 356.2 + 10.5 = 23.7$ kcal per gram-mole = 23,700 cal per gram-mole

Standard entropy change for this reaction at 25°C is:

$\Delta S = 35.0 - 42.0 + 45.1 = 38.1$ cal/(gram-mole)(°K)
$\Delta c_p = c_p(H_2O) = 6.89 + 3.283 \times 10^{-3}T - 0.343 \times 10^{-6}T^2$

At 500°K:

$$\Delta H = 23{,}700 + \int_{298}^{500} (6.89 + 3.283 \times 10^{-3}T - 0.343 \times 10^{-6}T^2)dT$$

$$= 23{,}700 + 6.89(500 - 298) + 1.641 \times 10^{-3}(500^2 - 298^2) - 0.114(500^3 - 298^3) \times 10^{-6}$$

$$= 23{,}700 + 1{,}393 + 264 - 11 = 25{,}346 \text{ cal per gram-mole}$$

$$\Delta S = 38.1 + \int_{298}^{500} \left(\frac{6.89}{T} + 3.283 \times 10^{-3} + 0.343 \times 10^{-6}T\right) dT$$

$$= 38.1 + 6.89 \times 2.3 \log_{10} ({}^{500}\!/_{298}) + 3.283 \times 10^{-3}(500 - 298) - 0.172 \times 10^{-6}(500^2 - 298^2)$$

$$= 38.1 + 3.57 + 0.66 - 0.03 = 42.3 \text{ cal/(gram-mole)(°K)}$$

$$\Delta G^\circ = 25{,}346 - 500 \times 42.3 = +4{,}196 \text{ cal/(gram-mole)}$$

$$\log K = \log P_{(H_2O)} = -\frac{\Delta G^\circ}{2.3RT} = -\frac{4{,}196}{2.3 \times 1.987 \times 500}$$

$$= -1.835 = \frac{1}{1.835}$$

$$P_{(H_2O)} = \frac{1}{68.4} = 0.0146 \text{ atm} = 11.1 \text{ mm Hg}$$

At 700°K:

$$\Delta H = 23{,}700 + \int_{298}^{700} (6.89 + 3.283 \times 10^{-3}T - 0.343 \times 10^{-6}T^2)dT$$

$$= 27{,}093 \text{ cal per gram-mole}$$

$$\Delta S = 38.1 + \int_{298}^{700} (6.89/T + 3.283 \times 10^{-3} - 0.343 \times 10^{-6}T)dT$$

$$= 45.2 \text{ cal/(gram-mole)(°K)}$$

$$\Delta G^\circ = 27{,}093 - 700 \times 45.2 = -4{,}547 \text{ cal per gram-mole}$$

$$\log P_{(H_2O)} = +\frac{4{,}547}{2.3 \times 1.98 \times 700} = 1.420$$

$$P_{(H_2O)} = 26.3 \text{ atm} = 386 \text{ psi}$$

The thermal dehydration of the acid appears to be commercially feasible in the temperature range of 500 to 700°K without the use of any powerful desiccating agents.

2.09 *Reference:* Hougen and Watson, "Chemical Process Principles," Part 3, pp. 834–835, Wiley, 1936.

$$\text{Eq. } (b) = \frac{Vr}{F} = \frac{n_0^2}{K\pi^2}\left[Hx_A + J\frac{x_A}{n_{A_0}(n_{A_0} - x_A)} + M\, ln\left(\frac{n_{A_0}}{n_{A_0} - x_A}\right) + N(\cdot\ \cdot\ \cdot)\right]$$

V_r = volume of reactor = 5 cu ft
F = feed rate = 1 lb-mole per hr
$n_0 = 1$ (assumed), $n_{A_0} = 1$, $w = -\frac{1}{2}$
$x_A = \frac{1}{2}$, $\pi = 1$ atm
$H = \omega^2 = \frac{1}{4}$, $J = (1 + \omega n_{A_0})^2 = \frac{1}{4}$
$M = -2\omega(1 + \omega n_{A_0}) = \frac{1}{2}$
$N = 0$

$$\frac{5}{1} = \frac{(1)^2}{K \times (1)^2}\left[\left(\frac{1}{4}\right)\left(\frac{1}{2}\right) + \left(\frac{1}{4}\right)\frac{1/2}{1(1 - 1/2)} + \frac{1}{2}\, ln \left(\frac{1}{(1 - 1/2)}\right)\right]$$

$$K = \frac{1}{5}\left[\frac{1}{8} + \frac{1}{4} + \frac{2.3}{2}\log_{10} 2\right]$$

$$= 0.1442 \text{ lb-mole/(cu ft) (hr)(atm}^2)$$

Let rate constant at 300°C = K'

$$\log\left(\frac{K}{K'}\right) = \frac{30{,}000}{4.576}\left(\frac{773 - 573}{773 \times 573}\right) = 2.97$$

$$K' = \frac{0.1442}{932} = 1.55 \times 10^{-4} \text{ lb-mole/(cu ft)(hr)(atm}^2)$$

$$\text{Feed rate} = \frac{PV}{RT} = \frac{5 \times 10{,}000}{0.730 \times 573 \times 1.8} = 66.5 \text{ lb-mole per hr}$$

$H = J = 1/4$, $M = 1/2$, $N = 0$ as before but $x_A = 1/4$ and $\pi = 5$ atm

$$\frac{V_r}{66.5} = \frac{1}{(1.55 \times 10^{-4})(5)^2}\left\{\left(\frac{1}{4}\right)\left(\frac{1}{4}\right) + \left(\frac{1}{4}\right)\left[\frac{1/4}{1(1 - 1/4)}\right] + \frac{1}{2}\ln\left[\frac{1}{(1 - 1/4)}\right]\right\}$$

$$V_r = \frac{66.5 \times 0.2886}{(1.55 \times 10^{-4})(25)} = \mathbf{4{,}960} \text{ cu ft} = \text{volume of reactor}$$

2.10 Since the vapor pressures of the two pure components are given, this question will be solved on the assumption that Raoult's law and Dalton's law hold.

Total pressure = $P = 0.50 \times 3.0 + 0.50 \times 0.9 = 1.95$ atm

Composition of the vapor phase:

Yn-butane $= 1.50/1.95 = 0.769$ mole fraction
Yn-pentane $= 0.45/1.95 = 0.231$ mole fraction

This question may also be solved using K constants (Thermodynamics books give p-x data).

Assume $P = 2$ atm:

	x	K	K_x	$Y = K_x/\Sigma K_x$
n-Butane	0.50	1.8	0.90	0.773
n-Pentane	0.50	0.53	0.265	0.227
			1.165	

Assume $P = 3$ atm:

n-Butane	0.50	1.2	0.60	0.769
n-Pentane	0.50	0.36	0.18	0.231
			0.78	

Interpolating for $\Sigma K_x = 1.00$

$$P = 2 + (3 - 2)\frac{(1.165 - 1.000)}{(1.165 - 0.780)} = 2.43$$

Yn-butane $= 0.771$ mole fraction
Yn-pentane $= 0.229$ mole fraction

2.11 The conversion of SO_2 to SO_3 is a heterogeneous catalytic reaction: $SO_2 + \frac{1}{2}O_2 = SO_3$.

Since the reaction is exothermic, the percentage conversion of SO_2 to SO_3 decreases with increasing temperature and for this reason the process should be operated at the lowest temperature which gives a satisfactory rate of conversion. In order to take advantage of the high rates of conversion obtainable at high temperatures and at the same time to attain a high equilibrium conversion, which is only possible at lower temperatures, the reaction is usually carried out in two stages. The rectants enter the first converter at about 400°C and leave it at about 600°C. The reaction mixture is then cooled, entering the second converter at 400°C and leaving it at about 460°C. Conversions of about 80 per cent are obtained in the first converter and of about 96 to 97 per cent after passage through the second converter. First-class commercial plants attain within 1 to 2 per cent of the equilibrium conversion.

The percentage conversion of SO_2 to SO_3 is favored by the presence of excess oxygen, as may be seen from the equation. Feed gases may be prepared by burning sulfur (brimstone) in air. The higher the SO_2 content of the burner gas, the lower the O_2 content. Thus, with brimstone-burner gas containing 10 per cent SO_2, the equilibrium conversion to SO_3 is 96.8 per cent at 460°C, while with 5 per cent SO_2 gas the equilibrium conversion is 97.8 per cent at this temperature. However, gas rich in SO_2 requires less gas-handling equipment and less catalyst and is therefore used in preference to the weaker gas in spite of slightly smaller conversions.

While an increase in the total pressure of the system should result in increased equilibrium conversion of SO_2 to SO_3, as may be seen by applying Le Châtelier's principle to this reaction, the effect would be so small that it would not compensate for additional costs of operation at high pressure. Hence, operation at atmospheric pressure is practiced.

Reference: Rogers, "Manual of Industrial Chemistry," Vol. I, Chap. 7, Van Nostrand, 1942.

2.12 *Reference:* Hougen and Watson, "Chemical Process Principles," 2d ed., Part 3, p. 824, Wiley, 1936.

$$kt = ln\left(\frac{n_{A0}}{n_{A0} - x_A}\right) = 2.3 \log_{10}\left(\frac{100}{(100 - 99)}\right) = 4.606$$

$$t = 4.606/0.0098 = 470 \text{ min}$$

2.13 Synthetic methods of preparation have been chosen as answers to this question in order to emphasize that the attempt to utilize elementary carbon in the production of organic compounds is an active and successful field. The hydrocarbons are still produced from petroleum and alcohol from grains and other materials, but the production of these materials from carbon is ever increasing.

1. During World War II, a large part of Germany's liquid fuels were produced by the hydrogenation of low-grade oils and tars and by the reduction of carbon monoxide by hydrogen in the presence of a catalyst. The latter process, known as the Fischer-Tropsch synthesis is an excellent example of hydrocarbon synthesis.

The raw materials are carbon monoxide produced from coal and hydrogen. Successful catalysts employed in the process are: cobalt, thoria, and kieselguhr (1:0.08:1); and iron, copper, and alkali (5:1:0.1). For a complete discussion of the process variables, refer to the current literature (e.g., Schlesinger, Cromwell, Leva, and Storch, *Ind Eng Chem,* Vol. 43, p. 1474, 1951; and Groggins, "Unit Processes in Organic Synthesis," McGraw-Hill, 1952). The products are used as liquid and gaseous fuels.

2. Synthetic methanol. The synthesis of methanol from carbon monoxide by means of the Fischer-Tropsch synthesis has been carried out in this country for 25 years. An excellent review of synthetic methanol production is to be found in *Ind Eng Chem,* Vol. 40, p. 2230, 1948. About one-half of the methanol produced is oxidized to formaldehyde. The remainder is used as antifreeze solvent, etc. The raw materials are coke or natural gas, and the catalysts consist of metal-metallic oxide mixtures. A typical catalyst is copper with oxides of zinc, chromium, manganese, and aluminum. When contact with iron is excluded, methanol of 99 per cent purity can be produced. For a discussion of process variables see Groggins, "Unit Processes in Organic Synthesis," McGraw-Hill, 1952.

3. Ketone. Acetone is a typical example of a ketone produced on a large scale. It may be produced from starch or sugar by fermentation and the products of butanol, ethanol, and acetone are separated by distillation. Acetone is also prepared from propylene obtained from cracking still gas. The propylene is treated with sulfuric acid in a packed tower. The product of the tower is heated in a lead lined tank and isopropyl alcohol is distilled. The isopropyl alcohol in the presence of a copper catalyst yields acetone.

4. Ester.

Reference: Groggins, "Unit Processes in Organic Synthesis," 4th ed., McGraw-Hill, 1952, for a complete discussion of the large-scale production of esters.

5. Metallic organic compounds. Lead tetraethyl is perhaps one of the best known organo-metallic compounds and is used in the prevention of "knocking" in internal-combustion engines.

Tetraethyl lead is produced by the interaction of ethyl chloride with a lead-sodium alloy in a dry and inert atmosphere.

2.14 *Reference:* Perry, pp. 1870–1872.

It is assumed that the plant has been properly designed so as to include the proper materials of construction, venting and ventilating systems, fire equipment, etc.

(1) An active safety- and fire-protection organization should exist in the plant. (2) Special safety-protection equipment should be available and used. (3) Special fire-protection equipment should be available and its proper use should be common knowledge in the plant. (4) Preventive maintenance should be practiced continuously.

2.15 *a.* Fats are glycerol esters of saturated and unsaturated fatty acids. Hydrolysis or splitting of the fat may be accomplished in either alkaline or acid media. The alkaline media method is described here.

$$\begin{array}{lcccl} C_xH_yCOO\text{—}CH_2 & & & & CH_2OH \\ \qquad\qquad\quad | & & & & \quad | \\ C_xH_yCOO\text{—}CH & + \; 3NaOH & \rightarrow & 3C_xH_yCOONa \; + & CHOH \\ \qquad\qquad\quad | & & & \text{Soap} & \quad | \\ C_xH_yCOO\text{—}CH_2 & & & & CH_2OH \\ \qquad \text{Fat} & & & & \text{Glycerol} \end{array}$$

The fat is heated to approximately 80°C with live steam, and sodium hydroxide is added. The removal of the acid radical in the fat is a stepwise procedure. The partially hydrolyzed fat is "salted out" with sodium chloride and the procedure is repeated until the fat is completely hydrolyzed, the soap appearing in the top layer and the glycerol in the bottom layer.

b. Sodium chloride is added to "salt out" the soap.

Reference: Riegel, "Industrial Chemistry," 4th Ed., Reinhold, 1942, or Groggins, "Unit Processes in Organic Synthesis," 4th Ed., McGraw-Hill, 1952, for a description of acid hydrolysis.

2.16 $$\frac{50{,}000 \text{ units} \times 0.020/100}{1{,}000{,}000 \text{ units}} = \frac{10 \text{ units}}{1{,}000{,}000 \text{ units}}$$

Use 50/1,000 or 5 per cent of 0.020 per cent manganese by weight.

2.17 (*a*) Formic acid. (*b*) Alcohol. (*c*) Acid. (*d*) Glycerol and salts of higher fatty acids. (*e*) Glucose and fructose.

2.18 When resistance offered by press and cloth is negligible, $V^2 = K\theta$, where V = volume of filtrate collected in time θ and K = constant for constant pressure filtration. The volume of filtrate to be collected is directly proportional to the thickness of the cake. Hence, new time of filtration is $\theta_2 = \theta_1(V_2/V_1)^2 = 2(3/2)^2 = 4.50$ hr. The rates of washing are in each case inversely proportional to the final volumes of filtrate. Hence, the wash rate, $R_2 = R_1(V_1/V_2) = R_1(2/3)$. The time for washing is proportional to the volume of wash water and inversely proportional to the wash rate. Hence, $(\theta_{\text{wash}})_2 = (\theta_{\text{wash}})_1(V_2/V_1)(R_1/R_2) = (30)(3/2)(3/2) = 67.5$ min $= 1.125$ hr. The new total time per cycle $= 4.50 + 1.125 + 0.500 = 6.125$ hr. The new gal per cycle $= 3/2$(old gal per cycle). Therefore,

$$\frac{\text{New output of press, gal per hr}}{\text{Old output of press, gal per hr}} = \frac{1.5(3.00)}{1\ (6.125)} = 0.735$$

Hence, average output from press is reduced by 26.5 per cent.

2.19

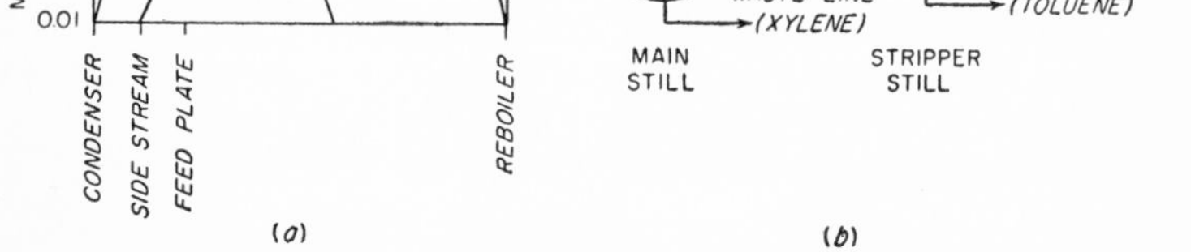

Fig. 2.19

2.20 Modern industrial chemical operations in many cases require water which is purer than the naturally occurring supply. Since in most chemical plants large quantities of process steam are used, requirements for boiler feedwater are large. Treatment of boiler water includes, when necessary, removal of solids by sedimentation, coagulation, settling, and filtration, and removal of dissolved salts by lime-soda, zeolite, and hydrogen-cation exchange methods. Large amounts of water are used in chemical process plants for cooling purposes in condensers and heat exchangers. Such waters, particularly when recirculated through cooling towers or spray ponds, may need to be treated for prevention of scale by the lime-soda, zeolite, or hydrogen-cation exchange methods and may have to be chlorinated to inhibit organic growths. Water used directly in the manufacture of chemicals should in general be clear, colorless, and free from iron, manganese, hydrogen sulfide, and organic growths. Hardness in water is generally objectionable in such industrial uses as dyeing, laundering, bleaching, paper making, tanning, etc. The lime-soda or zeolite process is usually used to remove hardness caused by calcium and magnesium salts. In the manufacture of fine chemicals and drugs distilled water has been used in the past, but the present trend is toward the use of demineralized water obtained by ion-exchange methods.

So-called temporary hardness in water is caused by dissolved calcium bicarbonate, while permanent hardness is due to dissolved noncarbonate calcium salts such as $CaCl_2$ and to magnesium salts such as $MgHCO_3$ and $MgCl_2$.

1. In the lime-soda process, slaked lime and soda ash are used to remove calcium and magnesium by precipitation:

$$Ca(HCO_3)_2 + Ca(OH)_2 = 2CaCO_3\downarrow + 2H_2O$$

$$Mg(HCO_3)_2 + 2Ca(OH)_2 = Mg(OH)_2\downarrow + 2CaCO_3\downarrow + 2H_2O$$

$$CaCl_2 + NaCO_3 = CaCO_3\downarrow + 2NaCl$$

$$MgCl_2 + Na_2CO_3 + Ca(OH)_2 = Mg(OH)_2\downarrow + CaCO_3\downarrow + 2NaCl$$

2. The zeolite softening process is a cation-exchange process in which the zeolite reacts chemically with the hard water, removing Ca and Mg ions and liberating Na ions in their stead. The process may be represented by the equation

$$Na_2Ze + CaCl_2 = CaZe + 2NaCl$$

When the zeolite is spent, it may be regenerated by treatment with brine:

$$CaZe + 2NaCl = Na_2Ze + CaCl_2$$

Zeolite-treated waters tend to be alkaline because bicarbonate hardness is transformed by the treatment to dissolved sodium bicarbonate.

3. The demineralizing process involves the use of cation and anion exchange resins which remove dissolved salts by first replacing cations with hydrogen ions, then replacing the anions with hydroxyl ion:

$$CaCl_2 + 2HR = 2HCl + CaR_2$$
$$2HCl + 2R'OH = 2R'Cl + 2H_2O$$

The demineralizing process yields the purest product but is also the most expensive method of the three. The zeolite treatment is convenient and works with a minimum amount of attention or supervision. The zeolite treatment is cheaper than the cold lime-soda process for removing noncarbonate hardness while the reverse is true in the case of bicarbonate hardness. Zeolite-treated water may in some cases be objectionable because of its usually high alkalinity and will also have a tendency to foam because of the presence of dissolved sodium salts.

The lime-soda process is not as effective in removing all hardness as the zeolite process but is cheaper with waters high in bicarbonate hardness. A combination lime-zeolite process is sometimes used, the lime to remove the bicarbonate hardness and the zeolite to remove all remaining hardness. The cost of equipment in this combination process is, however, high.

Reference: Nordell, "Water Treatment for Industrial and Other Uses," Reinhold, 1951.

2.21 *Polarimeter* is an instrument useful in the measurement of the concentration of an optically active substance in solution. It may also be used to identify optically active substances. The essential elements of a polarimeter are a polarizer for producing polarized light, a tube containing the solution to be studied, and an analyzer by means of which the degree of rotation of the polarized light from the optically active solution is determined.

Potentiometer is an electrical instrument by means of which the emf of a cell may be determined with a very high degree of accuracy by balancing it against a known potential drop in a calibrated circuit. A standard cell of known emf is used to adjust the current in the calibrated circuit. The potentiometer is useful whenever accurate measurements of emf or potential differences are required, and it operates without drawing any appreciable current from the emf source. Potentiometers are commonly used with thermocouples in the measurement of electrode potentials and in potentiometric titrations.

Refractometer is an instrument for measuring the index of refraction of a substance or solution. A refractometer contains one or more prisms and an arrangement by which light may be passed through these prisms and through the substance whose index of refraction is to be measured. By observing the angle at which the light emerges from the instrument, the desired index of refraction is either read directly on a scale or calculated. Refractometers are useful in identifying substances from their index of refraction and in measuring compositions of solutions when the relation between composition and index of refraction has been established.

Spectrophotocolorimeter. This is a spectrophotometer adapted to the measurement of the amount of light of a definite wavelength (within a narrow range) absorbed by a solution. A spectrophotometer usually contains a prism or a grating by means of which a narrow color band of light is produced. This monochromatic light beam is then passed through a cell containing the sample to be tested. The intensity of the transmitted light is then measured by a photoelectric cell. Spectrophotocolorimeters are particularly useful in the determination of constituents, and in the study of mixtures of constituents which are chemically related and which have absorption curves which differ only in certain narrow regions of the spectrum.

Calorimeter is an instrument for measuring various heat effects such as heats of reaction, heats of mixing, sensible heats, and latent heats. The instrument is usually heat insulated and is provided with a sensitive thermometer or thermocouple for measuring temperature changes. The calorimeter may also be provided with an electric heating element by means of which a measured amount of heat may be supplied.

2.22 The rod mill is classified as an intermediate mill and the ball mill and tube mill are classified as fine grinding mills.

The rod mill consists of a cylinder whose length is greater than its diameter. The grinding agent consists of rods whose length is approximately that of the mill enclosure. The distinguishing characteristic of the rod mill is the absence of fines in the product. The product is usually of the order of 50 mesh.

The tube mill consists of a horizontal rotating tube-like cylinder whose length is several times its diameter. The grinding agent is usually flint or steel balls. Its product is characterized by the fineness of grind, the actual mesh being dependent on ball diameter and method of operation. The feed to the mill is of the order of 20 mesh and the product 325 mesh.

The ball mill is a horizontal rotating cylindrical or conical chamber, which may or may not be lined. The grinding medium is steel or iron balls, or flint stones. The charge of balls or stones, their size, and the speed of rotation are parameters which determine the fineness and efficiency of grinding. The ball mill is a "fine" grinder and is less expensive to operate than a rod mill. Ball mills have largely replaced tube mills.

2.23 The reactants in the Fischer-Tropsch synthesis of motor fuels are carbon monoxide and hydrogen. This synthesis gas may be prepared from coal, coke, natural gas (i.e., CH_4), etc.

The principle reactions, which are a function of

1. Temperature (200–300°C)
2. Pressure (1–25 atm)
3. Type of catalyst (CO, Ni, Fe, or Cu with alkali oxide promotors)
4. Carbon monoxide–hydrogen ratio
5. Purity of synthesis gas

are of two general types:

$$aCO + \frac{(2a + b)H_2}{2} \rightarrow C_aH_b + aH_2O$$

$$2aCO + \frac{bH_2}{2} \rightarrow C_aH_b + aCO_2$$

The products of the reaction vary in chain length from 1 to 40 or more carbon atoms and a variety of saturated and unsaturated products. The principle by-products are alcohols and ketones.

2.24 *a.* In order to concentrate a solution of a material whose solubility decreases with increase in temperature, the latent heat of vaporization for the solvent must be supplied at reduced temperatures. This can be done by operating at reduced pressures, i.e., vacuum evaporators. Care must be taken in designing the heating unit so that there is not an accumulation of solute at this point. A vertical-tube, forced-circulation evaporator is indicated (see Perry, p. 507). If multiple effects are used, forward feed should be used.

b. (See Perry, p. 1061) In cases where solutes have a large positive temperature coefficient of solubility, cooling without evaporation can produce enough supersaturation to yield crystallization. Typical equipment for this type of operation are Wulft-Bock crystallizers, Swenson-Walker crystallizers, agitated batch crystallizers, etc.

c. Sodium chloride has a very small positive temperature coefficient of solubility and is typical of solutes in this class. In this case cooling has very little influence and crystallization is dependent on evaporation. Crystallizing evaporators are used.

d. Use a selfpriming centrifugal pump. If temperature is high, consideration of cooling the packing is important.

e. Use vacuum or vacuum freeze driers and spray driers.

f. Use an exchanger which produces high linear rates of flow on the viscous fluid side and which permits easy cleaning.

g. Use a vacuum still which permits distillation at "safe" temperatures.

h. The drier must be supplied with adequate means for controlling drier temperature and humidity. A tunnel-vertical-turbo type is suitable for lumber. A recirculating drier control system is described in Perry, p. 1335.

2.25 *a.* The weight of sulfur conveyed from the storage pile to the melting tank may be controlled automatically by a Harding weigh feeder, a Schaeffer belt system, or a Jeffrey vibrating feeder if the process is continuous. An automatic hopper scale or conveyor-type batching scale may be used in a batch operation. (See Perry, p. 1293.)

b. A two-control valve system for the heating tank is described in Perry, p. 1330. A control system for a continuous process is described in Perry, p. 1334.

c. A ratio flow-control system is described in Perry, pp. 1333 and 1334.

2.26 *a*. Iron and aluminum removal is costly since the precipitate of the iron and aluminum ion drags down, by adsorption, appreciable quantities of phosphate which must be reclaimed. Finely ground limestone is added to the phosphoric acid. Soluble CO_2HPO_4, CaH_2PO_4, and a precipitate of iron and aluminum phosphate and calcium fluoride are formed. The precipitate must be washed thoroughly to remove the soluble phosphates. The wash water is added to the acid solution of CaH_2PO_4 and pure sulfuric acid is added with the resulting precipitate of $CaSO_4$. After the removal of the $CaSO_4$, the acid solution is concentrated in a vacuum evaporator or a spray chamber.

b. There are three general methods of defluorination of phosphate rock to produce tricalcium phosphate, which is used as an ingredient in animal food products. The chief difference in the two methods which employ SiO_2 and steam is in the heat treatment. One process involves fusion and the other does not. The principle reaction is $Ca_{10}F_2(PO_4)_6 + H_2O + SiO_2 \rightarrow 3Ca_3(PO_4)_2 + CaSiO_3 + 2HF$. For a complete discussion, refer to Waggaman, "Phosphoric Acid, Phosphates, and Phosphate Fertilizers," p. 390, Reinhold.

c. $Na_3PO_4 \cdot 12(H_2O)$ is used as an internal "softening agent" in cases where the boiler acidity and/or the natural hardness of the water is relatively low. Phosphates when added internally produce a flocculant precipitate of the scale-producing ions, which is easily removed in boiler blowdown. The principle reactions for the removal of scale-producing ions are:

$$3Ca(HCO_3)_2 + 3Na_3PO_4 \rightarrow Ca_3(PO_4)_2\downarrow + 6NaHCO_3$$
$$3MgSO_4 + 2Na_3PO_4 \rightarrow Mg_3(PO_4)_2\downarrow + 3Na_2SO_4$$
$$FeCl_3 + Na_3PO_4 \rightarrow FePO_4\downarrow + 3NaCl$$

The phosphates have an added advantage in that they control the pH of the boiler water.

2.27 24,000 gal water is equivalent to $24{,}000 \times \dfrac{62.4}{7.5} \times \dfrac{1}{2{,}000}$ or 100 tons water.

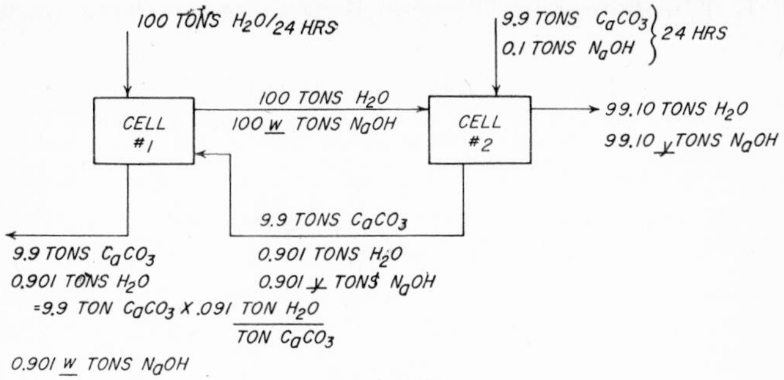

FIG. 2.27

Let w = equilibrium concentration of NaOH in cell #1 in tons NaOH per ton H_2O

Let y = equilibrium concentration of NaOH in cell #2 in tons NaOH per ton H_2O

Material balance of NaOH in cell #1

$$0.901w + 100w = 0.901y$$

Material balance of NaOH in cell #2

$$0.901y + 99.10y = 0.1 + 100w$$

(1) $100.901w = 0.901y$ or $100w = 0.89y$
(2) $100.001y = 0.1 + 100w = 0.1 + 0.89y$
(3) $98.91y = 0.1$ and $y = 1.01 \times 10^{-3}$ tons NaOH per ton H_2O

Therefore $w = 9 \times 10^{-6}$ tons NaOH per ton H_2O

Therefore, since each ton of $CaCO_3$ carries 0.091 tons of water and each ton of water carries 9×10^{-6} ton NaOH, the product will contain per ton $CaCO_3$

$$1 \text{ (ton } CaCO_3) \times 0.091 \text{ (ton } H_2O \text{ per ton } CaCO_3) \times 9 \times 10^{-6} \text{ ton NaOH per ton } H_2O = 8.19 \times 10^{-7} \text{ ton NaOH}$$

2.28 *a.* The principle methods of preparing rayon in order of production are the viscose and acetate processes.

b. I. *Viscose process*

$$\underset{\text{Cellulose}}{(C_6H_9O_4OH)_y} + yNaOH \rightarrow \underset{\text{Alkali cellulose}}{(C_6H_9O_4ONa)_y} + yH_2O$$

$$(C_6H_9O_4ONa)_y + yCS_2 \rightarrow \underset{\text{Cellulose xanthate}}{\left(C_6H_9O_4{-}O{-}C\begin{smallmatrix} {/\!\!/}S \\ \diagdown SNa \end{smallmatrix}\right)_y}$$

$$3\left(C_6H_9O_4{-}O{-}C\begin{smallmatrix} {/\!\!/}S \\ \diagdown SNa \end{smallmatrix}\right)_y + 2yH_2O \rightarrow$$

$$\left[C_{18}H_{27}O_{12}(OH)_2{-}O{-}C\begin{smallmatrix} {/\!\!/}S \\ \diagdown SNa \end{smallmatrix}\right]_y + 2yCS_2 + 2yNaOH$$

$$\left[C_{18}H_{27}O_{12}(OH)_2{-}O{-}C\begin{smallmatrix} {/\!\!/}S \\ \diagdown SNa \end{smallmatrix}\right]_y + \frac{y}{2}H_2SO_4 \rightarrow \underset{\text{Viscose rayon}}{(C_6H_9O_4OH)_y}$$

$$+ yCS_2 + \frac{y}{2Na_2SO_4}$$

II. *Acetate process*

$$\underset{\text{Cellulose}}{(C_6H_9O_4OH)_y} + \underset{\text{Acetic anhydride}}{3y(CH_3CO)_2O} \rightarrow \underset{\text{Cellulose acetate}}{[C_6H_7O_2(O_2CCH_3)_3]_y} +$$

$$3yCH_3COOH$$

An excellent description of the unit operations and unit processes involved is to be found in Shreve, "The Chemical Process Industries," McGraw-Hill, 1945.

c. Nylon is a polymerized condensation product of adipic acid and hexaphenylene-diamine.

$$C_6H_5OH \rightarrow C_6H_{11}OH \rightarrow (CH_2)_4(COOH)_2$$

Phenol Cyclohexanol Adipic acid

$$(CH_2)_4(COOH)_2 + NH_3 \xrightarrow{\text{catalyst}} NC(CH_2)_4CN$$

Adiponitrile

$$\downarrow \text{reduces}$$

$$H_2N - (CH_2)_6NH_2$$

Hexamethylene-diamine

$$xHO_2C(CH_2)_4COOH + xH_2N - (CH_2)_4NH_2 \rightarrow [OC(CH_2)_4COOH(CH_2)_6NH]_y$$

2.29 See Mantell, "Industrial Electrochemistry," McGraw-Hill, 1950.

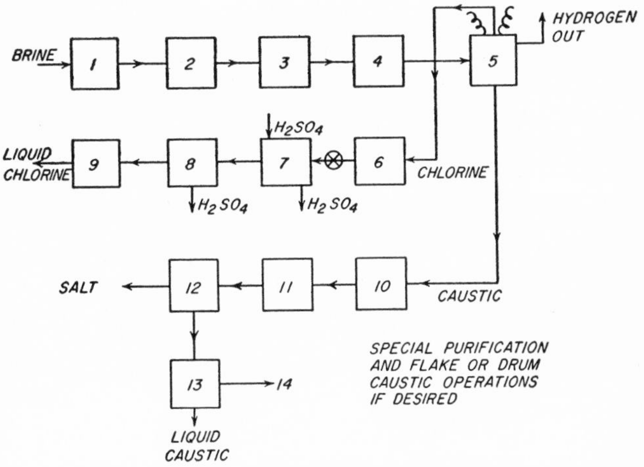

Fig. 2.29

1. Brine heater
2. Brine purification (calcium and magnesium removed)
3. Brine storage
4. Brine heater
5. Cell
6. Chlorine cooler
7. Drying tower
8. Expansion drum
9. Refrigeration unit
10. Caustic storage (weak)
11. Evaporator and separator
12. Filter
13. Liquid caustic storage
14. Salt may be crystallized and water removed if so desired.

One ton salt		
Na_2CO_3 (58 per cent)	30 lb	Refrigeration 0.5 ton
H_2SO_4 (66° Br)	118 lb	Caustic 0.45 ton (anhydrous)
Steam	11,750 lb	Chlorine 0.5 ton
Electricity	1,475 (kwhr)	Hydrogen 5,100 cu ft

2.30

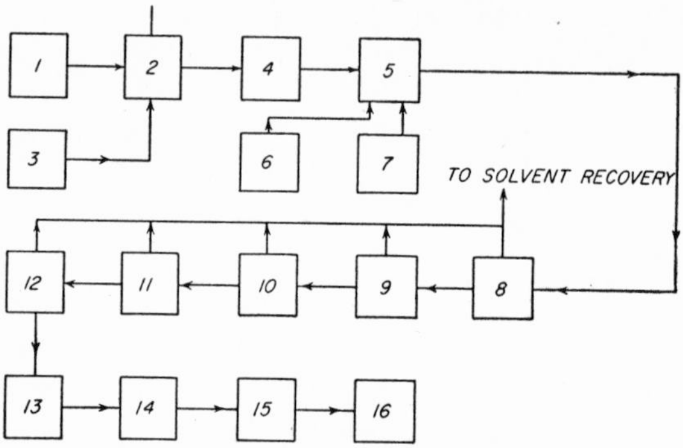

Fig. 2.30

1. Water-wet nitrocellulose (12.6% N_2)
2. Dehydrating press
3. Ethyl alcohol
4. Block breaker
5. Mixer
6. Ether
7. Diphenylamine stabilizer
8. Press
9. Macaroni press
10. Blocking press
11. Graining press
12. Dryer
13. Water wash
14. Dryer
15. Blender
16. Packing

For complete discussion see Shreve, "Chemical Process Industries," McGraw-Hill, 1945.

2.31 *a*. Solvent recovery by adsorption of solvent vapors on activated adsorbing agents operates efficiently and safely for the recovery of solvent vapors over a wide range of concentrations of solvent in solvent-laden air.

The solvent-laden air is removed from the drying operation by means of a suction blower. The air is usually passed through a dust-removal device and then to adsorbers.

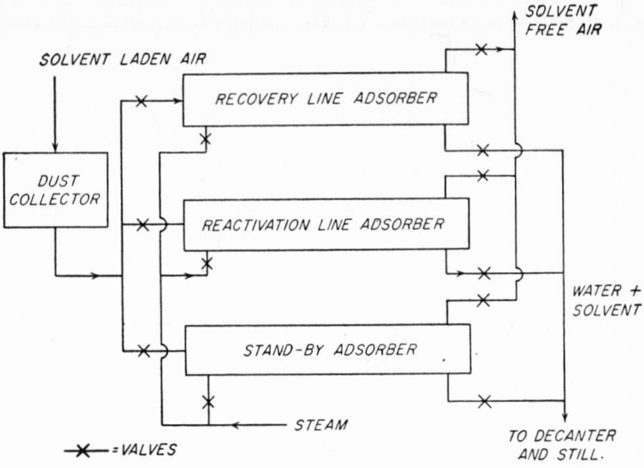

FIG. 2.31

The solvent-laden air then passes to an adsorber where the solvent is selectively adsorbed. When the adsorbing agent becomes "saturated" the solvent-laden gas is directed to a recently activated adsorber. Steam is directed to the "saturated adsorber" and the solvent and water are sent to decanters and stills.

b. Other methods of solvent recovery to be considered are:

1. Scrubbers
2. Compression and cooler

References: Perry, "Chemical Engineers' Handbook," 3d ed., McGraw-Hill, 1950.

Robinson, "The Recovery of Vapors," Reinhold, 1942.

2.32 Technical Paper No. 141, "Use of Oxygen in the Bessemer Steel Converter," U.S. Steel Corp., reprinted from *Journal of Metals,* September, 1952, evaluates in detail the effect of oxygen in bessemer-converter operation. A summary of this report indicates:

a. The use of oxygen may increase the life of the bottom of the converter when it becomes necessary to blank more than 50 per cent of the tuyères;

b. The use of oxygen makes possible a more uniform production rate by increasing its use as tuyères are blanked off;

c. More steel scrap can be used when oxygen is used than when air is used;

d. A greater percentage of the cold pig iron can be charged when oxygen is used; and

e. The use of oxygen does not affect (1) the bottom life, (2) final steel quality, and (3) final teeming temperature.

2.33 *Chemical and Engineering News*, Vol. 30, p. 5449, 1952, reports a world production of natural rubber during the first 10 months of 1952 of 1,445,000 tons and a world production of synthetic rubber for the same period of 740,500 tons. The processing of crude or natural rubber involves approximately the same operations as that of the synthetic rubber. Neoprene latex was quoted at 35 to 43 cents per pound in December, 1951, and natural rubber at 25 to 28 cents per pound. The principle advantage in the synthetic elastomers is the possibility of picking products of particular physical and chemical characteristics. Some have superior resistance to sunlight, some have superior solvent resistance, and others have greater elasticity. The following table gives typical cases of trade name, raw materials, and some of the important characteristics.

Trade name	Raw materials	Resistance to	
		Sun	Gasoline solvent
Buna S	Butadiene and styrene	Fair	Poor
Buna N	Butadiene and acrylonitrile	Fair	Poor
Butyl	Isobutylene and isoprene	Fair	Poor
Neoprene	Chloroprene	Fair	Good
Thiokol A	Ethylene dichloride and sodium tetrasulfide	Fair	Excellent

For a discussion of the unit processes see Shreve, "The Chemical Process Industries," McGraw-Hill, 1945.

2.34 *a.* First law: "Whenever any process occurs, the sum of all the energy changes taken over all the systems participating in the process is zero." Since heat and work are forms of energy being transferred to or from a system to its surroundings, the first law makes it possible by means of energy balances to compute unknown heat or work quantities as well as energy changes in systems.

Second law: "All spontaneous processes are irreversible." The tendency of heat to flow from a body at a higher temperature to one at a lower temperature or of a chemical reaction to come to equilibrium are specific instances of the second law. This law makes it possible to handle quantitatively such problems as the conversion of heat into work or the feasibility of chemical reactions.

Third law: "The entropy of pure crystalline substances is in general zero at the absolute zero of temperature." This law makes it possible to compute the absolute entropy of a substance from heat-capacity measurements extending to very low temperatures in the neighborhood of the absolute zero of temperature.

b. With the aid of thermodynamics, experimental data on chemical equilibriums, heats of reaction, and heat capacities have been correlated and systematized. As a result, it is now possible to predict chemical equilibriums and heats of reaction at various temperatures and pressures from limited experimental data at other temperatures and pressures or for related reactions.

c. 1. Reduced pressure—the ratio of actual pressure of a substance to its critical pressure.

2. Free energy—the difference between the enthalpy and the product of the absolute temperature and the entropy of a substance.

3. Fugacity—this property is defined by its relation to the free energy. At any given temperature the difference between the free energy of a substance in the given state and in the standard state is proportional to the logarithm of the ratio of its fugacity in the given state to that in the standard state.

4. Reduced temperature—the ratio of the temperature of a substance to its critical temperature.

5. Compressibility factor—the ratio of the pressure-volume product of a given substance to that in the ideal-gas state at the same temperature and pressure.

2.35 This a trial-and-error solution. As a first approximation, assume that the theoretical deliverabilities of the parallel lines are in the ratio to their diameters:

$$\frac{Q_{22}}{Q_{20}} = \left(\frac{22}{20}\right)^{2.67} = 1.29$$

The actual deliverabilities will be in the ratio:

$$\frac{Q'_{22}}{Q'_{20}} = 1.29\left(\frac{0.88}{0.92}\right) = 1.233$$

This gives an estimated actual flow of

$$Q'_{22} = (1.233/2.233) \times 6 \times 10^6 \text{ per hr} = 3{,}310{,}000 \text{ cu ft per hr}$$

for the 22-in. line, and

$$Q'_{20} = (1.000/2.233) \times 6 \times 10^6 \text{ per hr} = 2{,}690{,}000 \text{ cu ft per hr}$$

for the 20-in. line. The theoretical flow, assuming smooth pipes, is then computed as

$$\begin{aligned} Q_{22} &= 3{,}310{,}000/0.88 = 3{,}760{,}000 \text{ cu ft per hr, and} \\ Q_{20} &= 2{,}690{,}000/0.92 = 2{,}930{,}000 \text{ cu ft per hr} \end{aligned}$$

The Weymouth equation is

$$(P_1)^2 - (P_2)^2 = \frac{fLW^2zRT}{Dg_cMA^2}$$

where P_1 and P_2 are the inlet and outlet pressures in psf (abs), f is the friction factor for smooth pipe, L is the length of the pipe line in feet, W is the theoretical rate of flow in pounds per second, z is the compressibility factor, R is the universal gas constant, T is the absolute temperature, D is the internal diameter of the pipe in feet, g_c is 32.17 ft per sec^2, M is the molecular weight of the gas in pound-seconds per cubic feet, and in this case equals 0.65×29, and A is the cross section of the pipe in square feet. The Weymouth equation is used to compute the pressure drop in each line. If the calculated values of P_2 for the two lines agree within reason, an average P_2 value may be taken as the answer. If there is no close agreement of the calculated values of P_2, the assumed ratio of Q_{22}/Q_{20} is readjusted and the calculations repeated.

2.36 Approximate calculations for the amount of heat transfer: Temperature of steam = 228°F, and temperature in condenser =

101°F. Assume forward feed and boiling-point elevations of 3°F in the first effect and 6°F in the second effect, giving temperatures estimated to be 170°F for boiling point in first effect and 107°F for boiling point in second effect.

Pounds of water evaporated per pound of NaOH $= (90/10 - 84/16) = 3.75$

Heat transferred for vaporization in the two effects

$$= 3.75 \times \frac{(997 + 1{,}033)}{2} = 3{,}800 \text{ Btu per lb NaOH}$$

Heat required to preheat feed if admitted to first effect = $9(170 - 70) = 900$ Btu per lb NaOH

It is seen that approximately 24 per cent of the heat-transfer requirement is for preheating the feed to its boiling point. Accordingly, it is recommended that for a 10 per cent increase in production available heat exchangers be used to preheat the feed to about 160°F by means of steam bled from the vapor line leaving the first effect. The evaporators are to be operated as a double effect with forward feed. It is estimated that the resultant increase in capacity will be well over 10 per cent and that there will be no loss in steam economy as compared with normal operation with backward feed.

In order to handle a temporary 50 per cent overload, it will be necessary to operate the two evaporators in parallel, using the regular condenser on one of the effects and the spare condenser on the other one. High-pressure steam (5 psi) will be admitted to the steam chest of each evaporator and the feed will enter both effects in parallel. If the capacity of the spare condenser is insufficient to give a 50 per cent increase in production, then available heat exchangers may be used to preheat the feed, thus taking some load off the evaporators. High-pressure steam will have to be used for preheating the feed in the heat exchangers. Since high-pressure steam will be the heating medium in both evaporators and in the heat exchangers, there will be a resultant loss in steam economy which can be tolerated on a temporary overload basis.

2.37 *Reference:* Walker, Lewis, McAdams, and Gilliland, "Principles of Chemical Engineering," pp. 415–416, McGraw-Hill, 1937.

$$\frac{1}{V^2} = a + b\theta \text{ and } a = \frac{1}{(225)^2} \text{ and } \theta = 160$$

$$\frac{1}{(50)^2} = \frac{1}{(225)^2} + 160b \text{ and } b = 2.38 \times 10^{-6}$$

$$V_{av}\theta = \frac{Q}{A\Delta t} = \frac{2(\sqrt{a + b\theta} - \sqrt{a})}{b}$$

a. It is assumed that the evaporator is operated for 160 hr and cleaned for 8 hr, both each week. It follows that on substituting values for "*a*" and "*b*,"

$$V_{av} = \frac{Q}{A\Delta t(\theta - \theta_c)} = 1.27 \times \frac{10^4}{168} = 77.7 \text{ Btu/(hr)(sq ft)(°F)}$$

b. Let time of operation $= \theta$
Let time of cleaning $= \theta_c$

It is required that $\dfrac{Q}{(\theta + \theta_c)}$ be a maximum.

$$\text{Hence } \frac{d}{d\theta}\left[\frac{Q}{(\theta - \theta_c)}\right] = \frac{d}{d\theta}\left[2A\Delta t\frac{(\sqrt{a + b\theta} - \sqrt{a})}{b(\theta + \theta_c)}\right] = 0$$

$$\text{When } \frac{d}{d\theta}\left[\frac{\sqrt{a + b\theta} - \sqrt{a})}{(\theta + \theta_c)}\right] = 0, \text{ then } \theta = \theta_c + 2\sqrt{\frac{a\theta_c}{b}}$$

Substituting values of a, b, and θ_c, $\theta = 24.3$ hr.

This time corresponds to a value for $V_{av} = \dfrac{2\sqrt{b\theta_c}}{b(\theta + \theta_c)}$ $= 113$ Btu/(hr)(sq ft)(°F) as compared with $V_{av} = 77.7$ in part *a*.

Accordingly, for maximum capacity the evaporator should be cleaned after 24.3 hr of operation, corresponding to a total time for the cycle of 32.3 hr. It is suggested that the evaporator be operated during three shifts and cleaned during the fourth shift, corresponding to a 32-hr cycle.

2.38 *a*. Plate and frame presses are suitable for batch operation with both compressible and noncompressible sludges. This press is the cheapest per unit filtering surface and requires the smallest floor space, but involves a large amount of hand labor. This press is best adapted to sludges which either contain small amounts of solids or in which the solids are highly valuable, as in the manufacture of dyes.

b. Rotary continuous filters are used where the process is continuous, where large amounts of solids must be handled, and where labor costs must be kept low. These filters are well adapted to homogeneous sludges of high solid concentrations and low compressibility, which require little washing and do not require high pressures.

c. The Sweetland press is a pressure leaf filter which involves batch operation and has high washing efficiency, the wash water displacing the filtrate when admitted into the press. This filter is suitable for handling slurries when the filtrate is valuable and dilution with wash water is to be held to a minimum.

d. The Moore filter is an intermittent vacuum filter adapted to batch operation. Vacuum is applied to the inside of the leaves during filtration, while compressed air is applied to discharging the cake. The filter basket is moved from filtering tank to washing tank and dump tank with a traveling crane. This filter is suitable for sludges which do not easily settle out and which form an adherent cake. It may be used with compressible sludges provided that a high rate of filtration is not required.

2.39 The problem is the application of the phase rule in metallurgy. Precipitation hardening is applied to alloy systems in which there is a decrease of solid solubility in solid solutions with decreasing temperature.

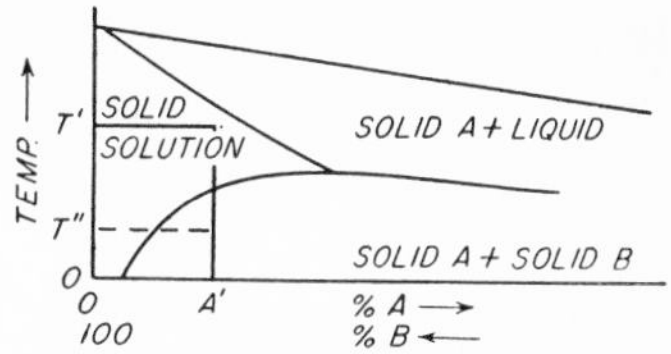

Fig. 2.39

If an alloy whose composition is represented by A' is heated to a temperature T', a single phase of solid solution results. If this solution is cooled suddenly to T'', the solid solution will persist but will be unstable with respect to precipitation of component B (i.e., the solid solution is supersaturated with respect to component B). The precipitation of component B distorts the space lattice and interferes with the normal slip of the alloy. This in turn hardens and strengthens the alloy. There is an optimum value in this process, beyond which the strength and hardness of the alloy are decreased. If this process takes place at room temperature or is the result of cold working, the process is known as age hardening.

The two terms—precipitation hardening and age hardening—have currently become synonymous. The "Metals Handbook," Wiley, however, still gives the following definitions: 1. "Precipitation hardening is a process which increases the hardness of an alloy by the controlled precipitation of a constituent from a supersaturated solid solution"; and 2. "Age hardening is a process that increases hardness and strength and usually decreases ductility. The process usually involves rapid cooling or cold work."

2.40 In checking the efficiency of combustion of flue gases it is desirable to ascertain the CO_2, CO, and O_2 content of the flue gases. All three can be determined by means of a manually operated Orsat analyzer which works by chemical absorption of each gas in a separate unit. A commercial automatic Orsat is manufactured which measures the CO_2 content only. Thermal-conductivity analyzers are in use which take advantage of the fact that the conductivity of CO_2 is considerably less than that of air. In one type of thermal-conductivity meter the CO_2 content is first determined. The sample is then passed over a heated carbon rod to burn CO to CO_2, and the CO_2 content is then redetermined. A thermal-flow meter is available which takes advantage of the magnetic property of oxygen and determines the oxygen by measuring the thermal conductivity of the gas sample in a magnetic field. Thermal conductivity methods are not suitable when components of unknown thermal conductivity are present in the gas mixture, and in any case require calibration for the type of gas mixture tested. They have the advantage of being fully automatic. The CO_2 content may also be determined by an automatic and recording instrument measuring the density of flue gases. Such instruments have no provision for the determination of the CO or O_2 content.

2.41 Instruments for the measurement of temperature are:

1. Liquid-in-glass thermometers, which depend on the expansion of the liquid with rise in temperature. Ranges covered are from −40°F to 1000°F. Use is limited by fragility. Exposed stem corrections and radiation corrections may be necessary to give

accurate results. Accuracy obtainable may be as high as ±0.01°F with calibrated instruments.

2. Pressure-type thermometers, in which the pressure of a liquid, gas, or vapor is used to distort a spiral or helix. These instruments are suitable in ranges from −40°F to 1200°F. These instruments are simple and easily installed, but accuracy is limited and varies from ±1°F to ±10°F.

3. Thermocouples, which may be used for measuring temperatures in the range of −250°F to 2800°F. When used in conjunction with a millivoltmeter, precautions should be taken against changes in the resistance of the thermocouple wires with use. If the indicating instrument is a potentiometer, changes in the resistance of the thermocouple wires will not affect readings. Proper compensation must be made for any variation in the cold-junction temperatures. These instruments are capable of high accuracy when calibrated.

4. Resistance thermometers, in which the electrical resistance of a coil is measured by means of a wheatstone bridge. These instruments are useful in the range of from −250°F to 1500°F. They are fragile and may lose calibration as a result of contamination or volatilization of coil material. When properly calibrated, these instruments are capable of high accuracy, to better than ±0.1°F. Contact resistances must be avoided since they make readings unreliable.

5. Optical pyrometers, which are used for measurement of high temperatures by visually matching the intensity of monochromatic light emitted by the heat source against that from a calibrated constant source. They are useful for temperatures above 1200°F. Commercial instruments are accurate to ±10°F. Correction for emissivity is necessary when sighting upon materials in the open. These instruments cannot be made to record temperature automatically.

6. Radiation pyrometers, which measure the total intensity of radiated light and heat. The radiation is absorbed by a battery of thermocouples in series and the electromotive force generated is a measure of the temperature of the heat source. They are useful for temperatures above 1200°F, are less accurate than optical pyrometers, and are more subject to error due to accumulation of dust and dirt and in the presence of cold strata

of absorbing gases. To obtain correct readings with radiation pyrometers the diameter of the source must exceed the minimum required by the geometry of the instrument. Corrections for emissivity must be made when sighting on material in the open.

2.42 Four methods of removing dust from a gas:

1. Cyclone separators—most widely used dust-collection equipment. The dust-laden gas enters a cylindrical or conical chamber tangentially and leaves through a central opening. Cyclones are applicable for removal of solid or liquid particles of 5 to 200 microns in diameter. Cyclones are designed for an inlet velocity of about 50 ft per sec. Friction loss through cyclones may range from 1 to 20 inlet velocity heads. A cyclone may be placed on either the suction or pressure side of a fan.

2. Cloth collectors (bag filters)—dust-laden gases are passed through a woven fabric which filters out the dust. Such filters have a pressure drop of 2 to 6 in. of water and are rated at 1 to 8 cu ft/(min)(sq ft) of cloth area. In operation it is essential that the gas be kept above its dew point to avoid plugging of the bag pores.

3. Scrubbers—a liquid is employed in this equipment to assist in the removal of dust. The equipment may take the form of spray chambers, water jets, cyclones, packed towers, and mechanical liquid disintegrators. Dust particles down to diameters of 5 microns may be handled. Depending on the type of scrubber used, pressure drops may amount to from 0.1 to 8 in. of water. Water consumption may range between 3 and 100 gal/(min)(1,000 cu ft) of gas handled.

4. Electrical precipitators—best adapted to electrically conducting dusts. Electrical power consumption is in the range of 0.2 to 0.6 kw/(1,000 cu ft)/(min) of gas handled. Very high collection efficiencies may be obtained.

For the given case of a gas entering at 95°C and with a dew-point of 70°C, a chamber spray scrubber is recommended. The humidification of the gas by the spray will tend to flocculate the finer particles. Since the gas will be cooled below its dew point by the spray, condensation will take place on the dust particles, increasing their effective size. The dust is then eliminated by impingement against baffles. This method will involve low first cost and low operating cost.

2.43 See Perry, p. 844.
Initial mixture in pounds alcohol per pound air

$$0.05 \times 46 = 2.30 \text{ lb alcohol}$$
$$0.95 \times 29 = 27.60 \text{ lb air}$$
$$\therefore H = \frac{2.3}{27.6} = 0.0833$$

Hs for final air:

$$Hs = \frac{60}{\{[(114.7/14.7) \times 760] - 60\}} \times \frac{46}{29} = 0.0162 \frac{\text{lb alcohol}}{\text{lb air}}$$

and $\dfrac{0.0833 - 0.0162}{0.0833} \times 100 = 80.6$ per cent recovery of ethanol.

2.44 $$6{,}000 \times 500 \times \frac{144}{163} \times \frac{1}{33{,}000 \times 60 \times 0.25} = 5.4 \text{ hp}$$

$$6{,}000 \times (4{,}200 - 500) \times \frac{144}{163} \times \frac{1}{33{,}000 \times 60 \times 0.30} = 33.0 \text{ hp}$$

Total power = **38.4** hp

2.45 *a.* Use aluminum or chromium alloys (over 18 per cent Cr) for cold acid where strength is over 68 per cent.

b. Use iron or steel, or use monel or nickel when contamination must be avoided.

c. Use iron or steel when the benzol is water and acid free.

d. Use ordinary cast iron when slight contamination is permissible. Use monel metal or nickel when contamination must be avoided.

e. Use iron or steel when there is less than 20 per cent water and when the H_2SO_4 is greater than 15 per cent. Use high-silica cast iron when the water content is between 20 and 30 per cent. Use lead when the water content of the mixture is greater than 30 per cent.

2.46 Basis of solution: 1 sq ft and capacity of 1 in. cake on leaf.

1. $$K'\theta = \frac{V^2}{A^2} = K' \times 5 = \frac{(3.8)^2}{(1)^2}$$
$$K' = 2.89$$

2. Differentiating equation 1, the rate of filtration at a given time is obtained

$$\frac{dV}{d\theta} = \frac{2.89A^2}{2V}$$

3. The cake thickness will be described in terms of t. When $t = 2$, then the cake thickness will be $1/t$ or one-half the thickness of the original cake and the volume of the filtrate delivered will be one-half the value delivered at $t = 1$.

Time Schedule for Leaf Press

Cycles, number	Cake thickness, in.	Time, hr				
		Filter cycle	Wash cycle	Clean	Total time	Time (n) cycles
1	1	5	5	0.5	10.5	10.5
2	½	1.25	1.25	0.5	3	6
3	⅓	0.549	0.549	0.5	1.6	4.8
4	¼	0.312	0.319	0.5	1.12	4.48
5	⅕	0.200	0.200	0.5	0.9	4.5
6	⅙	0.139	0.139	0.5	0.78	4.68

Sample calculations:

1 cycle ($V = 3.8$ cu ft):

$$\text{Wash rate} = \frac{2.89 \times 1^2}{2 \times 3.8} = 0.38 \text{ cu ft per hr}$$

$$\text{Wash time} = \frac{3.8/2}{0.38} = 5 \text{ hr}$$

2 cycles ($V = 1.9$ cu ft):

$$\text{filter time} = \theta = \frac{(1.9)^2}{1^2 \times 2.89} = 1.25 \text{ hr}$$

$$\text{wash rate} = \frac{dv}{d\theta} = \frac{2.89 \times 1^2}{2 \times 1.9} = 0.76 \text{ cu ft per hr}$$

$$\text{wash time, } \theta = \frac{1.9/2}{0.76} = 1.25 \text{ hr}$$

2.47 $H_w - H = \frac{0.26}{\lambda}(t_g - t_w)$

where $t_g = 100°F$
$t_w = 75°F$
$H_w = 0.019$
$\lambda = 1{,}050$

$$\textit{Air in: } H = 0.019 - \frac{0.26}{1{,}050}(100 - 75)$$

$$H = 0.019 - 0.006 = 0.013 \frac{\text{lb water}}{\text{lb air}}$$

$$\textit{Air out: } H = 0.059 \text{ (psychometric chart)}$$

$$\therefore 0.059 - 0.019 = 0.040 \text{ lb water removed per lb air}$$

and $\frac{1}{0.04} = 25$ lb air circulated per lb water removed

$$q = \underset{\text{(lb air)}}{25} \times \underset{(c_p \text{ air})}{0.238} \times \underset{(\Delta t)}{20} + \underset{\text{(lb water)}}{0.013 \times 25} \times \underset{(c_p)}{0.48} \times \underset{(\Delta t)}{20} + \underset{(\lambda)}{1{,}032}$$

$$q = 1154 \text{ Btu per lb of water removed}$$

See Perry for experimental data, *T-H* charts, and steam tables.

2.48 *a.* Methanol may be synthesized from mixtures of CO and H_2 or CO_2 and H_2. The principle method, however, is the synthesis from water gas (CO and H_2) that has been scrubbed to remove CO_2 and sulfur compounds. The pressure is usually of the order of 3,500 to 4,000 psi and the temperature 575 to 580°F.

When pure methanol is the desired product, the reacting gases should not be permitted to come in contact with iron. The usual catalysts are copper and oxides of manganese, chromium, zinc, and aluminum.

Approximately 90 per cent of the methanol production is obtained by this method.

b.

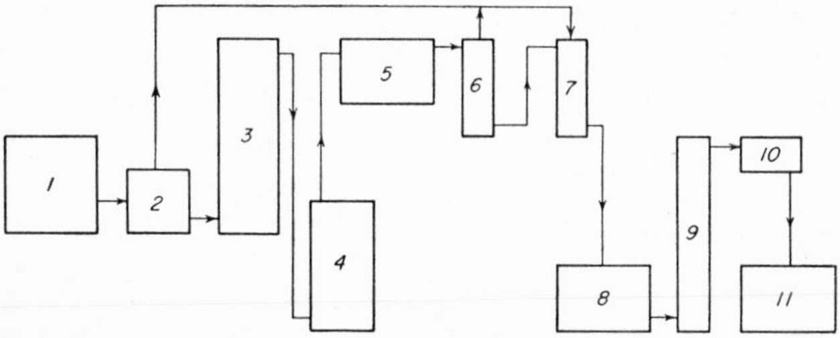

FIG. 2.48

1. CO–H_2 mixture
2. Compressor
3. Scrubber
4. Reactor
5. Condenser
6. High-pressure separator
7. Low-pressure separator
8. Methanol storage
9. Rectifying unit
10. Condenser
11. Methanol storage

2.49 *a.* The packed volume is a function of the column diameter and the height of the column required to give the desired separation. The column diameter is determined on the basis of permissible vapor velocity. This information must be determined for individual types of packing and is usually presented under flooding data.

The height of the column is a function of:

1. The degree of removal of solute
2. The vapor-liquid equilibrium and solubility data for the solvent chosen
3. Height-of-transfer-unit, $K_g a$, or heat-equivalent-t-a-transfer-plate data for the system involved

b. 1. 50 to 75 per cent of the flooding velocity is chosen as vapor velocity.

2. An economic balance of cost of solute waste vs. cost of column is the ultimate aim of most design calculations. In order to calculate the column height, the following steps are used:
   (*a*) Plot equation data
   (*b*) choose liquid-gas ratio
   (*c*) (1) Determine the number of transfer units by calculation or graphically, and the height equals the number of transfer units × HTU, or

   (2) Evaluate $\frac{dx}{(x^x - x)}$ (liquid phase controlling) or $\frac{dy}{(y^x - x)}$ (gas phase controlling) by graphical integration

   and solve $\frac{dx}{(y^x - x)} = \frac{K_l a S\, dL}{L}$

$$\text{or } \frac{dy}{(y^x - x)} = \frac{K_y aS \, dL}{L}$$

when K_ya or K_la are known and where y^x and x^x are equilibrium values.

c. The advantage of the HTU over the HETP is that the HTU is based on a true differential countercurrent process rather than a stepwise countercurrent process. The HTU method is essentially the same as capacity of K_ga and K_ya methods, but the HTU method has an advantage in that it involves only one dimension and does not vary appreciably with gas velocity. When the operating line and equilibrium line are parallel, HTU, HETP, and capacity methods are identical.

2.50 A multiple-effect, probably a triple-effect, evaporator would be used. If necessary, an economic balance could be carried out to determine the number of effects for which the sum of the fixed charges and operating costs is a minimum. To design the evaporator, it would be necessary to know the temperature of the steam available for heating in the first effect and the temperature of the cooling water for the condenser in the last effect. The boiling-point elevations of caustic solutions of various strengths between 8 and 50 per cent would be required.

For the purpose of making heat balances around the effects, it would be desirable to have an enthalpy concentration chart for caustic solutions or at least data on heats of mixing and specific heats of caustic solutions. The temperature of the feed to the evaporator would determine whether forward feed (for hot feed) or backward feed (for cold feed) should be used. The three effects would normally be designed for equal areas. In carrying out the calculations it would first be necessary to assume the concentrations of the solutions in the three effects. An approximation would be to assume equal evaporations. The over-all coefficients of heat transfer in each effect would then be estimated from some available correlation. The temperatures of the vapors leaving each effect would then have to be estimated, either assuming equal temperature drops across the heat-transfer surface in each effect or by assuming the temperature drops inversely proportional to the over-all coefficients. Allowance must be made for the boiling-point elevations of the solutions. A heat balance is then made around each effect and the amounts evaporated in each effect are calculated from these heat balances. The calculated amounts of heat transferred may now be used to readjust the assumed temperature drops across the heat-transfer surfaces, while the calculated evaporations can be used to correct the assumed concentrations and over-all coefficients in the effects. The calculations are then repeated until the calculated evaporations and temperature drops agree with the assumed ones.

Materials of construction will be determined by the degree of corrosiveness of the solutions which will depend on the concentrations and the temperatures. In the case of caustic solutions up to concentrations of 50 per cent and temperatures of 200°F, mild steel can be used. With forward feed, the effect containing the most concentrated solutions (50 per cent) could be operated below 200°F so that mild steel could be used for all effects. With backward feed, however, the first effect would contain the 50 per cent solution at some temperature above 200°F, so that stainless steel or nickel-clad steel or monel metal would then have to be used, at least in the first effect, and for any lines, valves, or pumps leading out of this effect. The higher cost of these materials may be a deciding factor in the choice between backward feed and forward feed.

SECTION THREE

3.01–3.50

CIVIL ENGINEERING

3.01 *a. Engineering News* formula.

b. $R = \dfrac{2WH}{S + 1}$ for drop hammers

$R = \dfrac{2E}{S + 0.1}$ for double-acting steam hammers

where R is the allowable pile load in pounds

W is the weight of striking part of the hammer in pounds

H is the effective height of fall in feet

E is the actual energy delivered by the hammer in foot-pounds per blow

S is the average net penetration of the pile in inches per blow for the last five blows after a depth has been reached where successive blows produce approximately the same net penetration

c. For the given data the allowable load per pile is

$$R = \frac{2 \times 500 \times 20}{1 + 1} = 10{,}000 \text{ lb per pile}$$

It must be pointed out that the *Engineering News* formula does not always give safe values for friction piles in clay soil because of many other factors, chief of which are the stress-time history of the clay and its properties of consolidation.

d. The number of piles required $= 80{,}000/10{,}000 = 8$

Use nine piles, placed in three rows of three so that the outside eight piles form a square. Use 5-ft 0-in. center-to-center spacing of piles with 1-ft 6-in. edge distance, making pile cap 13 ft 0 in. by 13 ft 0 in. Column will be centrally placed on pile cap. The minimum pile spacing is usually about 3 ft 0 in. but for friction piles in clay soils this spacing should be larger in order to develop more shearing resistance in the clay.

3.02 In classifying material for excavation, rock shall be ledge rock, concrete, or masonry which requires drilling or blasting for removal and also all boulders larger than ⅓ cu yd in volume. All excavation other than rock shall be considered earth. The contractor shall notify the architect or resident engineer before the removal of the rock.

3.03 *a. Atterberg limits* comprise the liquid, plastic, and shrinkage limits. The liquid limit is the water contents at which the soil has such a small shearing strength that it flows to close a preformed groove of standard width when jarred in a specified manner. The plastic limit is the water content at which a soil begins to crumble when rolled into threads of a specified diameter. The shrinkage limit is the water content that is just sufficient to fill the pores when the soil is at its minimum volume attained by drying. These limits furnish a sound basis for the identification and classification of soils and predict qualitatively their general behavior when they are correlated with soil tests of a more specific nature. The information furnished by these tests may be misleading, since, for the most part, they are performed on remolded soil.

For determining the liquid limit, a special standard-cup device is used. All the dimensions of the device are fixed and the jarring is accomplished by turning the crank at the rate of 2 revolutions per second. The moisture content when the groove is closed by 25 blows of the cup is defined as the liquid limit.

To find the plastic limit, a thread of soil is rolled out on a glass plate to a diameter of ⅛ in. When the moisture content has been reduced to the point where crumbling starts, the moisture content is measured.

The shrinkage limit is found by measuring the volume (by displacement of mercury) of a soil pat which has been dried in a desiccator. The volume is then used to determine volume of the voids remaining in the soil pat.

b. Permeability test. This test is used to determine the coefficient of permeability in Darcy's equation, $q = kiA$, for a given soil. In the constant-head permeameter, the net head of water on the soil sample of a known length and area is kept constant, and the rate of flow is measured. The permeameter tube or container holds the sample in place by means of screens or fitted porous stones. Before running the test it is necessary to rid the system of any entrapped air.

c. The Direct-shear test is used to measure the cohesion and angle of internal friction of a given soil under somewhat arbitrary conditions of loading rates, seepage conditions, and internal stresses.

The test is performed on a soil sample which is either an undisturbed sample or is representative of the true soil condition which is being investigated. The equipment for the test consists principally of the following: (1) a split rectangular box for holding the specimen constructed so that the upper half of the box can move horizontally with respect to the lower half; (2) a jacking arrangement by which a given vertical pressure can be applied to the specimen; (3) a means of pulling the upper half of the box with respect to the lower half; (4) a means of measuring the shearing resistance of the soil to the horizontal shearing displacement; and (5) a means of measuring the change of thickness of the sample during the test. At the start of a particular run the vertical pressure is applied and maintained constant. As shearing displacement is applied the shearing resistance is measured by a proving ring dial and the vertical displacement by means of an Ames dial.

In cases where seepage takes place under actual conditions, the test is performed with porous stones or plates top and bottom of the specimen and the load applied slowly or quickly depending on whether or not consolidation takes place.

d. Consolidation test. In this test the time rate of consolidation for an undisturbed soil sample is measured. From these measurements the coefficient of consolidation, Cv, in $T = Cvt/H^2$ can be found.

A carefully prepared undisturbed soil sample is cut to fit into the consolidometer. The consolidometer is equipped with porous stones to allow seepage of the pore water to take place. A constant vertical pressure is applied to the specimen during which time its change in thickness is observed at various intervals. Several such runs are made with different soil pressures in order to include the pressures to be encountered in the actual soil.

3.04 *a.* Concrete can be placed under water by means of a tremie, which is a pipe with a hinged plate closure at the bottom. The concrete is placed in the tremie and the latter is lowered to the proper location on the bottom. The pouring is started by opening the hinged plate. As the concrete slumps from the tremie, the tremie is raised but the bottom of it is always kept below the surface of the deposited concrete in order to prevent the passing of the concrete through the water which might cause segregation of the concrete mix.

b. A pneumatic caisson consists essentially of a weighted shell with a cutting edge, working chambers in which the air pressure can be varied, and air locks through which men, equipment, and excavated material can pass. As the material is taken out, the caisson sinks due to its own weight. Tilting of the caisson can be controlled by using several air compartments and varying the pressure in them. As the caisson sinks, additional sections are added to the top, and the locks are also raised.

c. Heads of timber piles are protected either by slipping a steel ring or band around the head of the pile or else the bonnet of the pile hammer serves as a restraint against brooming.

d. The heads of concrete piles are protected by placing either a braided rope mat or a steel-banded wood block between the top of the pile and the underside of the hammer anvil. The protective device is prevented from slipping off the pile head by the bonnet or fingers which extend down (from the hammer case) around the pile top.

e. For a pump to be used where the water level rises 40 to 50 ft it is best to use a vertical type suspended from an *A* frame by a cable in such a way as to be able to readily raise or lower the pump. To prevent locking, an open-type impeller should be used and the motor should be low voltage and not of the induction type.

f. Pointing is the finishing up and smoothing of masonry joints to a given contour for the purpose of achieving a more durable joint and for the sake of appearance. A pointed tool with the required contour is used after the masonry units have been set and the mortar has stiffened.

g. Wales are beams used to support the sheeting in a cut which is braced to prevent collapse of the side walls.

h. Cast-iron lintels are made in the form of an inverted T because this material is stronger in compression than in tension. The tension stress in such a member is considerably lower than the compression stress since the stress is proportional to the distance from the neutral axis which lies nearer to the bottom side of the section. In this way the material in tension and compression may be stressed up to the allowable limits.

i. Stiffeners in a plate girder are used to prevent diagonal buckling and also to prevent lateral buckling at points of concentrated vertical loads.

j. 1. In hot weather it is necessary to keep the concrete cool enough to avoid a flash set and to prevent subsequent rapid evaporation. The first can be achieved by cooling the aggregates and the mixing water. Coverings are usually used to control rapid evaporation.

2. In freezing weather the concrete must be kept above 40 to 50°F to ensure hardening. The time required for hardening depends on the type of cement used and can be shortened by the addition of not more than 2 per cent calcium chloride by weight of cement.

3.05 *a*. The piling interlock being in heavy tension, straight webbed piling is recommended. Special *T* and *Y* pieces are necessary for the junctures. Where piling is over 60 ft long or where penetration is difficult, special leads to prevent lateral deflection during driving may be necessary. In any case the driving must be vertical, with the hammer as vertical as possible and the driving gradual. The open interlock should be plugged so that it may remain clean while being driven. In cellular cofferdams particularly, guide templets are necessary to hold the sheet piling plumb. All sheet piling for a cell should be interlocked and the closure made before any driving of the piling is started. No sheet piling should be driven more than one-third its length before adjacent sheet piling is equally driven.

b. The arch-web type of steel-sheet piling increases the resistance to bending under exterior pressures, and it also resists buckling better while being driven.

c. Treating timber with preservatives, if properly done, has no appreciable effect on the structural strength of the timber. It does however substantially increase the life of the timber.

d. Uncoursed masonry (also called uncoursed rubble) is masonry composed of unsquared stones laid with no attempt at regular courses.

e. The sand and stone (never the cement) may be heated. The mixing water may also be heated. After deposition in the forms, the forms themselves usually supply sufficient side protection. Radiation of heat from the top may be lessened by covering with tar paper or a similar covering and then adding a layer of hay or straw. In very cold weather, tarpaulins may be spread and steam circulated under the canopy through pipes. The area under the tarpaulins may also be heated by salamanders or heat pots. Sand or earth in thickness above 4 in. will protect against normally cold weather.

f. Cofferdam is the term used to describe the walled structure built in place to isolate the area around a proposed foundation to permit dewatering operations and allow construction under comparatively dry conditions. The cofferdam is temporary and is usually removed after the need for it ends.

The caisson, while serving the same purpose of permitting construction in watered areas, is initially built off the site, floated to position, and sunk in place, and remains as an integral part of the foundation of the proposed structure.

g. This value varies among states. Almost all, however, consider 18 psi the critical pressure above which labor rates increase and hours of work decrease. New York state allows working pressures up to 50 lb maximum, while other states consider 48 lb as the maximum.

3.06 *a.* 1. Vertical sheeting is used where earth is wet and there is a tendency for it to flow and in very loose sand or gravel. It should also be used where the settlement of pipes or other adjacent underground structures would be undesirable.

2. Skeleton sheeting is used where the trench is in varied material and compact enough in some cases to require only partial sheeting. In the areas where tight sheeting is required additional planks may be used to close the gaps. Most common use is in hardpan, clay, or dry loam.
3. Stay bracing is used where it is only necessary to keep banks from caving in large masses. This is the simplest type of trench bracing. This type is intended as a temporary measure and should be used for only a day or two. Most often used in hardpan, dry clay, or dry loam.
4. Box sheeting is also called horizontal sheeting. The most frequent use is to increase the depth that can be reached with a single stage. If the piling is 6 ft long and the depth of trench is 9 ft, the top 3 ft could be box sheeting. It may be used where the material such as coarse gravel and dry sand is unstable, but the most common usage is where the banks can remain untimbered for quite a while with no great danger of caving.
5. Poling boards are most commonly used where there is little danger of the material running out from behind the short planks called "poling boards." Serious deformation and/or collapse of the timbering may result from this running out.
6. Plywood panels could be used where there is little danger of the material collapsing over short intervals of time until the large panels can be placed in position.

b. Sheeting should be left in place any time it is dangerous to personnel or to the construction equipment or to adjacent structures to dismantle the sheeting in its entirety. In particular in soft soil, loose sand, gravel, quicksand, or where a heavy rainstorm has created such soft-soil conditions it may be desirable to sacrifice parts of the sheeting to avoid bank movements. Equipment, such as cranes, may be unable to approach the trench after some of the bracing has been removed due to the danger of the sides caving.

c. The benefits usually attributed are that water gain is reduced, less cement is required for the same concrete strength, and greater effectiveness in combining with water is attained. There is some doubt as to the degree to which these benefits accrue.

3.07 *a*. To prevent the rapid drying of concrete the exposed surfaces should be covered. In some instances spraying with a resin-base solution or a covering of impregnated paper is used. For high early-strength concrete the curing period should be at least three days; and for ordinary concrete one week is required.

b. In freezing weather fresh concrete should be at a temperature of at least 50°F at the time of pouring. This can be accomplished by heating the aggregates to 70 to 80°F. The concrete should be protected by covers and in the case of a building heaters should be installed to maintain the temperature at a minimum of 50°F for a period of one week for concrete with Type I cement and three days for concrete with Type III cement. If 2 per cent calcium chloride is added to the mix the above curing periods may be reduced to three days for Type I cement and two days for Type III cement.

c.

Type of structure	*Length of time in days before forms and supports should be removed*
Arch centers	14–21
Centering under beams	14
Floor slabs	3–10
Walls	1–3
Columns	7–14
Sides of beams	3–10

d. Time limit between the addition of water at the mixer and the point of deposition may be 30 to 90 min depending on the degree of agitation of the mix during transit or during the waiting period.

e. Concrete may be admitted through temporary openings in the side of the forms, lowered into the form in bottom dump buckets, or allowed to slump down a pipe from the top, but concrete should never be dumped into the form from any height that will permit segregation of the mix. Filling should not be so rapid as to cause undue hydraulic pressure on the forms. Concrete should be sufficiently vibrated, as it is placed, to produce a dense concrete free of air pockets.

3.08 *a*. The cofferdam-frame dimensions must be a multiple of an even number of sheet piles and a whole number of sheet piles along any straight side. Sheet piles must be held in a plumb position while being interlocked and driven. The closure should be made before the driving of any sheet piles and no sheet pile should be driven more than one-third its length ahead of an adjacent sheet pile.

b. The shear adapters will increase the effective moment resistance of the structure by making it possible for the concrete slab and the steel stringer to act together.

c. Deck beam or girder bridges should have cross bridging at their third points or not farther apart than 25 ft, whichever is the shorter distance.

d. The preservative may soften the timber fibers slightly but causes no appreciable lessening of the structural strength.

e. Unless the timber is to be used only temporarily, the working stresses for untreated timber should be reduced by one-third if the structure is to be fully exposed to the weather and by one-eighth if the structure is roofed over but open to atmospheric moisture variations.

f. A voussoir is one of the wedge-shaped blocks of stone or concrete of which the arch is composed. The skewback is the inclined surface or joint upon which the voussoir at the end of the arch rests.

g. The stringers are beams placed lengthwise of a bridge which carry the loads from the floor to the floor beams. The floor beams run transverse to the length of the bridge and are connected to the trusses or girders at opposite panel points.

h. A bay is the space between two adjacent bents or piers. The term bent is used to describe trestle construction in which each bent consists of two or more vertical posts, two outside battered posts, a cap, sway bracing if posts are driven piles, and a sill if posts are framed timbers.

3.09 *a.* Pour cinders into the water along the outside face of sheet piling. The flow of water will carry the cinders into the interlocks in the sheet piling and greatly reduce these leaks. The sump pumps will take care of the remainder of the leakage.

b. Using a mix of 1 to 1 sand and cement, "grout" the river bottom for about 10 ft around the outside of the sheet piling. The mix is forced through a pipe by air pressure and the pipe is "air jetted" down through the ooze of the river bottom. Bags filled with sand and bags containing cinders should be stacked at convenient points around the cofferdam to be available if and when needed.

c. A pile should be completely driven before stopping for lunch, particularly when driving in a clay soil. If stoppage is permitted, redriving to completion may be very difficult because of the additional shearing resistance that the soil has acquired during the lunch interval (frictional take-up on the pile).

d. Fairly heavy boulders if the velocity of the stream is apt to be high.

e. Prefabricating timber that is to be pressure-creosoted allows every part of the completed member to be protected. The exposed timber in holes bored subsequent to creosoting could be treated by plugging one side of the hole and applying creosote from a pressure gun at the other side of the hole.

3.10 *a.* A relatively shallow trench dug in hardpan in dry weather would not require sheeting. In the case of a deep trench which might stand exposed for some time before backfilling, some bracing would be required because of the possibility of rain and water entering the trench with the subsequent loss of cohesion in the soil.

b. Paint the steel with a coat of oil. Lead paints under the heat of the torch produce a gaseous vapor that may be poisonous to the welder.

c. Oiling the forms is beneficial to concrete since it prevents drying out of the surface and renders the concrete more impervious.

d. Gunite is a rich cement mortar which is applied by spraying under high air pressure.

e. The major advantage of a-c over d-c welding is in the reduction of arc blow. Alternating current usually increases welding speeds and produces a higher quality weld. Where single-phase current is available the a-c current will be more economical.

3.11 Data to be secured in the field would include:

1. A study of the inadequacies of the present route including points of excessive grade or curvature with a view to relocating only portions of the existing route.
2. A traffic survey to determine volume and type of traffic to aid in selecting type of new facility.
3. A series of topographic strip maps covering the possible alternate routes.
4. A series of strip maps evaluating soil conditions on the alternate routes.
5. A study of natural drainage conditions.
6. A real-estate map to predict possible cost of right-of-way acquisition.
7. A study of the location of possible borrow pits or waste areas.
8. A study of the location of water supplies where concrete is to be used as a paving material.
9. An evaluation of the area as to possible future development of industrial or residential areas.
10. For some types of facilities it would also be necessary to study scenic attractions as the location of some routes would be affected by this.

3.12 *a.* A balanced design is one in which both the concrete and the steel are so proportioned as to work to their full working stresses when the member carries its full allowable load.

b. The transformed section is one in which the flexure steel is conceived to be replaced by a large area of imaginary concrete which can take tension. This gives a homogeneous section of concrete to which ordinary beam analyses may be applied.

c. 1. In a new design the neutral axis is located by the allowable working stresses in the steel and the concrete.

2. In an investigation of an existing beam the neutral axis is located at the centroid of the existing transformed area.

d. The fiber stress in a beam is assumed to be proportional to the distance of the fiber from the neutral axis.

e. Fireproofing in columns should consist of at least $1\frac{1}{2}$ in. of concrete or a thickness of concrete equal to $1\frac{1}{2}$ times the maximum size of the coarse aggregate. Where the concrete is to be exposed to weather or be in contact with the ground, the fireproofing shall be not less than $\frac{5}{8}$ in. in diameter and $1\frac{1}{2}$ in. for bars $\frac{5}{8}$ in. or less in diameter.

f. In a T beam the shear is assumed to be carried by an area whose width is equal to the width of the stem and whose depth is equal to the depth of the T beam.

g. The function of the stirrups is to prevent diagonal tension cracks.

h. Stirrups are not needed in slabs because the depth of the slab is so proportioned that the intensity of shearing stress is kept below the critical limit which indicates that diagonal tension would require stirrups.

i. Diagonal tension is computed by means of a formula for the shearing stress, but the failure to be guarded against is one of diagonal tension and not shear. Concrete is rarely used in a manner which would subject it to shearing failure and thus shear is only used as a measure of tensile stress.

j. Three inches of concrete should intervene between the reinforcement and the ground surface of the footing.

3.13 To stabilize a soil is to increase its supporting capacity and at the same time decrease its compressibility and possibly also its susceptibility to frost heave. Soil may be stabilized merely by adequate compaction or it may be stabilized by the addition of: (*a*) calcium chloride, (*b*) portland cement, (*c*) road oil, (*d*) clay, (*e*) sand, (*f*) gravel, or any combination of these ingredients. Probably the best way to introduce these admixtures into the soil is to scarify the soil with a disk harrow and then mix the material in, turning it over by using the harrow, or a blade grader or a multiple blade drag. Since the material is probably only stabilized to a depth of about 6 in., compaction where it is desired can be accomplished by the use of a three-wheel roller of light weight (less than 5 tons). A truck-mounted water sprinkler would be necessary for some types of stabilization (calcium chloride, portland cement, sandclay). For road oil a pressure distributor would also be required. Soil analyses necessary would include a grain-size analysis and a Proctor compaction test. The purpose of the compaction test would be to determine the best means of compacting the finished material. The grain-size analysis would aid in determining what size fractions to add to the natural subgrade (clay, sand, or gravel).

3.14 *a*. The way to prevent frost heave in a clay subgrade is to intercept the capillary rise. This can be done by installing at a depth of 3 ft (depth of frost penetration) an intercepting layer consisting of a water-tight membrane of asphalt and a sand cushion of 3 in. thickness or else a layer with low capillarity such as 18 in. of coarse-to-medium sand may be used. It is almost impossible to drain a subgrade containing large quantities of clay. The best thing to do is to seal the pavement and shoulders so that no moisture can enter the subgrade and drainage will not be necessary.

b. The strength of the concrete will be affected by the water-cement ratio, the length and type of curing, the quality of the aggregate, the thoroughness of mixing, any admixtures which may be used, and the type of cement used; the mix used may affect strength where the quantity of aggregate is excessive. To insure adequate strength a low water-cement ratio consistent with workability should be used. The curing should continue for at least 10 days. The aggregate should be clean and sound and should not include smooth or flat particles nor should the sand be excessively micaceous. The sand should not include large quantities of fine material. Mixing time should be around one minute. The water-cement ratio should be lowered to restore any strength lost by addition of admixtures. Try a mix 1:2:3½ by volume and 5.75 gal water per sack cement.

c. Reinforcing steel is used in concrete pavements to control cracking. The steel should be placed about 2 in. below the surface of the slab. The steel is placed near the surface in order to better control surface cracks and prevent the entrance of water and other foreign matter. Reinforcing steel is not designed inasmuch as it serves not as full reinforcing, but rather as a crack-controlling medium. The size and spacing of the bar is chosen arbitrarily and varies widely from state to state.

d. Vibration makes the mixture more plastic and thus allows the use of a lower water-cement ratio thus increasing the strength of the concrete. In some cases of low slump concrete vibrating develops honeycombing. Also the concrete may become hard making it difficult to handtool around the edges and near the joints. High-spots may also prove difficult to reduce. The essential reason for vibrating concrete is to assure proper placement of concrete even where a stiff mix is used.

e. Concrete may be cured by:

1. Spraying a plastic coating on the surface of the concrete thus preventing loss of water through the surface.
2. Using calcium chloride in the concrete mixture thus retaining moisture in the concrete by the hygroscopic action of the material.
3. Periodically spraying the pavement with water providing excess moisture on the surface to replace any which may have been lost.
4. Ponding water and allowing it to stand to a depth of 2 in. or so on the surface.

Ponding probably provides the best method, where the water is prevented from leaking off the slab into the subgrade. The seal provided against moisture loss is probably the most secure and the presence of excess moisture is beneficial to the concrete.

3.15 *a.* The original cracking of the concrete pavement is probably traceable to inadequate subgrade support. In order to reinforce the subgrade without removing the old pavement

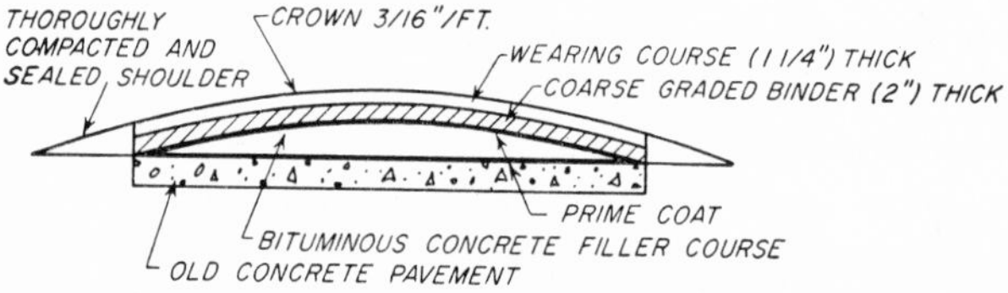

FIG. 3.15

it is necessary to drill a series of holes in the pavement and pump in a high-penetration slow-curing road oil under pressure. Thus we can realign the old slabs and seal and stabilize the subgrade. The shoulders should also be sealed against lateral encroachment of water into the subgrade.

b. The base should be thoroughly brushed clean and all joints and cracks should be sealed with a high-penetration rapid-curing asphalt. Then the old surface should receive a prime coat of low-penetration medium-curing road oil. A leveling course of coarse bituminous concrete may be used if the base requires to be brought to a true cross section.

c. The wearing course would consist of a coarse aggregate bituminous concrete binder, depth 1½ to 2½ in. and a wearing course 1 to 1¾ in. in depth. The binder course should have the aggregate distributed as follows: between 1½-and ¾-in. screens, 20 to 30 per cent; ¾ to ¼ in., 25 to 40 per cent; ¼-in. to No. 10 sieve, 5 to 15 per cent; passing No. 10 sieve, 20 to 35 per cent; bitumen 4 to 7 per cent. All percentages are by weight. The asphalt should have a penetration of 60–70. For the surface course the proportions are: aggregates, between 1¼ and ¾ in., 15 to 25 per cent; ¾ to ¼ in., 20 to 35 per cent; ¼ in. to No. 10 sieve, 5 to 15 per cent; No. 10 to No. 200 sieve, 25 to 35 per cent; passing No. 200 sieve, 4 to 6 per cent; bitumen 5 to 8 per cent. The asphalt used is the same as for the binder course. The materials are mixed in a standard highway mixing plant using the hot-mix method at a temperature of 300°F. Application temperature should not fall below 225°F. The mixtures may be spread by hand using rakes and hoes although most jobs of any size use mechanical spreaders with a helical worm spreader and a strike-off screed. The mixture is then rolled longitudinally from the edges to the center with a small overlap on each subsequent trip. The roller used is a 10- to 12-ton three-wheel roller. A subsequent rolling in a diagonal direction by a tandem roller of 5 tons weight may be used for the wearing course.

3.16 *a.* Fills may be compacted by: (1) jetting, which involves forcing water into the fill under pressure using nozzles on high-pressure hoses and relying on the downward pressure of the water to align the grains in a dense condition; (2) tamping, which may be accomplished using hand tampers or pneumatically or gasoline-driven vibratory tampers and compacting in layers; and (3) rolling in layers using a sheep's-foot roller and a number of passes for each layer. Jetting has the advantage that it can be used for relatively thick layers and can be accomplished rather quickly. It has the disadvantage of introducing large quantities of water into the embankment which greatly decreases the embankment's strength and stability. Hand tamping when properly executed is very effective, but it has the disadvantage of being expensive and lengthy. Rolling using a sheepsfoot roller is probably the most effective method for getting adequate compaction on jobs of fairly large extent. It has the disadvantage that its effectiveness is not quite as great with noncohesive soils as with cohesive ones.

b. Shrinkage refers to the fact that a cubic foot of soil in its natural state will not yield a cubic foot as artificially compacted in the embankment due to greater relative density in the embankment and incidental losses as the material is transported from one place to the next. The amount of shrinkage is determined by the comparative relative densities from the natural state to the embankment and the amount of material lost in transit. A shrinkage factor must be used in balancing cuts and fills or it will be found that there is not sufficient material to complete the embankment. In order to compensate for the shrinkage all fill quantities are multiplied by an amount equal to $1/(1 - S)$ where S = shrinkage factor expressed as a ratio.

c. The temporary pavement should be a bituminous macadam. Lay a foundation of 6 to 8 in. of crushed stone ranging 4 to 1 in. in size. Roll using a 10-ton three-wheel roller moving longitudinally with subsequent passes from the edges of the pavement toward the center. Then sweep in choke stone and continue to roll wetting down the surface as you go. The wearing course should consist of broken stone with a range of sizes from 2½ to 1 in. The depth of the wearing course is about 4 in. This course is rolled just as the base course was rolled. High-penetration asphalt is then applied at the rate of 2 gal per sq yd. Choke stone is then spread immediately on the surface and broomed and rolled in. Then a seal coat of asphalt is applied at the rate of ¾ to 1 gal per sq yd. Then sand or cover stone is applied and rolled into the surface. All excess is swept off and the surface is ready for use. The strength and durability of this pavement depends partly on the subgrade and partly on the waterbound macadam base course used. This type of pavement was recommended because it is relatively inexpensive, does not require a curing period before it can be used, and is flexible so that it can withstand a certain amount of settlement in the newly compacted approach embankment.

3.17 *a.* See the answer to 3.16*c*.

b. See the answer to 3.16*c*.

c. This type of surface will require a surface treatment to be applied periodically. The surface treatment consists of a prime coat of emulsified or cut-back asphalt, a binder coat, cover stone, a seal coat, and screenings. From time to time patches may be required where weaknesses have developed. Where such patches are necessary the subgrade should be stabilized and compacted and then a base course and wearing course similar to the original should be placed. A stock of material from the original stockpiles should be kept for this purpose to ensure that the patch will become integral with the surrounding pavement and have the same composition.

3.18

List 1	List 2
1	*b*
2	*e*
3	*a*
4	*c*
5	*d*
6	*f*

3.19 *a.* Centrifugal force is a lateral force exerted 6 ft above the top of the rail by a train rounding a curve. Allowance must be made for this force in the sway bracing of the bridge.

b. Dead load is the always-present dead weight of the structure. This weight does not change although it may move where the bridge has a moveable span.

c. Cooper's standard loading is a scheme of axle loads representing a double locomotive and a train. This loading is widely used in designing railroad bridges. The load can be varied giving weights of driver-wheel axles from 10 to 90 kips by even 10-kip increments or by variable amounts.

d. Live load is that load which may be moved on or off the bridge and does not represent an integral part of the structure. This load is always placed to give maximum effect. Cooper's loading in part *c* is an example of a live load. Snow, ice, or wind would also represent a live load.

e. Impact represents a percentage increase which is applied to all moving live loads to take into account any shock or vibratory stresses which may be set up due to the nature of the moving load or any irregularities which may exist in the road bed. This includes rolling effect, hammer blow, car impact, etc.

3.20 *a.* A sole plate is a steel plate attached to the lower flange of the girder below the end stiffeners which distributes the girder reaction to the masonry bearing plate. It shall have a thickness of not less than ¾ in. and not less than the thickness of the flange angles plus ⅛ in. Preferably it shall not be longer than 18 in.

b. 1. Stiffeners shall be placed at all points of end bearing and bearing of concentrated loads. According to the American Railway Engineering Association "if the depth of the web between the flanges or side plates of a plate girder exceeds 60 times its thickness, it shall be stiffened by pairs of angles riveted to the web."

2. The clear distance between stiffeners shall not exceed 72 in.

3. The clear distance between stiffeners shall not exceed

$$\frac{10{,}500t}{\sqrt{S}}$$

where t = thickness of web in inches

S = unit shearing stress, gross section, in web at point considered

Other specifications have similar requirements.

c. Stiffener angles at points of concentrated load shall have milled ends.

d. One-eighth of the web may be included in the net area of the flange and one-sixth of the web may be used for the gross area.

e. Anchor bolts shall be not less than 1¼ in. in diameter. Anchor bolts not carrying uplift shall extend 12 in. into the masonry. Those carrying uplift shall be designed to engage a mass of masonry the weight of which is 1½ times the uplift

f. Combined stresses include dead-load stresses, live-load stresses, impact stresses, wind stresses, snow stresses, ice stresses, etc., in such a combination as to give both maximum negative and maximum positive effect.

g. Alternate stresses are those used to design a member which goes through a reversal of stress. The alternates would be the maximum positive and the maximum negative stresses.

h. A gusset plate is a plate used to connect the various members of a truss which comes together at a joint. It is made large enough to include the necessary number of connection rivets.

i. A filler plate is used at truss joints to compensate for any difference in the depth or thickness of the members being joined so that connection may be made to a flat gusset plate.

j. Where the open sides of truss members are joined by latticing, stay plates are used as near the end of the member as possible and at intermediate points where the lacing is interrupted. The purpose of the stay plates is to lend a little additional rigidity to the member.

3.21 It may be inferred from (3) that a distribution reservoir is to be provided, rather than pumping directly from a small, clear well to the mains. Therefore filter capacity can be designed for normal rather than maximum flow.

1. Daily consumption = 14,000 × 100 = 1.4 mgd

Water filtered, including wash water = 1.4/0.96 = 1.46 mgd

Required filter area = (1.46/125) × 43,560 = 509 sq ft

For a plant as small as this, the filters can be operated on 1 eight-hour shift

Area = 3 × 509 × (8/7.5) = 1,628 sq ft

Provide 3 units 20 × 275 ft in plan = 1,650 sq ft

If one unit is out of service for extensive repairs the plant can be operated on a double shift to provide the required flow. An alternative would be to install 4 units.

2. Alum = 4.5 grains per gal

1 grain per gal = 142.5 lb per million gal

4.5 × 142.5 × 1.46 = 936 lb of alum per day

3. National Board of Fire Underwriters

$$Q = 1{,}020\sqrt{P}\,(1 - 0.01\sqrt{P})$$

when P = population in thousands

$$\begin{aligned} Q &= 1{,}020\sqrt{14}\,(1 - 0.01\sqrt{14}) \\ &= 1{,}020 \times 3.74(1 - 0.037) \\ &= 1{,}020 \times 3.74 \times 0.963 = 3674 \text{ gal per min} \end{aligned}$$

National Board of Fire Underwriters recommends providing for a 10-hr fire in towns exceeding 2,500 in population. Therefore required storage $= 3{,}674 \times 60 \times 10 = 2{,}204{,}000$

Peak of daily flow may occur during fire. Therefore domestic storage $= 2.25 \times 1.46$ mgd $= 3.29$ million gal. Total storage, fire plus domestic use $= 2.20 + 3.29 = 5.49$ million gal.

3.22 *a.* Detention period 30 to 60 sec. Sixty seconds recommended by most states.

b. Maximum rate of flow 0.5 to 1 ft per sec. The higher figure is generally used.

c, d, e. $wd = Q/V, \quad wL = A$

For medium-size grit particles the recommended rate of flow is 50,000 gal per day per sq ft of surface area. For 1 mgd the required surface area would be 20 sq ft. Assume $w = 1$ ft (d). Then $L = 20$ ft (c) and $d = \dfrac{Q}{wV} = \dfrac{1.547}{1 \times 1} = 1.547$ ft since 1 mgd $=$ 1.547 cfs. To provide grit storage capacity (g) make depth $=$ 2 ft (e).

f. Use three units in parallel to take care of variations in flow.

g. Grit will vary in amount from 0.5 to 10 cu ft per million gal. Increasing depth to 2 ft will provide storage for $1 \times 20 \times 0.453 = 9+$ cu ft

h, i. Clean daily, manually, for so small a plant.

3.23 *a.* For raw sewage containing 250 ppm suspended solids 1.5 hr sedimentation should effect a reduction of ± 45 per cent or ± 138 ppm in the effluent (a).

b. $V = 1.5 \times 500{,}000/24 =$ **31,250** gal

c. $V = 31{,}250/7.48 = 4{,}180$ cu ft

Assume $\pm 1{,}000$ gal per sq ft per day loading. Then $wl = 500{,}000/1{,}000 = 500$ sq ft. Take $l = 4w$, then $4w^2 = 500$, $w^2 = 125$, $w = 11.2$ using width $= 12$ ft; length $= 48$ ft; surface area $=$ 576 sq ft; depth $= V/A = 4{,}180/576 = 7+$.

Use 8 ft.

$$w = \mathbf{12}\text{ ft},\ L = \mathbf{48}\text{ ft},\ D = \mathbf{8}\text{ ft}$$

d. On basis of 45 per cent removal we have 112 ppm settled out. This equals $\dfrac{112 \times 8.33}{2} = 468$ lb per day.

468 lb solids + 8,900 lb water = 9,368 lb
9,368 lb at 63 lb per cu ft = 148+ cu ft, say 150 cu ft

3.24 *a.* 500 ft maximum spacing between manholes. 300 ft preferable. On small sewers spacing is controlled by maximum convenient length of cleaning rods. On lines large enough for a man to enter, a greater spacing might be used, but is undesirable because of difficulty of removing a possible victim of noxious gases.

b. Twenty-five years minimum for sewers, ten years for treatment works. Sewers are buried in trenches. Additional units are readily constructed at a treatment plant and improvements in treatment methods may increase the efficiency of new units. Treatment-plant area should be adequate for long-term expansion.

c. 50 to 300 gal per capita per day average depending on character of district sewered. 130 gal is a reasonable value in most localities. Peak flow may be double average flow. Factor of safety should be applied to take care of errors in population estimates, etc. 130 × 4 = 520 gal per capita per day, sewer flowing full.

d. Sanitary sewers—2 ft per sec, sewer flowing full. Storm drains—3 ft per sec, sewer flowing full.

e. Sanitary sewers—8 in. minimum to minimize clogging. Storm drains are seldom less than 12 in.

f. Rational method is best for small areas. $Q = ciA$ where Q is flow in ft per sec, A is drainage area in acres, c is relative imperviousness of the contributory surface, and i is the rate of precipitation in inches per hour. A time-intensity curve of appropriate frequency is selected and the rainfall rate for the concentration time is used. This concentration time consists of time of flow to an inlet plus time of flow in the sewer.

g. Catch basins should be used on unpaved streets and on paved streets when the slopes are so steep that the velocity of surface wash exceeds the velocity of flow in the sewer at points further down the valley.

h. Crowns should be continuous. If invert of 24 in. is at elevation 100.00, invert of 15 in. would be at elevation 100.75 and invert of 8 in. would be at elevation 101.33.

3.25 The rational method of storm-drain design employs the equation $Q = ciA$ in which Q is the runoff in ft per sec to be carried by the drain from an area of A acres; c is the runoff coefficient or expected ratio of runoff to rain fall; i is the intensity of precipitation in second-feet per acre. Since 1 in. of rain per hour falling on an area of an acre is substantially equal to 1 cu ft per sec, the intensity of precipitation may be expressed more conveniently in inches per hour.

The acreage is measured directly from a map of the area. The value of c is estimated from a consideration of the relative imperviousness and the slope of the surface.

The value of i must be taken from a time-intensity curve of precipitation for a storm of a certain frequency of occurrence or from a rainfall formula derived for such a storm. The frequency of storm for which the curve in formula is to be used will depend upon the value of the property to be served by the drain and the magnitude of probable flood damage resulting from inadequate capacity of the drain. The greater the probable flood damage, the more it is necessary to design for infrequent storms of great magnitude.

Theoretically, the drain should be designed for such a storm that the increased flood damage resulting from a storm of greater magnitude would be slightly less than the increased construction cost to carry the flow from the latter storm. Practically, much judgement is required in selecting the storm-frequency curve to be used; for, while construction costs of various-sized drains can be estimated closely, it is difficult to estimate flood damages resulting from inadequate capacity of drain.

When an appropriate rainfall curve or formula has been selected, it is necessary to determine the concentration time since the rate of precipitation decreases with an increase in the concentration time t. This concentration time is made up of the inlet time, that is the time required for water to flow over the surface from the upper limit of a drainage area to the inlet, and the time of flow in the drain to the point under consideration.

For example, if the area contributing to the upper inlet of a drain is 2 acres, the runoff coefficient is 0.8, the inlet time is 5 min, and the rate of rainfall corresponding to this inlet time is 6 in. per hr, the drain would be designed for a Q equal to $0.8 \times 6 \times 2 = 9.6$ ft per sec. By drawing the profile of the street from the first to the second inlet we can determine the necessary slope for the drain. Then, with Q and S known, we can use pipe-flow diagrams or nomographs to determine the diameter of pipe necessary and the velocity of flow in the drain.

Suppose that this velocity works out to be 3 ft per sec and that the distance from the first to the second inlet is 360 ft. Then the time of flow in the drain is 2 min. At the second inlet then, the quantity of flow would be the product of the total contributary area, the runoff coefficient and the intensity of precipitation corresponding to a concentration time of $5 + 2 = 7$ min. This general procedure is continued as the drain is designed from inlet to inlet to the point of outfall.

3.26 Obtain or prepare a topographic map of the subdivision showing street and lot lines. A scale of 1 in. = 100 ft is generally suitable. Contour interval will vary from 1 to 10 ft depending upon steepness of slopes.

Show on this map the existing sewer into which the new sewers are to discharge and locate the new sewers to flow by gravity wherever possible.

Obtain or run profile levels for all streets to be sewered.

Locate all known underground utilities or structures on both plan and profiles. Obtain data on soil characteristics and, particularly, depths to ground water or rock.

Obtain data on probable population to be served 25 years hence, expected sewage flow per capita, probable ground-water infiltration, and expected flow from any commercial or industrial districts within the area.

Obtain data on depths of cellars, particularly on the downhill side of sidehill streets so the sewers may be placed deep enough to drain such cellars, using normal slopes for house connections.

Starting at upper end of a lateral carry design to a junction, then start at upper end of another lateral entering this junction. Proceed in this manner until entire system has been designed. Profiles of 1 in. = 100 ft horizontal and 1 in. = 10 ft vertical, should be prepared as work is carried out on plan since breaks in grade on profile will control location of intermediate manholes.

Manholes should be located at all intersections, at every change in grade or alignment, and at intervals not exceeding 500 ft, preferably less. Manholes should be numbered in a logical sequence.

Computations for each line should be arranged in tabular form and should show streets, manhole numbers, population, domestic sewage and infiltration, distances between manholes, slopes, size and kind of pipes required, surface elevations at manholes to 0.1 ft, invert elevations of sewers at manholes to 0.01 ft, velocity of flow when full, and capacity when full.

Much of this information is shown on both plan and profiles, together with arrows to indicate direction of flow.

3.27 *a*. An Imhoff tank is a two-story sedimentation and sludge-digestion tank used for sewage treatment. It is normally rectangular in plan with horizontal flow of sewage taking place longitudinally in the upper chamber. Settled solids pass through a slot to the digestion chamber below. The slot is trapped so that gases evolved in digestion cannot carry solids upward into the sedimentation chamber. Gases are diverted to one or more gas vents alongside the upper chamber. Provision is made for drawing off digested sludge from the bottom of the lower chamber under hydrostatic pressure.

b. The rapid sand filter is the most common type of filter used in water treatment. It consists of a concrete filter box containing an underdrainage system. Above this there is usually 12 to 18 in. of graded gravel to keep the filter medium from entering the underdrains. Supported on the gravel are 24 to 36 in. of filter sand or anthrafilt. Raw water, after coagulation and sedimentation, enters the filter and passes downward through the filter medium to the underdrains, thence through a rate controller set to filter at a constant rate of usually 125 million gal per acre per day, thence to a clear well. The water above the sand is maintained at a constant depth. Some of the coagulant and finer suspended matter forms a zoogloeal film, or *schmutzdecke*, on top of the sand and the main filtering action occurs here.

When the loss in head through the filter becomes excessive, the influent and effluent lines are closed, and filtered water stored in a wash water tank flows into the underdrains under pressure, passing upward to expand and clean the sand, and eventually flowing to the sewer through wash water troughs located above the top of the sand.

c. An Imhoff cone is a cone-shaped glass of 1 liter capacity used to determine the proportion of sewage solids which will settle out in various periods of time. The approximate volume of settleable solids can be observed directly.

d. A sludge bed is an underdrained bed of sand some 12 in. deep overlying 6 to 8 in. of gravel. Sewage sludge is run on to the bed and left to dry. The beds may be open or may be protected from precipitation by a greenhouse-type structure.

3.28 Secondary treatment of sewage effluents embrace various methods for filtering the sewage, oxidizing the organic material through the action of aerobic bacteria, and usually disinfecting the effluent before final discharge into the receiving waters.

These processes include the intermittent sand filter, contact beds, standard-rate and high-rate trickling filters, and the activated sludge process. The latter process has a number of modifications. Final disinfection usually consists of chlorination.

An intermittant sand filter consists of a prepared bed of sand, usually 3 ft deep, provided with underdrains. Sewage which has received at least primary treatment is applied to the bed intermittently and allowed to percolate slowly downward. The top few inches of sand will eventually become clogged and will have to be removed for washing or replacement.

The method yields a very high quality effluent but dosage rates are low so that a large acreage is required. Initial costs are likely to be high unless land values are low and sand of the proper quality is available locally. Some difficulties are experienced in winter operation.

A contact bed consists of a concrete tank filled with large crushed rock or other appropriate filter media and provided with distribution pipes and underdrains. Sewage is allowed to fill the bed and is given a period of contact. The bed is then slowly drained and is allowed a period of rest during which air can enter the voids to provide oxygen for the bacteria in the zoogloeal film which collects on the stones. The efficiency is not high. Since the trickling filter and activated sludge processes are more satisfactory, contact beds are little used today.

A trickling filter is similar in construction to a contact bed but the sewage is sprayed over the bed or distributed by a rotary distributor and allowed to trickle downward through the bed in contact with the air.

Dosage rates are high, particularly with the high-rate filters so the acreage needed is much less than required by intermittent sand filters or contact beds. Efficiency is high but the quality of the effluent is not as good as that from a sand filter. A final sedimentation tank is necessary since the accumulated solids are unloaded periodically. The trickling filter requires a high operating head. Because of the spraying action, there may be an odor nuisance when the sewage is stale. The breeding of the Psychoda fly in the filters also presents a problem.

Activated sludge consists of sludge settled out of sewage which has been previously agitated in the presence of abundant free oxygen. When a quantity of such sludge is added to the effluent from primary sedimentation tanks and the mixed liquor is then passed through an aeration tank where it is agitated by compressed air, paddles or other mechanical aerating devices, we have the activated sludge process.

The sludge contains an abundance of aerobic bacteria. When it is circulated through the mixed liquor by the air action, it picks up many of the smaller suspended solids and comes in contact with the colloidal and dissolved solids. Thus there is an opportunity for all solids to become oxidized.

Final sedimentation tanks are necessary. Return sludge amounting to about 25 per cent by volume of the effluent is pumped back to the influent. Excess sludge goes to a digestor.

The process uses small acreage at little head. Quality of effluent can be varied to meet various needs by using short or long periods of aeration. Operating costs are rather high because of air consumption and sludge pumping. The sludge produced is large in volume and is somewhat difficult to treat.

3.29 See answer 3.28 for a general description of the activated-sludge process. Authorities are not in complete agreement as to all biologic phenomena which occur. It is chiefly a biochemical process with adsorbed organic matter being oxidized by various bacteria present in the zoogloeal sludge. Nitrogenous matter is oxidized by other bacteria. Clarification may be produced partly by bioprecipitation and partly as a result of a base exchange.

3.30 *a.* The separate sludge-digestion process comprises the collection of sewage solids in primary sedimentation tanks (and also in the final tanks of certain secondary treatment processes) and the passing of these solids, by pumping or by gravity flow, to one or more tanks where digestion of the sludge occurs. Digestors are generally provided with floating covers, devices for the collection and utilization of sludge gases, and arrangements for heating and controlling the reaction of the sludge to reduce the time required for digestion. Many plants use two-stage digestion, the primary stage of about a week taking place in one digestor and the sludge then being transferred to a second digestor for about three weeks.

b. Sludge may be dewatered on open or covered drying beds or on vacuum filters. Sand beds require considerable acreage and may be high in first cost, particularly when covered. Drying is slow but does not require skilled attendance.

Vacuum filters require little space and dry the sludge quickly. They are not low in either first cost or maintenance. Skilled attendance is necessary since conditioning of the sludge may be required to obtain a satisfactory filter cake.

3.31 *a*, 2; *b*, 2; *c*, 4; *d*, 4; *e*, 4; *f*, 2; *g*, 2; *h*, 1; *i*, 4; *j*, 2.

3.32 Recommended capacity of septic tank for 10 persons = 900 gal. Recommended dimensions 3.5 ft wide, 8.5 ft long, 4.5 ft liquid depth, 5.5 ft total depth. If a domestic garbage grinder is to be installed, the capacity should be increased by 50 per cent. Capacity shown above provides for 2 years' accumulation of sludge plus 50 gal per capita sewage flow per day.

For fairly porous soil allow 450 sq ft of absorption area in bottom of disposal trenches. For 18-in. width of trench, length will equal $450/1.5 = 300$ ft.

Sewage from house will flow into septic tank shown in Fig. 3.32*a*. Clarified effluent will flow out to distribution box and thence to 300 ft of 4-in. open-joint tile drain, Fig. 3.32*b*. Top of tile should be about 15 in. beneath ground surface. Tile should be surrounded with gravel, coarse sand, or cinders for a distance of at least 6 in. on sides and bottom and at least 2 in. above top of pipe. Open joints should be covered by tar paper. A more effective septic tank than that shown in Fig. 3.32*b* would involve a small secondary chamber following the main septic tank. This would be provided with an automatic siphon to permit dosing the entire tile field periodically instead of permitting the effluent

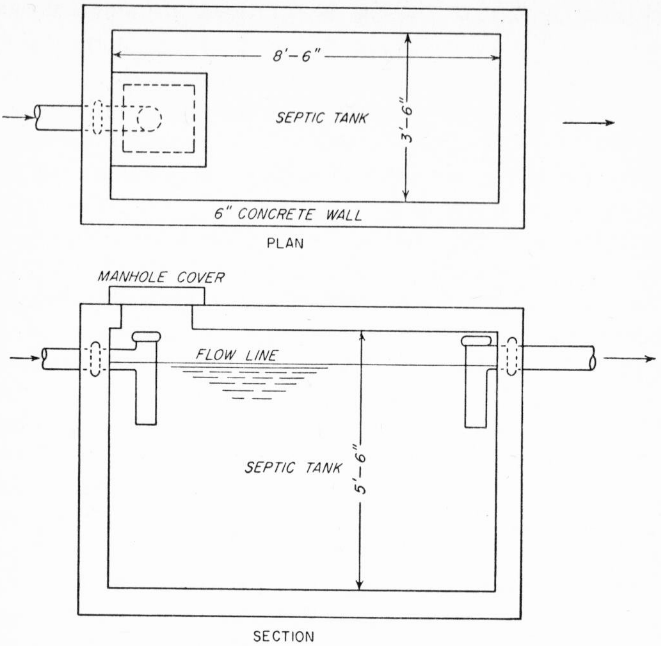

FIG. 3.32*a*

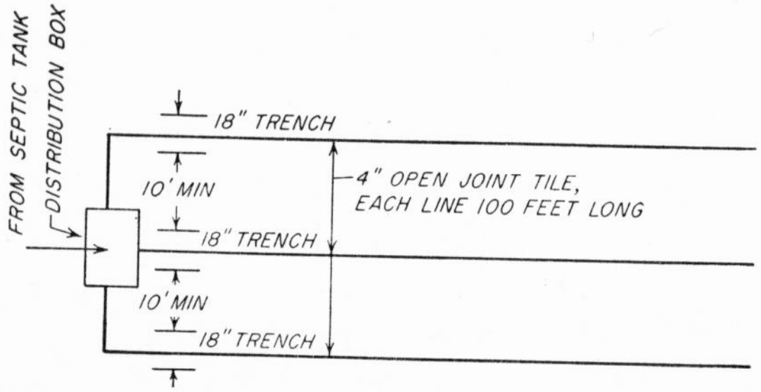

FIG. 3.32*b*

to trickle slowly through the first few joints as is likely to occur when no siphon is provided.

3.33 Malaria is transmitted by various mosquitoes of the *Anopheles* group. *Anopheles quadrimaculatus* is the most important vector of the disease in the eastern United States.

The mosquito must bite persons whose blood contains the malaria parasites. Certain stages in the life cycle of the parasite must then take place in the mosquito before the insect can transmit the disease by biting others. Obviously, if there are no cases in the area, there can be no transmission of the disease even though the density of *quadrimaculatus* infestation may be heavy.

Where there are cases in the area there are a number of control measures possible: (1) Infected persons should receive proper medical treatment to reduce or eliminate the parasites from their blood. (2) Infected persons should be protected from the bites of the insects. This is not difficult with proper screening since *quadrimaculatus* is predominantly a dusk and night biter. (3) The raising of cattle in rural areas reduces the incidence of the disease since the insect prefers cattle to man for a blood meal. (4) Standard mosquito-control measures aimed principally at the insect in the larval stage are effective in reducing mosquito density. (5) Blood tests of all persons in a heavily infected area should be carried out so that all infected persons can receive proper medical treatment. (6) DDT can be used as a residual spray in inhabited buildings so that adult mosquitoes are killed before they can transmit the disease. (7) Educational campaigns are effective in informing the public concerning the steps necessary to eliminate the disease or to reduce its incidence.

3.34 *a.* 1. Case rate = 2,891/2,000 = 1.446 per thousand
2. Death rate = 1,304/2,000 = 0.652 per thousand
3. Fatality rate = 1,304/2,891 × 100 = 45 per cent

b. Morbidity is the number of cases of a disease occurring during a year in terms of the population in hundred-thousands. While generally computed for the entire population, it may also be determined for certain age groups or classes.

3.35 *a.* While many diseases are transmitted by milk, tuberculosis and undulant fever are those most readily prevented by protecting the dairy herd. The tuberculin test is applied periodically, usually annually or semiannually, to detect tubercular cows in the herd. Such animals are destroyed. Undulant fever can be controlled by removal of infected animals from the herd and by pasteurization of the milk.

b. Measures to protect the milk line are designed to assure healthy cows, clean and healthy workmen, clean and dustless barns, prompt cooling of the milk in a separate milk house, proper utensils and the effective cleaning and sterilization thereof, and pasteurization of the milk.

c. The above steps will minimize or eliminate the transmission of typhoid, scarlet fever, diphtheria, undulant fever, and other diseases by milk.

d. Milk is an ideal medium for the development of many bacteria and bacterial growth is rapid in dirty milk. Pasteurization is not a sterilization process and hence a high-count raw milk still has considerable numbers of bacteria in it after pasteurization. The most effective measures to eliminate this danger are the provision of sanitary conditions in the dairy and the proper pasteurization and bottling of the milk.

e. Milk may be pasteurized at 143°F for 30 min or flash pasteurized at 160°F for 15 sec. Control of early flash pasteurizers was uncertain and the method was consequently but little used until recently. Modern flash pasteurizers provide excellent control and are as safe as the holder types. They require much less space and are consequently increasing in use.

3.36 *a.* Bubonic plague is transmitted to men by the bite of fleas from an infected rat.

b. Murine typhus fever (endemic) is transmitted by the bite of fleas or mites from an infected rat.

c. Malaria is carried by various mosquitoes of the *Anopheles* genus.

d. The common vector of dengue is the *Aedes aegypti* mosquito.

e. Smallpox is commonly communicated by discharges from the nose and throat of persons suffering from the disease. It may also be transmitted through the agency of material from pustules or skin lesions.

f. Undulant fever may be transmitted by unpasteurized milk, by contact with infected slaughtered animals, by contact with the dust of pens containing infected animals, and by contact with these animals when they abort since the disease causes infectious abortion in cows, sows, and goats.

g. Tularemia is usually communicated to man in skinning or plucking rabbits, quail, and other game. It may also be transmitted by certain biting flies.

h. The common vector of yellow fever is the *Aedes aegypti* mosquito. In jungle areas other mosquitoes are involved including *Sabethini* and *Haemagogus*.

i. Rocky Mountain spotted fever is transmitted from various small wild animals to man by ticks.

3.37 The steps to be taken and data to be collected in determining the source of the typhoid outbreak would include:

1. Prompt reporting to the local health department of all cases by the attending physicians.
2. The filling in of questionnaires relative to the sources of milk, water, shellfish, and other foods consumed by those persons affected by the disease.
3. The preparation of spot maps showing the areas within the community where there are cases of the disease.
4. The prompt bacteriological analysis of supplies of water, milk, shellfish, and other foods.
5. The check of restaurants and other establishments where food had been served or sold to victims of the disease for possible typhoid carriers.
6. A check of private well supplies and of cross connections between potable and industrial water supplies.

3.38 Two methods suitable for the disposal of garbage are sanitary fill and incineration.

Sanitary fill differs from open dumping in that the garbage is covered with about 2 ft of earth at the end of each working day. It is suitable where there are low areas, abandoned borrow pits, and other suitable land within or near the municipality and where suitable earth, preferably sandy soil, is available for covering. The method is generally cheaper than incineration and permits the eventual utilization of tracts of land for parks, housing developments, and other uses.

Incinerators will provide for the complete stabilization of organic materials and a great reduction in volume of the wastes collected. First costs and operating costs are high. They are particularly useful where extensive tracts of land for sanitary fill are not locally available.

3.39 There are several methods for determining the safe yield of a watershed from the storage which can be developed economically at a given reservoir site or, conversely, the storage which will be necessary to furnish a desired yield. One of the most satisfactory procedures is to use a mass curve of modified runoff.

Actual records of runoff, usually monthly, are obtained for a stream-gaging station on the stream relatively close to the site of the proposed dam. The longer the period of years for which records are available the greater the likelihood of the record including a period of extreme drought which will control the yield or the required storage.

If the records are given in cubic feet per second at the gage, they are converted to inches of depth on the watershed area above the gage and these figures are then used for the slightly different watershed area above the site of the proposed dam.

When the proposed reservoir will have a large surface area the actual runoff records can be modified downward to account for the expected increased evaporation losses from the reservoir. The amount of water to be released downstream for the use of riparian owners below the reservoir site is also deducted from the monthly values of actual runoff. The remainder will be water available for storage, for power or water supply use, and for waste over the spillway at times when the reservoir is full.

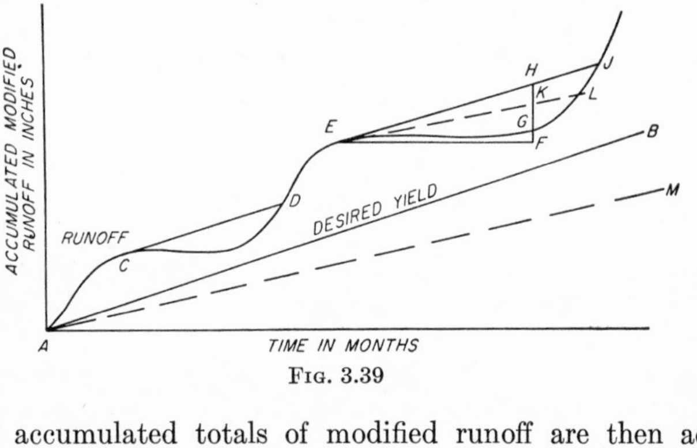

Fig. 3.39

The accumulated totals of modified runoff are then added month by month and plotted as a mass curve (Fig. 3.39). If, let us say, a yield of 100 mgd is desired, this value is expressed in inches depth per month on the watershed area and plotted as the sloping line *AB*. Lines *CD* and *EJ* are drawn parallel to *AB* from points *C* and *E* where the runoff starts to decline. It is obvious that the worst period of drought has occurred between *E* and *F*. During this period the total inflow is represented by the ordinate *FG*. The total required yield is represented by *FH*. Therefore water in the amount *GH* must be released from storage to supply the demand. This storage, shown here as inches depth on the watershed, can be converted into acre feet, billions of gallons, or other convenient units.

It may be uneconomical to develop this volume of storage at the site. If the storage which can be developed is *GK* we draw the dotted line *EKL*. The safe yield is then reduced to that represented by *AM*, drawn parallel to *EJ*.

3.40 *a*. The reduction of losses through leakage and waste in a water-distribution system is becoming ever more important as the cost of supplying water to a community increases year after year. Water pressures will also improve as waste is minimized. In some cities the actual flow of water in the system may be from 1½ to 2 times the necessary consumption.

b. The complete metering of a city is most effective in reducing wastes. Leakage from broken mains may be detected by visual inspection. The Cole pitometer is widely used to detect leaks in mains. Audio devices to amplify the sound of escaping water are also used. Periodic waste-water surveys and careful maintainance of the distribution system may reduce the unaccounted-for water to perhaps 2 per cent of the delivered water.

c. When water shortages exist, educational campaigns have been quite effective in reducing actual consumption and minimizing the actual waste of water.

3.41 A rapid sand water filtration plant normally includes the following units or items: (1) screens for the removal of leaves and other large objects; (2) a chemical storage house for the storage of chlorine, ammonia, lime, alum, activated carbon, and soda ash; (3) a mixing device such as a flash, mixer, baffled mixing chamber, hydraulic jump, a low-lift pump suction to provide intimate mixing of activated carbon, lime, and alum, or other coagulant with the raw water; (5) one or more flocculators in which gentle stirring action permits satisfactory floc formation; (6) one or more sedimentation basins in which the coagulant can settle out, removing turbidity, color, and many bacteria;

(7) one or more filter units as described in 3.27*b*; (8) a clear well for the storage of filtered water; (9) provisions for final chlorination and pH adjustment in the clear well; (10) wash-water pumps and a wash-water tank to permit back washing the filters; (11) air compressors for air washing of filters in some cases; (12) a sewer connection for the dirty wash water; (13) suitable meters and gages to show the quantity of water being processed at any time; and (14) a well-equipped laboratory, adequately staffed, for analyses of the raw, finished, and delivered water. Low-lift and high-lift pumps and power-generation equipment will be required in some cases.

3.42 *a*. The zeolite softening process is essentially one of base-exchange. The zeolite, through which the water passes, consists of a chemical compound so loosely bound that it will readily exchange its sodium radical for the calcium and magnesium radicals in the water to be treated. The process is also reversible, depending upon the concentration of dissolved chemicals. Zeolites may be natural, such as glanconite or greensand, or synthetic, such as Permutit.

In passing the raw water through the zeolite the reactions are as follows:

$$NaZ + {}^{Ca}_{Mg}(HCO_3)_2 \rightarrow {}^{Ca}_{Mg}(Z) + ZNaHCO_3$$

Sodium zeolite	Calcium or magnesium bicarbonate hardness	Calcium or magnesium zeolite	Sodium bicarbonate

$$NaZ + {}^{Ca}_{Mg}(SO_4) \rightarrow {}^{Ca}_{Mg}(Z) + Na_2SO_4$$

Sodium zeolite	Sulfate hardness	Calcium or magnesium zeolite	Sodium sulfate

The end products of these reactions are soluble and do not produce hardness in the water.

When the softening capacity of the zeolite is exhausted, the raw-water flow is cut off and the zeolite is backwashed with a brine solution. The reaction of the salt with the calcium zeolite is as follows:

CaZ	$+ NaCl \rightarrow$	NaZ	$+$	$CaCl$
Calcium zeolite		Sodium zeolite		Calcium chloride

After such backwashing, the restored zeolite can again be used to soften water.

b. The effect of H_2S in raw water to be chlorinated is to increase the required dosage of chlorine to provide a disinfecting residual in the water since a part of the chlorine added will react with the hydrogen sulfide.

c. Lime and soda ash are added to water to remove the bicarbonates and sulfates of calcium and magnesium which cause hardness. The chemical reactions with the bicarbonates and sulfates of calcium are as follows:

$Ca(HCO_3)_2$ +	$Ca(OH)_2 \rightarrow$	$2CaCO_3$ +	$2H_2O$
Calcium bicarbonate	Lime	Calcium carbonate	Water
$CaSO_4$ +	$Na_2CO_3 \rightarrow$	$CaCO_3$ +	Na_2SO_4
Calcium sulfate	Soda ash	Calcium carbonate	Sodium sulfate

The reactions with magnesium compounds are similar.

The addition of the lime and soda ash results in insoluble compounds which will settle out or in soluble compounds which do not cause hardness.

3.43 *a.* Chloramines are used in water treatment: (1) for disinfection; (2) for taste and odor control; (3) as algicides; (4) for weed control in reservoirs.

b. Sodium hexametaphosphate (Calgon) is used to control the solubility equilibrium of calcium carbonate in water-softening plants; in the processing of industrial water supplies; and in the "threshold treatment" of water in an attempt to inhibit corrosion.

c. Sodium bisulfite is a reducing agent. As such, it may be used in the deaeration of water to minimize its corrosiveness. It may also be used in dechlorination, to avoid chlorinous tastes after heavy applications of chlorine. Because careful chemical control is necessary, its use has not become widespread in water treatment.

d. Sulfur dioxide in aqueous solution has been used to clean rapid sand filters which have become coated with iron or manganese. This process is patented. Sulfur dioxide is also used in dechlorination.

e. Activated carbon is chiefly useful in water treatment to control tastes and odors.

f. Aluminum sulfate (alum) has a variety of uses in water treatment. The chief use is as a coagulant to remove color, turbidity, and bacteria in connection with rapid sand filtration.

g. Hydrated lime is sometimes used before filtration in an attempt to reduce the bacterial load on filters; it is frequently used after filtration to combat the corrosive quality of the water resulting from the presence of oxygen and carbon dioxide and also to adjust the pH value; it is widely used in water softening.

h. Sodium chloride is most widely used in water treatment in the regeneration of zeolite water-softening tanks.

i. Sodium carbonate is added to waters of low alkalinity to permit the use of alum as a coagulant; it is used in cleaning filters; and it is widely used with lime in water softening.

3.44 *a.* (1) *A single-stage centrifugal pump* is one having a single impeller. It is not, in general, economical to use when the operating head exceeds 300 ft (*b*).

(2) In a *centrifugal* pump a rotating impeller imparts velocity to the water entering from the suction line and forces it to flow under pressure into the discharge line.

(3) For higher heads (*c*) a *multistage* pump is used. Here two or more impellers are connected in series, the discharge from the first impeller passing to the suction of the second, etc.

(4) Both the reciprocating and the rotary pumps are *positive-displacement* pumps.

(5) *Reciprocating pumps* are provided with a piston or plunger moved by reciprocating action in a cylinder provided with the necessary inlet and outlet valves. The movement of the piston alternately draws water into the cylinder from the suction line and forces it out under pressure into the discharge line.

(6) In the single-acting reciprocating pump the flow is intermittent and unsteady. This condition is largely corrected by using a *double-acting plunger pump* in which there are two sets of inlet

and outlet valves so that continuous discharge of water is obtained.

(7) *A rotary pump* has cams or gears which rotate in a casing, thus forcing the incoming water around the casing and out the discharge line on each revolution.

3.45 *a. Bacillus coli* and other bacteria of *coli-aerogenes* group are normally found in the intestinal tracts of man and animals. The presence of these organisms in water supplies is indicative of sewage pollution. Although not in themselves pathogenic, their presence indicates possible pollution of the water by pathogenic intestinal bacteria such as *B. typhosus*, and hence the need for purification of the supply.

The *E. coli* index for a sample of water is the reciprocal of the smallest quantity of the sample, in cubic centimeters, which gives a positive test for coliform organisms. The determination of the "most probable number" is in greater use today for determining the numbers of *E. coli* present in a sample.

b. Anaerobic bacteria thrive in the presence of suitable nutrients and in the absence of free oxygen.

Aerobic bacteria require free oxygen for their development.

c. Hardness in water is commonly expressed in terms of parts per million of $CaCO_3$ even though the total hardness may be made up of the carbonates and sulfates of calcium and magnesium. A carbonate hardness of 100 ppm is indicative of a water supply about on the border between slightly and moderately hard. Such a supply would not, as a rule, be softened for municipal use.

3.46 The factors which control the accuracy of computation of the lengths of the sides of a triangulation network include: (1) precision of measurement of base line; (2) precision of measurement of angles; (3) size of "distance angles" involved in the computations; (4) number of side and angle equations provided by the geometrical figures used in the network; (5) number of stations occupied by the transit party; and (6) frequency with which check base lines are measured.

The effects of items (1) and (2) are obvious. Since the lengths of triangle sides are computed by the law of sines, the angles used in the computations (distance angles) should be of such size that their sines are changing slowly so that errors of angular measurement will have a minimum effect upon the computations. Thus, the closer the angles used approach 90°, rather than 0° or 180°, the less effect errors in angular measurement will have on the computed lengths of network sides. The effect of the size of the angles is indicated by

$$\delta A^2 + \delta A\,\delta B + \delta B^2$$

in the strength of figure equation. δA equals the tabular difference for 1 sec. in the log sine of angle A in the sixth decimal place. δB is the corresponding value for log sine of angle B.

Items (4) and (5) reflect the number of geometrical checks on the computed lengths permitted by the network. They are included in the $(D - C)/D$ term in the strength of figure equation. D represents the number of new directions observed. C is the number of geometrical conditions (side and angle equations) in the network figure.

If a triangulation network is extended indefinitely, its strength gradually becomes less. Specifications accordingly provide for the measurement of a check base periodically in extending a network.

3.47 Such a traverse should be executed using taping bucks or stools since stakes cannot be driven. A minimum of three bucks is required. Tape measurements, each of substantially the full length of the tape where possible, should be made from the end monument to a mark on the first buck, and then carried successively from buck to buck. A tension balance and thermometers should be provided. Where a long tape (200 ft or 50 m) is used, a center support, adjusted to grade by eye, may be necessary.

A transit party consisting of an instrument man and one helper is required to align the bucks as they are successively moved from the rear to the head of the line. A levelman and rodman must establish the differences in elevation between each pair of bucks to permit computation of the inclination corrections. The taping party will normally consist of front and rear chainmen, front and rear stretchermen, and a recorder who may also hold the center support when needed. Necessary corrections include standardization, temperature, slope, and sag.

3.48 Surveys by transit and tape permit work of a high degree of accuracy and are used for surveys of valuable property and for construction surveys. Because of the time involved, they are expensive.

The transit stadia method is well adapted to mapping and to surveys of limited extent and of a relatively low order of accuracy. Distance measurements are made much more rapidly than by taping, particularly in rugged terrain, hence the cost of the work is much less.

The plane table is a specialized instrument particularly adapted to topographic mapping and surveys of low accuracy. The combined field and office time required for such surveys is less than when the stadia method is used and there is greater likelihood that field errors will be detected when this method is used since all plotting is done in the field. The method has several advantages, such as the graphical solution of the three point problem, not available in the stadia method. On the other hand, the instrument and the usual field sheets are not well adapted for use in foul weather and some engineers believe the transit-stadia method to be better adapted to wooded terrain.

The aerial-survey method is particularly adapted to mapping of extensive areas, to preliminary route surveys and to soil- and land-use surveys.

3.49 At the surface three permanent monuments should be placed along the line of the tunnel so that this line can be transferred to the shaft collar whenever necessary. Three points are desirable to permit detection of any displacement of one of the monuments by construction operations.

Points on line are then transferred to the shaft collar. From the points so established, two and preferably three wires supporting heavy plumb bobs are hung in the shaft. Care must be taken that these wires are not displaced by flowing water, by air currents, or by impingement on the shaft framing. The wires should be of small diameter. The bobs should be heavy. Movement of the bobs and wires should be dampened by immersion of the bobs in buckets of oil or other viscous liquids. In wet shafts or where high-velocity air currents are encountered, the wires should be lowered through wooden or pipe chimneys to prevent disturbance. If the three wires are in line and the distances between them are the same at the top and bottom of the shaft it is probable that they are hanging plumb.

If the wires hang without appreciable vibration, a transit set in the heading near the bottom of the shaft can be jigged into line with the three wires. In many cases it will be necessary to place illuminated scales behind each of the three wires and obtain the mean scale readings of the vibrating or swinging wires. The transit is then jigged into line with the mean scale readings.

As the tunnel heading advances, this transit line is transferred to three scales hung from the roof of the heading. With further advancement of the heading, the transit is set up ahead of these scales, backsighted upon them and the line projected forward as the excavation proceeds. Great care must be exercised in this work to obtain maximum accuracy and to eliminate all the instrumental errors since a base line of but a few feet is being projected for a long distance.

Where the tunnel line is projected through the air lock, it is necessary to set up the transit in the lock, backsight on three scales in the free air portion of the tunnel, close the rear-lock door, admit compressed air, open the forward door and project the line onto three scales in the portion of the heading under air. This must be done several times to eliminate all instrumental errors.

3.50 Referring to Fig. 3.50, a base *AB* is taped along one bank, the quadrilateral *ABCD* is triangulated and tied into the bridge center line *EF*. *CD* is measured as a check base and the control net is adjusted by least squares.

With the design stationing of *E*, *F*, and the center lines of piers 1, 2, 3, 4, and 5 known, we may set range flags on shore at *G*, *H*, *J*, *K*, *L*, *M*, *N*, and *O*, drive batter frames upstream from each pier as shown at pier 2, and compute the necessary angles to be laid off from the bases on either shore to set *P* and *Q* on these batter frames on the center line of pier 2. Then range flags can be set at *R*, *S*, *T*, and *U*, to permit driving the sheet piles

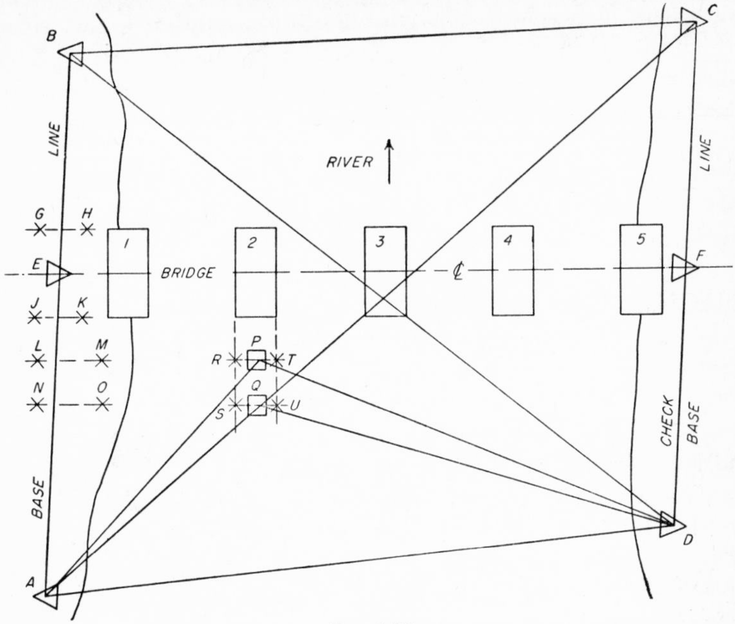

Fig. 3.50

for the long side of the pier-2 cofferdam. A similar procedure is applied to all other piers.

With the cofferdams in place the system of triangulation is applied to the center of each cofferdam in turn to permit the establishment of points controlling the placing of forms, stone facing, and arch hinges.

SECTION FOUR

4.01–4.50

ELECTRICAL ENGINEERING

4.01 *References:* "I.E.S. Lighting Handbook," 1947.
Krachenbuehl, "Electric Illumination," Wiley, 1951.
Sharp, "Introduction to Lighting," Prentice-Hall, 1951.

For parking lots, recommended illumination is 1 to 2 ft-c. For a downtown area assume 2 ft-c. A broad-beam (30° or more) general-service type of floodlight is indicated for this area of $200 \times 300 = 60{,}000$ sq ft. Select a 500-watt floodlight unit having initial beam lumens = 3,400. Assume a depreciation factor = 0.7.

$$\text{No. of units} = \frac{\text{ft-c} \times \text{area}}{0.7 \times \text{initial beam lumens}} = \frac{2 \times 60{,}000}{0.7 \times 3{,}400} = 50$$

Refer to table 8-8, "I.E.S. Lighting Handbook," 1947, p. 8–27.

For a 25-ft mounting height = D, assume Z = 40 ft for a 40° beam. The coverage of one unit = 2,300 sq ft. 60,000/50 = 1,200 sq ft minimum coverage required, so the 50 (500-watt) units will give ample uniformity. The 50 units could be mounted five to a pole on 10 poles spaced 60 ft along the two long sides of the lot. A more efficient but less diversified arrangement could be made by using 1,000-watt general-service lamps in 18- to 24-in. broad-beam reflectors which would give 8,900 initial beam lumens.

$$\text{No. of 1,000-watt units} = \frac{2 \times 60{,}000}{0.7 \times 8{,}900} = 20.$$

Area to be covered by one unit = 60,000/20 = 3,000 sq ft. Refer to table 8-8, "I.E.S. Lighting Handbook," p. 8–27.

For $D = 25$ and $Z = 50$ ft, a 35° beam would cover 3,270 sq ft.

The 1,000-watt units could be mounted in groups of two on 10 poles spaced 60 ft along each long side of the lot.

4.02 *Reference:* "I.E.S. Lighting Handbook," 1947, pp. 8–38 to 8–40.

The formula for this point-by-point calculation is

$$E_h = (I/h^2) \cos^3 \theta_h$$

where E_h = the horizontal illumination in foot-candles at a point p in a plane h ft below a point-source of intensity I candlepower in the direction of p, and θ_h = the angle between a vertical line at p and the line connecting p and the source.

a. At the center, the contribution of one lamp is

$$E_{h_1} = (800/10^2) \cos^3 21.8° \text{ (where } \tan \theta_h = 4/10 \text{ and } \theta_h = 21.8°) = 6.4 \text{ ft-c}$$

The contribution of the other lamp is the same, so at the center of the table (both ways) $E_h = 2 \times 6.4 = 12.8$ ft-c.

b. At the center of either end of the table, from the nearer lamp, $E_h = 6.4$ ft-c. (as in *a*), but from the farther lamp, $E_h = (800/10^2) \cos^3 50.2° = 2.1$ ft-c. The resultant $E_h = 6.4 + 2.1 = 8.5$ ft-c.

c. At any corner, $E_h = 8 \cos^3 26.5° + 8 \cos^3 51.2° = 5.6 + 2.0 = 7.6$ ft-c.

4.03 *Reference:* "I.E.S. Lighting Handbook," p. 6–10.

Take efficiency of a 750-watt PS Mazda lamp as 20 lumens per watt. Assume the same luminaire efficiency and depreciation factor for incandescent and fluorescent lamps:

The power ratio of fluorescent to incandescent for 20 ft-c = $20/42$. If the illumination is raised to 30 ft-c, $30/20$ more lumens will be required. The ration of power for a change would be $20/42 \times 30/20 = 0.715$, and the power-cost saving would be $(1 - 0.715)100$ or 28.5 per cent.

4.04 *Reference:* "I.E.S. Lighting Handbook," 1947.

Recommended illumination level = 50 ft-c (Table *A*-1, p. *A*-2).

A general diffusing or semi-indirect type of luminaire, as shown in Table 8-2, pp. 8–9 to 8–11, is indicated. The room index, Table 8-3, $=F$. Assume ceiling and wall reflectances = 50 per cent. From Table 8-2, pp. 8–9 to 8–10, the coefficient of utilization for semi-indirect luminaires is about 0.30. Assume the maintenance factor = 0.60. The total initial light flux required is: $F = 50(20 \times 30)/0.30 \times 0.60 = 167{,}000$ lumens. The maximum spacing of luminaires is 12 ft, and if six luminaires are used, they could be arranged in two rows of three per row with 10-ft spacing. The lumens per luminaire would be 167,000/6 = 28,000. If incandescent lamps are used, one 1,500-watt, two 750-watt, or three 500-watt lamps per luminaire would be required (Table 6-3, p. 6–10). If fluorescent lamps are used, seven 100-watt lamps per luminaire would be required (Table 6-8, p. 6–35). A more uniform installation with lower brightness contrast would be to use more luminaires, say 12, spacing them in three rows, 7 ft between rows, and four in each row spaced on 7.5-ft centers. The lumens per luminaire would then be 167,000/12 = 14,000. One 750-watt incandescent lamp per luminaire would be sufficient, or four 100-watt fluorescent lamps, soft white.

Wiring. Reference: "The National Electrical Code," 1949.

If two rows of three luminaires per row are used, a separate two-wire branch circuit should be used for each row. Assuming 120-volt lamps, the current per circuit would be $3 \times 1{,}500/120 = 37.5$ amp. Two #6 AWG for each circuit with 50-amp protection would be adequate. If three rows of four luminaires per row are used, separate branch circuits for each row should be used. The current per circuit would be $4 \times {}^{750}\!/_{120} = 25$ amp. Two #10 AWG for each circuit with 30-amp protection would be adequate.

4.05 *Reference:* "I.E.S. Lighting Handbook," 1947.

a. Table *A*-1. For rough bench and machine work, 20 ft-c illumination level is recommended. For medium bench and machine tool work, 30 ft-c is recommended.

b. Page 10–105. Current practice is to use direct fluorescent-lamp luminaires for general industrial lighting and to provide uniform illumination level throughout every work area.

c. Assume 30 ft-c illumination on 30-in. work plane. Assume ceiling and wall reflectances = 50 per cent, and luminaires mounted 2 ft below ceiling. The mounting height above floor =

18 − 2 = 16 ft. From Table 8-3, p. 8-13 the room index = *D*. Select a direct fluorescent-lamp luminaire, as on Table 8-2, p. 8–6. The coefficient of utilization is 0.58 for the two 100-watt types. Maintenance factor, assumed poor, = 0.45. The total lumens = 30(40 × 250)/0.58 × 0.45 = 1,150,000. From Table 6-8, p. 6–35, the 100-watt white lamp has an initial output of 4,300 lumens. The number of two-lamp luminaires required is 1,150,000/2 × 4,300 = 134. These luminaires are approximately 5 ft long, and for uniform illumination the spacing should not be greater than the mounting height of 16 ft. Four rows of two-lamp luminaires, with 34 luminaires lengthwise per row (about 7-ft 4-in. centers) would be a suitable arrangement.

d. Four-wire three-phase branch circuits for each row with the luminaires balanced between the three phases and neutral would be a suitable circuit arrangement.

e. The walls and ceiling should be painted a light color. In part *c.*, 50 per cent reflectance was assumed. If higher reflectance than this could be maintained, fewer lamps would have been required for the same level of illumination and brightness contrast would have have been lower.

4.06 No. "The National Electrical Code," Vol. V, 1949, Table 4, p. 326, specifies that a 1-in. conduit be used for two or three #6 wires.

4.07 Some defects which would justify an inspector to order the wiring torn out of a new residence and reinstalled are:

1. Noncontinuous runs. Conductors must be continuous from outlet to outlet.

2. Improper size of conduit for conductors or too small conductors for main and branch circuits.

3. Discontinuity of metal raceways, cable armor, or other metal enclosures for conductors.

4. Insufficient free length of conductors at outlets. Six in. is specified.

5. Junction boxes not accessible without removing some part of the building.

4.08 Rated current, flowing before the fault, is

$$I_L = P_L/E_L = 10{,}000/250 = 40 \text{ amp}$$

The generated emf under these conditions is

$$E_g = E_L + I_0R_a = 250 + 40 \times 0.50 = 270 \text{ volts}$$

On short-circuit, it is assumed that E_g, the inductance L, and the armature resistance R_a remain constant. The circuit resistance becomes $R = R_a + R_{sc} = 0.5 + 0.2 = 0.7$ ohm. The equivalent circuit from $t = 0$, when the fault occurs, until the breaker opens is 0.02 sec.

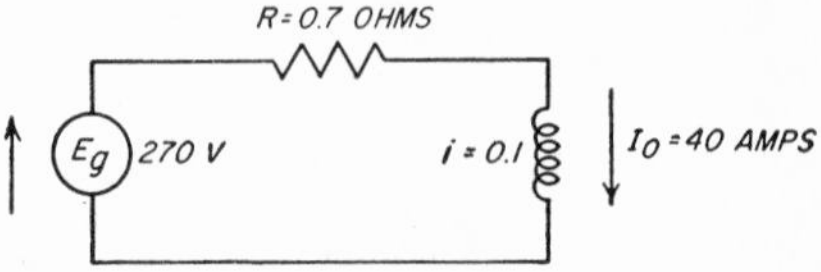

FIG. 4.08

The current I_0 is the initial current flowing in the inductive circuit at $t = 0$, and the current $I = E_g/R = 270/0.7 = 386$ amp is the current which will flow eventually if the breaker never operates. The transient equation for this case is

$$i = I - (I - I_0)e^{-Rt/L} \text{ for } 0 \leq t \leq 0.02$$

The maximum current withstood by the armature will occur at $t = 0.02$ sec:

$$I_{\text{max}} = 386 - (386 - 40)e^{-0.7 \times \frac{0.02}{0.1}} = 386 - 346 \times 0.869$$
$$= 386 - 301 = 85 \text{ amp}$$

4.09 At the instant the field is disconnected from the line, the circuit will be as shown, where R_d is the field-discharge resistance, and by Ohm's law, $R_f = 120/8.4 = 14.3$ ohms, is the field resistance. Because of the field inductance, L_f, the field current cannot change instantaneously; hence it remains at 8.4 amp.

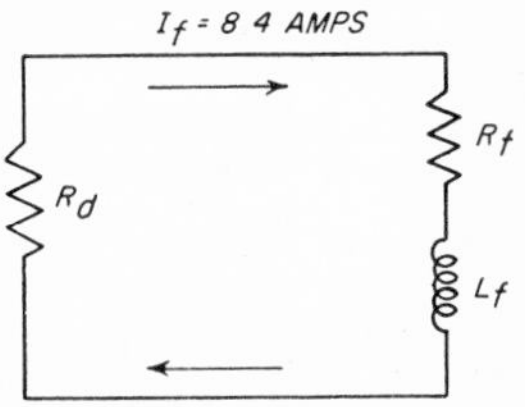

FIG. 4.09

The voltage across the two resistances will be equal to the induced voltage across L_f, and this value must be kept to one-third of the standard high-potential test voltage of 1,000 plus twice the voltage rating of the machine. We then have the voltage equation: $I_f(R_d + R_f) = \dfrac{(1{,}000 + 2 \times 120)}{3} = 413.3$ whence,

$R_d = \dfrac{(413.3 - I_fR_f)}{I_f} = \dfrac{(413.3 - 120)}{8.4} = 34.9$ ohms required. It will be noted that the values of the field inductance and, for that matter, field resistance, were not required for a solution.

4.10 From the first measurement we have (1) $3C_g = 0.5$ where C_g = the capacitance of each conductor to the sheath. From the second measurement we have (2) $2C_m + C_g = 0.6$ where C_m = the capacitance between any two conductors. From (1), $C_g = 0.5/3 = 0.167$ μf. Substituting (1) in (2), $C_m = (0.6 - 0.167)/2 = 0.217$ μf. We thus have a balanced Y load of three 0.167-μf capacitors and a balanced Δ load of three 0.217-μf capacitors. By a ΔY impedance transformation, the balanced Δ is equivalent to a balanced Y having capacitors of $0.217 \times 3 = 0.651$ μf each.

The charging current is thus due to an equivalent balanced Y load each leg of which consists of a capacitor of $0.167 + 0.65 = 0.818$ μf.

Then the charging current per phase is

$$I_L = I_\phi = E_\phi B_\phi = E_\phi(2\pi f C) = \frac{25{,}000 \times 377 \times 0.818}{\sqrt{3} \times 10^6}$$

$$= 4.45 \text{ amp}$$

4.11 Any text or electrical handbook gives the following transformer equation: $E = 4.44 K_s N f B A\ 10^{-8}$ volt

where K_s = stacking factor = 0.9
N = number of turns = 1,500
f = frequency = 60 cps
B = flux density = 62,000 lines psi
A = area of core in square inch
E = rms voltage of winding having N turns

Here $2{,}300 = 4.44 \times 0.9 \times 1{,}500 \times 60 \times 62{,}000 \times A \times 10^{-8}$ volts

So $A = 10.3$ sq in.

4.12 *a.* $N_{600} = \dfrac{600 \times 200}{2{,}400} = 50$ turns

$$N_{240} = \frac{240 \times 200}{2{,}400} = 20 \text{ turns}$$

b and *c*. $I_p = \dfrac{200{,}000}{2{,}400} = 83.3$ amp

d. $I_{600} = \dfrac{100{,}000}{600} = 166$ amp

$I_{240} = \dfrac{100{,}000}{240} = 416$ amp

e. $I_p = A\underline{/\alpha°} + B\underline{/\beta°} = \dfrac{600 \times 166}{2{,}400}\underline{/-45.6°}$

$+ \dfrac{416 \times 240}{2{,}400}\underline{/0°} = 29.5 - j29 + 41.6$

$I_p = 76.6$ amp

4.13 $I_R = 15{,}000/2{,}300 = 6.52$ amp

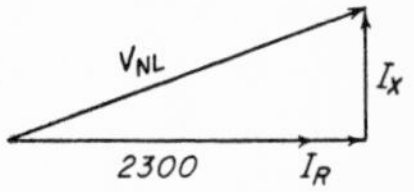

FIG. 4.13

$Z_H = \dfrac{V}{I} = \dfrac{65}{6.52} = 9.96$ ohms

$R_H = \dfrac{P}{I^2} = \dfrac{350}{(6.52)^2} = 8.22$ ohms

$X_H = \sqrt{Z_H{}^2 - R_H{}^2} = 5.65$ ohms

a. $Ix = 6.52 \times 5.65 = 36.8$ volts

$IR = 6.52 \times 8.22 = 53.6$ volts

$V_{NL} = \sqrt{(2{,}354)^2 + (37)^2} = 2{,}354$ volts

Regulation $= \dfrac{(V_{NL} - V_{FL})}{V_{FL}} \times 100 = \dfrac{(2{,}354 - 2{,}300)}{2{,}300}$

$\times 100 = 2.34$ per cent

b. Maximum efficiency occurs when $I^2R = CL$

$I^2R = I^2 \times 8.22 = 245$ watts

$I = 5.45$ amp

Power out (pf = 1.0) = 2,300 × 5.45 = 12.5 kw (neglecting regulation)

Maximum efficiency $= \dfrac{\text{power out}}{\text{power in}} = \dfrac{12{,}500}{12{,}500 + 245 + 245}$

$= \dfrac{12{,}500}{12{,}990} = 0.962 = 96.2$ per cent

4.14 Assuming rated voltage out:

$Z_{\text{rated}} = 2{,}200/45.5 = 48.5$ ohms

$Z_{A_{po}} = 72/2{,}200 = 0.0326$

$R_{A_{po}} = 1{,}000/100{,}000 = 0.01$
$\cos\theta_A = 0.01/0.0326 = 0.307,\ \theta_A = 72.1°$
$Z_{B_{po}} = 75/2{,}200 = 0.0341$
$R_{B_{po}} = 1{,}100/100{,}000 = 0.011$
$\cos\theta_B = 0.011/0.0341 = 0.322,\ \theta_B = 71.1°$
$\dot V = \dot E_1 + \dot I_1 Z_1 = \dot E_2 + \dot I_2 Z_2$
$\dot E_1 = \dot E_2$ and $\dot I_1 + \dot I_2 = \dot I_T = 2\underline{/-37°}$
$E_1 + \dot I_1(0.0326\underline{/72.1°}) = 1$
$E_1 + \dot I_2(0.0341\underline{/71.1°}) = 1$

$$\dot I_1 = \frac{0.0341\underline{/71.1°}}{0.0326\underline{/72.1°}}\dot I_2 = (1.04\underline{/-1°})\dot I_2$$

$(1.04)\underline{/-1°}\dot I_2 + \dot I_2 = 2\underline{/-37°}$
$\dot I_2(1.04 - j0.017 + 1) = (1.6 - j1.2)$

$$\dot I_2 = \frac{2\underline{/-37°}}{2.04\underline{/-0.5°}} = 0.98\underline{/-36.5°}$$

$\therefore |I_2| = 0.98PO = 98$ per cent rated

$$\dot I_1 = (1.04\underline{/-1°})\dot I_2 = (1.04\underline{/-1°})(0.98\underline{/-36.5°}) = 1.02\underline{/-37.5°}$$

$\therefore |I_1| = 1.02PO = 102$ per cent rated

4.15 A = ratio 2,400/240
B = ratio 4,160/240

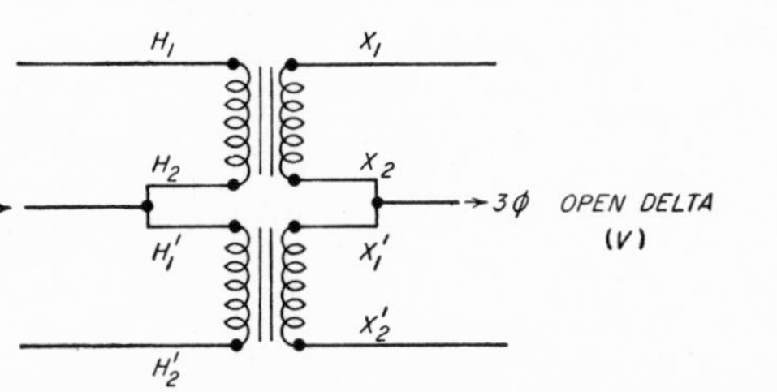

FIG. 4.15. (Continued on page 298.)

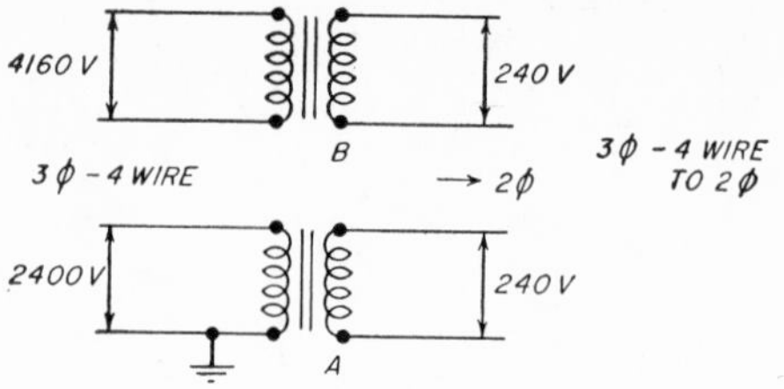

FIG. 4.15. (Continued.)

4.16 Although the power could be transmitted at 11,000 volts, it would be preferable to increase the transmission voltage to about 33 kv. Transformers at each end would then be required. Assuming the use of Y-Y banks, the line voltages and turn ratios are shown in the following diagram, with each bank rated at 3,000 kva.

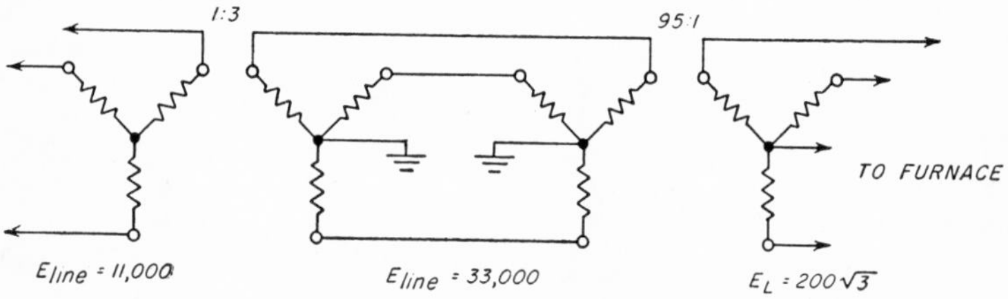

FIG. 4.16

At 33,000 volts each wire will have

$$I_{\text{line}} = \frac{VA}{\sqrt{3} \times E_{\text{line}}} = \frac{3{,}000 \times 10^3}{\sqrt{3} \times 33 \times 10^3} = 52.5 \text{ amp}$$

The allowable loss for each of the three wires is

$$P_{\text{loss/wire}} = P_{\text{phase}} \times 0.05 = \frac{3{,}000 \times 10^3 \times 0.8}{3} \times 0.05$$

$$= 40{,}000 \text{ watts}$$

Hence the maximum allowable resistance per wire per mile (where "d" is the length of the transmission line in miles) is

$$R_{\text{wire mile}} = \frac{P_{\text{loss/wire}}}{I_L{}^2 \times d} = \frac{40{,}000}{(52.5)^2 \times 10} = 1.45 \text{ ohms per mile}$$

This requirement may be met with selection of #4 AWG standard annealed copper wire having 1.34 ohms per mile at 25°C. On wooden poles with 250-ft span, a minimum spacing of 5 ft between wires should be allowed. The resistance drop in this line is $IR = 52.5 \times 14.5 = 760$ volts. Tables for this size wire and spacing give 0.80 ohm reactance per mile per wire at 60 cps. Hence, the reactive drop for 10 miles is $IX = 52.5 \times 8.0 = 420$ volts. Therefore, the total drop (neglecting charging current) is

$$IZ = \sqrt{(IR)^2 + (IX)^2} = \sqrt{(760)^2 + (420)^2} = 870 \text{ volts}$$

This is only 4.6 per cent of $33{,}000/\sqrt{3}$ volts and is completely negligible for a furnace application. Regulation of generator and transformer have not been included.

4.17 Lower transmission voltages result in larger wire size or in high resistance and low efficiency. On the other hand, higher transmission voltages require more expensive tower and protective equipment, but the larger spacing required results in higher inductive reactance. Furthermore, for economical pole spacing, there is a minimum size wire for sufficient mechanical strength. In this problem construction costs are neglected.

$$I_{\text{line}} = \frac{P_{\text{delivered}}}{(\text{pf} \times \sqrt{3} \times E_{\text{line}})} = 25{,}000 \times \frac{10^3}{(0.85 \times \sqrt{3} \times E_{\text{line}})}$$

The allowable voltage drop and power loss in each wire are respectively

$$IZ_{\text{per wire}} = 0.08E_{\text{phase}} = 0.08 \times E_{\text{line}}/\sqrt{3}$$
$$P_{\text{loss per wire}} = 0.06P_{\text{phase}} = 0.06 \times 25{,}000 \times 10^3/3 = 500 \times 10^3 \text{ watts}$$

Based on allowable power loss only, the allowable resistance of wire per mile is, where $d = 25$ miles,

$$R_{\text{wire mile}} = \frac{P_{\text{loss per wire}}}{d \times I_{\text{line}}^2} = \frac{500 \times 10^3}{25 \times I_{\text{line}}^2}$$

For the three available transmission voltages, the values are tabulated below per wire:

kv	I_{line} (amp)	P_{loss} (kw)	R_{mile} (ohms)	Wire size, AWG
12.5	1,360	500	0.0108	
66.0	256	500	0.303	4-0
115.0	143	500	0.970	2

The last column gives the nearest standard copper-wire size, taken from wire tables at 25°C, having a resistance a trifle lower than the allowable ohms per mile. On this basis, the 12.5 kv is immediately eliminated as requiring impracticable size (large) wire.

In determining IZ drop, as this line is short, neglect capacitance (charging current). The inductive reactance depends on spacing, and minimum spacing for safety and minimal corona loss depend on voltage. Consider the data in the following table (at sea level):

Kv	Wire size, AWG	$R_{(\text{ohms per mile})}$	Minimum allowance spacing (ft)	$X_{(\text{ohms per mile})}$
66	4-0	0.264	9	0.770
115	2	0.840	60	
115	2-0	0.420	20	0.895

None of these choices satisfies the regulation requirement. The 60-ft spacing (approximated) is too great even to consider the reactance. Choosing a larger wire size, e.g., #2-0 as shown in the third line of the table, gives $Z_{\text{wire mile}} = \sqrt{R^2 + X^2} = 0.990$ ohm and the drop per wire is then $(IZ)_{\text{drop per wire}} = I_{\text{line}} \times Z_{\text{wire mile}} \times d = 143 \times 0.990 \times 25 = 3{,}550$ volts which satisfies with ample margin both the loss and regulation requirements.

4.18

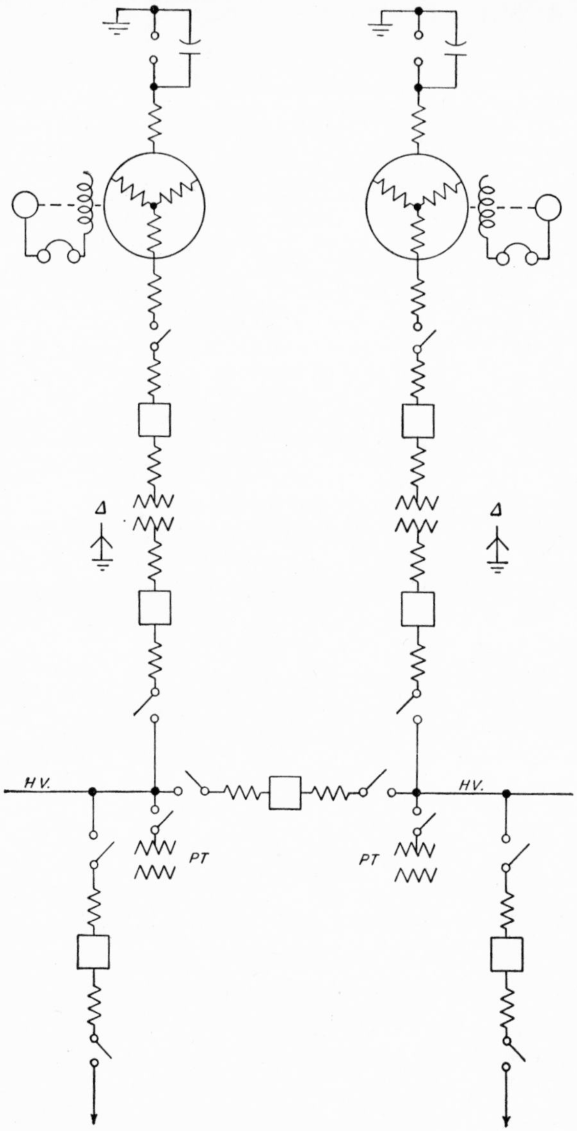

Fig. 4.18

4.19 If all reactive kva are supplied by the synchronous condenser, 5,000 kw, including the 300-kw loss in the condenser, may be added.

a. This leaves 4,700 kw for the new motors. At 80 per cent pf, this means 4,700/0.8 = **5,875** kva in motors.

b. For a pf of 0.8, the reactive factor is 0.6, and 0.6 × 5,875 = 3,525 kvars in the new motors. Total kvars to be supplied by the condenser are 8,667 + 3,525 = **12,192** kva = condenser rating.

c.

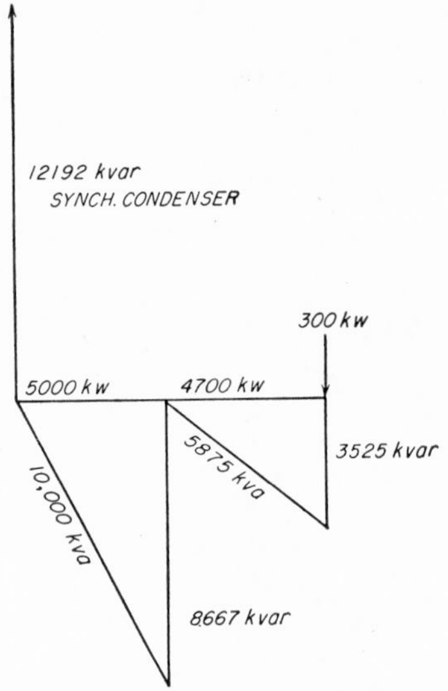

Fig. 4.19

4.20

(1)	(2)	(3)	(4)	(5)	(6)	(7)	(8)	(9)
Rating	Load		Efficiency	Input	Factors		Input	
	hp	kw		kw	Power	reactance	kva	Kvar
(Given)	(Given)	0.746 × (2)	(Given)	(3)/(4)	(Given) cos θ	sin θ	(5)/(6)	(7) × (8)
1–50 hp	30	22.4	0.86	26.05	0.70	0.715	37.20	26.60
1–100 hp	75	56.0	0.89	63.00	0.80	0.60	78.75	47.20
2–15 hp	15	11.2	0.92	12.20	0.85	0.527	14.35	7.56
1–300 hp	310	231.5	0.92	252.00	0.85	0.527	296.00	156.00
1–33 kw	—	33.0	1.00	33.00	1.00	0	33.00	0
							459.35	−237.36
1–500 hp	(×0.746)	373	1.000	373.00	0.80	0.60	466.0	+280.00
	300	224	0.925	242.00				
Total				628.25				42.64

This combination can be adjusted to unity pf where kw = kva. Otherwise

$$\text{kva} = \sqrt{(\text{kw})^2 + (\text{unbalanced kvar})^2}$$

The above figures indicate almost unity power factor so that kva in this case will be very close to 629.5 kva.

4.21 *a.* A 2,300-volt three-phase synchronous motor would allow constant speed and also a means of power-factor control of the plant load. This could be started through a compensator as an induction motor with the field short-circuited. Assuming 80 per cent over-all efficiency, the input to the motor at rated generator output would be 100/0.80 = 125 kw. At unity pf the line current to the motor would be

$$\frac{125{,}000}{(\sqrt{3} \times 2{,}300 \times 1)} = 31.3 \text{ amp}$$

b. A 200-hp 2,300-volt three-phase 12-pole squirrel-cage induction motor would be best suited for this application because the speed would be nearly constant and it is the most reliable the least expensive type of motor that can be used when high starting torque is not required. It could be started through a compensator. Assuming 90 per cent efficiency and 90 per cent pf at rated output, the line current would be

$$\frac{(200 \times 746)}{(\sqrt{3} \times 2{,}300 \times 0.90 \times 0.90)} = 46.3 \text{ amp}$$

c. The 2-hp machine-tool motors could be 220-volt single-phase squirrel-cage induction motors, across-the-line start, split phase or capacitor. Any larger motors up to 15 hp should be 440-volt three-phase squirrel-cage induction motors because this is the most rugged and least expensive type for constant-speed drive where high-starting torque is not required. They could be across-the-line start. The input current for 2-hp 220-volt single-phase motor at rated load, assuming 80 per cent efficiency and 80 per cent pf would be

$$\frac{(2 \times 746)}{(220 \times 0.80 \times 0.80)} = 10.6 \text{ amp}$$

The input current for 15-hp 440-volt three-phase motor at rated load, assuming 85 per cent efficiency and 85 per cent pf would be

$$\frac{(15 \times 746)}{(\sqrt{3} \times 440 \times 0.85 \times 0.85)} = 20.4 \text{ amp}$$

d. A 15-hp 440-volt three-phase squirrel-cage induction motor with stator leads brought out so that they could be connected for 6, 8, or 12 poles would afford the three required speeds at 60 cps. High-starting torque is not required in a blower, so this is the most reliable and least expensive type of motor to use. The line current at full load, assuming 85 per cent efficiency and 85 per cent pf would be

$$\frac{(15 \times 746)}{(\sqrt{3} \times 440 \times 0.85 \times 0.85)} = 20.4 \text{ amp}$$

e. A 50-hp 440-volt three-phase wound-rotor (slip-ring) induction motor with rotor-resistance starting and speed control is best suited for a crusher drive. Considerable adjustment of speed may be obtained as well as rather heavy starting torque. The line current at full load, assuming 85 per cent efficiency and 90 per cent pf would be

$$\frac{(50 \times 746)}{(\sqrt{3} \times 440 \times 0.85 \times 0.90)} = 63.4 \text{ amp}$$

f. One-sixth hp 110-volt single-phase squirrel-cage induction motors are best suited for ventilating fans. They could be split phase or shaded pole starting across the line. Starting torque for fans is low, and these are the most reliable and least expensive motors to use. The full-load current, assuming 75 per cent efficiency and 75 per cent pf would be

$$\frac{[(1/6) \times 746]}{(110 \times 0.75 \times 0.75)} = 2.0 \text{ amp}$$

4.22 The propagation constant per loop mile for the transmission line with uniformly distributed parameters is

$$\gamma = \alpha + j\beta = \sqrt{(r + jl\omega)(g + jc\omega)}$$

At a frequency of 796 cps, $\omega = 2\pi f = 5{,}000$

$$\begin{aligned}\gamma &= \sqrt{(10.44 + j18.3)(0.300 + j41.9)(10^{-6})} \\ &= \sqrt{21.1\underline{/60.2^\circ} \times 42.0 \times 10^{-6}\underline{/90^\circ}} \\ &= 0.0298\underline{/75.1^\circ} = 0.00766 + j0.0287\end{aligned}$$

whence

$$\begin{aligned}\alpha &= 0.00766 \text{ neper per loop mile (attenuation)} \\ \beta &= 0.0287 \text{ radian per loop mile (phase shift)}\end{aligned}$$

a. The wavelength is $\lambda = 2\pi/\beta = 6.28/0.0287 = 219$ miles.

b. The phase velocity is given by $v = \omega/\beta = 5{,}000/0.0287 =$ 174,000 miles per sec or $(174{,}000/186{,}000) \times 100 = 93.5$ per cent of the speed of light.

c. The attenuation, if the line is properly matched at the load is $\alpha = 0.00766$ neper per loop mile. There are 8.68 db in one neper, hence the attenuation is

$$0.00766 \times 8.68 = 0.0665 \text{ db per loop mile}$$

d. For distortionless transmission it is necessary that

$$1g = rc \text{ or } 1 = \frac{rc}{g} = \frac{(10.44 \times 0.00838 \times 10^{-6})}{(0.300 \times 10^{-6})}$$
$$= 0.290 \text{ henry per loop mile}$$

As the line has but 0.00366 henry per loop mile, it is necessary to use additional loading of 0.290 − 0.00366 = 0.286 henry per loop mile.

4.23 To match properly the generator to the line, the latter must have a characteristic impedance $Z_0 = 100 + j0$ ohms, equal to the generator impedance. Since the stub is to be connected in parallel with the line, it is convenient to work with admittances.

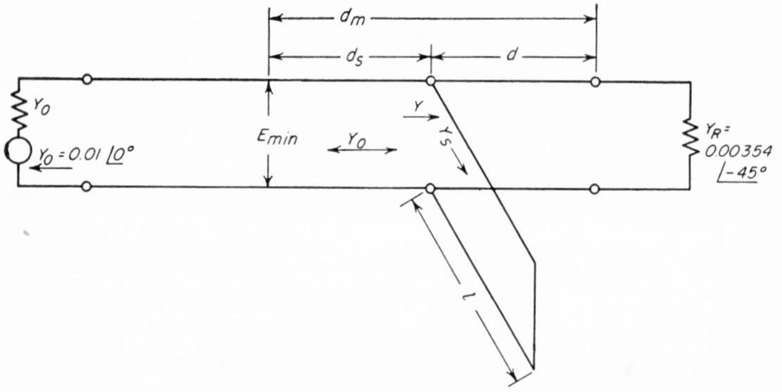

FIG. 4.23

In this case there is a conductive characteristic admittance

$$Y_0 = \frac{l}{Z_0} = G_0 = 0.01 \text{ mho}$$

The stub must be connected to the line at a distance d, preferably as near the load as possible, where the line admittance looking toward the load, $Y = G + jB$, has a real or conductive component $G = G_0$. To determine this location, compute first the receiving-end reflection factor

$$N_R = \frac{[(Z_R/Z_0) - 1]}{[(Z_R/Z_0) + 1]} = \frac{(2 + j2 - 1)}{(2 + j2 + 1)}$$
$$= 0.62\underline{/30°}$$

The standing-wave ratio of the line prior to stubbing is

$$\frac{(1 + N_R)}{(1 - N_R)} = \frac{(1 + 0.62)}{(1 - 0.62)} = 4.27$$

Next compute the location, d_m, at which the standing wave of voltage is at its minimum, $d_m = \frac{(\varphi + \pi)\lambda}{4\pi}$ where

φ = angle, in radians, of $N_R = 0.525$

λ = wavelength, in meters, $= \frac{(3 \times 10^8)}{f} = 0.5$

Consequently, $d_m = (0.525 + \pi) \times \frac{0.5}{4\pi} = 0.136$ meter. Now the stub must be connected a distance d_s either side of the point of voltage minimum, where

$$d_s = \frac{(\lambda \times \cos^{-1} N_R)}{4\pi} = 0.5 \times \frac{(51.6/57.3)}{4\pi} = 0.0358 \text{ meter}$$

As it is desirable to place the stub as close to the load as possible, locate it at $d = d_m - d_s = 0.136 - 0.036 = 0.1$ meter. As mentioned above, a point has been located at which the admittance of the line looking toward the load is $Y = G_0 + jB$. The lossless stub has an admittance $Y_s = 0 + jB_s$. By adjusting the length of the stub so that $B_s = -B$, then the admittance of the line and stub in parallel, Y', will be $Y' = Y + Y_s = G_0 + jB + 0 - jB = G_0$, and the line is matched, as desired, to the left of the stub.

The length of the lossless short-circuited stub required is given in terms of the standing-wave ratio of the line without the stub as

$$1 = \frac{\lambda}{2\pi} \times \tan^{-1} \frac{\sqrt{\rho}}{(\rho - 1)} = \frac{0.5}{6.28} \times \tan^{-1} \frac{\sqrt{4.27}}{(4.27 - 1)}$$
$$= 0.045 \text{ meter}$$

It should be noted that answers to questions of this type are obtained with much greater facility by means of a universal transmission line diagram, such as the Smith chart.

4.24 *a.*

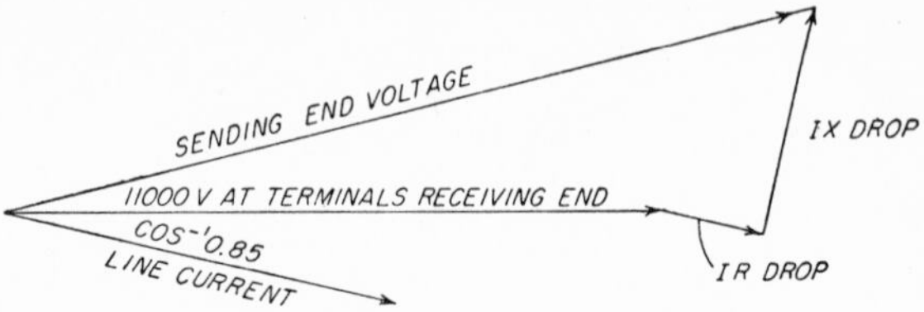

FIG. 4.24

b. Line current $= \dfrac{\text{watts}}{E \cos \theta} = \dfrac{1{,}200 \times 10^3}{11{,}000 \times 0.85} = \mathbf{128.4}$ amp

7.5 per cent of 1,200 kw = 90 kw

$I^2R = (128.4)^2R \leq 90{,}000$ watts

$$R \leq \frac{90{,}000}{(128.4)^2} = 5.45 \text{ ohms or } 0.2725 \text{ ohms}$$

per mile of wire

#4-0 solid copper wire has 0.264 ohms per mile and radius = 0.23 in.

c. Resistance per wire = 0.264 × 10 = **2.64** ohms

d. Inductance per mile = $0.7411 \times \log_{10} (18/0.23 = 78.2) + 0.080 = 0.7411 \times 1.8932 + 0.080 = 1.485$ millihenrys per mile

Reactance per wire = $2 \times \pi \times 50 \times 1.485 \times 10^{-3} \times 10 = \mathbf{4.66}$ ohms

e. Sending-end voltage, where $0.527 = \sin (\cos^{-1} 0.85)$,

$$= 2\sqrt{(5{,}500 \times 0.85 + 128.4 \times 2.64)^2 + (5{,}500 \times 0.527 + 128.4 \times 4.66)^2}$$

$$= 2\sqrt{(4{,}670 + 339)^2 + (2{,}900 + 596)^2} = \mathbf{12{,}220} \text{ volts}$$

f. Regulation, assuming no load, the receiving-end voltage becomes equal to the sending-end voltage, is

$$\frac{(12{,}220 - 11{,}000)}{11{,}000} = \frac{1{,}220}{11{,}000} = \mathbf{11.1} \text{ per cent}$$

g. Line loss = $I^2R = (128.4)^2 \times 2.64 \times 2 = 87{,}000$ watts

$$\text{Efficiency} = \frac{1{,}200{,}000}{(1{,}200{,}000 + 87{,}000)} \times 100 = \mathbf{93.2} \text{ per cent}$$

4.25 $Z = zl = (0.35 + j0.8)100$

$$= 100\sqrt{0.1275 + 0.64}\,\underline{/\tan^{-1} 80/35} = 87.3\underline{/66.4°}$$

$$Y \frac{\tanh \theta}{\theta} = \frac{Is}{Es} = \frac{j50}{100{,}000} = 5 \times 10^{-4}\underline{/90^\circ} \text{ (from tests with}$$

100,000 volts)

Assuming, for the moment, that $\frac{\tanh \theta}{\theta} = 1\underline{/0^\circ}$ and $Y =$ $5 \times 10^{-4}\underline{/90^\circ}$

$$ZY = (87.3\underline{/66.4^\circ})(5 \times 10^{-4}\underline{/90^\circ}) = 436.5 \times 10^{-4}\underline{/156.4^\circ}$$
$$= 0.04365\underline{/156.4^\circ}$$

From chart in Woodruff, "Principles of Electric Power Transmission," Chap. 5,

$$\frac{\tanh \theta}{\theta} = 1.003\underline{/-0.1^\circ} \text{ and } Y = \frac{5 \times 10^{-4}\underline{/90^\circ}}{1.003\underline{/-0.1^\circ}}$$

$$Y = 5 \times 10^{-4}\underline{/90.1^\circ}$$

The correction is negligible except in the angle.
Then for $ZY = 0.04365\underline{/156.5^\circ}$

$$\cosh \sqrt{ZY} = \cosh \theta = 0.98\underline{/0.05^\circ}$$

and
$$\frac{\sinh \theta}{\theta} = 0.993\underline{/0.018^\circ}$$

$$\text{Voltage to neutral} = \frac{132{,}000}{\sqrt{3}} = 76.3 \text{ kv}$$

$$\text{Line current} = \frac{50{,}000}{3 \times 76.3 \times 0.80} = 273 \text{ amp}$$
$$= 273(0.8 - j0.6) = (218.4 - j164) \text{ amp}$$

From Woodruff (as above),

$$E_S = E_R \cosh \theta + I_R Z \frac{\sinh \theta}{\theta}$$

$$= 76.3 \times 0.98\underline{/0.05^\circ} + \frac{(273\underline{/-36.9^\circ})(87.3\underline{/66.4^\circ})(0.993\underline{/0.018^\circ})}{1{,}000}$$
$$= 74.8\underline{/0.05^\circ} + 23.68\underline{/29.68^\circ}$$

$$\cos 29.68^\circ = 0.8688$$
$$\sin 29.68^\circ = 0.4952$$

$$E_S = 74.8 + j0 + 23.68(0.8688 + j0.4952)$$
$$= 74.8 + 20.55 + j11.7 = (95.35 + j11.7) \text{ kv}$$

$$I_S = I_R \cosh\theta + E_R Y \frac{\sinh\theta}{\theta} = (273\underline{/-36.8^\circ})(0.98\underline{/0.05^\circ})$$
$$+ (76{,}300\underline{/0^\circ})(5 \times 10^{-4}\underline{/90.1^\circ})(0.993\underline{/0.018^\circ})$$
$$= 267.5\underline{/-36.75^\circ} + 37.85\underline{/90.12^\circ}$$
$$\cos 36.75 = 0.5983$$
$$\sin 36.75 = 0.8012$$
$$I_S = 267.5(0.8012 - j0.5983) + j3785 = 214 - j160 + j37.85$$
$$= (214 - j122.15) \text{ amp}$$

Sending-end power

$$= \text{real part of } (95.35 + j11.7) \times (214 + j122.15)$$
$$= 20{,}400 - 1{,}430 = 18{,}970 \text{ kw per phase}$$

$$\text{Efficiency} = \frac{\text{receiving-end power}}{\text{sending-end power}} = \frac{50{,}000}{3 \times 18{,}970} \times 100$$
$$= \frac{50}{56.9} \times 100 = 87.9 \text{ per cent}$$

Check by finding approximate value of line current by assuming half of the charging current supplied at each end.
Charging current at 76.3 kv to neutral is

$$I_c = \frac{76.3}{100} \times 50 = 38.15 \text{ amp}$$

With half at each end, current at receiving end is

$$I_R + \frac{I_c}{2} = \text{line current} + \frac{38.5}{2} = 218.4 - j164 + j19.1$$
$$= 218.4 - j144.9 = 262.5\underline{/-33.5^\circ}$$
$$I^2R \text{ per line} = (262.5)^2(0.35 \times 100) = 2{,}890 \text{ kw}$$
$$\text{Efficiency} = \frac{50{,}000}{(50{,}000 + 3 \times 2{,}890)} \times 100 = \mathbf{87.4} \text{ per cent}$$

4.26 One phase of the circuit is

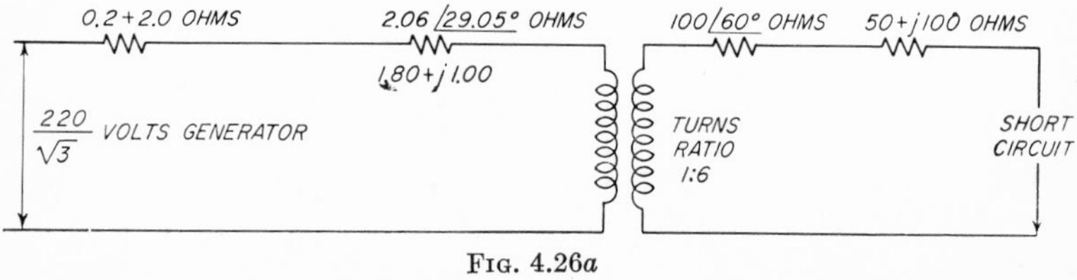

FIG. 4.26a

The equivalent circuit referred to generator voltage is

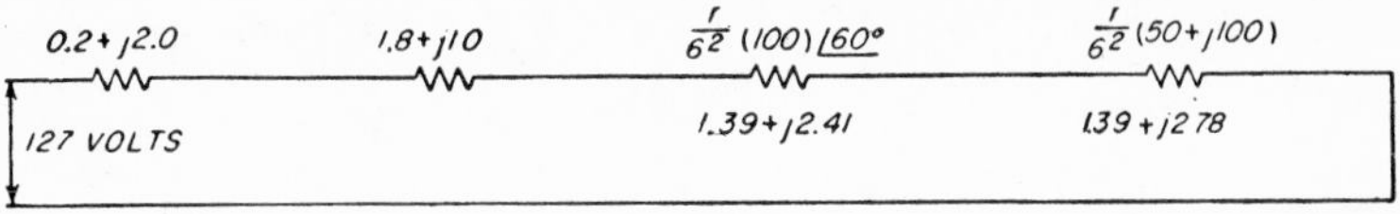

FIG. 4.26b

Simplified, this becomes

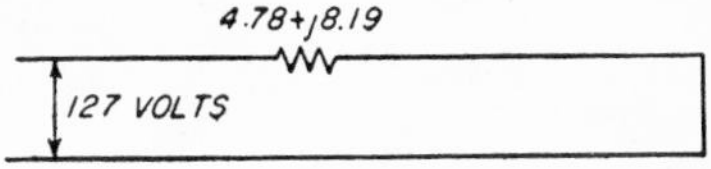

FIG. 4.26c

The current at the generator is

$$I_G = \frac{127}{4.78 + j8.19} = \frac{127}{9.48\underline{/59.7^\circ}} = 13.4\underline{/-59.7^\circ} \text{ amp}$$

The current at the short circuit is ⅙ of this or

$$I_{\text{short circuit}} = \tfrac{1}{6} \times 13.4 = 2.63 \text{ amp}$$

4.27 From blocked test

$$R_{eq} \text{ per phase} = \frac{P_B}{3I^2} = \frac{40{,}500}{3 \times (170)^2} = 0.466 \text{ ohm}$$

$$Z_{\text{equiv}} = \frac{V}{I} = \frac{440}{\sqrt{3} \times 170} = 1.5 \text{ ohm}$$

$$X_{\text{equiv}} = \sqrt{Z_{\text{equiv}}{}^2 - R_{\text{equiv}}{}^2} = \sqrt{2.25 - 0.22} = 1.42 \text{ ohm}$$

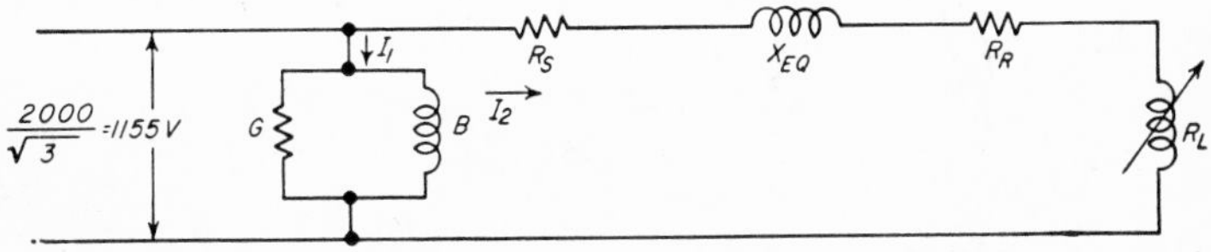

FIG. 4.27

$$R_S + R_R = 0.466 \text{ ohm}$$

Using d-c ratios for split

$$R_{S_{dc}} = 0.165 \text{ ohm}$$
$$R_{R_{dc}} = 0.0127 \times n^2 = 0.0127 \times 4^2 = 0.203 \text{ ohm}$$ (referred to stator)

$$R_S = \frac{0.165}{(0.165 + 0.203)} \times 0.466 = 0.21 \text{ ohm}$$

$$R_R = \frac{0.203}{(0.165 + 0.203)} \times 0.466 = 0.256 \text{ ohm}$$

$$R_L = R_R\left(\frac{1 - S}{S}\right) = 0.256\left(\frac{1 - 0.015}{0.015}\right) = 16.8 \text{ ohm}$$

From no-load test (assuming F and W inherent in R_L)

$$G = \frac{(10{,}100 - 2{,}000)}{3 \times (1{,}155)^2} = 0.00202 \text{ mho}$$

$$Y = \frac{I}{V} = \frac{15.3}{1155} = 0.0132 \text{ mho}$$

$$\text{pf} = \frac{p}{\sqrt{3}\,VI} = \frac{10{,}100}{\sqrt{3} \times 2{,}000 \times 15.3} = 0.191$$

$$B = Y \sin\theta = 0.0132 \times 0.9815 = 0.013 \text{ mho}$$

$$I_2 = \frac{V}{Z} = \frac{1{,}155}{0.21 + 0.256 + 16.8 + j1.42} = \frac{1{,}155}{17.27 + j1.42}$$

$$= \frac{1{,}155}{17.4\underline{/4.7^\circ}} = 66.4\underline{/-4.7^\circ} \text{ amp} = 66 - j5.5$$

$$I_1 = V(G - jB) = 1{,}155(0.00202 - j0.013)$$
$$= 2.33 - j15 = 15.2\underline{/-81.2^\circ}$$

a. $I_{\text{stator}} = I_1 + I_2 = 68.3 - j20.5 =$ **71.3**$\underline{/-16.7^\circ}$ amp

$I_{\text{rotor}} = nI_2 = 4 \times 66.4 =$ **265.6** amp

b. $P_{\text{out}} = (3I_2{}^2R_L - F \text{ and } W)$

$= [3 \times (66.4)^2 \times 16.8 - 2{,}000] = 220$ kw

hp $= 220/0.746 =$ **295** hp

c. $N = \frac{120f}{p}(1 - s) = 1{,}000 \times 0.985 =$ **985** rpm

d. Torque developed $= 3I_2{}^2(R_L + R_R) = 3 \times (66.4)^2(17.1)$

$= 226{,}000$ sync watts $= \frac{226{,}000}{105} =$ **2,150** newton meters

Net torque $= \frac{(226{,}000 - 2{,}000)}{105} = 2{,}130$ newton meters

e. pf $= \cos \underline{/I_{\text{stator}}} = \cos 16.7^\circ =$ **0.958**

f. Efficiency $= \frac{P_0}{P_I} \times 100 = \frac{220{,}000 \times 100}{\sqrt{3} \times 2{,}000 \times 71.3 \times 0.958}$
$= \mathbf{93.0}$ per cent

4.28 Present excitation $= 480 \times 11 = 5{,}280$ amp-turns per pole

Output current $= 35{,}000/125 = 280$ amp
Series field turns per pole $= 5{,}280/280 = 18.85$
Therefore, wind 19.5 turns per pole

4.29 *a.* At unity pf:

Output $= 2{,}500 \times 1$ kw

Current $= \frac{2{,}500}{(\sqrt{3} \times 6.6 \times 1)} = 219$ amp

Armature copper loss $= \frac{[3 \times (219)^2 \times 0.072]}{1{,}000} = 10.4$ kw

Field loss $= \frac{[(200)^2 \times 0.43]}{1{,}000} = 17.2$ kw

Friction loss $= 35.0$ kw
Core loss $= 47.5$ kw
Total loss $= 110.1$ kw

Efficiency $= \frac{\text{output}}{(\text{output} + \text{losses})} = \frac{(2{,}500 \times 100)}{2{,}610.1}$
$= 95.8$ per cent

b. At 0.8 pf:
Output $= 2{,}500 \times 0.8 = 2{,}000$ kw

Current $= \frac{2{,}000}{(\sqrt{3} \times 6.6 \times 0.8)} = 219$ amp

Armature copper loss $= \frac{[3 \times (219)^2 \times 0.072]}{1{,}000} = 10.4$ kw

Field loss $= \frac{[(240)^2 \times 0.43]}{1{,}000} = 24.8$ kw

Friction loss $= 35.0$ kw
Core loss $= 47.5$ kw
Total loss $= 117.7$ kw

Efficiency $= \frac{(2{,}000 \times 100)}{2{,}117.7} = 94.4$ per cent

4.30 $E_{av} = 2LI/T$ volts

where E_{av} = average induced voltage in time T

T = commutating period, or the time in seconds in which the coil current I is reversed

I = coil current = 100 amp

L = coil inductance in henrys = 0.10×10^{-3} henrys = 0.0001

$$T = \frac{(60 \times 2)}{(1{,}200 \times 100)} = 0.001 \text{ sec}$$

$$E_{av} = \frac{(0.0001 \times 2 \times 100)}{0.001} = 20 \text{ volts}$$

4.31 *a.* Current at start varies directly as the applied voltage. For rated current at start, $V_{start} = 550/4.25 = 130$ volts.

b. Starting torque varies as the square of the voltage. At 440 volts, $T_{start} = [(440)^2/(550)^2] \times 160$ per cent = 102 per cent of rated torque, and $I_{start} = (440/550) \times 425$ per cent = 340 per cent of rated current.

4.32 If 85 per cent efficiency is assumed, the rated motor current will be

$$I_m = \frac{(746 \times \text{hp})}{(E \times \text{efficiency})} = \frac{746 \times 5}{120 \times 0.85} = 36.6 \text{ amp}$$

Rated field current is, by Ohm's law

$$I_f = \frac{E}{R_f} = \frac{120}{50} = 2.4 \text{ amp}$$

Whence rated armature current is

$$I_a = I_m - I_f = 36.6 - 2.4 = 34.2 \text{ amp}$$

The starter is to limit the armature current to 200 per cent of rated value, or 68.4 amp. If the armature circuit resistance is R_a and the maximum starter resistance is R_s, then by Ohm's law

$$68.4 = \frac{E}{(R_a + R_s)}$$

Whence the starter resistance must be

$$R_s = \frac{E}{68.4} - R_a = \frac{120}{68.4} - 0.8 = 1.755 - 0.800 = 0.955 \text{ ohm}$$

4.33 $I_{28.8} = 100$ amp

$$= \frac{28{,}800}{(\sqrt{3} \times 208 \times 0.8)}$$

Using $V_{A_{\text{ground}}}$ as reference

$$I_B = 100\underline{/120° - 36.7°}$$
$$= 100\underline{/83.3°} \text{ amp}$$
$$I_A = 60\underline{/0°} + 100\underline{/-36.7°}$$
$$= 60 + 80 - j60$$
$$= 152\underline{/-23.2°} \text{ amp}$$
$$I_C = 60\underline{/-120°} + 100\underline{/-120° - 36.7°}$$
$$= 152\underline{/-143.2°} \text{ amp}$$
$$I_{\text{ground}} = 60\underline{/0°} + 60\underline{/-120°}$$
$$= 60\underline{/-60°} \text{ amp}$$

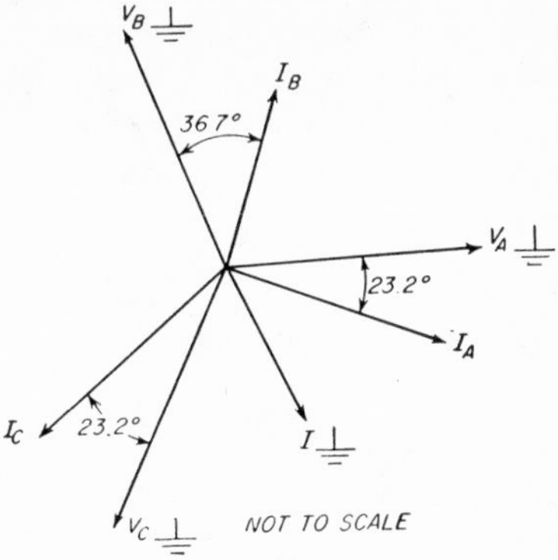

FIG. 4.33

4.34 *a.* Both short-time-current and interrupting-current ratings are higher than the continuous-current rating, with the interrupting-current rating much the larger.

b. The shape and spacing of the current-conducting parts and the shape, dimensions, and material of the insulating parts determine the voltage rating. The sign of the current-carrying parts, including the separable contacts, determines the continuous-current rating. Usually they are made large enough to carry the rated short-time- or intermittent-current overloads without excessive heating. The speed of separation of the contactor, and the design and efficiency of the arc quenching or interrupting means, determines the interrupting capacity of the breaker.

c. The actual load connected to the output side of the breaker determines the current actually passing through the breaker, on either a continuous or short-time basis. In the event of a fault, the worst condition is a short circuit, or a ground at the output terminals of the breaker. In that case the current to be interrupted is determined by the equivalent impedance of the distribution system between the breaker and the effective bus bar of the system.

4.35 Motor input $= 62.5 + 30.5 = 93$ kw

$$\text{Tangent of p-f angle} = \sqrt{3} \times \frac{(62.5 - 30.5)}{(62.5 + 30.5)}$$
$$= \sqrt{3} \times 32/93 = 0.596 = \tan 30.8°$$

Power factor $= \cos 30.8° = 0.859$

Power input $= \sqrt{3} \times EI \cos\theta$

$= \sqrt{3} \times 600 \times I \times 0.859 = 93{,}000$ watts

$I = 104.3$ amp in each line.

Power output $= 0.90 \times 93{,}000/746 = 112.2$ hp

4.36 Using complex notation

$$\text{kva} = \sqrt{3} \times \text{kv} \times I \cos\theta + j\sqrt{3} \times \text{kv} \times I \sin\theta$$

Total load kva $= 4{,}000 + j0$

Alternator No. 1

$$\text{kva}_1 = \sqrt{3} \times 6.6 \times 200 \times 0.85 + j\sqrt{3} \times 6.6 \times 200 \times 0.527$$

$$= 1{,}943 + j1{,}205$$

Alternator No. 2 must supply the difference

$$\text{kva}_2 = \text{kva} - \text{kva}_1 = (4{,}000 - 1{,}943) + j(0 - 1{,}205)$$
$$= 2{,}057 - j1{,}205 = 2{,}380\underline{/-30.4°}$$

Alternator No. 2 supplies 2,057 kw, at $\cos(-30.4°) = 0.863$ pf lagging. $I_2 = 2{,}380/(\sqrt{3} \times 6.6) = 208$ amp

4.37 For paralleling, the following conditions must be alike: frequencies, waveforms, voltages, phase rotation, and phasing. To share the load in proportion to their ratings, the two machines must have similar speed-load curves, their impedances must be inversely proportional to their ratings, and the ratio of R to Z must be the same in both machines. The load may be shifted from one machine to the other by shifting the input powers to the prime movers. Factors affecting power factor are: governor speed settings, internal impedances; power factor of load, speed-load characteristics, and field excitation.

4.38 *a.* 1. Capacitor. Capacitor changes the phasing between currents I_1 and I_2 in two windings spaced 90° from each other, treating a condition similar to a two-phase rotating field.

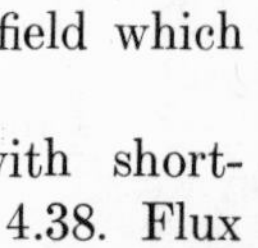

FIG. 4.38

2. Repulsion. Wound rotor with commutator. Brushes are short-circuited creating an induced field which acts similarly to a series field.

3. Shaded pole. Salient pole machine with short-circuited turn "C" as shown in Fig. 4.38. Flux

through "A" is delayed because of Lenz's law causing a sweeping of flux across the pole face.

b. Five hp for special applications.

c. Rotate the brushes to opposite side of hard neutral.

d. Reduced number of turns on field; compensating winding; laminated field structure; and increased armature size.

4.39 By definition, $db = 10 \log P_1/P_2$, and the power delivered to the coil based upon $P_2 = 0.005$ watts is

$$P_1 = 0.005 \text{ antilog } {}^{20}\!/_{10} = 0.5 \text{ watts}$$

Inasmuch as this power is $P_1 = I^2R$, the rms current in the 10-ohm voice coil must be $I = \sqrt{P_1/R} = \sqrt{0.5/10} = 0.224$ amp. If mks units are desired, which are easier and require no conversion factors, the flux density of 10,000 lines psi is

$$\mathrm{B} = 0.155 \text{ weber per sq meter}$$

and for the active length, which is the circumference of the voice coil

$$1 = -d = 3.14 \times 1 \times 0.0254 = 0.0799 \text{ meters}$$

Then the rms force exerted is simply $f = B1NI$

$$f = 0.155 \times 0.0799 \times 10 \times 0.224 = 0.0277 \text{ newtons}$$

(This force is equivalent to 1 ounce.) If the current is sinusoidal, the maximum thrust will be $\sqrt{2}$ times the rms value found above.

4.40 In the absence of characteristic curves, a linear power amplifier must be assumed. For a linear circuit, the maximum-power-transfer theorem states that for maximum power output the load resistance equals the generator resistance. By Thevenin's theorem, the tube may be considered as a constant-voltage source in series with its plate resistance as shown in Fig. 4.40.

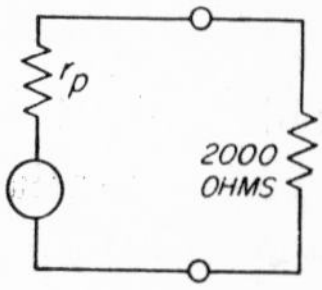

FIG. 4.40

As maximum power occurs when the load is adjusted to equal 2,000 ohms resistance, r_p of the tube must also equal 2,000 ohms. It may be noted that a load resistance equal to $2r_p$ or even greater is generally recommended because the tube is not a linear device and maximum "undistorted" power is desired.

4.41 *a*. Since the voice-coil impedance as seen through the transformer varies with the square of the turn ratio,

$$\frac{N_1}{N_2} = \sqrt{\frac{Z_1}{Z_2}} = \sqrt{\frac{2{,}500}{8}} = 17.7$$

b. For negligible primary resistance, the d-c plate voltage, E_p, equals the plate supply voltage, E_b. If the dissipated power is to be 15 watts, then the quiescent plate current is

$$I_b = \frac{P_b}{E_b} = {}^{15}\!/\!_{250} = 0.06 \text{ amp}$$

The coordinates $E_b = 250$ volts, $I_b = 60$ ma, locate the operating point at $E_c = -43.5$ volts.

c. As the tube is not permitted to draw grid current, the signal cannot be greater than 43.5 peak volts (and will therefore swing the grid from 0 to -87 volts). The value 43.5 peak volts corresponds to $43.5/\sqrt{2} = 30.75$ rms sinusoidal signal voltage.

d. The power output is given by

$$P_0 = \frac{(E_{\max} - E_{\min})(I_{\max} - I_{\min})}{8}$$

where $E_{\max}$, $E_{\min}$, $I_{\max}$, and $I_{\min}$ are values measured at 0 grid volts and -87 grid volts, on the load line. Here

$$P_0 = \frac{(365 - 105)(118 - 13)}{8} = 3{,}420 \text{ milliwatts}$$

The second harmonic current distortion is given by

$$\begin{aligned} D_2 &= (I_{\max} + I_{\min} - 2I_b) \times {}^1\!/\!_4 \\ &= (118 + 13 - 2 \times 60) \times {}^1\!/\!_4 = 2.75 \text{ ma} \end{aligned}$$

This value is not very accurate because of the subtraction of two substantially equal values, both of which were read from a small-scale graph.

e.

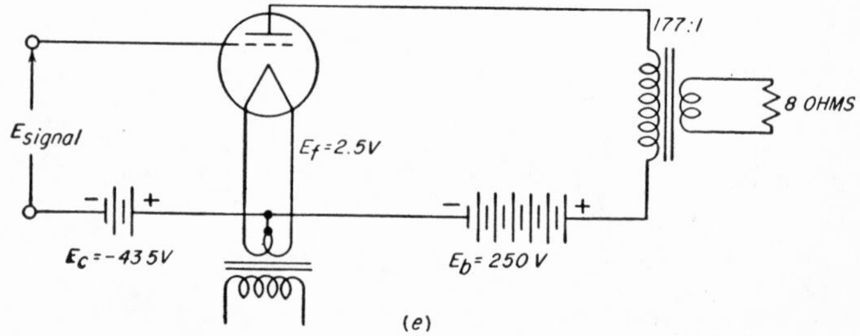

FIG. 4.41

4.42 *a.* $\sqrt{2} \times 120 = 170$-volt peak-to-neutral-peak inverse

$$\text{voltage per stack} = 2 \times \frac{\sqrt{3}}{2} \times 170 = 295 \text{ volts}$$

$$\frac{295}{20} \text{ volts} = 14.75 \text{ or } 15 \text{ disks}$$

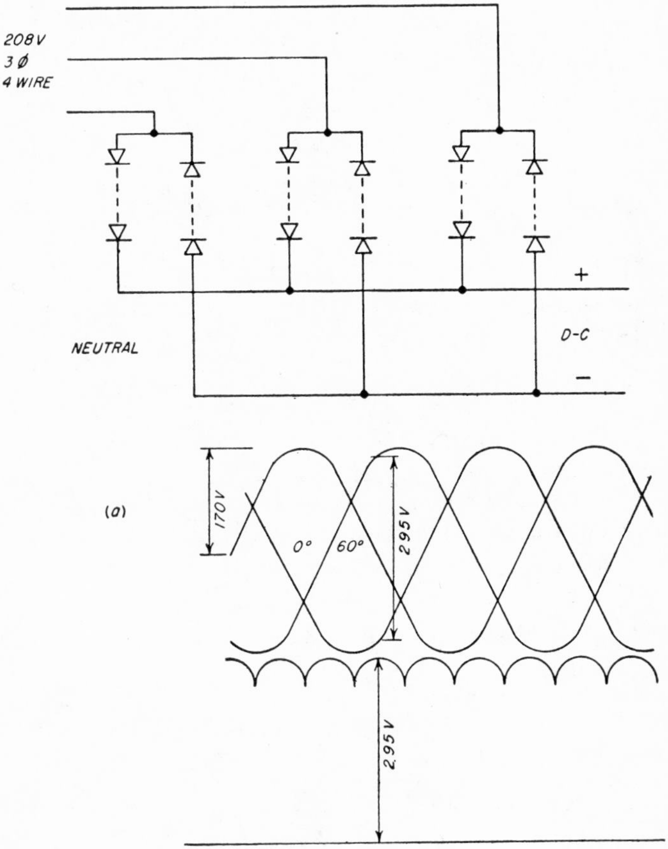

Fig. 4.42*a*

Six single stacks required, two stacks in series always. Current capacity, $3 \times 2 = 6$ amp.

Output voltage:

$$E_{av} = \frac{170}{\pi/6}\int_{0°}^{30°} [\cos\theta - \cos(120° + \theta)]\,d\theta$$

$$= \frac{170 \times 6}{\pi}\int_{0°}^{30°} (\cos\theta - \cos 120° \times \cos\theta + \sin 120° \times \sin\theta)\,d\theta$$

$$= 325\int_{0°}^{30°}\left[(1 + 0.5)\cos\theta + \frac{\sqrt{3}}{2}\sin\theta\right]d\theta$$

$$= 325(1.5\sin\theta - 0.866\cos\theta)\Big]_{0°}^{30°}$$

$$= 325(1.5 \times 0.5 - 0 - 0.866 \times 0.866 + 0.866)$$

$$= 325 \times 0.866 = 282 \text{ volt no load}$$

or $0.85 \times 282 = 240$ volt full load

Output capacity $= 6 \times 240 = 1{,}440$ watts

b. Rectifier of part *a* is also the rectifier that gives the smallest voltage ripples.

c. The rectifier that takes the smallest number of disks and still draws a balanced load is one-half of the rectifier of part *a*, which uses voltages to neutral only once. Peak inverse voltage is as in part *a*. Fifteen disks per stack are required but only three stacks current capacity $= 3 \times 2 = 6$ amp.

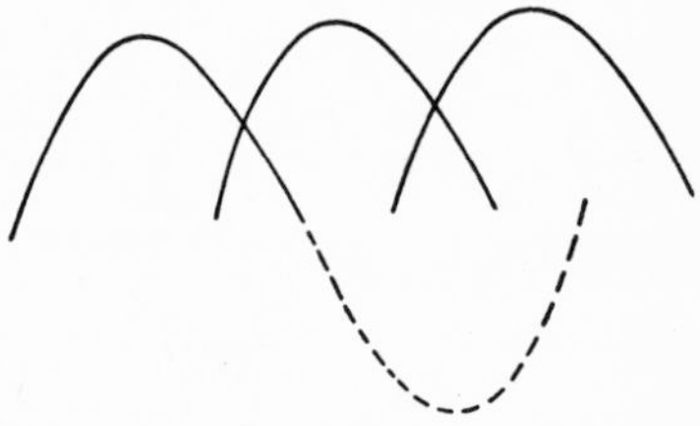

FIG. 4.42*c*

Output voltage

$$E_{av} = \frac{170}{\pi/3}\int_{0°}^{60°} \cos\theta\,d\theta = 162(\sin\theta)\Big]_{0°}^{60°}$$

$$= 162\left(\frac{\sqrt{3}}{2} - 0\right) = 140 \text{ volts no load}$$

$$= 0.85 \times 140 = 119 \text{ volts full load}$$

Voltage ripple in part $a = \frac{(295 - 255)}{2} = 20$ volts.

Voltage ripple in part $c = \frac{(170 - 85)}{2} = 42.5$ volts.

Voltage ripple in part c is $\frac{42.5}{20} = 2.13$ times voltage ripple in part a.

4.43 Power $= EI \cos \theta$

$$550 = 220 \times 2.5 \cos \theta$$

$$\cos \theta = \frac{550}{220 \times 2.5} = 1$$

$$\theta = 0°$$

a. The current in the main winding, 1.45A, lags the line voltage. The condenser current, 1.3A, must lead the other current if their sum, 2.5A, is to be in phase with the line voltage.

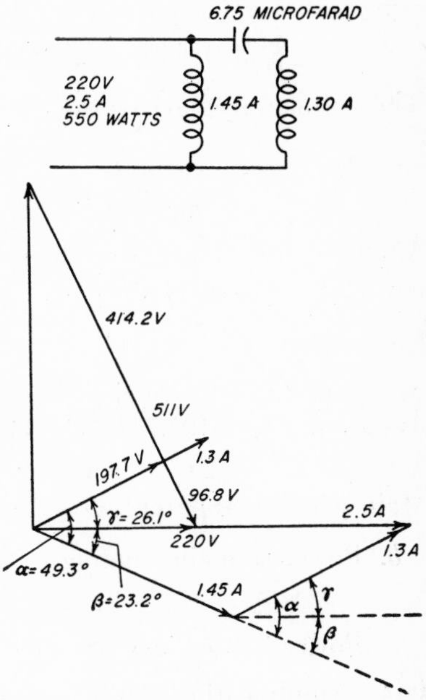

FIG. 4.43

By the cosine law

$$(2.5)^2 = (1.45)^2 + (1.3)^2 + 2 \times 1.45 \times 1.3 \cos \alpha$$

$$6.25 = 2.10 + 1.69 + 3.77 \cos \alpha$$

$$\cos \alpha = \frac{(6.25 - 3.79)}{3.77} = 0.652$$

$$\alpha = 49.3°$$

$$\sin \alpha = 0.758$$

By the sine law

$$\frac{2.5}{\sin (\pi - \alpha)} = \frac{1.3}{\sin \beta}$$

$$\sin \beta = (1.3/2.5) \times \sin \alpha$$

$$= 0.52 \times 0.758 = 0.394$$

$$\beta = 23.2°$$

$$\cos \beta = 0.918$$

Let $\gamma = \alpha - \beta = 49.3° - 23.2° = 26.1°$, $\cos \gamma = 0.898$

The components of the line voltage, 220, with respect to the condenser current, 1.3*A*, are $220 \cos \gamma = 220 \times 0.898 = 197.7$ volts.

$$220 \sin \gamma = 220 \times 0.440 = 96.8 \text{ volts}$$

The voltage drop across the condenser is

$$E_c = IX_c = \frac{1.3}{377 \times 6.75 \times 10^{-6}} = \frac{1{,}300}{2.545} = 511 \text{ volts}$$

Apparent impedance drop in condenser branch

$$220 = IZ = IR_W + j(IX_W - IX_C) = 197.7 - j96.8$$

$IX_W - 511 = -96.8$ volts and $IX_W = 511 - 96.8 = 414.2$ volts

Apparent $IZ_W = IR_W + jIX_W = 197.7 + j414.2$

Apparent $Z_W = 197.7/1.3 + j414.2/1.3 = 152 + j319$

$$= \sqrt{(152)^2 + (319)^2} = 353 \text{ ohms}$$

Main winding apparent $Z = 220/1.45 = 152$ ohms.

b. Power to main winding $= 220 \times 1.45 \times \cos 23.2°$
$= 293$ watts

Power to auxiliary winding $= 197.7 \times 1.3 = 257$ watts.

4.44 Amplification factor

$$\mu = \left.\frac{\Delta Ep}{\Delta Eg}\right]_{I_p \text{ constant}}$$

$$= \frac{(200 - 150)}{(-4) - (-6)} = \frac{50}{2} = 25$$

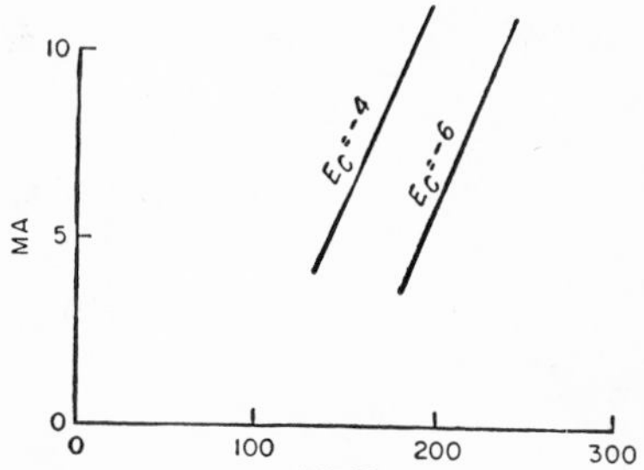

FIG. 4.44

Mutual conductance

$$g_m = \left.\frac{\Delta Ip}{\Delta Eg}\right]_{E_p \text{ constant}}$$

$$= \frac{(12 - 6)10^{-3}}{(-4) - (-6)} = \frac{6 \times 10^{-3}}{2}$$

$$= 3 \times 10^{-3} \text{ mhos} = 3{,}000 \text{ micromhos}$$

Plate resistance

$$r_p = \frac{\mu}{g_m} = \frac{25}{3 \times 10^{-3}} = 8{,}333 \text{ ohms}$$

4.45

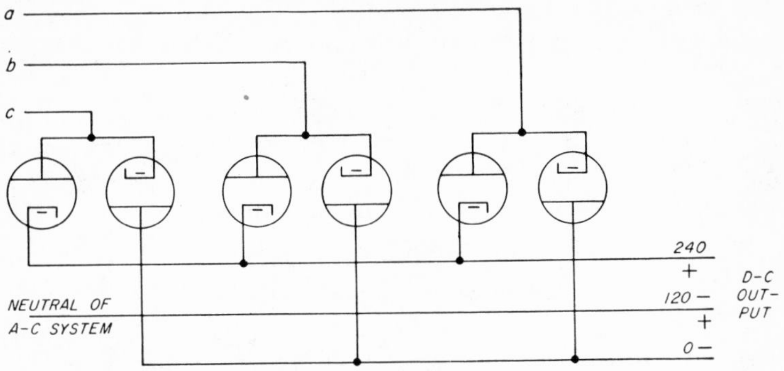

Fig. 4.45*a*. Internal connections for assembly of gas diodes for power rectifier.

Assuming a drop in each tube of 15 volts the rms voltage to neutral of the a-c system should be $(120 + 15) \times 0.707 = 95.5$ volts. With a 208-volts four-wire system giving 120 volts to neutral, an autotransformer is required to reduce this to 100 volts approximately.

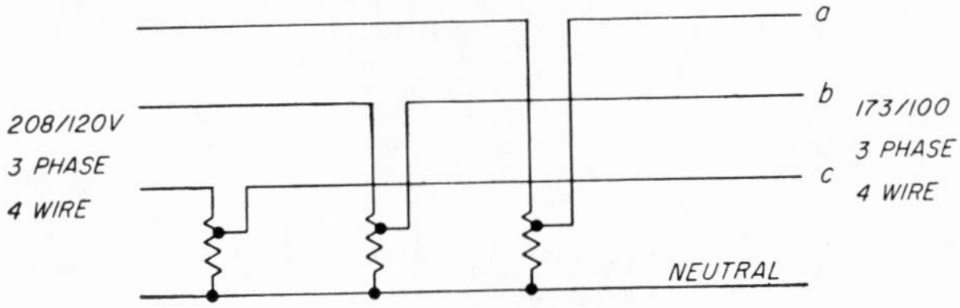

Fig. 4.45*b*

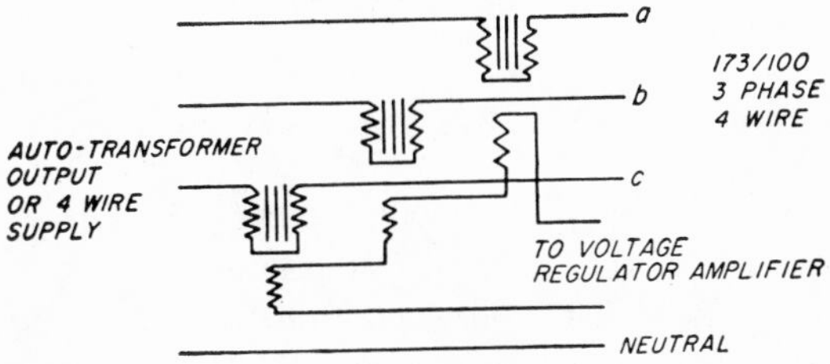

Fig. 4.45*c*

A standard electron-tube voltage regulator on the output can be made to control the d-c bias of a three-phase saturated core reactor which would replace part or all of the voltage reduction in the autotransformer and cause voltage reduction to vary inversely with the load, so as to reduce variations in the output voltage as the load current varies.

For 10 kw at 240 volts direct current, the current is 10,000/240 = 41.7 amp. The average current per tube = 41.7/3 = 13.9 amp. Current fluctuations are small in a rectifier of this type, so that any commercial rectifier tube with an average current rating equal to 13.9 amp will carry the peak currents of normal operation without a condenser filter. The tube should be able to carry a peak inverse voltage of

$$E_{pI} = 2 \times 120\sqrt{2} = 340 \text{ volts}$$

4.46 No resistance values being furnished, assume a dissipationless parallel or antiresonant circuit for which the angular frequency of antiresonance is merely

$$\frac{1}{\sqrt{LC}} = 2\pi f_0$$

Hence the required capacitance is given by

$$C = \frac{1}{(2\pi f_0)^2 xL} = \frac{1}{(6.28 \times 60 \times 10^3)^2 \times 260 \times 10^{-6}}$$
$$= 0.0271 \times 10^{-6} \text{ f}$$

4.47 It is first necessary to locate the load line on the characteristic curves. The resistance load seen by the tube is the voice-coil resistance multiplied by the impedance ratio of the output transformer

$$R_L = 8 \times 312.5 = 2{,}500 \text{ ohms}$$

A line having the slope $-1/2{,}500$ amp per volt is drawn through the point at which the -15-volt characteristic curve intersects the plate voltage of 250 volts. This d-c or quiescent operating point is found to be at a plate current $I_b = 65$ ma, and the load line drawn through this point with proper slope is seen to intersect the abscissa scale at 415 volts and the ordinate scale at 166 ma (415/0.166 = 2,500 ohms). Now a 10-volt rms sinusoidal signal has peak voltages of ± 14.14 volts. Thus swinging the grid from $-15.0 + 14.1 = -0.9$ volts to $-15.0 - 14.1 =$

−29.1 volts. The plate currents at these extremes of signal swing are, from the curves

$$I_{max} = 150 \text{ ma and } I_{min} = 10 \text{ ma}$$

To compute the harmonics with greater accuracy, determine the plate currents corresponding to half of the peak swings, namely at $-15.0 + 0.5 \times 14.14 = -7.93$ grid volts and at $-15 - 0.5 \times 14.14 = -22.1$ grid volts. The corresponding plate current values found are $I_{+0.5} = 112$ ma, and $I_{-0.5} = 33$ ma.

a. The change in operating point when the signal is applied is

$$\begin{aligned}\Delta I_b &= 0.167 \times (I_{max} + 2I_{+0.5} + 2I_{-0.5} + I_{min}) - I_b \\ &= 0.167 \times (150 + 2 \times 112 + 2 \times 33 + 10) - 65 \\ &= 75 - 65 = 10 \text{ ma}\end{aligned}$$

The dynamic operating point is at 250 volts, 75 ma.

b. The fundamental component of plate current (assuming harmonics above the fourth to be negligible) is given by

$$\begin{aligned}I_1 &= 0.333 \times (I_{max} + I_{+0.5} - I_{-0.5} - I_{min}) \\ &= 0.333 \times (150 + 112 - 33 - 10) = 73 \text{ ma}\end{aligned}$$

c. The second harmonic component of plate current is given by

$$\begin{aligned}I_2 &= 0.250 \times (I_{max} - 2I_b + I_{min}) \\ &= 0.250 \times (150 - 2 \times 65 + 10) = 7.5 \text{ ma}\end{aligned}$$

Hence the approximate percentage, second harmonic distortion, is

$$D_2 = 100 \times \frac{I_2}{I_1} = 100 \times 7.5/73 = 10.3 \text{ per cent}$$

4.48 A wound-rotor induction motor is substantially a three-phase transformer with one rotating set of windings. Usually the stator is the primary and the rotor is the secondary, across which the resistance grids are connected. If both windings are Y-connected, then the grids would be properly connected in series with the secondary even if the rotor and the stator functions are interchanged. If the turn ratio per phase is 1:1, then neither rotor nor stator will suffer from overvoltage operation if their connections are interchanged. In addition, if the rotor winding has a resistance as low as that of the stator, satisfactory torque characteristics should obtain for the reversed mode of operation, even if reactances are not identical.

4.49 $P_M = 3{,}600 \times R \times \frac{K_H}{S} = \frac{(3{,}600 \times 15 \times \frac{2}{3})}{50} = 720 \text{ watts}$

$$P_{\text{system}} = P_M \times (CT \text{ ratio})(PT \text{ ratio}) = 720 \times 20 \times 20 = 288 \text{ kilowatts}$$

4.50 Overhead ground wires are used to protect transmission lines against lightning by intercepting direct strokes and by providing multiple paths for stroke current. They also protect against induced strokes by increasing the capacitance between conductors and ground, thereby reducing the voltage from conductor to ground. Low ground resistance is important.

Alternative methods of affording a certain degree of protection to transmission lines are protector tubes, ground fault neutralizers, and automatic reclosing.

Protective tubes simply provide gaps to ground the high-voltage surge on the line and some means to extinguish the power-follow arc.

Ground-fault neutralizers are reactance coils placed between neutral and ground and especially proportioned in relation to the charging current of the system so as to neutralize the ground-fault current.

Circuit breakers disconnect the lines from the power source when lightning or switching disturbances cause overvoltage or overcurrent. Automatic reclosing permits the lines to be kept in service except for the momentary interruption necessary to clear the disturbance.

Reference: Lewis, "Protection of Transmission Systems Against Lightning," Wiley, 1950.

SECTION FIVE

5.01–5.25

ENGINEERING ECONOMICS AND BUSINESS RELATIONS

5.01 *a.* Standardization of equipment increases the productive ability of the average worker. The simplification which occurs permits the inexpert to become skilled more rapidly.

b. Certain materials are available only seasonally and substantial inventories of these must be maintained. The supply on hand of all raw materials must be enough to carry over a definite period of time. The comparison of the values of material and labor must indicate that proper economy of material use is being made. The kind and grade of material should be analyzed with the methods of manufacture, the use by the consumer, the expected life of the item and the price to be charged all being given proper weight.

c. A knowledge of this is prerequisite to establishing economy of operation. By recording the speed of operation, a base may thus be created for standardization of the materials, tools, equipment, and methods being used. The speed data gives some measure of the worker's ability and provides information for use in the training of new men.

d. Routing through the plant must be toward the end that maximum economy is attained. Not only the article itself but also its component parts must be so routed that the entire operation flows smoothly and interruptions due to breakdowns, overloaded departments, pileups, etc., are at a minimum. The functions of supply of stores, issue cards, labor timecards, and control forms must operate such that schedules may be maintained.

e. The work orders serve to alert the various departments of the work coming; thus, the engineering department may commence design work, the store clerks may anticipate stock requisitions, the production departments may look ahead and plans may be made towards providing any special equipment and facilities and adjusting the labor staff in accordance with anticipated volume of production.

5.02 *Job:* Specialization as applied to the job so subdivides the work that only one or a very few operations can be assigned to a worker. This both improves the quality and increases the quantity of output.

Individual: The end of improved quality and quantity of output is also achieved by assigning to each worker one or several manual or mental operations that he is particularly fitted to perform.

Machine: The simpler a machine or tool becomes, the less the attention and skill that is required for its operation or use.

Product: The quality is improved and the production cost reduced as the number of types and variety of sizes of a product are reduced.

5.03 *a. Craft union:* This is an association of employees possessing a common interest or skill or held together by employment in a single occupation or a group of closely related occupations, e.g., the Photo Engravers Union.

b. Industrial union: This is an association of all employees of an industry regardless of the type of work or the skill possessed by the individual, e.g., the United Automobile Workers.

c, and *d. Open shop* and *closed shop:* Normally these are phrases indicating that a plant has only nonunion members (open shop) or that it has only union members (closed shop) as employees. The answer, however, is more involved than this. A better distinction is to say that an open shop is one where the union is not recognized as such and is not therefore allowed to represent the workers in dealings with the employer, and that a closed shop is one where the union is the recognized bargaining agency.

e. Union shop: One where the union is the recognized bargaining agent. These may be open union shops, closed union shops with open unions, closed union shops with closed unions, or preferential union shops.

1. *Open union shop:* Both union members and nonunion members are employed.
2. *Closed union shop with open union:* Nonunion employees may be hired by the employer when union help is unavailable. However, these employees must join the union. The union cooperates by making membership easy to acquire.
3. *Closed union shop with closed unions:* The employer may hire new men only by going to the union. His right to discharge is also restricted.
4. *Preferential union shop:* As additional work becomes available, it is understood that union men are to receive initial preference. Nonunion men may be hired after the union file has been exhausted. In discharging during slack periods the nonunion men are to go first.

f. Industry-wide bargaining: Collective bargaining is conducted by the union with an association of employers. The agreements thus arrived at, therefore, may apply to an entire industry or major portion of it. The coal-mining industry and the clothing industry are good examples of this.

g. Down-time pay: A term used to describe pay provided to the employee for time lost on account of material supply shortages or machine breakdowns.

h. Maintenance of membership: This is a union security measure whereby a union employee pledges to remain a union member or an employee newly joining a union pledges to remain a member for the duration of the collective bargaining agreement if they have not resigned by a certain period.

i. Checkoff: Money which is remitted to the union is deducted from the employees' wages by the employer for union dues or assessments.

j. Seniority: A system by which length of service is the decisive element in deciding on promotions or layoffs. In some companies, periods of layoff or absence are deducted in computing length of service and in others it is not. Usually definite rules are set up regarding absences due to vacation periods, illness, leaves or governmental draft.

5.04 *a. Plant-wide seniority:* Length of service with the company regardless of the division or department is the yardstick employed.

b. Departmental seniority: Only length of service in a particular department is considered in computing seniority.

c. Superseniority: Agreements between the union and company may state that certain persons such as union shop stewards have seniority rights over and above those of any other employees in their departments.

Synthetic seniority: War veterans, even though not company employees before the war, may be given credit for their military service as years of company service.

d. Probationary employees: New employees who must serve a stated probation period varying from one month to even a year. It is understood that certain standards are to be met if their employment is to continue. Such employees have no seniority rights.

e. Grievance: This is a general term applied to an employee who feels that he is, or has, suffered an injustice. Such grievances may be those that affect only a few employees, e.g., a person feels that his work has been changed without pay adjustment or that he has been given work to do not within his duties. Another major category is that which affects all employees, e.g., a failure to agree between company and union.

f. Arbitration of grievances: This is the final step after a grievance has gone through the various channels of shop steward, department grievance committee, general company grievance committee, and possibly even the international union committee. Usually both parties agree in advance that the arbitration results shall be binding. The arbitration board may be a single person or a group of persons. Where several persons comprise the board, each party selects an equal number of members and these selectees choose an extra person to upset a possible tie vote.

g. Call-in pay: Where employees report for work and are sent home without working, a certain amount is paid to the employees. This varies from two to four hours pay. Similarly where an employee is called back to work after his regular day's work, if a minimum payment is required, it is termed call-back pay.

h. Portal-to-portal pay: A term used to describe payment of an employee for time spent on the property of an employer though not actually working at the job, e.g., time spent changing clothes to get ready for work or time spent traveling from the plant entrance to the place of work.

i. Featherbedding: A condition whereby payment is made for work not done. The term also applies to the case where more workers are used than are a reasonable requirement for efficient operation.

j. Boycotts: Primary boycott is one directed against an employer or company and consists of members of the union and their families withholding their patronage.

Secondary boycott is similar to the primary boycott but in addition attempts are made to induce others not directly concerned to withhold their patronage, e.g., the public may be asked not to purchase items offered or a contractor may be asked not to buy certain items.

5.05 Standard costs are planned predetermined costs which serve as a budget for setting standards of achievement and providing a check on attainment. They make for effective managerial control. Standards of costs (which must be revised from time to time) are set up for labor, material, and burden. For labor, operational studies are made and costs are the product of standard labor rates and standard labor times. Standard material costs are established for given periods from information provided by the purchasing department. Standard burden costs are the indirect expenses of the manufacturing departments charged against operations in the form of standard rates. Actual costs should be checked periodically against standard costs (usually by graphic charts) and variations investigated.

5.06 The law of diminishing returns, in very general terms, states that when the amount of a factor which is used in combination with comparatively fixed amounts of other factors is increased, the product will eventually fall after the increase reaches a certain variable amount. In the case of an office building, the rentable floor space is the profitable factor involved. As the height increases, the floor space will increase at a greater rate than the cost of adding more structure and providing more services. There will be a point, however, where increased height requires so much elevator space and service, so much lost traveling time, such large structural columns and members, and such increased utilities-installation costs and maintenance that the return per rentable square foot in spite of the additional floor space begins to fall off.

5.07 1. Provide ample aisles and stairs free of obstructions. Number of intersections of aisles kept at a minimum.

2. Ample room around all machines.

3. Sufficient and safe equipment-moving facilities; particularly hoisting and heavy-weight-lifting machinery.

4. Sufficient clear and well-marked exits to permit rapid escape in case of fire.

5. Design power system with minimum potentials and minimum exposure to human contact.

6. Provide for quick cutoff of electric power, steam, gas, and other utilities at individual machines, rooms, and buildings.

7. Provide quick ventilation facilities for removal of dust, fumes, and vapors.

8. Design adequate lighting for all areas.

9. Insure safe traffic rules.

10. Insist on proper housekeeping.

11. Keep visual aids and posters on safety effective, interesting, provoking, and new.

5.08 Preventive maintenance depends upon an adequate inspection program such that minor defects are remedied before they cause the need for major repairs and renewals may be made before failure of equipment.

Automobile Plant: All buildings, including foundations, walls, columns, girders, plaster cracks, etc., once a year. All roofs every six months. All floors depending on use from three months to two years. Paint, every six months, including not only cleanliness but also protection and light-reflection capacity. Drinking-water systems, toilets, and washbowls daily. Piping as follows: heat and low-pressure steam monthly; high-pressure steam weekly, oil and water every three months. All electric wiring every three months; all sprinklers, fire apparatus, and accessories every three months. Pressure tanks, ventilation, exhausters, and blowers weekly. Cranes, elevators, conveyors, lifting devices, hoists, crane runways, slings, ovens, furnaces, electric welders, grinders, and tools monthly. All fences, bridges, walks, driveways, fire escapes, manholes, and safety belts every six months.

5.09 The next best thing to a profit is to reduce the amount of loss. At half capacity, a loss of \$111,000 − \$96,000 (600 @ \$160) = \$15,000 will occur. Reduction of this loss is an obvious move.

Cost of 1,200 items	=	\$168,000	
Less 600 @ 160	=		\$ 96,000
600 @ 100	=		60,000
			\$156,000

Net loss = \$168,000 − \$156,000 = \$12,000

A loss of \$12,000 instead of \$15,000 is preferable and therefore the offer should be accepted.

5.10 This break-even type of problem is most easily solved by setting up an algebraic equation. In this case, let x = number of shoes to be manufactured. Then

$$3.00x - (0.90x + 0.80x + 0.40x) = 90{,}000$$
$$x = 100{,}000$$

Checking this:

100,000 @ \$3.00 =	\$300,000
100,000 @ \$2.10 =	\$210,000
Left to cover fixed charges:	\$ 90,000

5.11 Depreciation rate is the rate at which a physical asset lessens in value with the passage of time.

In the straight-line method, it is assumed that the depreciation is equal for each year of the asset's life. A formula for the depreciation per year would be

$$D = \frac{A - B}{n}$$

where D = depreciation per year
A = first cost
B = estimated salvage value at end
n = estimated life of asset in years

In the sinking-fund method of depreciation, one of a series of equal amounts is deposited into a sinking fund at the end of each year of the asset's life. This is usually compounded annually. This amount is equal to the estimated total depreciation times the sinking-fund factor corresponding to the estimated life and the interest-rate taken.

$D = (A - B)$sf where D, A, and B are as explained above and sf is a sinking-fund factor based on the well-known, equal-payment-series, sinking-fund-factor formula. The payments under the sinking-fund method becomes progressively greater. This method therefore is not as conservative as the straight-line method, particularly if there is any likelihood that an asset may be retired prior to the end of the estimated period of depreciation. The ICC, it would appear, is simply following the custom of imposing conservative practices on a public utility.

5.12 *a.* General partners are liable for all the firm's debts. In the case of joint liability, the individual is liable for his proportional part; e.g., if the firm is sued for $9,000 and there are three partners he is liable for $3,000. If the liability is joint and several (the usual case) he could become liable for the entire amount.

b. Limited partners have their liability limited to the original stake and are risking only this contribution.

c. Cumulative voting permits minority stockholders to elect members to the board of directors by concentrating their votes, e.g., ordinary voting permits each share of stock one vote each for directors. If five directors are to be elected, that would mean five votes per share or one for each director. Cumulative voting allows the five votes to be cast for one director.

5.13 *a.* In a partnership, two or more individuals associate themselves by contract in the common ownership, management, and control of a business enterprise. The partnership is not a separate legal entity but can only act in the names of its partners. Each partner may act for all and each generally bears unlimited liability. The death or withdrawal of one partner automatically dissolves the partnership. A corporation is a voluntary association of natural or legal persons, organized under and recognized by law as an artificial person separate from the persons who compose it, for the accomplishment of certain purposes specified in its charter. A corporation, unlike a partnership, can be formed only after authority has been granted by state (or Federal) government. The charter to do business nominally limits the corporation to certain lines of business. Ownership is vested in stockholders and shares are freely transferable. Liability is limited only to the amount paid for the stock shares. The enterprise has perpetuity. Capital is readily obtained through the sale of stock.

b. If an increase in the capital stock is made when actually no additional value has been paid either in cash or in money's worth, this is called "stock watering."

c. Certified check: A check drawn by a depositor against his account which the bank has marked "certified" indicating that sufficient funds have been set aside to satisfy it whenever presented. These funds are charged against the account of the person making the check. The bank has assumed an unconditional obligation to pay this amount.

d. Corporation bond: A written contract, under seal, whereby a corporation binds itself to pay a specific sum of money to the owner of the bond. Usually issued with coupons attached which, when severed, become promissory notes for the payments of installments of interest when the interest becomes due.

e. Letter of credit: A letter of request whereby one person, usually a merchant or banker, requests some other person to advance money or to give credit up to a certain amount to a third person named therein, charging it to the writer's account.

f. Bill of lading: A written acknowledgement by a carrier that he has received the goods for shipment. It is also a contract for transportation and a contract to make delivery to the person named or to his order.

g. Promissory note: A written promise to pay on demand, or at a fixed and determined future time, a certain sum of money to, or to the order of, a specified person or to bearer.

h. Damages: Liquidated damages means the sum agreed upon in advance by the parties as compensation for a breach. Unliquidated damages means sums such as a jury would award when the case is presented to them upon its own merits.

i. Money and barter: Money acts as a medium of exchange; as a common denominator of values; as an economic link between the present, past, and future. Barter is the process of exchange where no single medium of exchange is used. Where barter involves identical items (a rare situation) no problem is involved. Normally, however, barter involves different quantities of dissimilar items. Without some common denominator of value, as money, it becomes extremely difficult. Where the items are very different in value, as a diamond ring for a pound of steak, it is extremely tedious to trade for numerous commodities till the holder of the ring finally secures something approaching the value of the ring and still reasonable to the owner of the steak. When commodities are perishable, barter provides no link of present and future except promises to repay in the future for something received now.

5.14 The essential elements of a contract are:

1. *Competent parties:* Anyone can make a binding contract with these exceptions:

Minors (persons under 21)
Married women (permitted in most states by enabling statutes)
Lunatics (permitted in some states if made in good faith)
Drunken persons (permitted in some states if made in good faith)

2. *A lawful subject matter:* The subject contract may not violate a statute; may not be contrary to rules of common law; may not be forbidden by public policy.

3. *A proper consideration:* Consideration may be defined as the act or forbearance of one party which is given in exchange for the act or promise of the other. Examples would be a landlord giving up possession of premises in return for a promise to pay rent or a promise to buy goods at a fixed price when made in exchange for a promise to manufacture goods and sell them to the first party at that price. Love and affection are not regarded as a proper consideration in law.

4. *A genuine agreement or mutual assent:* Both parties must assent to the same thing in the same sense. The agreement must be voluntary and without force being used. In some cases, but not in all, the law requires that the agreement be in writing to be enforceable.

5.15 Contracts may be made illegal by the following ways:

1. By statute, e.g., gambling or betting contracts; usurious interest rates; Sunday contracts (in some states)

2. By being against public policy, e.g., contracts to bribe witnesses or jury members; contracts for votes in exchange for appointments after election; contracts agreeing never to marry

3. Certain mutual mistakes, as when both parties were mistaken about the item being sold at a sale

4. Fraud, where if the deceived party had known the true facts he would not have consented

5. Duress, when threats of actual physical violence against a person, his property, or someone related to him is used to force a person into a contract (the threat to sue, when there is ground for a lawsuit, is not duress)

6. Undue influence, where persuasion or capitalizing on another's trust and thereby taking unfair advantage of him can be proven

5.16 *a.* Contracts may be terminated before execution by

Mutual consent

Breach (damages may arise from this)

Death or disability in personal-service contracts

Subsequent change of law rendering subject matter illegal or impossible to perform

One party preventing the other from executing his part

Destruction of rare subject matter through no fault of the parties

b. A contract may be considered breached

When the contractor renounces his liability and refuses to perform

When by his acts he renders performance impossible

When he fails to perform what he agreed to do

5.17 Five rules of ethical behavior for a professional engineer:

1. No engineer should falsely or maliciously injure, directly or indirectly, the reputation, prospects, or business of another.

2. Every engineer should satisfy himself to the best of his ability that the enterprises with which he becomes identified are of legitimate character; and if not he should sever his connection as soon as practicable.

3. No engineer should attempt to supplant a fellow engineer after definite steps have been taken toward his engagement.

4. No engineer should attempt to conceal possible oversights or errors nor to shirk responsibility.

5. He should work towards a contract that is sound and fair to the owner, himself, and the contractor.

See also the next question.

5.18 It is not proper for a professional engineer to participate in competitive bidding against his colleagues to secure a professional engagement that is to go to the lowest bidder or to accept an engagement to review the work of another professional engineer without his knowledge. A professional man as such should be worthy of his hire. In committing his skill, education, and ability to a job it is presumed that he will give his best efforts and, therefore, to enter into competition with others implies that his abilities and fees are variable. Again, as a professional man of ethics, to review another's work without his knowledge is to question his ability and talents without giving him an opportunity to defend his work.

5.19 In these straight-line, depreciation-plus-average-interest problems, the most correct method of solution is to consider the first cost (minus salvage if any), divided by n (number of years involved) as capital recovery at 0 per cent capital recovery. Depreciation at 0 per cent $= \frac{(P - L)}{n}$. With a salvage value, the

$$\text{average interest} = (P - L)\frac{(i)}{(2)}\frac{(n + 1)}{(n)} + Li$$

Reinforced bridge:

$$\text{Depreciation} = \frac{9{,}000 + 13{,}000 - 10{,}000}{5} = \$2{,}400$$

Maintenance and inspection $= 300$

Average interest at 6 per cent; $(22{,}000 - 10{,}000) \times$

$$\frac{(0.06)}{(2)}\frac{(6)}{(5)} + 10{,}000(0.06) = 432 + 600 = 1{,}032$$

Total annual cost $= \$3{,}732$

New bridge:

$$\text{Depreciation} = \frac{55{,}000 - 13{,}000 - 15{,}000}{30} = \$\ 900$$

Average interest at 6 per cent; $(42{,}000 - 15{,}000) \times$

$$\frac{(0.06)}{(2)}\frac{(31)}{(30)} + 15{,}000(0.06) = 838 + 900 = 1{,}738$$

Total annual cost $= \$2{,}628$

5.20 *a.* Interest on 20,000 = 20,000(0.06) = \$1,200
Interest on present worth of
10,000 = 10,000(0.4173)(0.06) = 250
Total annual cost = \$1,450

b. Interest on 25,000 = 25,000(0.06) = \$1,500

This being the total annual cost, plan *a.* is the more economical.

5.21 Bridge *A*:

$$\text{First cost} = \$10{,}000$$

$$\text{Infinite renewals} = 10{,}000\,\frac{(0.01265)}{(0.06)} = 2{,}100$$

$$\text{Annual maintenance}\ \frac{50}{0.06} = 833$$

$$\text{Present worth of repairs}\ \frac{200(0.17740)}{0.06} = 591$$

$$\text{Total capitalized cost} = \$13{,}524$$

Bridge *B*:

$$\text{First Cost} = \$15{,}000$$

$$\text{Infinite renewals} = (15{,}000 - 3{,}000)\,\frac{(0.00470)}{(0.06)} = 940$$

$$\text{Annual maintenance} = 0$$

$$\text{Present worth of repairs}\ \frac{100(0.17740)}{0.06} = 296$$

$$\$16{,}236$$

5.22 The fundamental interest formula for this type of problem involving a systematic reduction of the principal of the debt by repayments of principal and interest uniformly is

$$R = P\left[\frac{i(1+i)^n}{(1+i)^n - 1}\right]$$

where R is the end of period payment
P is the present sum of money
i is the interest rate per period
n is the number of periods

$$R = 1{,}000\left[\frac{0.04(1.04)^5}{(1.04)^5 - 1}\right]$$

Solving this, R = \$224.63 to be paid each year. The term $\left[\frac{i(1+i)^n}{(1+i)^n - 1}\right]$ may be taken from tabulations such as in Grant, "Principles of Engineering Economy," Ronald Press, in which it is called the "capital-recovery factor." This type of question may be worded differently such as:

a. What 5-year annuity can be purchased for \$1,000 at 4 per cent interest?

b. What annual saving for 5 years must be made to justify an expenditure of \$1,000 now if money brings 4 per cent interest?

c. If \$1,000 is invested now at 4 per cent interest, what uniform amount may be drawn each year for 5 years so that nothing is left at the end of the fifth year?

5.23 Haskold's valuation formula

$$P = R\left[\frac{1}{i' + i/(1+i)^n - 1}\right]$$

is the most commonly used formula for finding present worth with two interest rates. Its greatest use seems to be in mine-valuation studies.

In this problem $R = 200000$
$i' = 0.10$
$i = 0.03$
$n = 30$

$$P = 200{,}000\left[\frac{1}{0.10 + 0.02102}\right] = \$1{,}652{,}620$$

This means that the \$200,000 is actually divided into two parts. One part, \$165,262 is a 10 per cent return on \$1,652,620. The other \$34,738 invested at 3 per cent will yield \$1,652,620 in 30 years. In other words, the syndicate will receive a 10 per cent return each year and in addition will recover the investment sum \$1,652,620 at the end of 30 years.

5.24 Comparing by annual costs:

Method *A*:

Tunnel interest	= 150,000 × 0.05	= \$7,500
Annual operation and upkeep		= 2,000
Total annual cost		= \$9,500

Method B:

Ditch interest $= 50{,}000 \times 0.05$	$=$ \$ 2,500
Annual operation and upkeep	$=$ 2,000
Flume capital recovery at 5 per cent	
$= (30{,}000 - 5{,}000)(0.12950) + 5{,}000(0.05)$	$=$ 3,487
Annual operation and upkeep	$=$ 4,000
Total annual cost	$=$ \$11,987

Note that where annual cost of a structure with perpetual life is involved, interest on the investment is used, i.e., as the number of years approaches infinity the capital-recovery factor approaches the interest rate. Also that where salvage is involved, it is necessary to make the capital-recovery factor equal to the interest earned on the prospective salvage value plus the recovery with interest the difference between first cost and salvage.

5.25 The net return on the sale was \$950,000 − \$20,000 = \$930,000. This problem becomes one of saying that the present worth of \$68,667 (i.e., 1,000,000/15 + 2,000) for 15 years plus 1,000,000, 15 years hence should equal \$930,000.

Try 7 per cent; $P.W. = 68{,}667 \times 9.108 + 1{,}000{,}000 \times 0.3624 = \$988{,}400.$

Try 8 per cent; $P.W. = 68{,}667 \times 8.559 + 1{,}000{,}000 \times 0.3152 = \$903{,}200.$

By straight-line interpolation, the interest rate is found to be 7.68 per cent or, to the nearest 0.5 per cent, say 7½ per cent.

SECTION SIX

6.01–6.50

MECHANICAL ENGINEERING

6.01 $Q = U \times A \times (t_{\text{in}} - t_{\text{out}})$ Btu per hr

U = over-all heat-transfer coefficient in Btu/(hr)(sq ft)(°F)

A = area of box $= 2 \times 2 \times 6 = 24$ sq ft

1 Btu = 0.000293 (kw-hrs)

$Q = (0.1)(24)(96 - 72) = 57.6$ Btu per hr

Total heat transferred $= Q$ hr $= 57.6 \times 24 = 1380$ Btu

Cost $= 1{,}380 \times 0.000293 \times 5$ (cents) $= 2.025$ cents

6.02 $$F = \frac{H(t - t_a)N}{E(t_d - t_o)C} = \text{quantity of fuel required}$$

(From "Heating, Ventilating, and Air Conditioning Guide," Chap. 17, ASHVE, 1950.)

H = calculated heat loss, Btu per hr, during the design hours, based on t_0 and t_d

t = average inside temperature maintained during heating period, in °F.

t_a = average outside temperature during estimate period, in °F (for cities, like Newark, with 212-day heating season, Oct. 1 to May 1)

t_d = inside design temperature, in °F (usually 70°F)

t_0 = outside design temperature, in °F

N = no. of heating hours in estimated period

E = efficiency of utilization of fuel

C = heating value of one unit of fuel

$$t = \frac{(9 \times 70) + (15 \times 50)}{24} = 57.5°\text{F}$$

Degree-days $= (65 - t_a)212 = 5{,}210$
$t_a = 65 - 5{,}210/212 = 40.4°F$
$N = 212 \times 24 = 5{,}088$ hr

$$F = \frac{650{,}000 \times (57.5 - 40.4) \times 5{,}088}{0.65 \times [70 - (-10)] \times 13{,}500} = 80{,}500 \text{ lb}$$
$$= 40.25 \text{ tons}$$

6.03 $F = \dfrac{H(t - t_a)N}{E(t_d - t_0)C}$ (as in the preceding answer)

Degree-days $= (t - t_a)212 = 7{,}000$
$t - t_a = 7{,}000/212 = 33°F$, where $t = 65°F$
$N = 24 \times 212 = 5{,}088$ hr

a. $F = \dfrac{240{,}000 \times 33 \times 5{,}088}{(0.60)(70 - 0) \times 12{,}000} = 80{,}000$ lb or 40 tons

Cost per season $= 40 \times \$4.50 = \$180$

b. $F = \dfrac{240{,}000 \times 33 \times 5{,}088}{0.75 \times 70 \times 142{,}000} = 5{,}410$ gal

Cost per season $= 5{,}410 \times \$0.06 = \$325$

c. $F = \dfrac{240{,}000 \times 33 \times 5{,}088}{0.70 \times 70 \times 550} = 1{,}495$ M cu ft

Cost per season $= 1{,}495 \times \$0.80 = \$1{,}200$

6.04

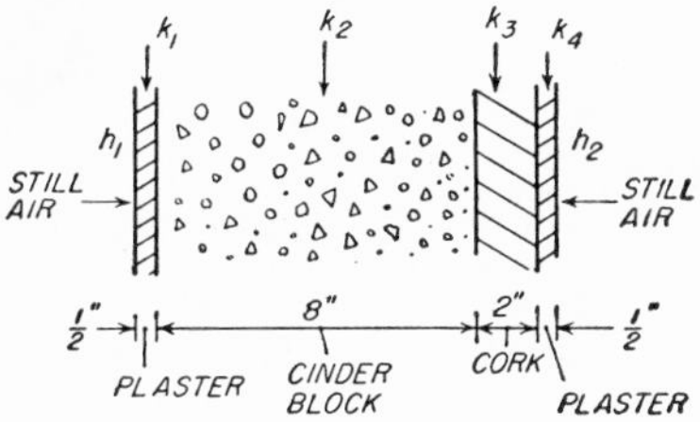

Fig. 6.04

Assume cement plaster: $k_1 = k_4 = 8.0$

$$Q = \frac{A(t_1 - t_2)}{1/h_1 + L_1/K_1 + L_2/K_2 + L_3/K_3 + L_4/K_4 + 1/h_2}$$
$$= \frac{1 \times 40}{1/1.65 + 0.5/8 + 1.61 + 2/0.30 + 0.5/8 + 1/1.65}$$
$$= \frac{40}{0.606 + 0.063 + 1.61 + 6.67 + 0.063 + 0.606}$$
$$= 40/9.62 = 4.16 \text{ Btu/(sq ft)(hr)}$$

where $t_1 - t_2 = 40°F$

A = area = 1 sq ft

L = thickness of material in inches

K = thermal conductivity [(Btu)(in.)/(hr)(sq ft)(°F)]

H = surface coefficient of heat transmission [Btu/(hr)(sq ft)(°F)]

(From Heating, Ventilating, and Air Conditioning Guide," ASHVE, 1950.)

For 8-in. cinder block, $L_2/K_2 = 1.61$

6.05 See preceding answer.

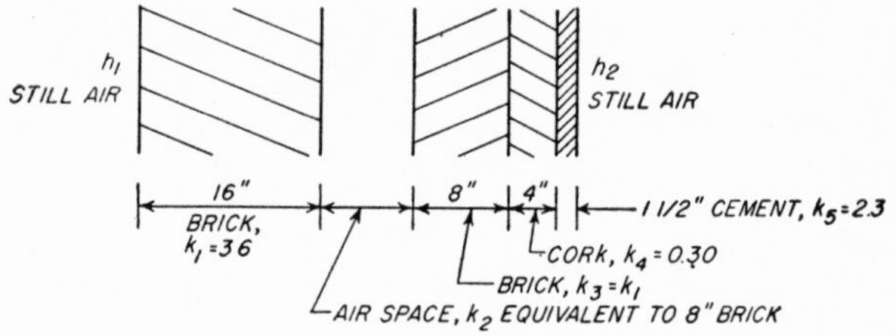

FIG. 6.05

$$Q = \frac{A(t_1 - t_2)}{1/h_1 + L_1/K_1 + L_2/K_2 + L_3/K_3 + L_4/K_4 + L_5/K_5 + 1/h_2}$$

$$= \frac{1(70 - 30)}{1/1.65 + 16/3.6 + 8/3.6 + 8/3.6 + 4/0.3 + 1.5/2.3 + 1/1.65}$$

$$= 40/24.1 = 1.66 \text{ Btu per sq ft} \times \text{hr} = 39.8 \text{ Btu per sq ft} \times \text{day}$$

6.06

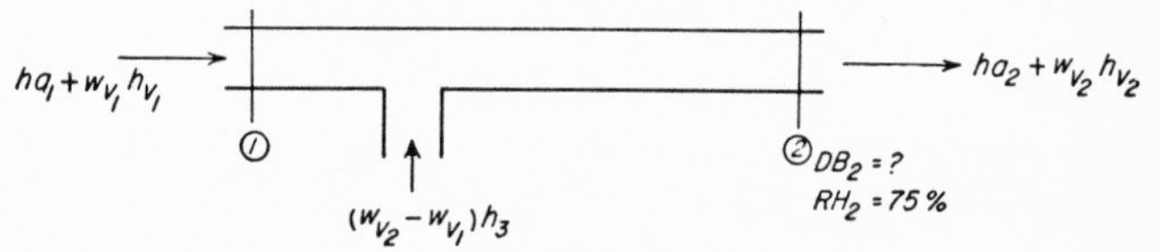

FIG. 6.06

Where RH = relative humidity

DB = dry-bulb temperature, °F

ha = enthalpy of dry air, Btu per lb dry air

hf = enthalpy of water spray = Btu per lb water

w_v = lb vapor per lb dry air

v = cu ft per lb dry air

w_a = lb dry air per cu ft

Evaluating the entering energy to the leaving energy for 1 lb dry air,

$$h_{a_1} + w_{v_1}h_{v_1} + (w_{v_2} - w_{v_1})h_3 = h_{a_2} + w_{v_2}h_{v_2} \qquad (1)$$

a. $h_{a_1} + w_{v_1}h_{v_1} = 23.7$ Btu per dry air*

$w_{v_1} = 44$ grains vapor per lb dry air* $= 44/7{,}000 = 0.0063$ lb vapor per lb dry air.

$$\therefore 23.7 + (w_{v_2} - 0.0063)18.1 = h_{a_2} + w_{v_2}h_{v_2} \qquad (2)$$

A trial-and-error solution is applicable. Assume DB_2. Use chart to find $(h_{a_2} + w_{v_2}h_{v_2})$ and w_{v_2} based on this assumption. Apply equation (2) to check validity of assumption. As an aid in choosing a trial DB_2, note that $(w_{v_2} - 0.0063)18.1$ is very small compared to the other quantities in equation (2). $\therefore (h_{a_2} + w_{v_2}h_{v_2})$ is approximately equal to 23.7 and $RH_2 = 75$ per cent (given)

First trial: $DB_2 = 61°F$, $RH_2 = 75$ per cent, gives: $(h_{a_2} + w_{v_2}h_{v_2}) = 24$ Btu per lb dry air* and $w_{v_2} = 60/7{,}000 = 0.0086$ lb vapor per lb dry air*

Check: $23.7 + (0.0083 - 0.0063)(18.1) = 24$ or $23.74 = 24$

Second trial: Assume $DB_2 = 60.5°F$

$\therefore (h_{a_2} + w_{v_2}h_{v_2}) = 23.8$ Btu per lb dry air.*

$w_{v_2} = 59/7{,}000 = 0.0084$ lb vapor per lb dry air*

Check: $23.7 + (0.0084 - 0.0063)(18.1) = 23.8$ or $23.74 = 23.8$

This is close enough. Therefore $v_1 = 13.48$ cu ft per lb dry air* and $w_{a_1} = 1/13.48 = 0.0743$ lb dry air per cu ft

Weight of incoming air $= (1{,}800)(0.0743) = 134$ lb per min

$\therefore$ Water required $= 134(w_{v_2} - w_{v_1}) = 134(0.0084 - 0.0063)$ $=$ **0.282** lb per min

$$DB_2 = \mathbf{60.5°F} \text{ and } WB_2 = \mathbf{55.8°F}$$

b. Equation (2) becomes $23.7 + (w_{v_2} - 0.0063)1{,}150 = h_{a_2} + w_{v_2}h_{o_2}$

First trial: As in (*a*), assume $DB_2 = 71°F$

$\therefore (h_{a_2} + w_{v_2}h_{v_2}) = 30.4$ Btu per lb dry air*

$w_{v_2} = 85/7{,}000 = 0.01214$ lb steam per lb dry air*

* Using psychrometric chart.

Check: $23.7 + (0.0121 - 0.0063)1{,}150 = 30.4$, or $30.4 = 30.4$

$$\text{Steam required} = \left(\frac{\text{lb air}}{\text{min}}\right)\left(\frac{\text{lb steam}}{\text{lb air}}\right) = \text{lb per min}$$

$134(w_{v_2} - w_{v_1}) = 134 \times 0.0058 =$ **0.785** lb steam per min

$DB_2 =$ **71**°F and $WB_2 =$ **65.5**°F

6.07 See previous answer for symbol notation.

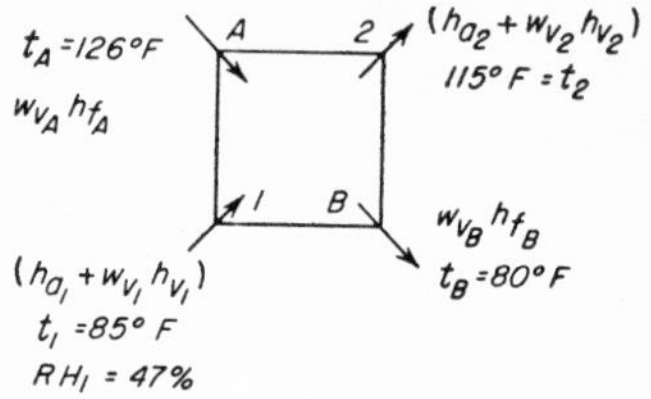

FIG. 6.07. Energy diagram for a cooling tower where weight of dry air is 1 lb. $h_{v2} = h_{g2}$ since air leaves in a saturated condition; P_v = vapor pressure, psi; P_{sat} = saturated vapor pressure, psi.

$w_{v_B} = w_{v_A} - (w_{v_1} - w_{v_2})$ = lb of departing water per lb dry air

$$\frac{\text{Dry air, lb}}{\text{Water, lb}} = \frac{1}{w_{v_A}} = \frac{(h_{f_A} - h_{f_B})}{0.24(t_2 - t_1) + w_{v_2}(h_{v_2} - h_{f_B}) - w_{v_1}(h_{v_1} - h_{f_B})}$$

$$= \frac{(93.91 - 48.0)}{0.24(115 - 85) + w_{v_2}(1{,}111.6 - 48) - w_{v_1}(1{,}098.8 - 48)}$$

$$\text{Eq. (1)} = \frac{45.9}{7.2 + w_{v_2}(1{,}063.6) - w_{v_1}(1{,}050.8)}$$

$P_{v_1} = RH_1 \times P_{sat} = 0.47 \times 0.596 = 0.280$ psi and $P_{v_2} = 1.471$ psi

$$w_{v_1} = 0.622\left(\frac{P_{v_1}}{P_a - P_{v_1}}\right) = 0.622\left(\frac{0.280}{14.7 - 0.280}\right) = 0.0121 \text{ lb vapor per lb dry air}$$

$$w_{v_2} = 0.622\left(\frac{1.471}{14.7 - 1.47}\right) = 0.0693 \text{ lb vapor per lb dry air}$$

$$a.\ \text{Eq. (1)} = \frac{45.9}{7.2 + 0.0693 \times 1063.6 - 0.0121 \times 1050.8}$$

$= 0.674$ lb dry air per lb water

$$V = \frac{WRT}{P} = \frac{0.674 \times 53.3 \times (85 + 460)}{(14.7 - 0.28) \times 144} = 9.43 \text{ cu ft}$$

dry air per lb water

= 9.43 cu ft wet air per lb water (by Dalton's law)

$$\frac{\text{Wet air, lb}}{\text{Water, lb}} = \frac{w_{v_1}}{w_{v_A}} + \frac{1}{w_A} = 0.0121 \times 0.674 + 0.674 = \mathbf{0.682}$$

b. $$\frac{\text{Air, cfm}}{\text{Air, cu ft per lb water}} = \frac{2{,}000}{9.43} = \mathbf{212}\text{ lb water per min}$$

6.08 Outside air = 7.5 cfm per person (not smoking)

a. Total outside air = 7.5 × 1,800 = 13,500 cfm

b. Sensible heat loss per person = 225 Btu per hr

Sensible heat loss of audience

= 225 × 1,800 = 405,000 Btu per hr

Solar heat loss = 120,000 Btu per hr

Total heat loss = Q_s = 525,000 Btu per hr

$$Q_s = W_s(0.24)(t_i - t_e)$$

where t_i = temperature in auditorium (°F)

t_e = temperature of conditioned air

W_s = conditioned air per hour, pounds

$$525{,}000 = W_s \times 0.24(78 - 65)$$
$$W_s = 168{,}000 \text{ lb air per hr}$$

From psychrometric chart, air at 65°F and at an estimated relative humidity = 70 per cent shows specific volume = 13.4 cu ft per lb dry air

$$\text{Air circulated} = \frac{\text{Air, lb per hr}}{60 \text{ min}} \times \frac{\text{cu ft}}{\text{lb dry air}} = \frac{168{,}000}{60} \times 13.4$$
$$= \mathbf{37{,}400}\text{ cfm}$$

c. From "Heating, Ventilating, and Air Conditioning Guide," Chap. 6, Fig. 7, curve D, ASHVE, 1950.

165 Btu per hr = latent heat loss per person

Latent heat loss of audience = 165 × 1,800 = 296,000 Btu per hr

Moisture per person = 1,100 grains

Moisture from audience, grains = 1,100 × 1,800

= 1,980,000 grains per hr

$$\frac{\text{Moisture per hr}}{\text{Dry air circulated per hr, lb}} = \frac{1{,}980{,}000}{168{,}000} = 11.8 \text{ grains}$$

moisture per lb dry air

Moisture content of inside air at 78°F to 67°F = 82 grains per lb dry air (from chart)

Moisture content of entering air = 82.0 − 11.8 = 70.2 grains per lb dry air

Air with 70.2 grains moisture per lb dry air and 65°F has a wet-bulb temperature = **60.2**°F

Specific volume = 13.43 cu ft per lb dry air is sufficiently close to 13.40 cu ft per lb dry air used in part *b*.

6.09 t_a = temperature (0°F) of outside air as it enters heating coils

t_b = temperature F° of air as it enters auditorium

t_c = temperature (70°F) of vitiated air

a. Heat loss from building = 1,250,000 Btu per hr

Heat gain from audience = (220 × 5,000) = 1,100,000 Btu per hr

Net heat loss = Q_s = 150,000 Btu per hr

Cubic feet air per hr entering = (1,800 × 5,000) = 9,000,000 cu ft per hr

$$PV = WRT \text{ and } W = \frac{PV}{RT} = \frac{144 \times 14.5 \times 9 \times 10^6}{53.3 \times (0 + 460)}$$

= 767,000 lb air per hr

$$Q_s = W \times C_p(t_b - t_c) \text{ and } (t_b - t_c) = \frac{Q_s}{W \times C_p}$$

$$t_b = t_c + \frac{Q_s}{W \times C_p} = 70 + \frac{150{,}000}{767{,}000 \times 0.24} = 70 + 0.81$$

= **70.81**°F

b. Heat supplied by heating coils per hr = $W \times C_p(t_b - t_a)$ = 767,000 × 0.24(70.81 − 0) = **13,000,000** Btu per hr

6.10 *a*. Sensible heat load = $Q_s = W \times C_p(t_a - t_b)$

$$W = \frac{Q_s}{c_p(t_a - t_b)} = \frac{450{,}000}{(0.24)(75 - 65)} = \mathbf{187{,}500} \text{ lb air per hr}$$

b. $$\frac{\text{Moisture, grains}}{\text{Dry air, lb}} = \frac{\text{grains moisture per hr}}{\text{lb dry air per hr}}$$

$$= \frac{1{,}200{,}000}{187{,}500} = 6.40 \text{ grains per lb dry air to be removed}$$

$$\frac{\text{Moisture, grains}}{\text{Supply air, lb}} = 78 - 6.40 = 71.6 \text{ grains per lb air}$$

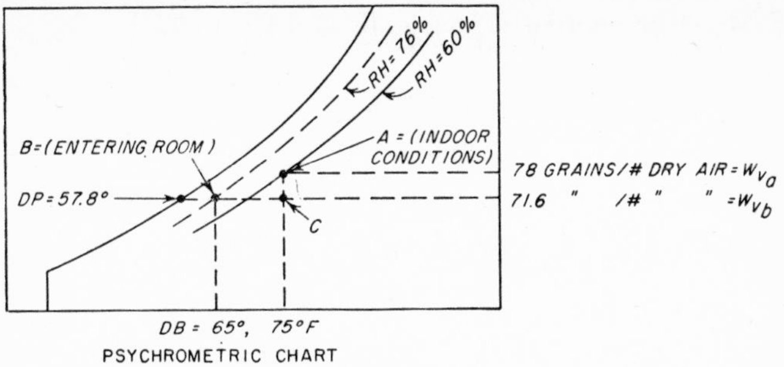

FIG. 6.10

From Fig. 6.10 at $BD = 65$°F at 71.6 grains per lb air and dew point = **57.8**°F and RH = **76** per cent

c. $\dfrac{1{,}200{,}000}{7{,}000}$ 171.2 lb moisture per hr

Heat load picked up in auditorium

$$= \left(\frac{\text{Pound moisture}}{\text{Hour}}\right)\left(\frac{\text{Btu}}{\text{lb moisture}}\right) = \left(\frac{\text{lb moisture}}{\text{hr}}\right) h_{f_g}$$

$$= 171.2 \times 1{,}051 = \mathbf{180{,}000} \text{ Btu per hr}$$

6.11 $$\text{Horsepower input} = \frac{0.0001573 \times \text{cfm} \times \text{static pressure}}{\text{static efficiency}}$$

$$\text{Horsepower input} = \frac{0.0001573 \times (60{,}000/60) \times 2}{0.40}$$

$$= 0.786 \text{ hp}$$

Use **1** hp motor.

6.12 $$\text{Velocity of air} = Q/A = \frac{9{,}300 \text{ (cfm)}}{(\pi/4) \times (3)^2 \text{ (sq ft)}} = 1{,}317 \text{ ft per min or } 21.95 \text{ ft per sec}$$

$$V = \sqrt{2g\,\frac{Dh_v}{12d}}$$

and

$$h_v = \frac{12dV^2}{2gD}$$

where D = 62.1 lb per cu ft H_2O at gage temperature
h_v = velocity pressure (in. H_2O)
d = density of air flowing
V = ft per sec
h_t = total pressure difference created by fan
h_s = static pressure

$$PV = WRT \quad \text{and} \quad d = \frac{W}{V}$$

$$\therefore d = \frac{P}{RT} = \frac{144 \times 14.1}{53.3(460 + 83)} = 0.0703 \text{ lb per cu ft}$$

where $P = \left(\frac{28.75}{29.9}\right)(14.7) = 14.1$ psi

$$h_v = \frac{12 \times 0.0703 \times (21.95)^2}{2 \times 32.2 \times 62.1} = 0.102 \text{ in. water}$$

$$h_t = h_s + h_v = 0.85 + 0.102 = 0.952 \text{ in. water}$$

$$\text{Air hp} = \frac{Qh_tD}{12 \times 33{,}000} = \frac{9{,}300 \times 0.952 \times 62.1}{12 \times 33{,}000} = 1.39 \text{ hp}$$

$$\text{Fan mechanical efficiency} = \frac{\text{Air hp}}{\text{input}} = \frac{1.39}{3.55} \times 100$$

$$= \mathbf{39.2} \text{ per cent}$$

$$\text{Static efficiency} = \text{mechanical efficiency}\left(\frac{h_s}{h_t}\right)$$

$$= 39.2\left(\frac{0.850}{0.952}\right) = \mathbf{35} \text{ per cent}$$

6.13 $Q = A \times V = (2 \times 3) \times 20 = 120$ cfm
For standard air conditions

$$V = 66.76\sqrt{h_v} \text{ and } h_v = \left(\frac{20}{66.67}\right)^2 = 0.09 \text{ in. water}$$

$$h_t = h_s + h_v = 3.00 + 0.09 = 3.09 \text{ in. water}$$

$$\text{Air hp} = \frac{Qh_t}{6{,}355} = \frac{120 \times 3.09}{6{,}355} = \mathbf{0.0583} \text{ hp}$$

6.14 Horsepower input $= \frac{Qh_t}{6{,}355 \times \text{eff}} = \frac{(60{,}000/60)(2)}{6{,}355 \times 0.40}$

$$= 0.786 \text{ hp}$$

Use 1-hp motor.

6.15 N = standard commercial ton
cop = coefficient of performance
1-ton capacity = 12,000 Btu per hr
20-ton capacity = 240,000 Btu per hr

a. $Q = W \times C_p(t_2 - t_1)$

$$W = \frac{240{,}000}{0.24(90 - 70)} = \textbf{50,000} \text{ lb per hr}$$

b. Assuming cop = 4

$$\text{hp} = \frac{(4.71)N}{\text{cop}} = \frac{4.71 \times 20}{4} = \textbf{23.5} \text{ hp}$$

6.16 Refer to ammonia tables or charts for property values.

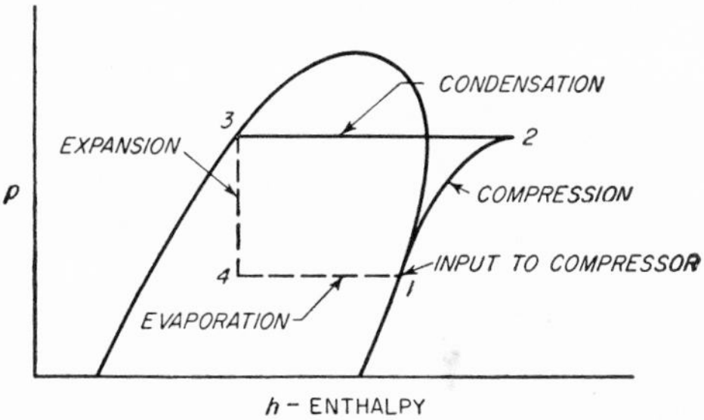

FIG. 6.16

a. $$\text{Volume efficiency} = \frac{\text{volume ammonia delivered per min}}{\text{piston displacement (rpm)}}$$

Volume ammonia delivered per min to compressor = 2 × (volume efficiency) × (piston displacement) (rpm)

$$= 2 \times 0.82 \left\{(1)\left[\frac{\pi}{4} \times (1)^2\right]\right\} (150) = 193 \text{ cfm}$$

Ammonia at 31.16 psi (from tables)—saturated, $v_1 = 8.92$ cu ft per lb

$$\text{Weight to be circulated} = \frac{193}{8.92} = 21.60 \text{ lb per min}$$

Refrigeration effect = $h_1 - h_3 = 612 - 143 = 469$ Btu per lb

$$\text{Capacity} = \frac{\text{lb per (min)(Btu per lb)}}{200} = \frac{(21.6)(469)}{200}$$

$= \textbf{50.5}$ standard commercial tons

b. $\dfrac{\text{Btu extracted}}{\text{Pounds ice at 16°F}} = C_{p_W}(t_2 - 32) + \text{heat of fusion} +$
$c_{p_I}(32 - 16) = 1(80 - 32) + 144 + 0.5(32 - 16) = 48$
$+ 144 + 8 = 200$ Btu per lb ice $= 400{,}000$ Btu per ton ice

$$\frac{\text{Ice, tons}}{24\text{ hr}} = \frac{\text{capacity} \times 288{,}000 \text{ Btu per 24 hr}}{\text{Btu extracted per ton ice}} = \frac{50.5 \times 288{,}000}{400{,}000}$$
$$= \mathbf{36.4} \text{ tons ice}$$

c. Ideal horsepower $= \dfrac{778W(h_2 - h_1)}{33{,}000}$ (for isentropic expansion) $= \dfrac{778 \times 21.6(724 - 612)}{33{,}000} = 57.0$ hp

$$\text{Brake horsepower} = \frac{\text{Ideal hp}}{\text{Over-all efficiency}} = \frac{57.0}{0.80} = \mathbf{71.2} \text{ hp}$$

6.17 P_D = diametral pitch
N = number of teeth
D = pitch diameter
T_V = train value
w = rpm

$$P_D = \frac{N}{D}, \quad N_A = P_D D_A = 12 \times 3 = 36 \text{ teeth}$$

$$N_C = N_A + 2N_B = 36 + 2 \times 18 = 72 \text{ teeth}$$

$$\frac{W_A - W_D}{W_C - W_D} = T_V = \frac{N_C}{N_A} = \frac{72}{36} = -2$$

Case I: Gear *A* clutched in, gear *C* fixed.

$$\frac{W_A - W_{D(\text{I})}}{0 - W_{D(\text{I})}} = -2, \quad W_A - W_{D(\text{I})} = 2W_{D(\text{I})}, \; W_{D(\text{I})} = \frac{W_A}{3} \qquad (1)$$

Case II: Gear A fixed, gear C clutched in.

$$\frac{0 - W_{D(\text{II})}}{W_C - W_{D(\text{II})}} = -2, \quad W_{D(\text{II})} = 2W_C - 2W_{D(\text{II})}, \; W_{D(\text{II})} = \frac{2W_C}{3} \qquad (2)$$

(For same input speed, $W_A = W_C$)

$$\therefore \frac{W_{D(\text{II})}}{W_{D(\text{I})}} = \frac{\frac{2}{3}W_C}{\frac{1}{3}W_A} = \frac{2W_C}{1W_C} = \mathbf{2}$$

6.18 $P_1 = 20$ psia
$P_2 = 190$ psia
$t_3 = 80°F$
$S_1 = S_2 = 1.3700$
$h_1 = 606.2$ Btu per lb
$h_2 = 753$ Btu per lb
$h_3 = h_4 = 132$ Btu per lb

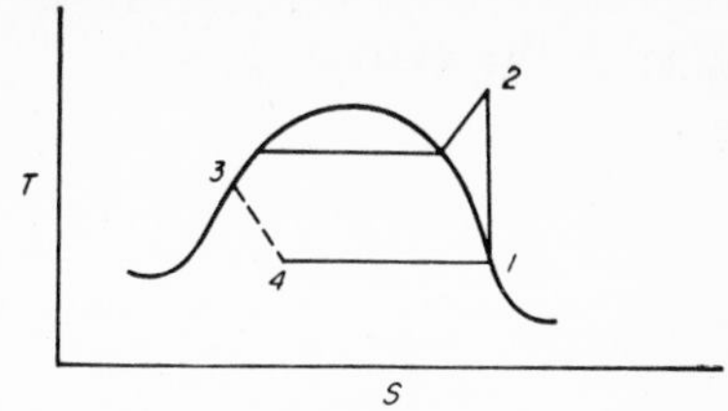

FIG. 6.18

a. $W = h_2 - h_1 = 753 - 606.2 =$ **146.8** Btu per lb
b. $Q_R = h_2 - h_3 = 753 - 132 =$ **621** Btu per lb
c. $Q_A =$ refrigeration $= (h_1 - h_4) = 606.2 - 132$
$=$ **474.2** Btu per lb

d. $\text{cop} = \frac{QA}{W} = \frac{474.2}{146.8} =$ **3.23**

e. $\text{Circulation} = \frac{200 \text{ Btu per min}}{474.2 \text{ Btu per lb}} =$ **0.422** lb per min per ton of refrigeration

6.19 *a.* Displacement volume = stroke × area

$$= 6.00 \times \frac{\pi}{4} \times (5.375)^2 = 136 \text{ cu in.}$$

Initial volume = displacement volume + clearance volume $= 136 + 23.4 = 159.4$ cu in.

$$\text{Compression ratio} = \frac{\text{initial volume}}{\text{clear volume}} = \frac{159.4}{23.4} = \mathbf{6.82 \text{ to } 1}$$

b. $$\text{Brake hp} = \frac{Tn}{63{,}000} = \frac{(12 \times 2{,}100) \times 2{,}500}{63{,}000} = 1{,}000 \text{ hp}$$

$$b_{\text{mep}} = \frac{33{,}000 \times \text{bhp}}{LAN} = \frac{33{,}000 \times 1{,}000}{0.5[(\pi/4)(5.375)^2] \times 17{,}500} = \mathbf{166 \text{ psig}}$$

where T = torque (in-lb)
n = rpm
L = stroke in feet
A = piston area (sq in.)

$$N = \text{power cycles per min} = \frac{14 \times 2{,}500}{2}$$

c. Brake hp per lb $= 1{,}000/1{,}450 =$ **0.689** hp per lb

6.20 *a.* Mean torque $= \dfrac{\text{maximum torque} + \text{minimum torque}}{2}$

$$T_m = \frac{20{,}000 + (-6{,}000)}{2} = 7{,}000 \text{ ft-lb}$$

Variable torque $= \dfrac{\text{maximum } T - \text{minimum } T}{2}$

$$T_v = \frac{20{,}000 - (-6{,}000)}{2} = 13{,}000 \text{ ft-lb}$$

Mean component of stress $= S_m = \dfrac{16T_m}{\pi D^3} = \dfrac{16 \times 7{,}000}{\pi D^3}$

$$= \frac{35{,}600 \text{ psi}}{D^3}$$

Variable component of stress $= S_v = \dfrac{16T_r}{\pi D^3} = \dfrac{16 \times 13{,}000}{\pi D^3}$

$$= \frac{66{,}200 \text{ psi}}{D^3}$$

$$S_n(\text{reversed torsion}) = S_{t_{ult}} \times \frac{0.50}{2} = \frac{97{,}000}{4} = 24{,}250 \text{ psi}$$

$$S_{s_{yp}} = 0.55\, S_{t_{yp}} = 0.55 \times 58{,}000 = 31{,}900 \text{ psi}$$

$$\frac{1}{\text{Factor of safety}} = \frac{S_v}{S_n} + \frac{S_m}{S_y}$$

$$\frac{1}{2} = \frac{66{,}200}{24{,}250\, D^3} + \frac{35{,}600}{31{,}900\, D^3} = \frac{2.73}{D^3} + \frac{1.12}{D^3} = \frac{3.85}{D^3}$$

$$D^3 = 7.70, \quad D = \mathbf{1.975} \text{ in.}$$

b. $\dfrac{S_{s_{yp}}}{\text{Factor of safety}} = \dfrac{16T}{\pi D^3} = \dfrac{31{,}900}{2} = \dfrac{16 \times 20{,}000}{\pi D^3}$

$$D^3 = 6.39, \quad D = \mathbf{1.855} \text{ in.}$$

c. Working stresses which have been determined from the ultimate or yield-point values of a material with a factor of safety will give safe and reliable results only for static loading. Failures in machine parts subjected to variable loading occur at stresses considerably below yield point. Because of this "fatigue" phenomenon, the diameter calculated on the basis of a static torque loading in part *b* would not stand up under the variable loading acting on the shaft in part *a*.

6.21 $e_L = BLv \times 10^{-8}$

e_L = volts (emf), B = gausses, L = length (cm), v = velocity (cm per sec)

44.70 cm per sec = 1 mph, 30.48 cm = 1 ft

$$e_L = 0.85(30.48 \times 88)(44.70 \times 150) \times 10^{-8} = \mathbf{0.117} \text{ volts}$$

6.22 *a.* A boiler hp is equal to the power necessary to evaporate 34.5 lb water per hr from saturated water at 212°F to saturated steam at 212°F.

$$1 - \text{boiler hp} = \mathbf{33{,}475} \text{ Btu per hr}$$

b. 1 − mechanical hp = 33,000 ft-lb per min, 1 Btu = 778 ft-lb

$$1 - \text{mechanical hp} = 33{,}000/778 = \mathbf{42.4} \text{ Btu per min}$$

$$\therefore 1 - \text{boiler hp} = \frac{33{,}475/60}{42.4} = \mathbf{13.15} \text{ mechanical hp}$$

c. The factor of evaporation is the ratio that changes the actual evaporation rate (lb per hr) to the rate that would result if the boiler were operated from and at 212°F.

Equivalent evaporation = (actual evaporation)(factor of evaporation) = 4,000 × 1.06 = 4,240 lb per hr

$$\text{Boiler hp} = \frac{(\text{evaporation})(\text{latent heat @ 212°F})}{33{,}475}$$

$$= \frac{4{,}240 \times 970}{33{,}475} = \mathbf{123} \text{ boiler hp}$$

6.23 Over-all boiler efficiency $= \dfrac{W_{bo}(h_2 - h_1)}{W f q_H}$

where W_{bo} = lb steam delivered by boiler per hr
h_2 = enthalpy of delivered steam
h_1 = enthalpy of water entering boiler
W_f = lb fuel fired per hr
q_H = higher heating value of fuel per lb

$$W_{bo} = \frac{885{,}000}{4} = 221{,}250 \text{ lb steam per hr}$$

h_2(at 400 psi, 700°F) = 1362.7 Btu per lb, h_1(280) = 249.1

$$Wf = \frac{221{,}250(1362.7 - 249.1)}{0.825 \times 13{,}850} = 21{,}500 \text{ lb per hr}$$

$$= 21{,}500/2{,}000 = \mathbf{10.75} \text{ short tons per hr}$$

6.24

$$\frac{W_{bo}}{Wf} = 12.77$$

$$\text{Boiler efficiency} = \frac{W_{bo}(h_2 - h_1)}{Wf \times q_H}$$

From chart, h_2(200 psia 87°F superheat) = 1251.5 Btu per lb
h_1(93°F) = 61 Btu per lb

$$q_H = \frac{12.77(1{,}251.5 - 61)}{0.828} = 18{,}400 \text{ Btu per lb}$$

6.25 *a.* The following items are required to complete a heat balance:

1. Heat absorbed by the steam-generating unit
2. Heat lost in dry flue gas
3. Heat loss due to moisture in fuel
4. Heat loss due to moisture resulting from combustion of hydrogen
5. Heat loss due to moisture in air
6. Heat loss due to unburned combustible gases
7. Heat loss due to unconsumed combustibles in the refuse
8. Heat loss due to unconsumed hydrogen and hydrocarbon compounds in the chimney gases (Losses due to radiation and losses due to unaccounted-for causes are generally included in this item also.)

b. Orsat apparatus:

Mercury thermometer 0 to 220°F for water-temperature measurement
Mercury thermometer (gas-filled) 0 to 1000°F for steam temperature
Thermocouple pyrometer to 1600°F for flue-gas temperature
Pressure gages to 200 psi
Draft gages
Throttling calorimeter
Oxygen-bomb calorimeter
Apparatus for weighing or metering fuels
Psychrometer
Scale for weighing refuse, etc.
Calibrated volumetric tanks for water measurement

Watch
Steam tables
Furnaces for approximate analysis

c. 1. Orsat apparatus
2. Water-weighing tanks
3. Fuel-weighing equipment
4. Throttling calorimeter
5. Thermometers
6. Thermocouple pyrometer
7. Psychrometer
8. Ash-weighing equipment

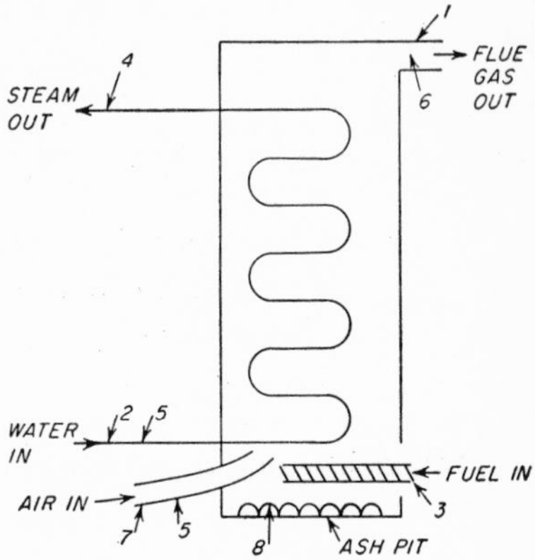

FIG. 6.25c

d. 1. Heat absorbed by generating unit $= w(h_2 - h_1)/w_f$
where w = amount of water evaporated (lb per hr)
w_f = fuel burned (lb per hr)
h_1 = enthalpy of steam entering unit (Btu per lb)
h_2 = enthalpy of steam leaving unit (Btu per lb)

2. Heat lost in dry flue gas $= 0.24\, w_g\, (t_g - t_a)$
where w_g = weight of dry flue gas per lb of fuel

$$= \frac{(4\ CO_2 + O_2 + 700)}{3(CO_2 + CO)}\left(Cb + \frac{S}{235}\right)$$ where Cb = carbon burned, lb, per lb fuel

t_g = temperature of gases leaving unit (°F)
t_a = temperature of air supplied for combustion (°F)

3. Heat loss due to moisture in fuel

$$\frac{M}{100}(1{,}066 + 0.5t_g - t_a) \text{ when } t_g > 575°\text{F}$$

$$\frac{M}{100}(1{,}089 + 0.46t_g - t_a) \text{ when } t_g < 575°\text{F}$$

where M = moisture, from approximate analysis, per cent by weight

4. Heat loss due to moisture resulting from combustion of hydrogen

$$\frac{9H}{100}(1{,}066 + 0.5t_g - t_a) \text{ when } t_g > 575°\text{F}$$

$$\frac{9H}{100}(1{,}089 + 0.46t_g - t_a) \text{ when } t_g < 575°\text{F}$$

where H = per cent hydrogen in fuel (from ultimate analysis)

5. Heat loss due to moisture in air = $0.47\, w_v\, (t_g - t_a)$

where $w_v = rdvw_a$ = weight of water vapor in air supplied for combustion

r = relative humidity of air supplied at temperature t_a

d = weight (lb) of water vapor to saturate 1 cu ft of dry air at temperature t_a

v = volume of 1 lb dry air at temperature t_a

w_a = weight of dry air supplied per pound of fuel

6. Heat loss due to unburned combustible gases

$$= C\left(\frac{10{,}160\ CO}{CO_2 + CO}\right)$$

where C = weight of carbon burned per pound of fuel

CO = per cent by volume, in dry gas leaving unit

CO_2 = per cent by volume, in dry gas leaving unit

7. Heat loss due to unconsumed combustible in refuse

$$= 14{,}600\left(\frac{w_a}{w_f} - \frac{A}{100}\right)$$

where w_a = weight of refuse and ash, lb per hr

w_f = weight of fuel, lb per hr

A = per cent ash (from ultimate analysis)

8. Losses due to radiation and not included above

$= F$ − (sum of items 1 to 7, inclusive)

where F = higher heating value of fuel, Btu per pound

Item 8 should be less than 2 per cent.

6.26 The operation of this stoker-fired plant during the second year was essentially carried out with a reduced amount of excess air. This is apparent from figures given: with 0 per cent CO and 10 per cent combustible in the ash pit there was 6.25 per cent O_2 left in the flue gas during the first year's operation. In the second year's operation, besides the 0.1 per cent CO and the increased combustible (16 per cent − 10 per cent = 6 per cent) in the ash pit, both of which would require O_2 to burn to CO_2, as in the first year, there was only 3.9 per cent O_2 left in the flue gas. This shows that much less air was supplied in the second year, causing more combustion losses due to incomplete combustion, i.e., CO in the flue gas and unburned carbon in the ash pit. The increase in per cent CO_2 occurred because less air passed into the flue gas during the second year. The per cent N_2 should not change much; therefore in the flue-gas analysis the per cent O_2 decreased and the per cent CO_2 increased.

The efficiency = heat transferred through boiler and tubes per pound of coal fired, divided by the heating value per pound of coal fired.

During the second year, because of reduced air supply and therefore less efficient combustion, less heat was liberated from each pound of coal. The temperature in the furnace, however, was higher because there was less excess air to absorb the heat that was released. The higher temperature in the furnace meant a greater temperature difference above the steam in the boiler and tubes. This temperature difference forced a greater rate of heat transfer to the steam. That is, although each pound of coal released less heat than in the first year, a greater portion of this heat was transferred to the steam because of the higher temperature difference. This compensated for the smaller amount of heat released from each pound of coal so that the numerator in the efficiency equation above remained unchanged, thus generating the same weight of steam from the same weight of coal each year. Since the same type of coal was used both years, the denominator did not change. Therefore the efficiency did not change.

The increased 2 per cent cost per thousand pounds of steam can be explained by (*a*) the faster deterioration and consequent replacement of furnace refractory and boiler tubes, due to operation at higher temperatures, (*b*) the increased slagging of boiler tubes at higher temperatures, requiring more frequent soot-blower operation, and (c) the greater refuse-handling cost, because of increased combustible in the ash pit.

6.27 Assumptions:

a. Steam generated at 190 psia from 60°F water.

b. Boiler rated at 250 boiler hp. Average operation consists of 3 boilers operating simultaneously at 200 per cent rating, 16 hr per day, 5 days per week.

c. Average pay of boiler-room personnel is \$4,200 per year.

d. Total cost of boiler-room installation, complete, including four boilers, all equipment, land and buildings, and 20-year amortization cost is \$200,000.

e. Steam generated per year = 33,480(Btu/hr × hp) × 250(hp/boiler) × 2(rating) × 16(hr/day) × 5(days/week) × 52(weeks/year) × 3 boilers all divided by (1,190 − 28) (Btu/lb steam) × 1,000(lb steam/1,000 lb steam)
= 180,000,000 lb steam per year

f. Cost of fuel
= 180,000,000(lb steam/year)
× 1162(Btu/lb steam) × \$4.50 (cost ton coal) all divided by 12,000(Btu/lb coal) × 0.75(efficiency)
× 2,000(lb coal/ton coal) = \$ 52,400 per year

g. Wages = 12 men at \$4,200 per man per year = \$ 50,400 per year

h. Water cost

$$= \frac{40(\text{per cent}) \times 180{,}000{,}000(\text{lb/year}) \times 0.07(\$/1{,}000 \text{ gal})}{8.34(\text{lb/gal}) \times 1{,}000(\text{gal}/1{,}000 \text{ gal})} = \$ \quad 605 \text{ per year}$$

i. Amortized cost and depreciation

$$= \frac{\$200{,}000}{20} = \$ \ 10{,}000 \text{ per year}$$

j. Lubricants and miscellaneous supplies = \$ 2,000 per year

k. Miscellaneous costs like taxes, overhead, insurance, power, special purchases = \$ 5,000 per year

Cost per year—total of items *e* to *k* = \$120,405 per year

$$\text{Cost per 1,000 lb steam} = \frac{120{,}405}{180{,}000} = \$0.67/1{,}000 \text{ lb steam}$$

Based on the above assumptions and the given boiler plant conditions, the cost is 67 cents per 1,000 pounds steam. It would be advisable to pay any price under 65 cents per 1,000 pounds steam. The 2 cents per 1,000 pounds difference will take care of \$0.02 × 180,000 = \$3,600 for part-time service of 1 man to check on steam flow meters, coordinate demand with the new supplier, and check the safety and condition of the steam distribution system. If the existing boiler plant is to be salvaged when steam is purchased, then depending on salvage value and additional factory space that becomes available, the price can be raised above 65 cents per 1,000 pounds steam to be purchased.

6.28 R_f = reheat factor
q_r = stage reheat, Btu per lb
n_{st} = stage efficiency
v_b = blade velocity, ft per sec
v_1 = steam entrance velocity, ft per sec

At 180 psia and 600°F,

$$h_0 = 1323.5 \text{ Btu per lb}$$
$$ih_2 = 1111.0 \text{ Btu per lb}$$
$$\Delta H_s = 212.5 \text{ Btu per lb}$$

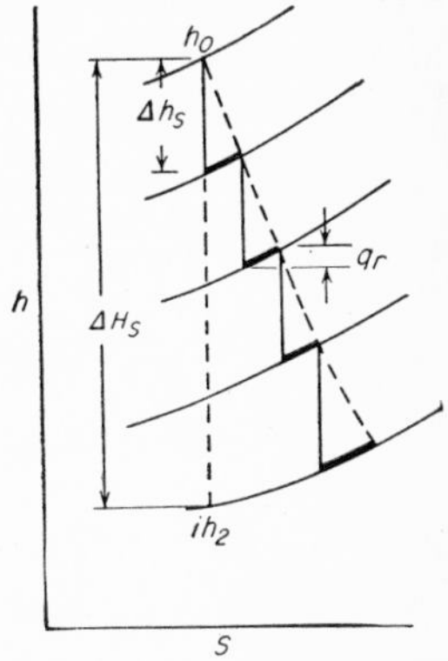

FIG. 6.28

$$\rho = \frac{V_b}{V_1} = \frac{\cos \alpha}{2} \text{ for maximum efficiency}$$

Let nozzle angle = α = 20°.

$$\rho = \frac{\cos 20°}{2} = \frac{0.940}{2} = 0.470$$

However, considering disk friction and fanning, ρ for maximum efficiency will be less, or say $\rho = 0.420$

$$V_1 = \frac{V_b}{\rho} = \frac{625}{0.420} = 1{,}490 \text{ ft per sec}$$

Assume nozzle velocity coefficient = K_n = 0.95

$$\text{Ideal entrance velocity} = iV_1 = \frac{V_1}{k_n} = \frac{1{,}490}{0.95} = 1{,}565 \text{ ft per sec}$$

$$\Delta h_s = \frac{iV_1^2}{2g778} = \frac{(1{,}565)^2}{64.4 \times 778} = 48.9 \text{ Btu per lb}$$

Find number of stages

$$Z = \frac{\Delta H_s \times R_f}{\Delta h_s} = \frac{212.5 \times 1.06}{48.9} = 4.6$$

Select turbine of four stages.

Find Δhs:

$$\Delta hs = \frac{\Delta H_s \times R_f}{Z} = \frac{212.5 \times 1.06}{4} = 56.3 \text{ Btu per lb, first trial}$$

$$q_r = \Delta h_s(1.00 - \eta_{st}) = 56.3(1.00 - 0.75) = 14.1 \text{ Btu per lb}$$

Stage	Nozzle or wheel	Enthalpy	Pressure
1	N	1,323.5 56.3	180
	W	1,267.2 14.1	
			107
2	N	1,281.3 56.3	
	W	1,225.0 14.1	
			59
3	N	1,239.1 56.3	
	W	1,182.8 14.1	
			31
4	N	1,196.9 56.3	
	W	1,140.6	15

Exhaust pressure should be 16 psia, which for this trial would give an enthalpy = 1146.0 Btu per lb. Another trial value of Δh_s will be necessary. An estimate of second trial Δh_s may be made using the following approach:

$$\Delta h_s = \text{first trial } \Delta h_s - \frac{\text{error in enthalpy}}{Z\eta_{st}}$$

$$\Delta h_s = 56.3 - \frac{(1{,}146 - 1{,}140.6)}{4(0.75)} = 54.5 \text{ Btu per lb}$$

$$q_r = 54.5(1.00 - 0.75) = 13.6 \text{ Btu per lb}$$

Assuming that the second trial yields sufficiently accurate results, the calculations may be continued as follows:

Total internal work per lb steam $= E_i = Z(\Delta h_s - q_r)$

$$= 4(54.5 - 13.6) = 164 \text{ Btu per lb}$$

$$\text{Actual engine efficiency} = \frac{E_i}{\Delta H_s} = \frac{164}{212.5} \times 100 = \mathbf{77.2} \text{ per cent}$$

$$\text{Ideal steam rate} = \frac{3{,}413}{212.5} = \mathbf{16} \text{ lb per kwhr}$$

Assuming radiation and mechanical losses as 2 per cent of the internal work of the turbine,

$$\frac{\text{Ideal steam rate}}{\text{Actual steam rate}} = 0.98 \times \eta_i = 0.98 \times 0.772 = 0.756$$

$$\text{Actual steam rate} = \frac{16}{0.756} = \mathbf{21.2} \text{ lb per kwhr}$$

6.29 For Corliss engine diagram factor = 0.85.

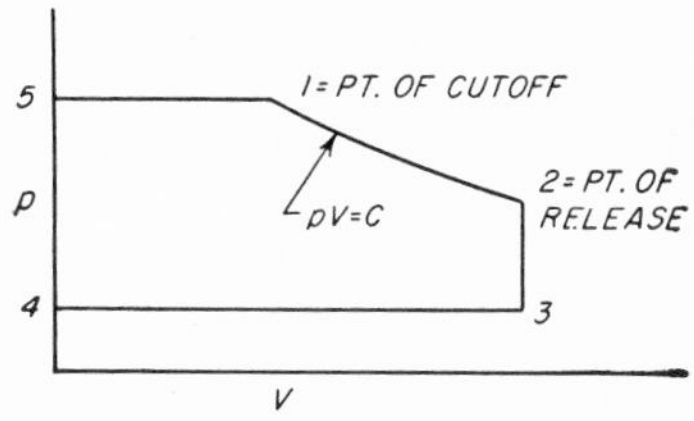

Fig. 6.29

$$\text{Conventional diagram } \frac{V_1}{V_2} = \frac{3}{8} = \frac{1}{r_e}, \text{ where } r_e = 2.67$$

$$\text{Head end piston area} = \frac{\pi}{4}(28)^2 = 615.0 \text{ sq in.}$$

$$\text{Piston rod area} = \frac{\pi}{4}(5)^2 = \underline{19.6 \text{ sq in.}}$$

$$\text{Crank end piston area} = 595.4 \text{ sq in.}$$

a. p_{m_e} = mean efficiency pressure (conventional)

$$= P_1\left(\frac{1 + \log_e r_e}{r_e}\right) - P_3 = 150\left(\frac{1 + \log_e 2.67}{2.67}\right) - P_3$$

$$= 56.3(1 + 0.981) - 15 = \mathbf{96.8} \text{ psia}$$

P_{m_a} = mean effective pressure (actual)
= (diagram factor) $\times P_{m_c}$
= $0.85 \times 96.8 =$ **82.3** psia

b. $ihp \text{ head end} = \dfrac{P_{m_a} L A_H N}{33{,}000} = \dfrac{82.3 \times (54/12) \times 615 \times 60}{33{,}000}$
= **413** hp

$ihp \text{ crank end} = \dfrac{P_{m_a} L A_C N}{33{,}000}$
$= \dfrac{82.3 \times (54/12) \times 595.4 \times 60}{33{,}000}$
= **401** hp

Indicated hp = 814

Assuming 90° mechanical efficiency, hp delivered at crankshaft = (mechanical efficiency)($i$hp) = 0.90×814
= **733** hp

c. Horsepower delivered to mill
= (brake hp)(0.90)(0.90)(0.85) = **505** hp

6.30 Load factor = (average power)/(peak power)
Efficiency of steam-generating unit = 80 per cent
Heating value of Pittsburgh bituminous coal = HV = 13,400 Btu per lb

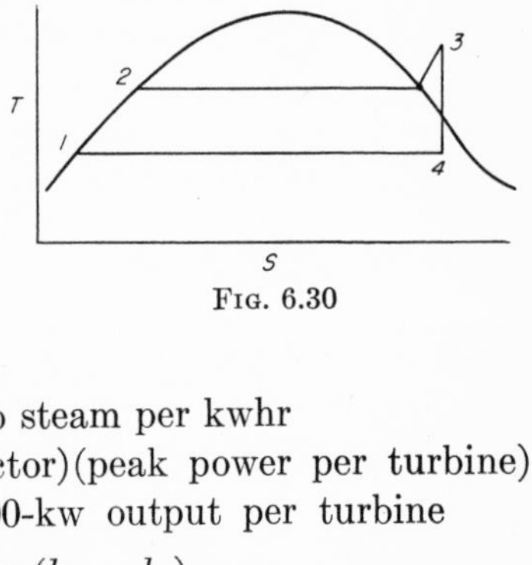

FIG. 6.30

Average steam rate = 11 lb steam per kwhr
Average power = (load factor)(peak power per turbine)
= $0.75 \times 10{,}000$ = 7,500-kw output per turbine

$$\text{Efficiency} = \frac{w_n(h_3 - h_1)}{w_f(HV)}$$

Obtain h_3 and h_1 from tables and charts

a. w_n = lb steam supplied per hr = (steam rate)(kw output)
= $11 \times 7{,}500$ = 82,500 lb steam per hr

w_f = weight of fuel fired
$= \dfrac{82{,}500(1{,}318 - 69.1)}{0.80 \times 13{,}400}$ = 9,620 lb/hr/turbine

Tons coal per day for four units $= \dfrac{4 \times 9{,}620 \times 24}{2{,}000} =$ **461** *b*. Assume 10°F rise in cooling water and no subcooling.

Q_R = (heat rejected by four turbines) $= 4w_n(h_4 - h_1)$

$= w_w(\Delta T) = 4 \times 82{,}500(921 - 69.1) = 281{,}000{,}000$ Btu per hr

$w_w = Q_R/\Delta T = 281{,}000{,}000/10 = 28{,}100{,}000$ lb per hr

$$\text{Gallons water per min} = \frac{28{,}100{,}000 \times 7.48}{60 \times 62.4} = \mathbf{56{,}200}$$

6.31 Assuming uniform wear which is proportional to product of velocity and pressure

$$T = \pi\mu P_{(\max)} r_i(r_0^2 - r_i^2)$$

with one side effective and twice with two sides effective

where T = torque(in-lb)

μ = coefficient of friction

$P_{(\max)}$ = maximum pressure

r_i = inside radius

r_0 = outside radius

$= 1.25\, r_i$

N = total axial pressure

$$\therefore\ T = 2\pi \times 0.3 \times 12 \times r_i^3[(1.25)^2 - (1)^2] = 6{,}516$$

$$r_i^3 = \frac{6{,}516}{22.7(1.562 - 1{,}000)} = 512$$

$r_i = \mathbf{8.00}$ in. and $r_0 = \mathbf{10.00}$ in.

$$N = \frac{T}{\mu(r_0 + r_i)} = \frac{6{,}516}{0.3(10 + 8)} = \mathbf{1{,}205}\ \text{lb}$$

6.32 $$\text{Indicated work per revolution} = \frac{(\text{output hp}) \times 33{,}000}{N \times \text{efficiency}}$$

$$= \frac{20 \times 33{,}000}{1{,}800 \times 0.80} = 458 \text{ ft-lb per revolution}$$

Let N = mean rpm

N_2 = maximum rpm

N_1 = minimum rpm

ω = radians per second

c_f = coefficient of fluctuation

J = mass moment of inertia = lb-sec² per ft

$\bar{r}$ = radius to concentrated mass (in.)

$$\omega = \frac{2\pi N}{60}$$

Excess energy delivered to flywheel = change in kinetic energy of fly wheel = ΔkE = (0.20)(458)

$$\Delta kE = 91.6 \text{ ft-lb} = \frac{1}{2} J(\omega_2^2 - \omega_1^2)$$

$$= \frac{1}{2}\frac{W}{g}\left(\frac{\bar{r}}{12}\right)^2 \left[\left(\frac{2\pi N_2}{60}\right)^2 - \left(\frac{2\pi N_1}{60}\right)^2\right]$$

$$= \frac{W}{2g}\left(\frac{\bar{r}\pi}{360}\right)^2 (N_2^2 - N_1^2)$$

since $N = \dfrac{N_2 + N_1}{2}$ and $c_f = \dfrac{N_2 - N_1}{N}$,

$$\begin{aligned} N_2 + N_1 &= 2N \\ N_2 - N_1 &= c_f N \\ \hline N_2^2 - N_1^2 &= 2c_f N^2 \end{aligned}$$

$$\Delta kE = 91.6 = \frac{W}{2g}\left(\frac{\bar{r}\pi}{360}\right)^2 2c_f N^2 = \frac{50}{64.4}\left(\frac{7\pi}{360}\right)^2 2c_f(1{,}800)^2$$

$$c_f = 0.00488$$

$$\begin{aligned} N_2 + N_1 = 2N &= 3{,}600 \text{ rpm} \\ N_2 - N_1 = c_f N &= 8.8 \text{ rpm} = \text{total speed variation} \\ \hline 2N_2 &= 3{,}608.8 \text{ rpm} \\ N_2 &= 1{,}804.4 \text{ rpm} \\ N_1 &= 1{,}795.6 \text{ rpm} \end{aligned}$$

6.33 Let V_1 = steam velocity leaving nozzle (ft per sec)
V_{1_r} = relative velocity entering blade (ft per sec)
V_2 = absolute exit velocity (ft per sec)
V_{2_r} = relative velocity leaving blade (ft per sec)
Δh = available energy (Btu per lb)
K = velocity coefficient
V_b = blade velocity (ft per sec)
β = blade-entrance angle (degrees)
F = force per lb steam per sec
w = lb steam per sec

a. $V_1 = 223.8\, k \sqrt{\Delta h} = 223.8 \times 0.95 \times \sqrt{100}$
$= 2{,}120$ ft per sec

b, *c*, *d*, and *e*.

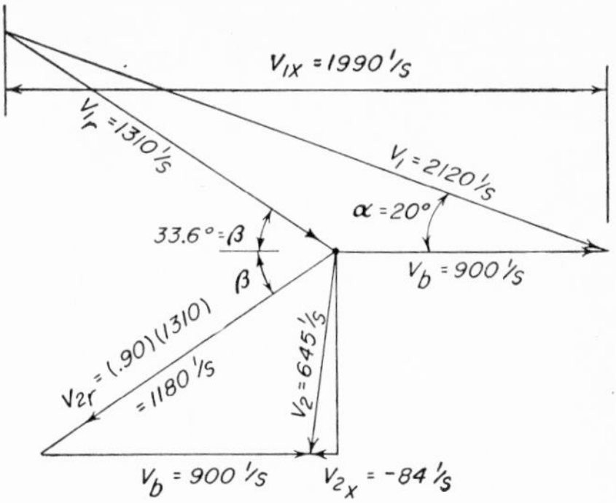

FIG. 6.33

$$f.\ F = \frac{V_{1_x} - V_{2_x}}{g} = \frac{1{,}990 - (-84)}{32.2} = \mathbf{64.4}\ \frac{\text{lb}}{\text{(lb steam per sec)}}$$

$$g.\ \text{Blade hp} = \frac{W(V_{1_x} - V_{2_x})V_b}{g \times 550} = \frac{1{,}800}{3{,}600} \times \frac{64.4 \times 900}{550} = \mathbf{52.6}\ \text{hp}$$

h. Shaft hp = blade hp − friction loss hp − windage loss hp
= 52.6 − 6 − 2 = **44.6** hp

i. Losses converted into enthalpy of steam

(1) Nozzle loss $= (1 - k^2)\ 100$
$= [1 - (0.95)^2]\ 100 = 9.75$ Btu per lb

(2) Blade friction loss $= \dfrac{V_{1_r}^2 - V_{2_r}^2}{2gJ}$

$$= \frac{(1{,}310)^2 - (1{,}180)^2}{64.4 \times 778} = 6.52 \text{ Btu per lb}$$

(3) Residual velocity loss $= \dfrac{V_2^2}{2gJ}$

$$= \frac{(645)^2}{64.4 \times 778} = 8.30 \text{ Btu per lb}$$

(4) Friction between steam and wheel

$$= \frac{\text{hp} \times 550}{wJ} = \frac{6 \times 550 \times 2}{778} = 8.48 \text{ Btu per lb}$$

total = 33.05 Btu per lb

Enthalpy of exhaust steam = 1,200 − 100 + 33 = 1133 Btu per lb

6.34 *Assumptions:*

a. The 125 psig steam supply at the source is saturated.

b. The 200 equivalent ft of pipe does not include resistance of pressure-reducing-valve control station.

c. Second fluid heat-transfer equipment is at higher than operating steam pressure.

d. Piping is insulated.

Solution: Let normal operating pressure be approximately 90 per cent of maximum working pressure at equipment. Therefore, normal operating pressure will be 0.9 (25 + 15) = 36 psia, or 21 psig. Let 7,000 fpm be a reasonable velocity of 125 psig steam in smaller pipe, and 8,000 fpm for 21 psig steam in larger pipe. Then for a 125-psig (140-psia) saturated steam line (assumption *a*) from the source to the p-r-v station, flow area =

$$3.22 \text{ cu ft/lb} \times 20{,}000 \text{ lb/hr} \times \frac{1}{60 \text{ min/hr}} \times \frac{1}{7{,}000 \text{ ft/min}} \times 144 \text{ sq in./sq ft} = 22.1 \text{ sq in.}$$

Use 5-in. schedule 40 pipe with flow area of 20.01 sq in.; since this pipe section is short, it will not normally operate under maximum conditions, and the cost of a 5-in. p-r-v station will be substantially less than that of a 6-in. p-r-v station. There is a trend away from the use of 5-in. pipe and valve sizes and, therefore, in some plants this size would be selected as 6 in. with consequent higher cost.

For a 21-psig (36-psia) steam line from the p-r-v station to the equipment, the throttled steam will be superheated since no heat is lost (assumption *d*).

Flow area =

$$11.28 \text{ cu ft/lb} \times 20{,}000 \text{ lb/hr} \times \frac{1}{60 \text{ min/hr}} \times \frac{1}{8{,}000 \text{ ft/min}} \times 144 \text{ sq in./sq ft} = 67.6 \text{ sq in.}$$

Use the next larger-size pipe which is 10-in. pipe with flow area of 78.85 sq in.

The 10-in. gate valve is located near the equipment since the p-r-v control station is located too far away from the equipment for convenient, quick shut off of steam (assumption *b*).

The 10-in. check valve will prevent the second fluid in the heat-transfer equipment from backing up to the p-r-v station and out of the relief valve if a tube or plate should rupture in the equipment (assumption *c*).

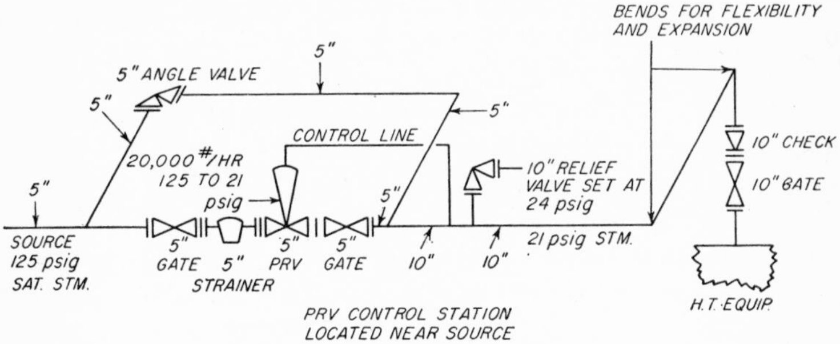

FIG. 6.34

6.35 c_{P_A} = specific heat of air (constant pressure)

c_{P_G} = specific heat of flue gas (constant pressure)

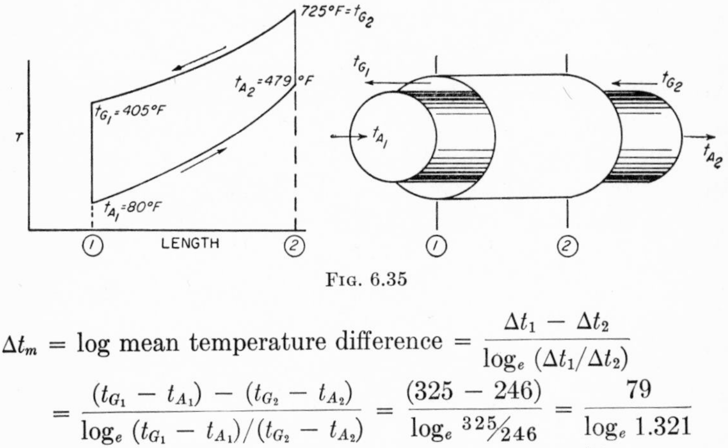

FIG. 6.35

$$\Delta t_m = \text{log mean temperature difference} = \frac{\Delta t_1 - \Delta t_2}{\log_e (\Delta t_1/\Delta t_2)}$$

$$= \frac{(t_{G_1} - t_{A_1}) - (t_{G_2} - t_{A_2})}{\log_e (t_{G_1} - t_{A_1})/(t_{G_2} - t_{A_2})} = \frac{(325 - 246)}{\log_e 325/246} = \frac{79}{\log_e 1.321}$$

$$= \frac{79}{0.278} = \mathbf{284°F}$$

$$Q = W_A c_{P_A}(t_{A_2} - t_{A_1}) = 357{,}000 \times 0.24 \times 399$$

$$= 34.2 \times 10^6 \text{ Btu per hr}$$

$$Q = W_G c_{P_G}(t_{G_2} - t_{G_1}) \text{ or } W_G = \frac{Q}{c_{P_G}(t_{G_2} - t_{G_1})}$$

$$W_G = \frac{34.2 \times 10^6}{0.24 \times 320} = 447{,}000 \text{ lb of flue gas}$$

Note: The specific heat of the flue gas is equal to the weighted average of the specific heats of its constituents. A typical flue-gas analysis is

$$
\begin{aligned}
CO_2 &= 0.15 \times 0.202 = 0.0303 \\
N_2 &= 0.80 \times 0.248 = 0.1983 \\
O_2 &= 0.05 \times 0.219 = 0.0110 \\
&\quad 1.00 \qquad\qquad\;\; 0.2396 \text{ or } 0.24
\end{aligned}
$$

6.36 For $P_1 = 1$ psig $= 15.75$ psia at 12 per cent moisture, $h_1 = 1{,}037$ Btu per lb

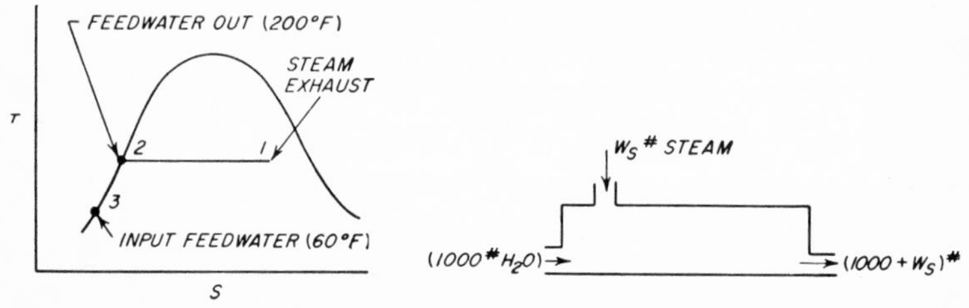

FIG. 6.36

Neglecting the effect of subcooling, which is nil in this case,
For $t_2 = 200°F$, $h_2 = 168$ Btu per lb
For $t_3 = 60°F$, $h_3 = 28.1$ Btu per lb
Heat absorbed by water = heat given up by steam.

$$
\begin{aligned}
1{,}000(h_2 - h_3) &= w_s \text{ lb } (h_1 - h_2) \\
1{,}000(168 - 28) &= w_s \text{ lb } (1{,}037 - 168) \\
w_s &= 1{,}000 \times {}^{140}\!/_{869} = \mathbf{161} \text{ lb}
\end{aligned}
$$

6.37 The equation of combustion is

$$C_{12}H_{26} + 18.5O_2 + 69.56N_2 + \underbrace{18.5O_2 + 69.56N_2}_{\text{Excess air}} \rightarrow$$

$$12CO_2 + 13H_2O + 69.56N_2 + \underbrace{18.5O_2 + 69.56N_2}_{\text{Excess air}}$$

The heat available to the heating system is the change in enthalpy of the products of combustion from 600°F (1060°R) to 75°F (535°R). Since it is possible that some of the H_2O vapor will condense at 75°F, giving off latent heat, this should be investigated. Assuming the products to be at 14.7 psia in the heating system, the partial pressure of the vapor will be

$$pp_{H_2O} = \frac{\text{No. of moles of } H_2O}{\text{No. of moles of products}} \times 14.7 \text{ psia} = \frac{13}{182.62} \times 14.7$$
$$= 1.048 \text{ psi or } 2.13 \text{ in. Hg}$$

The saturation pressure at 75°F = 0.875 in. Hg, and so H_2O will partially condense.

The number of moles of H_2O vapor at 75°F is

$$\frac{0.875}{29.92} \times 182.62 = 5.35 \text{ moles}$$

The number of moles that will condense = 13 − 5.35 = 7.65 moles.

The saturation temperature of steam corresponding to 2.13 in. of Hg is 103°F (563°R).

The ΔH of the H_2O from 1060°R to 535°R will be considered as: ΔH (5.35 moles from 1060 to 535°R) + ΔH (7.65 moles from 1060 to 563°R) + ΔH (7.65 moles condensing from 563 to 535°R)

h (Btu per lb-mole)

	CO_2	N_2	O_2
1060°R	9,350	8,129	7,544
535°R	−4,013	−3,716	−3,103
Δh	5,337	4,413	4,441

ΔH (Btu per lb-mole of product) = 12 × 5,337(CO_2) + 139.12 × 4,413 + 18.5 × 4,441 + $\Delta H(H_2O)$

$\Delta H(H_2O)$ = 5.35(8.595 − 4,242) + 7.65(8,595 − 4,474) + 7.65(1,098 − 43)18

ΔH = 64,000 + 615,000 + 82,200 + 23,300 + 31,500 +145,000
= 961,000 (Btu per mole of fuel)

Higher heating value = 20,550 (Btu per lb) × 170.2 (lb per lb-mole) = 3,500,000 (Btu per lb-mole)

$$\text{per cent utilization} = \frac{961,000}{3,500,000} \times 100 = 27.5 \text{ per cent}$$

6.38 W = indicated work
t = hours
T = torque (in-lb)
Q_A = heat added
e = thermal efficiency
w_f = fuel consumption (lb per hr)
L = stroke (ft)
q_L = lower heating value (Btu per lb)
A = area (sq in.)
P_m = mean effective pressure (psi)
N = explosions per min

$$\text{Indicated power} = P_m LAN = 110 \times 1 \times \left(\frac{121\pi}{4}\right) \times \left(\frac{300}{2}\right)$$

$$= 1{,}570{,}000\ \frac{\text{ft-lb}}{\text{min}} = \frac{1{,}570{,}000}{33{,}000} = 47.6 \text{ hp}$$

$$W \text{ per hr} = \frac{1{,}570{,}000 \times 60}{778} = 121{,}000 \text{ Btu per hr}$$

$$Q_A = q_L w_f = 18{,}000 \times 24 = 433{,}000 \text{ Btu per hr}$$

a. $$e = \frac{W \text{ per hr}}{Q_A} = \frac{121{,}000}{433{,}000} \times 100 = 28 \text{ per cent}$$

b. Mechanical efficiency = brake hp/indicated hp

$$\text{Brake hp} = \frac{T \times \text{rpm}}{63{,}000} = \frac{12 \times 700 \times 300}{63{,}000} = 40 \text{ hp}$$

$$\text{Mechanical efficiency} = \frac{40 \times 100}{47.6} = 84.2 \text{ per cent}$$

c. Specific gravity of fuel = 0.75
7.5 gal per cu ft

$$\frac{62.4 \times 0.75}{7.5} = 6.24 \text{ lb per gal,}$$

and $$\frac{24 \text{ lb per hr}}{6.24 \text{ lb per gal}} = 3.84 \text{ gal per hour}$$

Fuel cost per hr = 3.84 × 10 cents = \$0.384

$$\text{Fuel cost per hp per hr} = \frac{\$0.384}{40} = \$0.0096$$

6.39 T_1 = torque in
T_2 = torque out
n_1 = rpm in

n_2 = rpm out, and $n_1/n_2 = 4.11$
r = radius of wheel (ft)
F = tractive force
v = velocity (fpm)

a. hp out = efficiency × hp in

$$T_2 n_2 = \text{efficiency} \times T_1 \times n_1$$

$$T_2 = \frac{n_1}{n_2} \times T_1 \times \text{efficiency} = 4.11 \times 230 \times 0.97 = 915 \text{ ft-lb}$$

$$F = \frac{T_2}{r} = \frac{915}{(15/12)} = \frac{915}{1.25} = \mathbf{732} \text{ lb at both rear wheels}$$

$$b.\ \text{hp} = \frac{F_v}{33{,}000} = \frac{732 \times (40 \times 5{,}280/60)}{33{,}000} = \frac{732 \times 3{,}520}{33{,}000} = \mathbf{78.1} \text{ hp}$$

6.40 ihp = indicated horsepower per cylinder
bhp = brake horsepower
P_m = mean efficiency pressure (psi)
n = no. of cylinders
L = stroke (ft)
A = piston area (psi)
D = diameter (in.)
N = explosions per min

$$\frac{12 \times L(\text{ft})}{D(\text{in.})} = 1.4 \text{ and } D^2 = 73.5L^2$$

$$A = \frac{\pi D^2}{4} = 57.6L^2$$

$$\text{ihp} = \frac{\text{Bhp}}{(\text{mechanical efficiency}) \times n} = \frac{30}{0.85 \times 6} = 5.88$$

$$\text{ihp} = \frac{P_m LAN}{33{,}000} = 5.88 = \frac{90 \times L \times 57.6L^2 \times \left(\frac{1{,}800}{2}\right)}{33{,}000}$$

$$L^3 = 0.0416,\ L = \mathbf{0.346} \text{ ft or } \mathbf{4.15} \text{ in.}$$

$$D = \frac{4.15}{1.4} = \mathbf{2.97} \text{ in.}$$

6.41 *a.* Horsepower = hp = $Frn/63{,}000$
where n = rpm
r = pulley radius (in.)
F = net pull (lb) = $63{,}000 \times \text{hp}/rn$
$= 63{,}000 \times 10/3 \times 1{,}700 = 123.7$ lb

From Faires, "Design of Machine Elements," Macmillan, 1941, the net pull per inch of a single leather belt = 50 lb per in. Therefore, the belt width should be 123.7/50 or 2.5 in.

b. A crown holds a belt on the center of a pulley because the length of belt at each edge is less than it is at the center of the pulley. Thus as a belt travels to one side of center of the pulley, the opposite side of the belt tightens and pulls the belt toward the tight side. When the belt is centered, the edges have equal tensions, and the belt will run centered.

6.42 N = rpm
T = Number of teeth
x = number of gear pairs
F = force, lb
v = head velocity, fpm

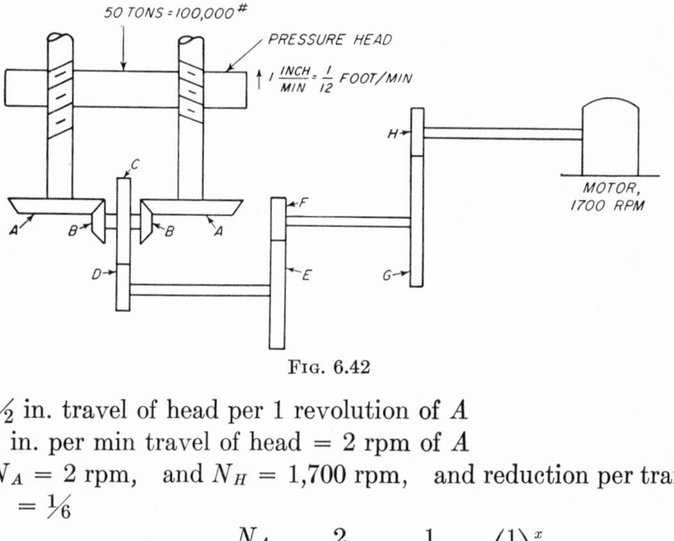

FIG. 6.42

½ in. travel of head per 1 revolution of A
1 in. per min travel of head = 2 rpm of A
$N_A = 2$ rpm, and $N_H = 1{,}700$ rpm, and reduction per train = ⅙

$$\text{Train valve} = T_V = \frac{N_A}{N_H} = \frac{2}{1{,}700} = \frac{1}{850} = \left(\frac{1}{y}\right)^x$$

when $x = 4$, as in sketch, $y = 5.4 < 6$ as required

$$T_V = \frac{T_H}{T_G} \times \frac{T_F}{T_E} \times \frac{T_D}{T_E} \times \frac{T_B}{T_A}$$

and assume y for spur-gear pairs to be 5, 5, and 6, and T multiples of 12

$$a.\ T_V = \frac{1}{850} = \frac{12}{60} \times \frac{12}{60} \times \frac{12}{72} \times \frac{T_B}{T_A}$$

$$\frac{T_B}{T_A} = \frac{150}{850} = \frac{15}{85} = \frac{1}{5.67}$$

Make T_B and T_A bevel gears, with teeth 15 and 85.

$$b.\ \text{hp} = \frac{F_v}{\text{efficiency} \times 33{,}000} = \frac{100{,}000 \times 1/12}{0.40 \times 33{,}000} = 0.632\ \text{hp}$$

Use a ¾-hp motor.

6.43 V = pitch line velocity
F_t = transmitted load
P_D = diametral pitch
n = number of teeth
b = face width
I = increment load
S_n = endurance limit
Y = form factor
F_w = wear load
N = rpm

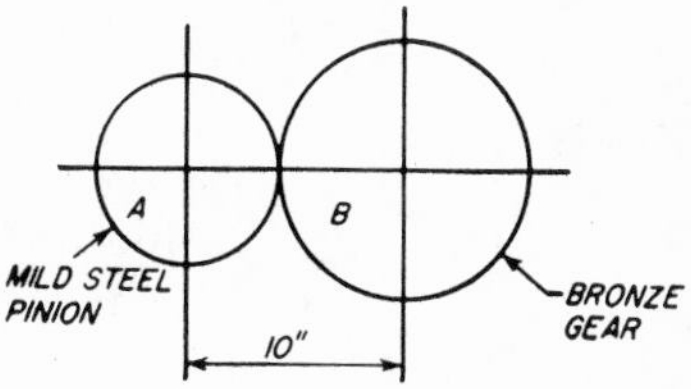

FIG. 6.43

$$\frac{R_A}{R_B} = \frac{\omega_B}{\omega_A} = 2/3 \text{ (given)}$$

$R_A = \frac{2}{3}R_B$

$R_A + R_B = 10$ in. (given)

$\frac{2}{3}R_B + \frac{3}{3}R_B = \frac{5}{3}R_B = 10$

$R_B = 6$ in. and $R_A = 4$ in.

$D_B = 12$ in. and $D_A = 8$ in.

$V = 2\pi N_A R_A = 2\pi \times 150 \times 4 = 3{,}770$ in. per min
$= 314$ ft per min

$$\text{hp} = \frac{F_t V}{33{,}000}, \quad F_t = \frac{33{,}000 \times 8}{314} = 841\ \text{lb}$$

All references to tables and pages are in Faires, "Design of Machine Elements," Macmillan, 1941.

e = maximum permissible error = 0.0045 (p. 216)
Use first-class commercial gears ($P_D > \frac{1}{2}$) (p. 216)
Assume $P_D = 6$ and expected error = 0.002 in. (p. 216)

Recommended proportions for cut teeth:

$$\frac{9.5}{P_D} < b < \frac{12.5}{P_D} \quad \text{or } 1.58 < b < 2.08$$

Use $b = $ **2** in.

Find dynamic load F_D

For 14½° full depth, $k = 0.107e$

$$C = \text{deformation factor} = \frac{kEgEp}{(Eg + Ep)}$$

$$= \frac{0.107 \times 0.002 \times 15 \times 10^6 \times 30 \times 10^6}{(15 + 30)10^6} = 2{,}140$$

$$F_D = \frac{0.05V(bC + F_t)}{0.05V + (bC + F_t)^{0.5}} + F_t = I + F_t$$

$$(bC + F_t) = 2 \times 2{,}140 + 841 = 5{,}121$$

$$I = 910 \text{ (p. 214) and } 920 \text{ (from the equation)}$$

$$F_D = 910 + 841 = \mathbf{1{,}751} \text{ lb}$$

Design is based on gear having smallest product of S_nY, where

$$F_s = \frac{S_nY_b}{P_D}$$

For gear (phosphor bronze):

$$T = P_D \times D = 6 \times 12 = 72 \text{ teeth,} \quad \text{and } Y = 0.360 \text{ (p. 204)}$$

$$S_nY = 24{,}000 \times 0.360 = \mathbf{8{,}640}$$

For pinion (SAE 1035):

$$T = P_DD = 6 \times 8 = 48 \text{ teeth,} \quad \text{and } Y = 0.345 \text{ (p. 204)}$$

$$S_nY = \frac{S_{ultimate}}{2} \times Y = \frac{87{,}000}{2} \times 0.345 = \mathbf{15{,}000}$$

∴ Bronze gear is weaker

$$F_s = \frac{24{,}000 \times 2 \times 0.360}{6} = 2{,}880 \text{ lb}$$

$$\text{Margin of safety} = \frac{F_s}{F_d} - 1 = \frac{2{,}880}{1{,}751} - 1 = 0.643$$

∴ Suitable for speed reducers, pumps, mining machinery, etc.

Check for wear:

$$Q = \frac{2D_B}{(D_A + D_B)} = \frac{2 \times 12}{(8 + 12)} = 1.2$$

Use SAE 1035 steel, tempering temperature = 600°F
Brinell No. 240 (Tables XXX and XXXIII)
By interpolation, $K = 126$

$$F_W = D_A bKQ = 8 \times 2 \times 126 \times 1.2 = 2{,}420 \text{ lb}$$
$$F_W > F_D, \quad 2{,}420 \text{ lb} > 1{,}751 \text{ lb}$$

$\therefore$ ($b = 2$ in.) and ($P_D = 6$) is suitable
b could be decreased somewhat to obtain a more economical design.

Recalculate for $b = 1\frac{7}{8}$ in. or $b = 1\frac{3}{4}$ in.

6.44 N = rpm of driving pulley
n = rpm of driven pulley
D = diameter of driving pulley
d = diameter of driven pulley

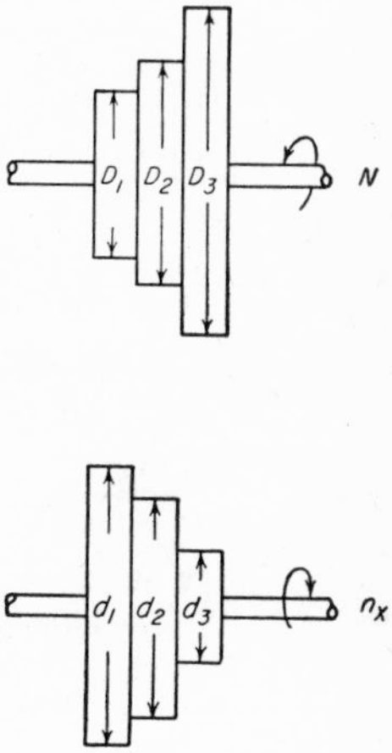

FIG. 6.44

For crossed belts

$$D_x + d_x = D_3 + d_3 \qquad (1)$$

and

$$\frac{n_x}{N} = \frac{D_x}{d_x} \qquad (2)$$

a. Find D_3 using equation (2)

$$\frac{n_3}{N} = \frac{D_3}{d_3} \text{ and } D_3 = \frac{n_3}{N} d_3$$
$$= \frac{500}{200} \times 6 = \mathbf{15} \text{ in.}$$

b. Find D_2 and d_2

$$D_2 + d_2 = D_3 + d_3 = 15 + 6 = 21 \text{ in.}$$
$$\frac{n_2}{N} = \frac{150}{200} = \frac{D_2}{d_2}, \quad \therefore D_2 = 0.75d_2$$
$$0.75d_2 + d_2 = 21, \ d_2 = \mathbf{12} \text{ in. and } D_2 = \mathbf{9} \text{ in.}$$

d. Find D_1 and d_1

$$D_1 + d_1 = 21 \text{ in.}$$
$$\frac{n_1}{N} = \frac{50}{200} = \frac{D_1}{d_1}, \quad \therefore D_1 = 0.25d_1$$
$$0.25d_1 + d_1 = 21 \text{ in.}, \ d_1 = \mathbf{16.8} \text{ in. and } D_1 = \mathbf{4.2} \text{ in.}$$

6.45

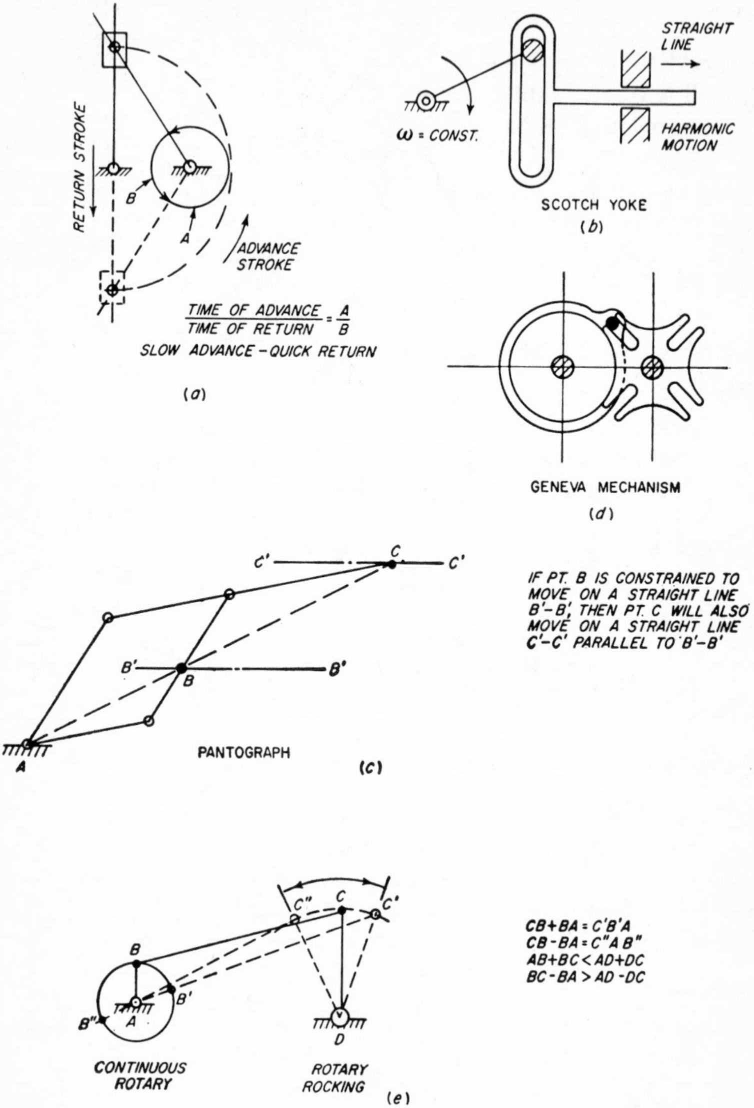
RETURN STROKE
B
A
ADVANCE STROKE
TIME OF ADVANCE / TIME OF RETURN = A / B
SLOW ADVANCE - QUICK RETURN
(a)
STRAIGHT LINE
ω = CONST.
HARMONIC MOTION
SCOTCH YOKE
(b)
GENEVA MECHANISM
(d)
C'
C
C'
B'
B
B'
A
PANTOGRAPH
(c)
IF PT. B IS CONSTRAINED TO MOVE ON A STRAIGHT LINE B'–B', THEN PT. C WILL ALSO MOVE ON A STRAIGHT LINE C'–C' PARALLEL TO B'–B'
C"
C
C'
B
B'
B"
A
D
CONTINUOUS ROTARY
ROTARY ROCKING
(e)
CB+BA = C'B'A
CB-BA = C"A B"
AB+BC < AD+DC
BC-BA > AD-DC

Fig. 6.45

6.46 *a.*

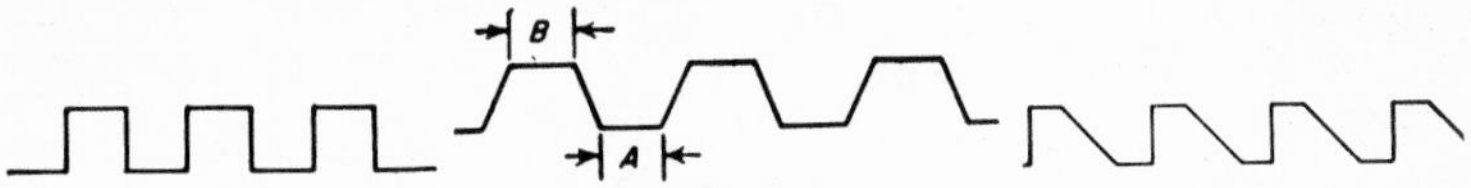

SQUARE THREAD

FIG. 6.46*a*. Most efficient (theoretically). A strong form. No means of adjustment for wear. Difficult to cut.

ACME THREAD

A is 0.0952 in. smaller than *B*, and therefore has self-locking values. A strong form. Easily machined with precision. Wear can be taken up.

BUTTRESS THREAD

Used for the translation of load in one direction only. A strong form that combines the advantages of the other two types.

b. 1. $S_s = \frac{S_t}{2}$ (allowable working)

S_s = shearing stress (psi)
S_t = tensile stress (psi)
A_t = area in tension (sq in.)
A_s = area in shear (sq in.)

2. $L = 2nt$, or $\frac{L}{2} = nt$

3. $S_t = \frac{F}{A_t} = \frac{F}{(\pi/4)D^2}$

4. $S_s = \frac{F}{A_s} = \frac{F}{\pi D \times nt}$

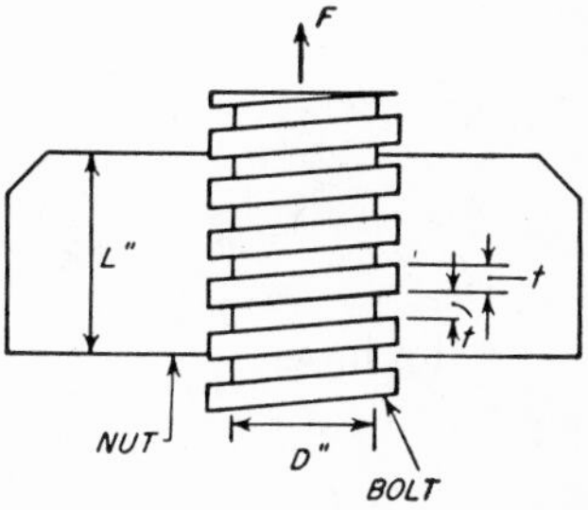

FIG. 6.46*b*

Substituting 2, 3, and 4 in 1,

$$\frac{F}{\pi D \times L/2} = \frac{F}{2 \times (\pi/4)D^2}, \quad \frac{1}{L} = \frac{1}{D}, \quad \text{and } L = D$$

6.47 F = 50 lb (in horizontal plane and at right angles to bar)

$$\frac{\text{Work (out)}}{\text{Revolutions}} = \text{efficiency} \times \frac{\text{Work (in)}}{\text{Revolutions}}$$

$W \times \text{pitch} = \text{efficiency} \times F \times 2\pi R$

$W \times \frac{1}{2} = 0.80 \times 50 \times 2\pi \times 30$

W = **15,100** lb

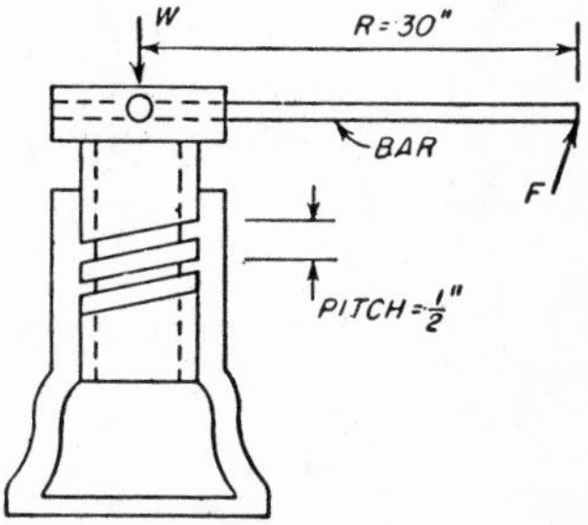

FIG. 6.47

6.48 $R = 12 + \frac{1}{2} \times \frac{7}{8} = 12.438$ in. $= 1.0365$ ft

Since lead of worm = two pitch distances, 40 revolutions of worm = one revolutions of drum

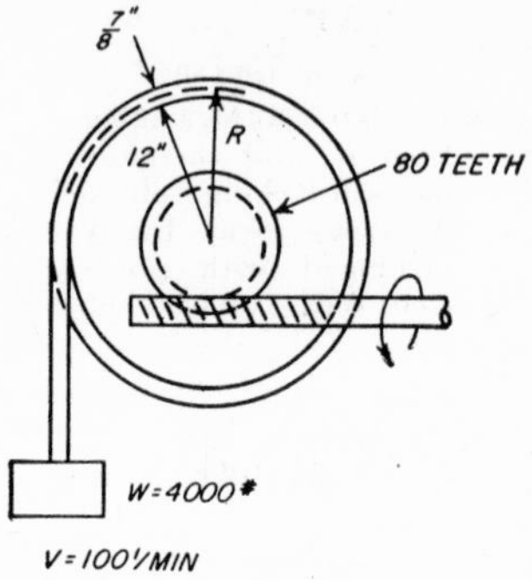

FIG. 6.48

$$\text{hp in} = \frac{\text{hp out}}{\text{efficiency}}$$

$$\text{hp in} = \frac{W \times V}{\text{efficiency} \times 33{,}000} = \frac{4{,}000 \times 100}{0.60 \times 33{,}000} = \mathbf{20.2}\ \text{hp}$$

$$\text{rpm drum} = \frac{V}{2\pi R} = \frac{100}{6.28 \times 1.0365} = 15.33\ \text{rpm}$$

$$\text{rpm worm} = 40 \times 15.33 = 613\ \text{rpm}$$

$$T_{(\text{in.})} = \frac{63{,}000 \times \text{hp}}{\text{rpm worm}} = \frac{63{,}000 \times 20.2}{613} = 2{,}075\ \text{in-lb}$$

$$T_{(\text{ft})} = \mathbf{173}\ \text{ft-lb}$$

6.49 $P = pA = 205 \times \frac{\pi}{4} \times (1.25)^2 = 252$ lb

N = effective coils = total coils − 2 = 9.5 − 2 = 7.5 coils
D = diameter of coil
d = diameter of wire, and y = deflection (in.)

$$C = \frac{D}{d} = \frac{(4.5 - 0.5)}{0.5} = 8$$

$$y = \frac{8\,PC^3N}{E_s d} = \frac{8 \times 252 \times 8^3 \times 7.5}{11.5 \times 10^6 \times 0.5} = 1.345\ \text{in.}$$

Initial compressed length = free length − y
= 8.00 in. − 1.345 in. = **6.66** in.

Solid length = $dN + 2d = 0.5 \times 7.5 + 2 \times 0.5 = 4.75$ in.
Deflection from free length to solid length = $y_c = 8.00 - 4.75 = 3.25$ in.

$$P_c = \frac{y_c}{y} \times P = \frac{3.25 \text{ in.}}{1.345 \text{ in.}} \times 252 \text{ lb} = 609 \text{ lb}$$
$$k = 1.18$$

(See curves of stress factors vs. spring index, Fig. 322, Faires, "Design of Machine Elements," Macmillan, 1941.)

$$S_s = \frac{k \times 2.55 P_c D}{d^3} = 1.18 \times 2.55 \times 609 \times 4 \times 8 = \mathbf{58{,}800} \text{ psi}$$

6.50

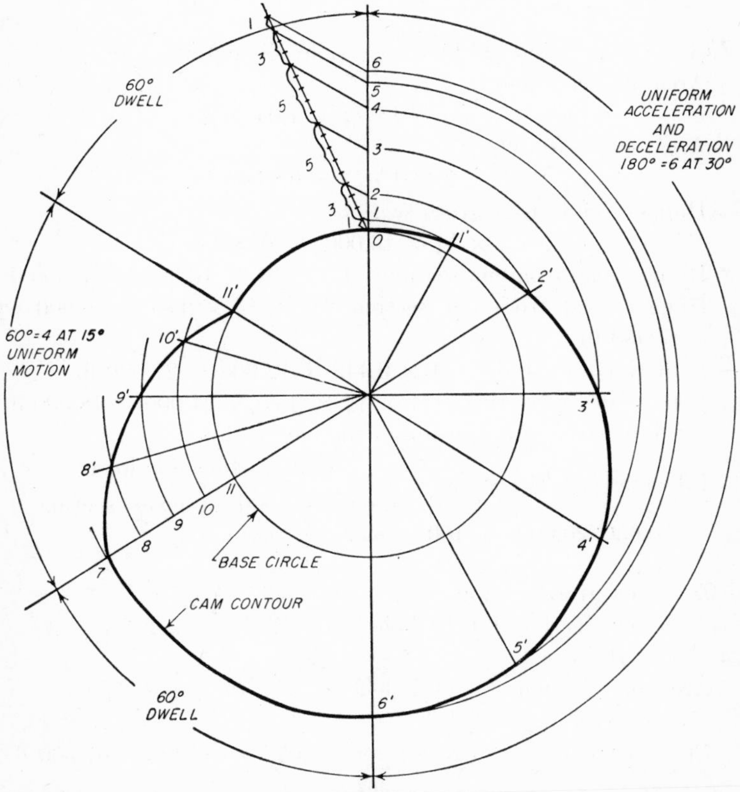

FIG. 6.50

SECTION SEVEN

7.01–7.75

STRUCTURAL ENGINEERING

7.01 Assume punched hole = $1\frac{3}{16}$ in. diameter

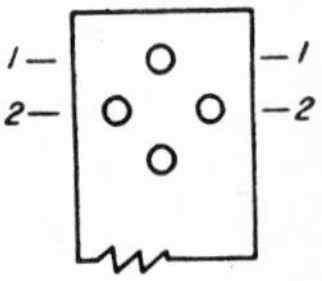

FIG. 7.01

Area net section 1-1

$= \frac{1}{4} \times (5 - 1\frac{3}{16}) = 1.04$ sq in.

Area net section 2-2

$= \frac{1}{4} \times (5 - 2 \times 1\frac{3}{16}) = 0.84$ sq in.

Hanger load from gross section

$= 5 \times \frac{1}{4} \times 16{,}000 = 20{,}000$ lb

Hanger load from net section 1-1 $= 1.04 \times 16{,}000 = 16{,}650$ lb

Hanger load from net section 2-2 $= \frac{4}{3} \times 0.84 \times 16{,}000 =$ 17,950 lb

Four rivets in shear $= 4 \times 0.442 \times 12{,}000 = 21{,}000$ lb

Four rivets in bearing $= 4 \times \frac{1}{4} \times 0.75 \times 24{,}000 = 18{,}000$ lb

Joint is weakest in tension in the net section 1-1

$$\text{Efficiency of the joint} = \frac{\text{smallest allowable load}}{\text{allowable load in gross section}} =$$

$(16{,}650/20{,}000) \times 100 = 83.3$ per cent

7.02 Area gross section $= \frac{3}{8} \times 9 = 3.37$ sq in.

Area net section 1-1 (2 holes) $= \frac{3}{8} \times (9 - 2 \times \frac{3}{4})$ $= 2.81$ sq in.

Area net section 2-2 (4 holes) $= \frac{3}{8} \times (9 - 4 \times \frac{3}{4})$ $= 2.25$ sq in.

Plate tension from gross section $= 3.37 \times 20{,}000 = 67{,}500$ lb

Plate tension from net section 1-1 = 2.81 × 20,000 = 56,200 lb
Plate tension from net section 2-2 = $\frac{8}{6}$ × 2.25 × 20,000 = 60,000 lb
Eight rivets in shear = 8 × 0.442 × 16,000 = 56,500 lb
Eight rivets in bearing = 8 × $\frac{3}{8}$ × $\frac{3}{4}$ × 32,000 = 72,000 lb
Maximum permissible tension in the plate is 56,200 lb
Efficiency of the joint = (56,200/67,500) × 100 = 83.3 per cent

7.03 p = three rivet diameters = 3 × $\frac{3}{4}$ = 2.25 in., $2p$ = 4.50 in.
Investigate on the basis of 4$\frac{1}{2}$ in. length of main plate
Area gross plate = 4.5 × $\frac{1}{2}$ = 2.25 sq in.
Area net section 1-1 (1 hole) = $\frac{1}{2}$(4.5 − $\frac{13}{16}$) = 1.84 sq in.
Area net section 2-2 (2 holes) = $\frac{1}{2}$(4.5 − 2 × $\frac{13}{16}$) = 1.44 sq in.
Tension in plate from gross section = 2.25 × 16,000 = 36,000 lb
Tension in plate from net section 1-1 = 1.84 × 16,000 = 29,500 lb
Tension in plate from net section 2-2 = $\frac{3}{2}$ × 1.44 × 16,000 = 34,600 lb
Three rivets in shear = 6 × 0.442 × 10,000 = 26,500 lb
Three rivets in bearing = 3 × $\frac{1}{2}$ × $\frac{3}{4}$ × 20,000 = 22,500 lb
Allowable load per inch of seam = 22,500/4.5 = 5,000 lb
Working efficiency = (22,500/36,000) × 100 = 62.5 per cent

7.04 Six rivets in shear = 12 × 0.601 × 12,000 = 86,500 lb
Six rivets in bearing = 6 × $\frac{7}{8}$ × $\frac{3}{4}$ × 24,000 = 94,500 lb
Tension in gross section of main plate = $\frac{3}{4}$ × 16,000 = 12,000 lb
($2p$ − $\frac{15}{16}$) × $\frac{3}{4}$ × 16,000 = 86,500 lb
($32p$ − 15) = 86,500/750 = 115.4
$32p$ = 130.4, p = 4.08 in. Use p = 4 in.
Tension 8-in. wide plate from gross section = 8 × $\frac{3}{4}$ × 16,000 = 96,000 lb
Tension 8-in. wide plate from section 1-1 = (8 − $\frac{15}{16}$) × $\frac{3}{4}$ × 16,000 = 84,500 lb
Tension 8-in. wide plate from section 3-3 = $\frac{6}{4}$(8 − $\frac{15}{8}$) × $\frac{3}{4}$ × 16,000 = 110,000 lb

In cover plates tension from section 4-4
$= (8 - 1\frac{5}{8}) \times 1\frac{4}{16} \times 16{,}000 = 85{,}600$ lb
Efficiency $= (84{,}500/96{,}000) \times 100 = 88.5$ per cent

7.05 Tension main plate must carry $= \dfrac{\text{diameter tank in inches}}{2}$ $\times$ psi $= (60/2) \times 500 = 15{,}000$ lb per in. $= 180{,}000$ lb per ft.

Minimum thickness of plate is probably $\dfrac{1\frac{2}{11} \times 15{,}000}{20{,}000} =$ 0.818 in., or say $1\frac{3}{16}$ in.

Assuming $\frac{7}{8}$-in. rivets are used, the pitch for the inside row of rivets $= 3 \times \frac{7}{8}+ = 2\frac{5}{8}+ = 3$ in.

Shear 11 rivets $= 22 \times 0.601 \times 15{,}000 = 198{,}500$ lb

Bearing 11 rivets (double shear) $= 11 \times \frac{7}{8} \times 1\frac{3}{16} \times 30{,}000 = 235{,}000$ lb

Tension in plate fıom gross section $= 12 \times 1\frac{3}{16} \times 20{,}000 =$ 195,000 lb

Tension in plate from section 1-1
$= 1\frac{1}{11}(12 - 0.94) \times 1\frac{3}{16} \times 20{,}000 = 178{,}000$ lb

Tension in plate from section 2-2
$= 1\frac{1}{10}(12 - 1.88) \times 1\frac{3}{16} \times 20{,}000 = 181{,}000$ lb

Tension in plate from section 3-3
$= 1\frac{1}{8}(12 - 3.76) \times 1\frac{3}{16} \times 20{,}000 = 184{,}000$ lb

Assume splice plate $= \frac{9}{16}$ in. thick

Tension in splice plate at section 4-4
$= 1\frac{1}{11}(12 - 3.76) \times 2 \times \frac{9}{16} \times 20{,}000 = 185{,}000$ lb

Bearing 11 rivets (single shear)
$= 11 \times \frac{7}{8} \times 2 \times \frac{9}{16} \times 24{,}000 = 260{,}000$ lb

Design is satisfactory: $p = 3$ in., $t_{\text{main plate}} = 1\frac{3}{16}$ in., $t_{\text{splice plate}} = \frac{9}{16}$ in.

Efficiency $= (178{,}000/195{,}000) \times 100 = 91.2$ per cent

7.06 Longitudinal tension $= \dfrac{\text{diameter tank in inches}}{4} \times$ psi $=$ $\frac{60}{4} \times 500 = 7{,}500$ lb per in.

Shear five rivets $= 9 \times 0.601 \times 15000 = 81{,}100$ lb (four in double shear, one in single shear)

$81{,}100 \div 7{,}500 = 10.8$ in. Use pitch $= 5\frac{1}{4}$ in.

Actual tension per $10\frac{1}{2}$ in. $= 10.5 \times 7{,}500 = 78{,}750$ lb

Tension gross section = $10.5 \times {}^{13}\!/_{16} \times 20{,}000 = 171{,}000$ lb
Tension in two cover plates at net section (inner row of rivets)
$= (10.5 - 1.62) \times t \times 20{,}000 = 78{,}750$ lb

$$t = \frac{78{,}750}{8.88 \times 20{,}000} = 0.442 \text{ in.}$$

This is split $5/9 \times 0.442 = 0.25$ in. minimum (to inside plate) and $4/9 \times 0.442 = 0.20$ in. minimum (to outside plate)
Use two splice plates $7/16$ in. thick to take care of bearing of five rivets $= 9 \times 7/16 \times 7/8 \times 24{,}000 = 82{,}700$ lb
Efficiency of splice [(81,100/171,000) × 100 = 47.4 per cent] is low because thickness of main plate was dictated by hoop tension and not by longitudinal tension

7.07 Eleven rivets; eight in double shear, three in single shear, eight in bearing on ¾-in. plate, 3 on ½-in. plate
Single shear one rivet $= 0.994 \times 8{,}800 = 8{,}750$ lb per rivet
Bearing one rivet on ¾-in. plate $= 1.125 \times 3/4 \times 19{,}000 =$ 16,060 lb per rivet
Bearing one rivet on ½-in. plate $= 1.125 \times 1/2 \times 19{,}000 =$ 10,700 lb per rivet
Allowable shear in 11 rivets $= 19 \times 16{,}060/2 = 152{,}600$ lb
Tension gross section main plate $= 16.5 \times 3/4 \times 11{,}000 =$ 136,000 lb
Tension in main plate from section 1-1
$= (16.5 - 1.19) \times 3/4 \times 11{,}000 = 126{,}200$ lb
Tension in main plate from section 2-2
$= {}^{19}\!/_{18}(16.5 - 2.38) \times 3/4 \times 11{,}000 = 111{,}800$
Tension in main plate from section 3-3
$= {}^{19}\!/_{16}(16.5 - 4.76) \times 3/4 \times 11{,}000 = 97{,}900$ lb
Tension in the inner cover plates section 4-4
$= {}^{19}\!/_{11} \times 1/2(16.5 - 4.76) \times 11{,}000 = 112{,}000$ lb
Splice is apt to fail by tension in section 3-3 in the main plate.
Efficiency of the splice = (97,900/136,000) × 100 = 72 per cent

7.08 Tension in tank shell per inch $= (D/2) \times \text{psi} = {}^{72}\!/_{2} \times 125 = 4{,}500$ lb
Assume rivet pitch = 3 in.
Rivet diameter = ⅞ in., hole = $^{15}\!/_{16}$ in.

Minimum thickness main plate $= \dfrac{1}{3 - 0.96} \times \dfrac{3 \times 4{,}500}{16{,}000} =$ 0.41 in.

Use $\frac{7}{16}$-in. plate, two rows of rivets.

Shear one rivet $= 0.601 \times 12{,}000 = 7{,}200$ lb, two rivets $=$ 14,400 lb

Bearing one rivet $= 0.875 \times 0.437 \times 24{,}000 = 9{,}200$ lb

Tension gross section of plate $= \frac{7}{16} \times 3 \times 16{,}000 = 21{,}000$ lb

Tension section 1-1 of plate $= \frac{7}{16}(3 - 0.94) \times 16{,}000 =$ 14,420 lb

Efficiency of splice $= (14{,}400/21{,}000) \times 100 = 68.5$ per cent

7.09 Slot the 3-in. leg of the angle with a $\frac{1}{2}$-in. slot just inside the 4-in. leg for a length of $6\frac{3}{4}$ in.

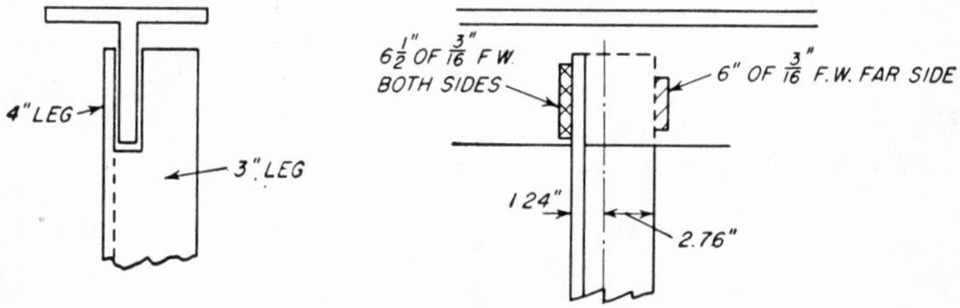

FIG. 7.09

Because of rounded edge of angle, fillet weld should not exceed $\frac{3}{16}$ in. in size (AISC)

Throat depth $= 0.707 \times \frac{3}{16} = 0.1325$

Allowable load per inch of fillet weld $= 0.1325 \times 15{,}000 =$ 1,990 lb per in.

Tensile strength $4 \times 3 \times \frac{1}{4}$ angle $= 1.69 \times 20{,}000 = 33{,}800$ lb

Number of inches of fillet weld needed $= 33{,}800/1{,}990 =$ 17.0 in.

Take moments about back of 3-in. leg of angle

$$1.24 \times 33{,}800 = 4 \times L_R \times 1{,}990$$

$$L_R = \frac{1.24 \times 33{,}800}{4 \times 1{,}990} = 5.27 \text{ in.}$$

Use one length $= 5\frac{1}{2}$ in. $+ \frac{1}{2}$ in. $= 6$ in.

Take moments about edge of 4-in. leg of angle

$$2.76 \times 33{,}800 \times L_L \times 2 \times 4 \times 1{,}990$$

$$L_L = \frac{2.76 \times 33{,}800}{8 \times 1{,}990} = 5.86 \text{ in.}$$

Use two lengths = 6 in. + ½ in. = 6½ in.

7.10 Slot the stem of the T with a ¾-in. slot 10½ in. long just beneath the flange.

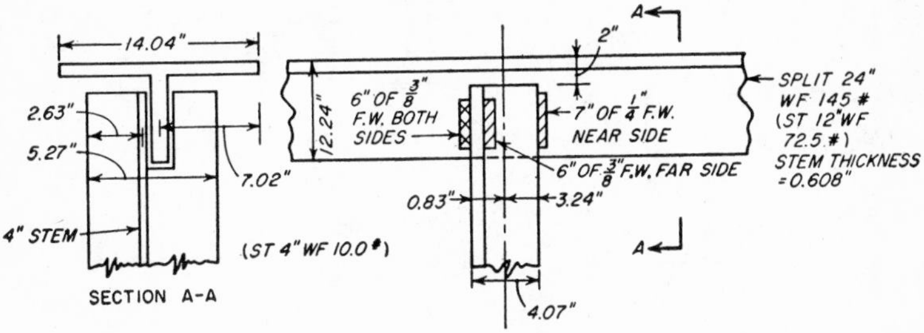

Fig. 7.10

(ST 4 WF 10.0)
Area = 2.94 sq in.
Flange thickness = 0.378 in.
Stem thickness = 0.248
Tensile strength T (ST 4 WF) = 2.94 × 20,000 = 58,800 lb
Take moments about back of flange (ST 4 WF)

$$0.83 \times 58{,}800 = 4 \times 2{,}000 \times L_R$$

$$L_R = \frac{0.83 \times 58{,}800}{4 \times 2{,}000} = 6.10 \text{ in.}$$

Use **6**½ in. + ½ in = **7** in.
Take moments about edge of stem (ST 4 WF)

$$3.24 \times 58{,}800 = 3 \times 4 \times 3{,}000 \times L_L$$

$$L_L = \frac{3.24 \times 58{,}800}{12 \times 3{,}000} = 5.30 \text{ in.}$$

Use three lengths of 5½ in. + ½ in. or **6** in.
Check: $6.5 \times 2{,}000 + 3 \times 5.5 \times 3{,}000$
$= 62{,}500 \text{ lb} > 58{,}800 \text{ lb}$

7.11 Let f = torsional force 1 in. from rivet group center of gravity

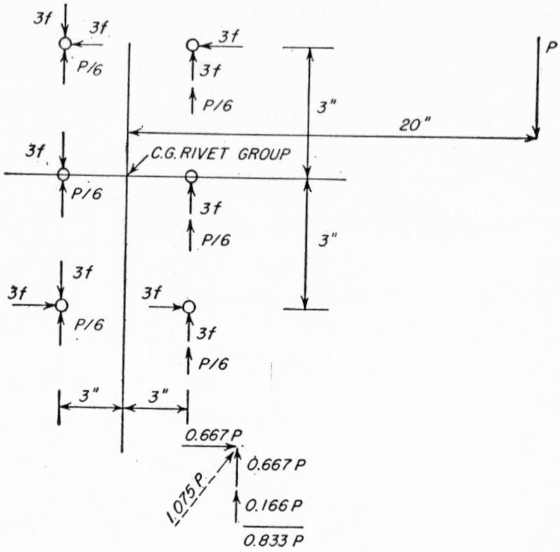

FIG. 7.11

Torsion M(about center of gravity of rivet group) = 0 =

$$+20P - 10 \times 3f \times 3, \quad \text{or } 3f = \frac{20p}{30} = 0.667P$$

Lower right-hand rivet = most stressed rivet

$$\sqrt{(0.667p)^2 + (0.833p)^2} = 1.075p$$
$$1.075p = 9{,}500 \text{ (given)}$$
$$\therefore p = 9{,}500/1.075 = \mathbf{8{,}850} \text{ lb}$$

A = area of bolt

$$A \times 16{,}000 = 9{,}500, \; A = \frac{9{,}500}{16{,}000} = 0.593 \text{ sq in.}$$

Use ⅞-in. diameter bolt ($A = 0.601$)
Thickness of plate for bearing = t_b

$$t_b \times 7/8 \times 32{,}000 = 9{,}500, \quad t_b = 9{,}500/28{,}000 = 0.34 \text{ in.}$$

Thickness of plate for tension (bending) = t_t

$$I_{(\text{net of plate})} = t_t \times 9^3 \times 1/12 - 2 \times (1 \times t_t) \times 3^2 = 42.75t_t$$

$$f = \frac{M_c}{I}, \quad 20{,}000 = \frac{17 \times 8{,}850 \times 4.5}{42.75t_t}$$

$$t_t = \frac{17 \times 8{,}850 \times 4.5}{42.75 \times 20{,}000} = 0.79 \text{ in.}$$

Use $13/16$-in. plate

7.12 Let f be the force in a rivet 1 in. from the center of the rotation. Then torsion in the rivets of one plate (about center of gravity of rivet group)

$$\begin{aligned} 10 \times 2.75 \times 2.75f &= 76f \\ 4 \times 4 \times 4f &= 64f \\ 4 \times 7 \times 7f &= \underline{196f} \\ & 336f \end{aligned}$$

$$\begin{aligned} M &= 0 \\ &= 2 \times 336f - 14.75 \times 50{,}000 \\ f &= 1{,}094 \text{ lb} \\ 7f &= 7{,}660 \text{ lb} \\ 2.75f &= 3{,}010 \text{ lb} \end{aligned}$$

A 1-in. rivet in single shear and bearing on a ½-in. plate may carry 11,780 lb.

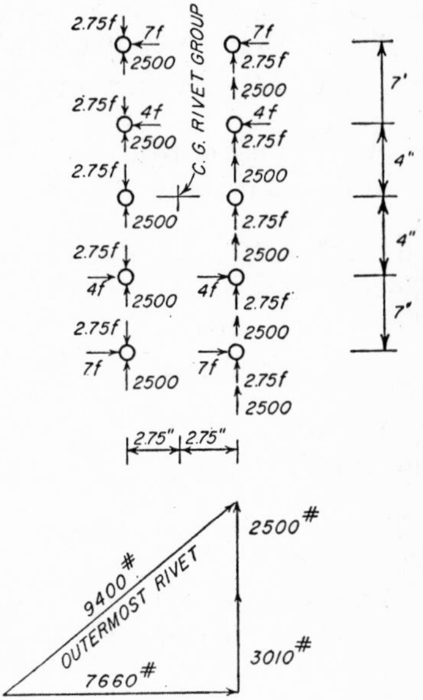

FIG. 7.12

$$I_{(\text{net})} \text{ of plates} = 1/12 \times 1 \times 17^3 - 2 \times 1 \times 1 \times (4^2 + 7^2) = 280 \text{ in.}^4$$

$$f = \frac{M_c}{I} = \frac{12 \times 50{,}000 \times 8.5}{280} = 18{,}200 \text{ psi}$$

7.13 Let f = shearing value of the weld 1 in. from center of gravity of welds

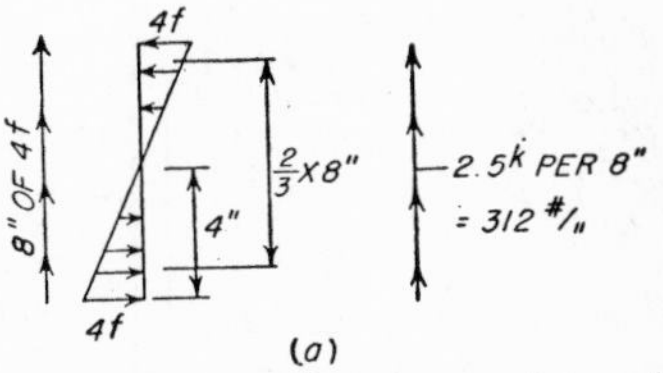

FIG. 7.13a. Shearing value of welds along one edge.

M of welds about center of gravity of welds =
$4 \times [4 \times 8 \times 4f + 4 \times (4f/2) \times (\frac{2}{3} \times 8)] = 512f + 171f = 683f$
$683f = 12 \times 10{,}000, \quad f = 176$ lb per in., $\quad 4f = 704$ lb per in.

Maximum weld force is 1,250 lb per in. Allowable for ¼-in. fillet weld = 2,000 lb per in., which is OK

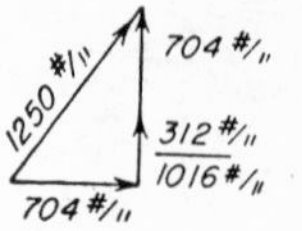

(b)
FIG. 7.13b

$$I = \frac{1}{12} \times \frac{1}{2} \times 8 \times 8 \times 8 = 21.3 \text{ in.}^4$$

$$f = \frac{M_c}{I} = \frac{8 \times 10{,}000 \times 4}{21.3} = 15{,}000 \text{ psi, which is OK}$$

A better use of welds is not to weld into corners.
If only 5 in. of weld is used on each of the four sides

$4[4 \times 5 \times 4f + 2.5 \times (2.5f/2) \times (\frac{2}{3} \times 5)] = 320f + 42f = 362f$
$362f = 12 \times 10{,}000, \quad f = 331, \quad 2.5f = 824, \quad 4f = 1{,}324$ lb per in.

$$\frac{10{,}000}{4 \times 5} = 500 \text{ lb per in.}$$

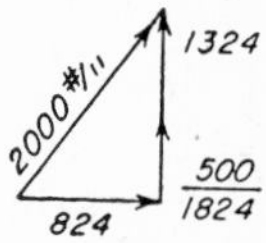

(c)
FIG. 7.13c

If four ⁵⁄₁₆-in. fillet welds are used, each 4 in. long, then

$$4[4 \times 4 \times 4f + 2 \times (2f/2) \times (\tfrac{2}{3} \times 4)] = 256f + 21f = 277f$$

$277f = 12 \times 10{,}000, \quad f = 433, \quad 2f = 866, \quad 4f = 1{,}733$ lb per in.

$$\frac{10{,}000}{4 \times 4} = 625 \text{ lb per in.}$$

2,500 lb per in. OK for ⁵⁄₁₆ = in. fillet weld.

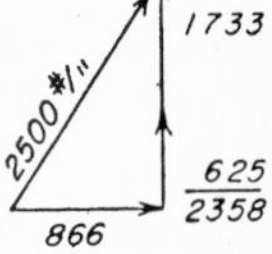

(d)
FIG. 7.13d

7.14 Gage from back of 4-in. leg to rivets in 3½-in. leg = 2 in.

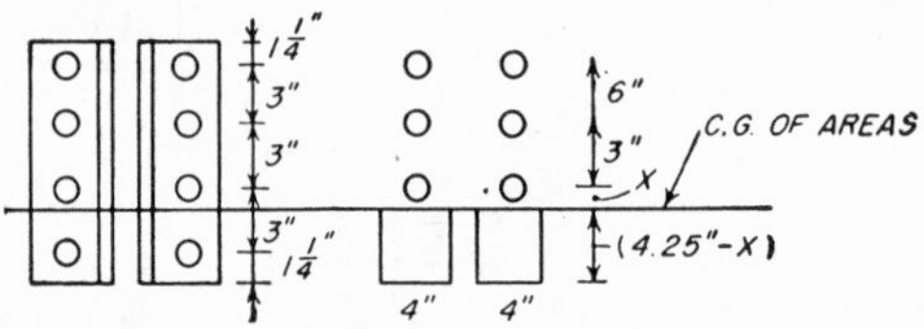

FIG. 7.14

Each ⅞-in. rivet good for **9,020** lb in shear and bearing on ⅜-in. leg. Area of two ⅞-in. rivets = 1.2 sq in. Assume that center of gravity of areas lies x distance below the second rivet from the bottom. Taking statical moments about the center-of-gravity line

$$\frac{8(4.25 - x)^2}{2} = 1.2[x + (x + 3) + (x + 6)] = 1.2(3x + 9)$$

$$(4.25 - x)^2 = \frac{1.2}{4}(3x + 9)$$

$$18.1 - 8.5x + x^2 = 0.9x + 2.7$$

$$(x^2 - 9.4x + 15.4) + 6.7 = 6.7$$

$$x - 4.7 = \pm 2.59, \quad x = +4.7 - 2.59 = 2.11 \text{ in.}$$

Let f be the intensity of tension or compression 1 in. from the center-of-gravity line

$$1.2(2.11^2f + 5.11^2f + 8.11^2f) + 8/3 \times 2.14^3f = 115.8f + 26.2f$$

$$= 142.0f = 8 \times 9{,}020 \times 2$$

= double shear in rivets through web of beam times the 2 in. of eccentricity.

$$f = 1{,}016 \text{ psi per in.}$$

Tension in top rivet = 0.601 × 1,016 × 8.11 = **4,950** lb

7.15 Similar to 7.14, assume that the center of gravity lies x distance below the third rivet above the bottom. M about center-of-gravity line is

$$\frac{8(7.25 - x)^2}{2} = 1.2[x + (x + 3) + (x + 6) + (x + 9)$$
$$+ (x + 12) + (x + 15) + (x + 18) + (x + 21)]$$

$$(7.25 - x)^2 = \frac{1.2}{4}(8x + 84)$$

$$52.6 - 14.5x + x^2 = 2.4x + 25.2$$

$$(x^2 - 16.9x + 27.4) + 44 = 44$$

$$(x - 8.45)^2 = 44$$

$$x - 8.45 = \pm 6.63$$

$$x = +8.45 - 6.63 = 1.82 \text{ in.}$$

Let f be the intensity of tension or compression 1 in. from the center-of-gravity line.

$$
\begin{aligned}
1.2 \times 1.82^2 f &= 1.2f \times 3.3 \\
1.2 \times 4.82^2 f &= 1.2f \times 23.2 \\
1.2 \times 7.82^2 f &= 1.2f \times 61.2 \\
1.2 \times 10.82^2 f &= 1.2f \times 117.3 \\
1.2 \times 13.82^2 f &= 1.2f \times 191.0 \\
1.2 \times 16.82^2 f &= 1.2f \times 283.0 \\
1.2 \times 19.82^2 f &= 1.2f \times 393.0 \\
1.2 \times 22.82^2 f &= 1.2f \times 522.0 \\
&\quad 1.2f \times 1596 = 1{,}915f \\
8 \times (5.433/3) \times f &= 427f \\
20 \times 9{,}020 \times 2 &= 2{,}342f \\
f &= 154.0 \text{ lb/(sq in.)(in.)}
\end{aligned}
$$

Tension in top rivets = 0.601 × 154.0 × 22.82 = **2,110** lb

7.16 Side dimension of fillet weld must be ⅝ in. or less.

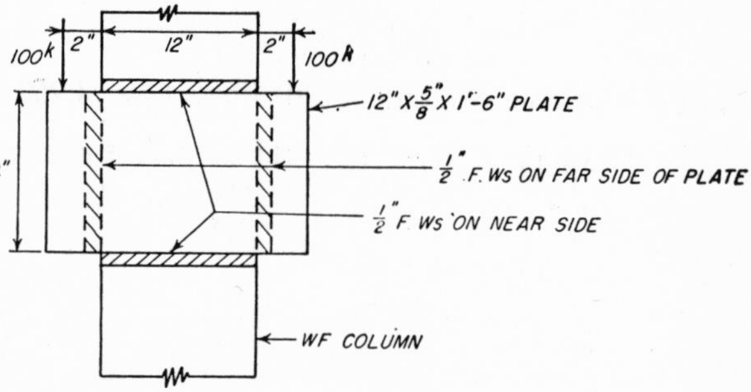

FIG. 7.16

Throat dimension of ½-in. fillet weld = 0.707 × ½ = 0.354 in.

½-in. fillet weld can carry 0.354 × 13,000 = 4,600 lb per in. in shear.

4 × 12 × 4,600 = 221,000 lb which is greater than 200,000 lb

7.17 Gross I of girder.

I of four angles about c.g of angles $= 4 \times 7.5 =$ 30 in.^{4}

plus $A\ d^2$ for angles

$= 4 \times 5.86(21.25 - 1.03)^2$ $=$ 9,600 in.^{4}

I of two cover plates

$= 2 \times 14 \times \frac{1}{2} \times 21.50^2$ $=$ 6,470 in.^{4}

I of web plate $= \frac{1}{12} \times \frac{3}{8} \times 42^3$ $=$ 2,320 in.^{4}

$I =$ 18,420 in.^{4}

$$f = \frac{Mc}{I} = 18{,}000 = \frac{\frac{1}{8} \times W \times 30 \times 30 \times 120 \times 21.75}{18{,}420}$$

W = 11,300 lb per ft = total uniform load per foot of girder

Center of gravity of flange is 1.05 in. below back of cover plate

Plate:	$14 \times \frac{1}{2} =$	7.00 in.^{2} $\times \frac{1}{4}$ in. $=$	1.75 in.^{3}
Angles:	$2 \times 5.86 =$	11.72×1.53	$= 17.92$
Flange:		$= 18.72\ (1.05)$	$= 19.67$

$$sb = \frac{VQ}{I} = \frac{75{,}000 \times 18.72 \times 20.70}{18{,}420} = 1{,}580 \text{ lb per in.}$$

One $\frac{3}{4}$-in. rivet may carry $2 \times 0.4418 \times 15{,}000 = 13{,}250$ lb in double shear and 11,300 lb in double bearing on $\frac{3}{8}$-in. web maximum rivet pitch for one line of rivets $= 11{,}300/1{,}580 = 7.15$ in. Use **6** in. (Maximum usually allowed by specifications for this condition)

7.18 *Try* four angles $6 \times 6 \times \frac{13}{16}$ in. placed $36\frac{1}{2}$ in. back to back of angles.

Gross I of girder:

I of four angles about their center of gravity

$= 4 \times 30$ $=$ 120 in.^{4}

plus Ad^2 for angles

$= 4 \times 9.09(18.25 - 1.80)^2$ $=$ 9,840 in.^{4}

I of web $= \frac{1}{12} \times \frac{3}{8} \times 36^3$ $=$ 1,460 in.^{4}

$I =$ 11,420 in.^{4}

Weight four angles $= 4 \times 31$ lb $= 124$ lb per ft
Weight web plate $= {}^{490}\!/_{144} \times 36 \times {}^{3}\!/_{8} = 46$ lb per ft
Weight girder $= 170$ lb per ft
Dead load moment
$= \frac{1}{8} \times 170 \times 50 \times 50 \times 12 = 637{,}000$ in-lb
Live load moment
$= \frac{1}{4} \times 70{,}000 \times 50 \times 12 = 10{,}500{,}000$ in-lb
$M = 11{,}137{,}000$ in-lb

$$f = \frac{Mc}{I} = \frac{11{,}137{,}000 \times 18.25}{11{,}420} = 17{,}800 \text{ psi, which is OK in bending}$$

$$V = 70{,}000 + 25 \times 170 = 74{,}250 \text{ lb}$$

$$sb = \frac{VQ}{I} = \frac{74{,}250 \times 18.18 \times 16.45}{11{,}420} = 1{,}942 \text{ lb per in.}$$

One ¾-in. rivet may carry $0.4418 \times 15{,}000 = 6{,}630$ lb in shear
Maximum pitch of ¾-in. rivets $= 6{,}630/1{,}942 = 3.42$ in.
Use 3¼ in.

7.19 Trial design by flange-area method.
Let girder be $\frac{1}{15}$ by 60 ft or 4 ft in depth
Shear at end $= 5{,}000 \times 30 = 150{,}000$ lb
Web area needed at 13,500 psi $= 150{,}000/13{,}500 = 11.1$ sq in.

Use web plate $48 \times \frac{3}{8} = 18.0$ sq in.

Assume lateral support of girder sufficient to permit a bending stress of 18,000 psi in compression.
Moment = flange area $\times 18{,}000 \times 45$ in. (couple arm)
$= \frac{1}{8} \times 5{,}000 \times 60 \times 60 \times 12 = 27{,}000{,}000$ in-lb

$$\text{Flange area} = \frac{27{,}000{,}000}{18{,}000 \times 45} = 33.33 \text{ sq in.}$$

⅛ area of web = flange area $= 2.25$ sq in.
31.08 sq in.
Area of two angles $8 \times 6 \times \frac{3}{4} = 19.88$ sq in.
11.20 sq in.
Area of one cover plate $18 \times \frac{5}{8} = 11.25$ sq in.

Check design by gross-moment-of-inertia method.

Distance back to back of 8-in. legs of angles	$= 48\frac{1}{2}$ in.
I of two angles about horizontal center of gravity of angles	$=$ 68 in.^{4}
Plus area of two angles × distance squared to N.A. of web $= 19.88(48.50/2 - 1.56)^2$	$=$ 10,250 in.^{4}
I of cover plate $= 18 \times \frac{5}{8} \times (48.50/2 + \frac{1}{2} \times \frac{5}{8})^2$	$=$ 6,775 in.^{4}
I of top flange	$=$ 17,093 in.^{4}
I of bottom flange	$=$ 17,093 in.^{4}
I of web plate $= \frac{1}{12} \times \frac{3}{8} \times 48^3$	$=$ 3,456 in.^{4}
I total	$=$ 37,642 in.^{4}

$$f = \frac{Mc}{I} = \frac{27{,}000{,}000 \text{ in-lb} \times 24.875 \text{ in.}}{37{,}642 \text{ in.}^4} = 17{,}850 \text{ psi, which is OK}$$

7.20 Center of gravity of T (above bottom of WF)

WF:	28.22 in.^{2} × 9.08 in.	= 256 in.^{3}	18.16 in.
			+ 0.40 in.
Channel:	9.90 in.^{2} × 17.77 in.	= 176 in.^{3}	18.56 in.
	38.12 in.^{2} (11.32 in.)	= 432 in.^{3}	− 0.79 in.
			17.77 in.
			−11.32 in.
			6.45 in.

I of T (about center of gravity):

Channel:	I about channel center of gravity	= 8.2 in.^{4}
	$A \times d^2 = 9.90 \times 6.45^2$	= 412.0 in.^{4}
WF:	I about WF center of gravity	= 1,674.7 in.^{4}
	$A \times d^2 = 28.22 \times 2.24^2$	= 141.5 in.^{4}
		I = 2,236.4 in.^{4}

Moment:

$$S = \frac{I}{c} \text{ (for top flange)}$$

$$= 2{,}236.4/7.24 = 309 \text{ in.}^3$$

$$M = f \times S = 17{,}050 \text{ psi} \times 309 \text{ in.}^3 = 5{,}260{,}000 \text{ in-lb}$$

$$S = \frac{I}{c} \text{ (for bottom flange)}$$

$$= 2{,}236.4/11.32 = 197 \text{ in.}^3$$

$$M = f \times S = 20{,}000 \text{ psi} \times 197 \text{ in.}^3 = 3{,}940{,}000 \text{ in-lb (use)}$$

$$\frac{P \times 30}{4} \times 12 + \tfrac{1}{8} \times 129.9 \times 30 \times 30 \times 12$$

$$= 3{,}940{,}000 \text{ lb}$$

$$90P = 3{,}940{,}000 - 175{,}500 = 3{,}764{,}500$$

$$P = \mathbf{41{,}900} \text{ lb}$$

Shear:

Two $\frac{5}{8}$-in. rivets in single shear $= 2 \times 0.307 \text{ in.}^2 \times 15{,}000$ psi $= 9{,}200$ lb

Horizontal shear per inch of beam (at end) may not exceed $\dfrac{9{,}200 \text{ lb}}{6 \text{ in.}} = 1{,}534$ lb per in. $= sb = \dfrac{VQ}{I}$

$$V = \frac{sh \times I}{Q} = \frac{1{,}534 \times 2{,}236.4}{9.90 \times 6.45} = 53{,}600 \text{ lb} = \frac{P}{2} + 15 \text{ ft} \times 129.9 \text{ ft-lb}$$

$$P = 2(53{,}600 - 1{,}950) = \mathbf{103{,}300} \text{ lb} > \mathbf{41{,}900} \text{ lb}$$

Deflection:

$$= \frac{1}{360} \times 30 \times 12 = \frac{P \times (30 \times 12)^3}{48 \times 30{,}000{,}000 \times 2{,}236.4}$$

$$P = \frac{4 \times 1{,}000{,}000 \times 2{,}236.4}{30 \times 30 \times 12 \times 12} = \mathbf{69{,}000} \text{ lb} > \mathbf{41{,}900} \text{ lb}$$

Permissible p = **41,900 lb**

7.21 (Refer to answer 1.616.)

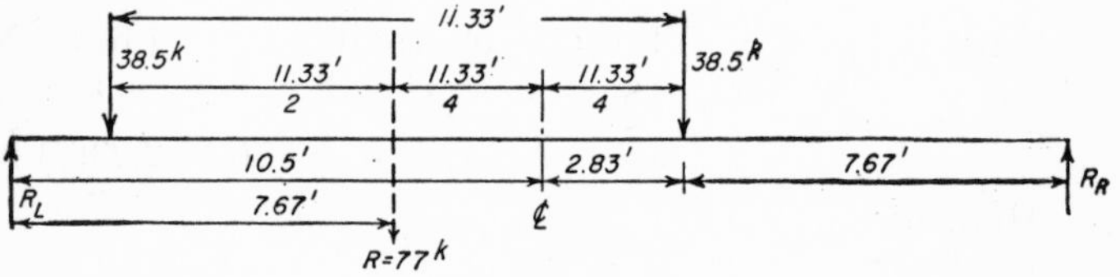

Fig. 7.21

Maximum live-load moment

$$= \frac{7.67 \text{ ft}}{21 \text{ ft}} \times 77 \text{ kips} \times 7.67 \text{ ft} \qquad = 215 \text{ ft-kips}$$

Dead-load moment at center line

$$= \tfrac{1}{8} \times 100.7 \text{ ft-lb} \times 21 \text{ ft} \times 21 \text{ ft} \qquad = 5.5 \text{ ft-kips}$$

Total moment $= 220.5$ ft-kips

Maximum end live-load shear

$$= 38.5 \text{ kips} + \frac{(21 \text{ ft} - 11.33 \text{ ft})}{21 \text{ ft}} \times 38.5 \text{ kips} = 56.2 \text{ kips}$$

Dead load shear = 10.5 ft × 100.7 lb = 1.06 kips

Total shear = 57.26 kips

Center of gravity of T (above bottom of WF)			24.280 in.
WF:	23.54 in.^{2} × 12 in.	= 282.5 in.^{3}	− 0.70 in.
Channel:	6.03 in.^{2} × 23.58 in.	= 142.0 in.^{3}	23.58 in.
	29.57 in.^{2} (14.35 in.)	= 424.5	−14.35 in.
			9.23 in.

I of T [about horizontal line through center of gravity]

	14.35 in.
	−12.00 in.
	2.35 in.
Channel: Ad^2 = 6.03 in.^{2} × 9.23 in. × 9.23 in.	= 514 in.^{4}
I about its center of gravity	= 4 in.^{4}
WF: Ad^2 = 23.54 × 2.35 × 2.35	= 130 in.^{4}
I about its center of gravity	= 2,230 in.^{4}
I total	= 2,878 in.^{4}

$S = \frac{I}{c} = \frac{2{,}878}{14.35} = 201$ in.^{3} (section modulus for bottom fiber)

$S = \frac{2{,}878}{9.93} = 290$ in.^{3} (section modulus for top fiber)

$$f(\text{bottom}) = \frac{Mc}{I} = \frac{220{,}500 \text{ ft-lb} \times 12 \text{ in. per ft} \times 14.35 \text{ in.}}{2{,}878 \text{ in.}^4}$$

$= 13{,}170$ psi

$$f(\text{top}) = \frac{220{,}500 \times 12 \times 9.93}{2{,}878} = 9{,}130 \text{ psi}$$

f(allowable) for $\frac{L}{b} = 21$ = 18,000 psi in compression (also tension)

Bridge crane runway girders are subjected to lateral loads = to 10 per cent of suspended load on crane plus an increase of vertical live loads due to impact. Full data not given in question, but fiber stresses will increase due to impact plus bending about vertical axis. Above bending stresses do not appear to be unreasonable. Horizontal shear per running inch of beam at plane between channel and

$$\text{WF} = sb = \frac{VQ}{I} = \frac{57{,}260 \text{ lb} \times 6.03 \text{ in.}^2 \times 9.23 \text{ in.}}{2{,}878 \text{ in.}^4}$$

$$= 1{,}108 \text{ lb per in.}$$

Single shear value of two ¾-in. rivets

$$= 2 \times 0.4418 \text{ in.}^2 \times 15{,}000 \text{ psi} = 13{,}250 \text{ lb}$$

$$\frac{13{,}250}{1{,}108} = 12 \text{ in.}$$

Use **6** in. maximum rivet pitch.

7.22 $R_L = R_R = \frac{3}{8}wL = \frac{3}{8} \times 10 \times 12 = 45$ kips
$R_C = 2 \times \frac{5}{8}wL = \frac{5}{4} \times 10 \times 12 = 150$ kips
M at R_C (no deflection of R_C) $= 45$ kips $\times$ 12 ft $-$ 10 kips per ft $\times$ 12 ft $\times$ 6 ft $= -180$ ft-kips

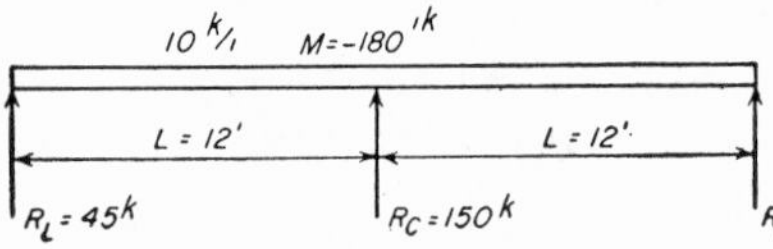

FIG. 7.22

1. Remove R_C and under 10 kips per ft load on 24 ft simple span Δ center line

$$= \frac{5}{384} \times \frac{240{,}000 \text{ lb} \times 24 \text{ ft} \times 24 \text{ ft} \times 24 \text{ ft} \times 1{,}728}{30{,}000{,}000 \text{ psi} \times 1{,}373 \text{ in.}^4}$$

$$= 1.81 \text{ in.}$$

2. R_C must push the load up 1.81 in. for no deflection or 1.31 in. for a ½-in. deflection

$$R_C \text{ for a ½-in. deflection} = \frac{1.31}{1.81} \times 150 \text{ kips} = 108.5 \text{ kips}$$

$$\text{and } R_L = R_R = 120 - \frac{108.5}{2} = 120 - 54.25 = 65.75 \text{ kips.}$$

M at R_C (½-in. deflection of R_C)
$= 65.75$ kips $\times$ 12 ft $-$ 10 kips per ft $\times$ 12 ft $\times$ 6 ft
$= +69$ ft-kips

3. Change in bending moment at $R_C = 180 + 69 = 249$ ft-kips. This may be found by $(65.75 - 45) \times 12 = 249$ ft-kips.

Alternate: Change in bending moment at $R_C = \Delta$ bending

$$\text{moment}_C = \frac{\Delta_{R_C}}{1{,}000} \times \frac{2 \times 12}{4}$$

where Δ_{R_C} is found from the deflection at C

$$\Delta_C = \tfrac{1}{2}\text{ in.} = \frac{1}{48} \times \frac{\Delta_{R_C}(24)^3 \times 1728}{30{,}000{,}000 \times 1{,}373}$$

$$\frac{\Delta_{R_C}}{1{,}000} = 41.5 \text{ kips}$$

$$\Delta \text{ bending moment}_C = \frac{41.5}{2} \times 12 = \mathbf{249.0} \text{ ft-kips}$$

7.23 1. Beam EF carries a moment of 499.7 ft-kips and end shear = 20.7 kips

$$\text{Section modulus required} = S \text{ in.}^3 = \frac{M \text{ in-lb}}{f \text{ psi}}$$

$$= \frac{499{,}700 \times 12}{18{,}000} = 333 \text{ in.}^3$$

Use 24 WF 140, $S = 358.6$ in.^{3} and standard end connection $A6$, good for $V = 108.2$ kips

2. Beam CD carries a moment of 251 ft-kips and end shear = 25.1 kips

$$S = \frac{251{,}000 \times 12}{18{,}000} = 167 \text{ in.}^3$$

Use 24 WF 74, $S = 170.4$ in.^{3}, and standard end condition $A6$

3. Beam AB carries a moment of 931 ft-kips and end shear = 39.4 kips

$$S = \frac{931{,}000 \times 12}{18{,}000} = 620 \text{ in.}^3$$

Use 36 WF 194, $S = 663.6$ in.^{3} and standard end connection $A10$, good for $V = 180$ kips.

7.24 (The following formulas for deflections of simple beams due to two concentrated loads at the third points are given in many texts and handbooks.)

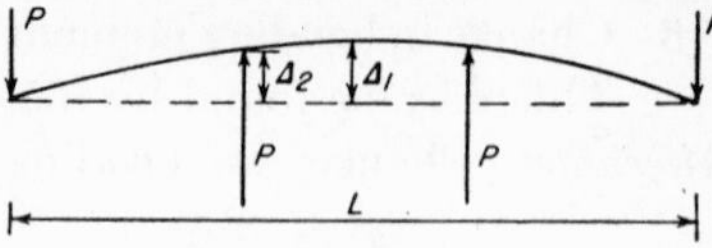

FIG. 7.24

First, neglect center line load of $4P$

$$\Delta_1(\text{at center line})\uparrow = \frac{P \times L/3}{24EI}\left(3L^2 - 4\frac{L^2}{9}\right)$$

$$= \frac{PL}{3 \times 9 \times 24EI}(27L^2 - 4L^2) = \frac{23PL^3}{648EI}$$

$$\Delta_2(\text{at third point})\uparrow = \frac{P \times L/3}{6EI}\left(3L \times \frac{L}{3} - 3\frac{L^2}{9} - \frac{L^2}{9}\right)$$

$$= \frac{4PL}{4 \times 3 \times 9 \times 6EI}(9L^2 - 3L^2 - L^2) = \frac{20PL^3}{648EI}$$

Deflection of center line point above third points $= \dfrac{3PL^3}{648EI}$

Second, neglect end loads of P

$$\Delta_3(\text{at center line})\downarrow = \frac{Fx^3}{48EI} = \frac{4P \times L^3/27}{48EI} = \frac{2PL^3}{648EI} = \text{deflection}$$

of center line point below third points

Resultant deflection at center line due to all P loads is $\dfrac{PL^3}{648EI}$ *upward*.

7.25 Solve by use of conjugate-beam method, requiring no handbook formulas.

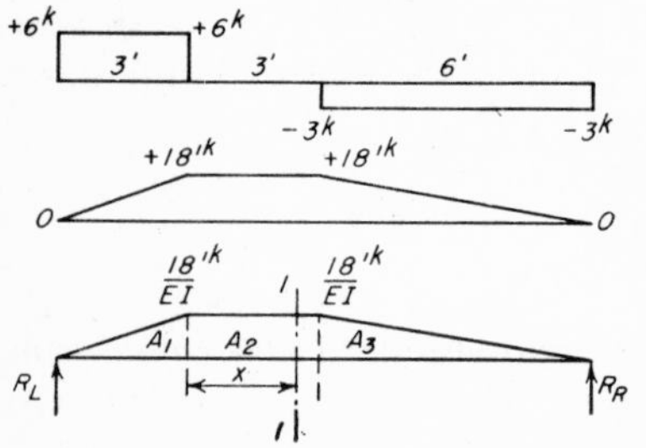

Normal shear diagram.

Normal moment diagram.

Normal moment diagram divided by EI becomes the loading for conjugate beam.

FIG. 7.25

R_L for conjugate beam, M about R_R

Area no.	Area	Arm (from R_R)	Area × arm = product
A_1	$= \frac{18}{EI} \times 3 \times \frac{1}{2} = \frac{27}{EI}$	$\times (9 + \frac{1}{3} \times 3)$	$= \frac{270}{EI}$
A_2	$= \frac{18}{EI} \times 3 = \frac{54}{EI}$	$\times (6 + \frac{1}{2} \times 3)$	$= \frac{405}{EI}$
A_3	$= \frac{18}{EI} \times 6 \times \frac{1}{2} = \frac{54}{EI}$	$\times (\frac{2}{3} \times 6)$	$= \frac{216}{EI}$
Σ areas =	$\frac{135}{EI}$		$\Sigma M = \frac{891}{EI}$

$$\text{and } R_L = \frac{891}{12EI} = \frac{74.25}{EI}\left(\frac{\text{ft}^2\ \text{kips}}{EI}\right)$$

R_R for conjugate beam, M about R_L

Area	×	Arm	=	M
$A_1 = \frac{27}{EI}$	×	$(\frac{2}{3} \times 3)$	=	$\frac{54}{EI}$
$A_2 = \frac{54}{EI}$	×	$(3 + \frac{1}{2} \times 3)$	=	$\frac{243}{EI}$
$A_3 = \frac{54}{EI}$	×	$(6 + \frac{1}{3} \times 6)$	=	$\frac{432}{EI}$

$$\Sigma M = \frac{729}{EI} \text{ and } R_R = \frac{729}{12EI} = \frac{60.75}{EI}$$

$$R_L + R_R = \frac{135}{EI} = \frac{74.25}{EI} + \frac{60.75}{EI}$$

Find where shear for conjugate-beam loading passes through zero.

$$R_L - A_1 = \frac{74.25}{EI} - \frac{27}{EI} = \frac{47.25}{EI}$$

which is less than $\frac{54}{EI}$ or A_2

Therefore shear passes through zero x distance to right of A_1 area. So

$$\frac{18x}{EI} = \frac{47.25}{EI} \text{ and } x = \frac{47.25}{18} = 2.625 \text{ ft}$$

and deflection is maximum at section 1-1, 5.625 ft to right of R_L.

Δ max = moment of conjugate-beam loading about section 1-1.

$$\Delta = +R_L \times 5.625 - A_1 \times (1 + 2.625) - \frac{47.25}{EI} \times \frac{2.625}{2}$$

$$= \frac{74.25}{EI} \times 5.625 - \frac{27}{EI} \times 3.625 - \frac{47.25}{EI} \times 1.312$$

$$= (+417.65 - 97.87 - 62.01) \times \frac{1}{EI} = \frac{257.77}{EI} \left(\frac{\text{ft}^3 \text{ kips}}{EI}\right)$$

7.26 For simplicity, divide this problem into two parts and solve by the conjugate-beam method.

1. *Concentrated load*

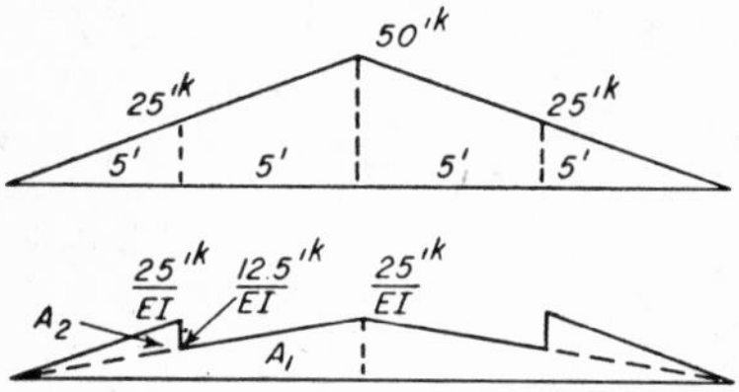

Max $M = \frac{1}{4} \times 10 \times 20 = 50$ ft-kips—normal moment diagram.

Conjugate beam loading—normal moment diagram divided by EI.

Fig. 7.26*a*

$$A_1 = \frac{1}{2} \times 10 \times \frac{25}{EI} = \frac{125}{EI}$$

$$A_2 = \frac{1}{2} \times 5 \times \frac{12.5}{EI} = \frac{31.25}{EI},$$

$$R_L = A_1 + A_2 = \frac{156.25}{EI}$$

$$M \text{ at center line} = \frac{156.25}{EI} \times 10 - \frac{125}{EI} \times \frac{10}{3} - \frac{31.25}{EI}\left(5 + \frac{5}{3}\right)$$

$$= (+1{,}562.5 - 416.7 - 208.3) \times \frac{1}{EI}$$

$$= \frac{937.5}{EI} \left(\frac{\text{ft}^3 \text{ kips}}{EI}\right)$$

2. *Uniform load*

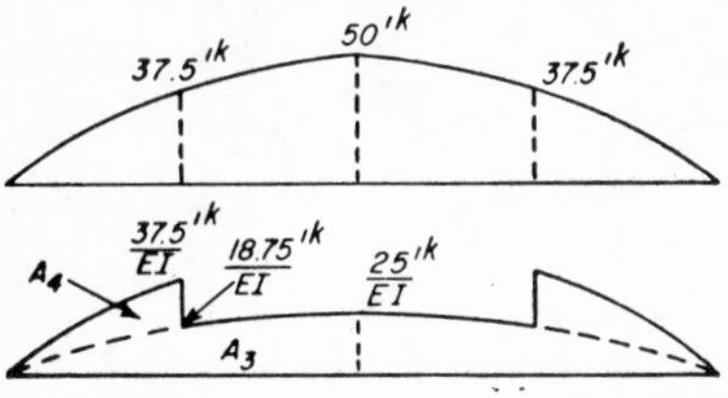

Max $M = \frac{1}{8} \times 1 \times 20 \times 20 = 50$ ft-kips—normal moment diagram is a parabola and M at quarter point $= \frac{3}{4}M$ at center line.

Conjugate beam loading – normal moment diagram divided by EI

FIG. 7. 26*b*

$$A_3 = \frac{2}{3} \times \frac{25}{EI} \times 10 = \frac{166.67}{EI}$$ (area under parabola from vertex outward = two-thirds area of enclosing rectangle)

$$A_4 = \frac{1}{2} \times 5 \times \frac{18.75}{EI} = \frac{46.87}{EI}$$ (it is close enough to treat area as a triangle)

$$R_L = A_3 + A_4 = \frac{213.54}{EI},$$ and M at center line

$$= + \frac{213.54 \times 10}{EI} - \frac{46.875}{EI} \times \left(5 + \frac{5}{3}\right) - \frac{166.67}{EI} \times \frac{3}{8} \times 10$$

$$M \text{ at center line} = (+2{,}135.4 - 312.5 - 625) \times \frac{1}{EI}$$

$$= \frac{1{,}197.9}{EI} \left(\frac{\text{ft}^3 \text{ kips}}{EI}\right)$$

$$\text{Total } \Delta \text{ at center line} = (937.5 + 1197.9) \times \frac{1}{EI}$$

$$= \frac{2{,}135.4}{EI} \left(\frac{\text{ft}^3 \text{ kips}}{EI}\right)$$

(To understand the conversion of Δ to inches, assume I of beam $= 344$ in.^{4})

$$\Delta \text{ max} = \frac{2{,}135{,}400 \times 1728}{344 \times 30{,}000{,}000} = 0.357 \text{ in.}$$ (use as 0.36 in. or 0.4 in.)

(The exact way in getting and dealing with A_4 would have shown in the fourth figure to the right of the decimal by about -1.)

7.27 Take statical moment from back of plate to find center of gravity.

Member	Area	×	Arm	=	Product
Plate	4.88	×	$\frac{3}{16}$	=	0.915
2 Channels	6.72	×	$4\frac{3}{8}$		29.400
	11.60 in.^{2}	×	(2.61 in.)	=	30.315 in.^{3}

Center of gravity lies 2.61 in. from back of plate and on axis of symmetry.

$I_{(1\text{-}1)}$

$$\begin{aligned}
&\text{Plates } \tfrac{1}{12} \times 13 \times \tfrac{3}{8} \times \tfrac{3}{8} \times \tfrac{3}{8} &&= 0.06 \text{ in.}^4 \\
&+4.88 \times (2.61 - 0.19)^2 &&= 28.80 \\
&\text{2 channels } 2 \times 32.3 &&= 64.60 \\
&+6.72 \times (4.37 - 2.61)^2 &&= 20.82 \\
&I \text{ (total)} &&= 114.28 \text{ in.}^4 \\
&r^2_{(1\text{-}1)} = \frac{I}{A} = \frac{114.28}{11.60} &&= 9.85 \text{ in.}^2 \\
&\frac{L^2}{r^2} = \frac{(20 \times 12)^2}{9.85} &&= 5{,}840
\end{aligned}$$

Permissible fiber stress = 17,000 − 0.485 × 5,840 = 14,170 psi

Allowable load = $A_s f_s$ = 11.60 × 14,170 = **164,300** lb

$I_{(2\text{-}2)}$

$$\begin{aligned}
&\text{Plate } \tfrac{1}{12} \times \tfrac{3}{8} \times 13 \times 13 \times 13 &&= 68.7 \text{ in.}^4 \\
&\text{2 channels } 2 \times 1.3 &&= 2.6 \\
&+6.72 \times 4.58^2 &&= 141.0 \\
& && 212.3 \text{ in.}^4 \\
&r^2_{(2\text{-}2)} = \frac{212.3}{11.60} &&= 18.3 > 9.85
\end{aligned}$$

Use $r^2_{(1\text{-}1)}$ only.

7.28 15 channel 50, $A = 14.64$ in.^{2}, $x = 0.80$ in.,
$I_1 = 401.4$ in.^{4}, $I_2 = 11.2$ in.^{4}

Center-of-gravity distance from top of cover plate = 5.42 in.

Member		Area	×	Arm	=	Product
Plate 22 × ¾	=	16.50	×	⅜	=	6.18
2 Channels	=	29.28	×	8.25	=	242.00
		45.78 in.²	×	(5.42 in.)	=	248.2 in.³

$I_{(1\text{-}1)}$

Plate = $\frac{1}{12} \times 22 \times \frac{3}{4} \times \frac{3}{4} \times \frac{3}{4}$	=	0.8
$+16.50\,(5.42 - 0.37)^2$	=	420.2
2 channels = 2×401.4	=	802.8
$+29.28\,(8.25 - 5.42)^2$	=	234.2
$I_{(1\text{-}1)}$	=	1,458.0 in.⁴
$r^2_{(1\text{-}1)} = \dfrac{I}{A} = \dfrac{1{,}458.0}{45.78}$	=	31.8 in.²

$I_{(2\text{-}2)}$ (axis of symmetry)

Plate = $\frac{1}{12} \times \frac{3}{4} \times 22 \times 22 \times 22$	=	665.0
2 channels = 2×11.2	=	22.4
$+29.28 \times (6.8)^2$	=	1,358.0
$I_{(2\text{-}2)}$	=	2,045.4 in.⁴
$r^2_{(2\text{-}2)} = \dfrac{2{,}045.4}{45.78}$	=	44.7 in.² > 31.8

$$\text{Permissible fiber stress} = 15{,}000 - \frac{(25 \times 12)^2}{4 \times 31.8} = 14{,}292 \text{ psi}$$

Allowable load = 45.78 × 14,292 = **655,000** lb

7.29

A of four angles	=	9.92
A of 8 × ¾ plate	=	3.00
		12.92 in.²
Plate = $\frac{1}{12} \times 8 \times \frac{3}{8} \times \frac{3}{8} \times \frac{3}{8}$	=	0.04
Four angles = 4×4	=	16.00
$+9.92\,(0.19 + 1.28)^2$	=	21.40
$I_{(1\text{-}1)}$	=	37.44 in.⁴
$r^2_{(1\text{-}1)} = \dfrac{I}{A} = \dfrac{37.44}{12.92}$	=	2.90 in.²
$r_{(1\text{-}1)}$	=	1.70 in.

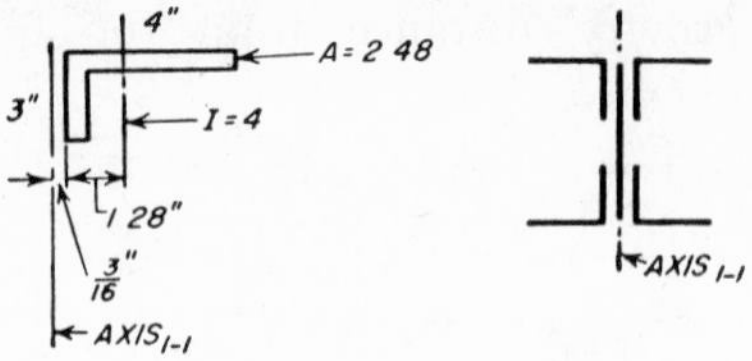

FIG. 7.29

By AISC column formula for $\frac{L}{r}$, less than 120 permissible fiber stress $= 17{,}000 - 0.485\left(\frac{L}{r}\right)^2$.

But $\frac{L}{r} = \frac{15 \times 12}{1.70} = 106 < 120$ and permissible $f = 11{,}550$ psi.

Allowable concentric load $= 12.92 \times 11{,}550 =$ **149,200** lb

7.30 Find A, I, and r of section.

$$A = 84.37 + 2 \times 22.00 \times 2 = 172.37 \text{ in.}^2$$

$I_{(1\text{-}1)}$: 14 WF 287 $= 3{,}912.1$ in.^{4}

Two 22 × 2 in. plates

$2 \times \frac{1}{12} \times 22 \times 2 \times 2 \times 2 = 29.4$

$2 \times 44 \times 9.40 \times 9.40 = 7{,}770.0$

11,711.5 in.^{4}

$I_{(2\text{-}2)}$: 14 WF $= 1{,}466.5$

Plates $2 \times \frac{1}{12} \times 2 \times 22^3 = 3{,}550.0$

5,016.5 in.^{4}

$$r^2 = \frac{I}{A} = \frac{5{,}016.5}{172.37} = 29.1 \text{ in.}^2$$

$$r = 5.4 \text{ in.}$$

$$F_b = 20{,}000 \text{ psi}$$

$$F_a = 17{,}000 - 0.485 \times \frac{(20 \times 12)^2}{29.1} = 17{,}000 - 960 = 16{,}040 \text{ psi}$$

$$f_a = \frac{P}{A} = \frac{1{,}250{,}000}{172.37} = 7{,}250 \text{ psi}$$

$$f_b = \frac{Pec}{I} = \frac{1{,}250{,}000 \times 8.40 \times 10.40}{11{,}711.5} = 9{,}325 \text{ psi}$$

$$\left(\frac{f_a}{F_a} + \frac{f_b}{F_b}\right) < 1.00$$

$$\frac{7{,}250}{16{,}040} + \frac{9{,}325}{20{,}000} = 0.452 + 0.466 = 0.918 < 1.00$$

7.31 Assume that eccentric loading causes moment about the axis of largest I.

Assume column is 14 WF 95

$A = 27.94$

$d = 14.14$

$I = 1063.5$ and 383.7

$r = 6.17$ and 3.71

$$\frac{l}{r} = \frac{20 \times 12}{3.71} = 65$$

$F_a = 14{,}950$

$F_b = 20{,}000$

$$f_a = \frac{P}{A} = \frac{210{,}000 + 40{,}000}{27.94} = 8{,}950 \text{ psi}$$

$$f_b = \frac{Pec}{I} = \frac{40{,}000 \times 24 \times 7.07}{1063.5} = 6{,}380 \text{ psi}$$

$$\frac{f_a}{F_a} + \frac{f_b}{F_b} = \frac{8{,}950}{14{,}950} + \frac{6{,}380}{20{,}000} = 0.598 + 0.319 = 0.917 < 1.000$$

A 14 WF 87 gives $0.655 + 0.348 = 1.003 > 1.000$.
Some designers would say OK, others would hold to 95 lb weight.

7.32 A ⅞-in. rivet in double shear and in double bearing on a ½-in. plate is good for 17,500 lb (AISC).
Four rivets required at each end.
Assume two angles 8 × 4 × 1 with 4-in. legs vertical and stitch-riveted.

Weight = 74.8 lb per ft

$A = 22.0$ in.^{2}

$I = 23.3$ in.^{4}

$y = 1.05$ in.

$r = 1.03$ in.

Rivet gage 4-in. leg = 2.50 in.

$$\frac{l}{r} = \frac{10 \times 12}{1.03} = 116.5 < 200, \text{ which is OK}$$

Distance of center of gravity for net section from back of 8-in. legs.

$$y \times A_{(\text{net})} = y[A_{(\text{gross})} - A_{(\text{holes})}] = A_{(\text{gross})} \times \text{arm} - A_{(\text{holes})} \times \text{arm}$$
$$y(22.00 - 2.00) = 22.00 \times 1.05 - 2.00 \times 2.50$$
$$y = \frac{(23.10 - 5.00)}{20.00} = \frac{18.10}{20.00} = 0.905 \text{ in.}$$
$$I_{(\text{net section})} = I_{(\text{gross section})} - I_{(\text{hole})} - A_{(\text{net})} \times d^2$$
$$= 23.30 - 2.00(2.50 - 1.05)^2 - 20.00(1.050 - 0.905)^2$$
$$= 23.30 - 2.00(1.45)^2 - 20.00(0.145)^2$$
$$= 23.30 - 4.20 - 0.42 = 18.68 \text{ in.}^4$$

Tension stress at end of member caused by

1. Direct stress $= \frac{P}{A} = \frac{65{,}000}{20.00}$ $= 3{,}250$ psi
2. Eccentric bending $= \frac{Pec}{I}$

   $= \frac{65{,}000}{18.68}(2.50 - 0.905)(4.00 - 0.905)$

   $= 3{,}480 \times 1.595 \times 3.095$ $= 17{,}200$ psi
3. Negative bending at end due to weight of member $= \frac{Mc}{I} = \frac{1}{12} wl^2 \times \frac{c}{I}$

   $= \frac{1}{12} \times 74.8 \times 10 \times 10 \times 12 \times \frac{3.095}{18.68}$ $= 1{,}240$ psi

   21,690 psi

7.33 Assume the weight of the member with rivets and lacing = 125 lb per ft.

Moment due to dead weight = $\frac{1}{12} \times 125 \times 25 \times 25 \times 12$ = 77,600 in-lb

Assume two 15-in. channels at 45 lb per ft with four holes out of web for ⅞-in. rivets.

$\frac{l}{r} = \frac{25 \times 12}{5.33} = 56.3$, which is OK for primary tension member

Area (gross) of 1 channel	= 13.17 sq in.
Area of holes = $4 \times 1 \times 0.618$	= 2.47 sq in.
Area (net)	= 10.70 sq in.

$$f = \frac{P}{A_{(n)}} + \frac{Mc}{I_{(g)}} = \frac{350{,}000}{2 \times 10.70} + \frac{77{,}600 \times 7.5}{2 \times 374}$$
$$= 16{,}350 + 778 = 17{,}128 \text{ psi}$$

∴ Assumed section is OK

7.34 Try an ST 8 WF 22.5 lb per ft.

$A = 6.62$ in.^{2}
$d = 8.06$ in.
$I = 37.8$ in.^{4}
$r = 2.39$ in.
$y = 1.87$ in.

Negative moment due to weight

$$= \tfrac{1}{12}wl^2 = \tfrac{1}{12} \times 22.5 \times 8 \times 8 \times 12 \quad = 1{,}440 \text{ in-lb}$$

Negative moment due to purlin $= \dfrac{PL}{8}$

$$= \frac{4{,}000}{8} \times 8 \times 12 \qquad = \underline{48{,}000 \text{ in-lb}}$$

$$M_T \qquad = 49{,}400 \text{ in-lb}$$

$$F_a = 17{,}000 - 0.485\left(\frac{l}{r}\right)^2 = 17{,}000 - 0.485\left(\frac{8 \times 12}{2.39}\right)^2$$
$$= 17{,}000 - 780 = 16{,}220 \text{ psi}$$

$$F_b = 20{,}000 \text{ psi}$$

$$f_a = \frac{P}{A} = \frac{60{,}000}{6.62} = 9{,}070 \text{ psi}$$

$$f_b = \frac{Mc}{I} = \frac{49{,}440}{37.8} \times (8.06 - 1.87) = 1{,}308 \times 6.19$$
$$= 8{,}090 \text{ psi}$$

$$\left(\frac{f_a}{F_a} + \frac{f_b}{F_b}\right) < 1.00, \quad \frac{9{,}070}{16{,}220} + \frac{8{,}090}{20{,}000} = 0.560 + 0.404$$
$$= 0.964 < 1.00$$

∴ Assumed section is OK

7.35 Choose two angles $3\tfrac{1}{2} \times 3\tfrac{1}{2} \times \tfrac{3}{8}$

$A = 4.96$ in.^{2}
$I = 5.8$ in.^{4}
$y = 1.01$ in.
$w = 17$ lb per ft

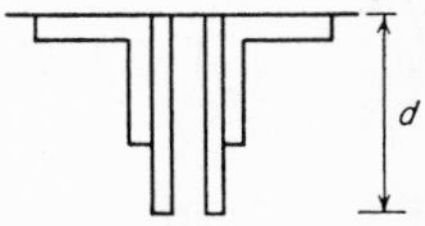

FIG. 7.35

Normal rivet gage for $3\tfrac{1}{2}$-in. leg is 2 in. from back of angle. Design plates to have center of gravity of plate and angle at rivet gage. Use $\tfrac{3}{8}$-in. plates.

For one angle and one plate: statical moment from back of L.

$$2.48 \times 1.01 \times \tfrac{3}{8} \times d \times \frac{d}{2} = (\tfrac{3}{8}d + 2.48) \times 2$$

$$\begin{aligned} 0.50 + 0.1875d^2 &= 0.75d + 4.96 \\ +d^2 &= 4d + 13.12 \\ d^2 - 4d + (4) &= +13.12 + (4) = +17.12 \\ (d - 2) &= \pm\sqrt{17.12} = \pm 4.14 \text{ in.} \\ d &= +4.14 + 2 = 6.14 \text{ in.} \end{aligned}$$

Try two plates $6\tfrac{1}{4} \times \tfrac{3}{8}$ in. (weight = 16.0 lb)

$$A = 2 \times \tfrac{3}{8} \times 6\tfrac{1}{4} + 4.96 = 4.68 + 4.96 = 9.64 \text{ in.}^2$$

I (for two angles and two plates)

(weight = 16.0 + 17.0) = (33 lb per ft)

$$\begin{aligned} &\text{Two angles} && = 5.80 \text{ in.}^4 \\ &+4.96 \times \overline{0.99}^2 && = 4.86 \\ &\text{Two plates} = \tfrac{1}{12} \times \tfrac{3}{4} \times \overline{6.25}^3 && = 15.25 \\ &+4.68 \times \overline{1.12}^2 && = 5.87 \\ & && \overline{31.78 \text{ in.}^4} \end{aligned}$$

$$r^2 = \frac{I}{A} = \frac{31.78}{9.64} = 3.3 \text{ in.}^2 \quad \text{and} \quad \frac{l^2}{r^2} = \frac{(8 \times 12)^2}{3.3} = 2{,}790 \text{ in.}^2$$

$\dfrac{l^2}{r^2}$ in the other plane is 1,112, as the unbraced length is 4×12

$$F_a = 17{,}000 - 0.485 \times 2{,}790 = 17{,}000 - 1{,}350 = 15{,}650 \text{ psi}$$

$$F_b = 20{,}000 \text{ psi}$$

$$f_a = \frac{P}{A} = \frac{75{,}000}{9.64} = 7{,}790 \text{ psi}$$

$$f_b = \frac{Mc}{I} = \frac{(48{,}000 + \tfrac{1}{12} \times 33 \times 8 \times 8 \times 12)}{31.78} \times 4\tfrac{1}{4}$$

$$= \frac{(48{,}000 + 2{,}110)}{7.47} = 6{,}700 \text{ psi}$$

$$\left(\frac{f_a}{F_a} + \frac{f_b}{F_b}\right) < 1.00 \text{ or } \frac{7{,}790}{15{,}650} + \frac{6{,}700}{20{,}000} = 0.497 + 0.335$$

$$= 0.832 < 1.00$$

$6 \times \tfrac{3}{8}$-in. plates would have been OK.

7.36 The vertical load is divided into two components:

$$\text{Normal (to roof surface)} = \frac{2}{\sqrt{5}} \times 160 = 143 \text{ lb per ft} = w_n$$

Parallel (to roof surface) $= \dfrac{1}{\sqrt{5}} \times 160 = 71.5$ lb per ft $= w_p$

Bending moment about the x-x axis

$= \frac{1}{8}w_{(n)}l^2 = \frac{1}{8}(143 + 90) \times 20 \times 20 \times 12 = 140{,}000$ in-lb

Bending moment about the y-y axis

$= \frac{1}{10}w_p\left(\dfrac{l}{3}\right)^2 = \frac{1}{10} \times 71.5 \times \dfrac{20 \times 20 \times 12}{3 \times 3} = 3{,}820$ in-lb

Assume 7-in. I beam 15.3 lb per ft $\quad S_{x\text{-}x} = 10.4$ in.^{3}

$S_{y\text{-}y} = 1.5$ in.^{3}

$$f = \frac{M_x}{S_x} + \frac{M_y}{S_y} = \frac{140{,}000}{10.4} + \frac{3{,}820}{1.5} = 13{,}460 + 2{,}540$$
$$= 16{,}000 \text{ psi}$$

Assumed section is OK.

7.37 Try a bolt of 1½-in. diameter.

Diameter at the root of thread = 1.283 in.

Area at the root of thread = 1.294 in.^{2}

$$S = \frac{P}{A} = \frac{20{,}000}{1.294} = 15{,}500 \text{ psi}$$

$$S_t = \frac{Tc}{J} = \frac{6{,}000 \times d/2}{\pi d^4/32} = \frac{6{,}000 \times 16}{\pi d^3} = \frac{30{,}600}{(1.283)^3} = 14{,}600 \text{ psi}$$

$$\text{Maximum normal stress} = \tfrac{1}{2}(S) + \sqrt{\left(\frac{S}{2}\right)^2 + (S_t)^2}$$

$$= \frac{15{,}500}{2} + \sqrt{(7{,}750)^2 + (14{,}600)^2} = 7{,}750 + 16{,}500$$
$$= 24{,}250 \text{ psi}$$

1½-in. bolt is OK

7.38

$$\frac{E_s}{E_w} = \frac{30{,}000{,}000}{1{,}500{,}000} = 20$$

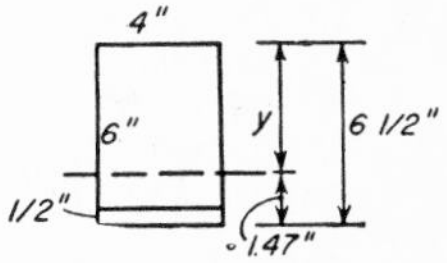

Fig. 7.38

$A \times \text{arm} = \text{product}$

$4 \times 6 = 24 \times 3 = 72$

$\frac{1}{2} \times (4 \times 20) = 40 \times 6\frac{1}{4} = 250$

$64(5.03) = 322$

$$\frac{f_t}{600} = \frac{1.47}{5.03}, \quad f_t = 600 \times \frac{1.47}{5.03} = 175.1 \text{ (equivalent wood)}$$

Stress in steel when wood is stressed to 600 psi

Compression = 20 × 175.1 = 3,502 psi tension

7.39

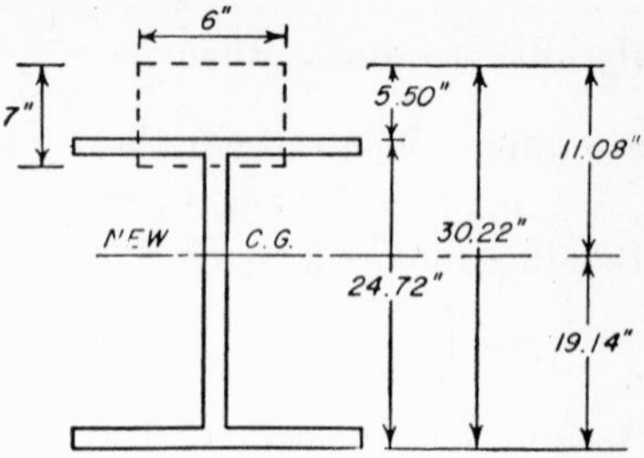

FIG. 7.39

$$f'_c = 3{,}000 \text{ psi},$$
$$f_c = 1{,}350 \text{ psi}$$
$$\frac{E_s}{E_c} = \frac{30{,}000{,}000}{3{,}000{,}000} = n = 10$$
$$I_{\text{WF}} = 5110.3 \text{ in.}^4,$$
$$A = 47.04 \text{ in.}^2$$

Assume concrete slab to be equivalent billet of steel = $\frac{5 \times 12}{n} = \frac{60}{10} = 6$ in. wide. Find new center of gravity (of composite section) from bottom of WF.

Member	Area	×	Arm	=	Product
WF	47.04	×	12.36	=	582 in.^{3}
Steel block	42.00	×	26.72	=	1,124 in.^{3}
	89.04	×	(19.14 in.)	=	1,706 in.^{3}

I of composite section:

$$\text{steel block } \tfrac{1}{12} \times 6 \times 7 \times 7 \times 7 = 171.5 \text{ in.}^4$$
$$+42(26.72 - 19.14)^2 = 42 \times 7.58^2 = 2{,}410.0$$
$$\text{WF} = 5{,}110.3$$
$$+47.04(19.14 - 12.36)^2 = 47.04 \times 6.78^2 = 2{,}160.2$$
$$9{,}852 \text{ in.}^4$$

Weight of concrete per foot

$$= \frac{7 \times 60}{144} \times 150 = 438 \text{ lb per ft}$$

Weight of WF per foot = 160 lb per ft

Weight_T = 598 lb per ft or say 600

$$\text{Dead moment} = \tfrac{1}{8} \times 600 \times 40 \times 40 \times 12 = 1{,}440{,}000 \text{ in-lb}$$

$$\text{Fiber stresses in WF} = \frac{Mc}{I} = \frac{1{,}440{,}000 \times 12.36}{5{,}110} = 3{,}480 \text{ psi}$$

Fiber stress in the bottom of the steel beam due to concentrated load may be 18,000 − 3,480 = 14,520 psi and the fiber stress in the top of the concrete may be $\frac{1}{10} \times \frac{11.08}{19.14} \times 14{,}520 =$ 840 psi

$$\text{Live load moment} = \frac{PL}{4} = \frac{P \times 40 \times 12}{4} = 120P$$

$$f = \frac{Mc}{I} = 840 \times 10 = \frac{120P \times 11.08}{9{,}852}$$

$$P = \frac{9{,}852 \times 70}{11.08} = \mathbf{62{,}300}\ \text{lb}$$

7.40 $sb = \frac{VQ}{I} = \frac{33{,}000 \times 42 \times 7.58}{9{,}852} = 1{,}068$ lb per in.

Two ⅞-in. rivets in single shear $= 2 \times 0.601 \times 15{,}000$
$= 18{,}040$ lb

End spacing of Z bars is $\frac{18{,}040}{1{,}068} = 16.9$ in.

Use **17**-in. spacing, maximum.

7.41 The total horizontal force at base of wall

$$= \frac{540 \times 18}{2} = 4{,}860 \text{ lb per ft.}$$

The permissible intensity of shearing stress without web reinforcement = 75 psi.

$$v = \frac{V}{bjd} \text{ or } d = \frac{V}{vbj} = \frac{4{,}860}{75 \times 12 \times \frac{7}{8}} = 6.2 \text{ in.}$$

The maximum moment $= 4{,}860 \times {}^{18}\!/_{3} \times 12 = 350{,}000$ in-lb.

$$k = \frac{f_c}{f_c + f_s/n} = \frac{1{,}125}{1{,}125 + 18{,}000/12} = 0.429,$$

$$j = 1 - \frac{k}{3} = 0.857$$

$$M \text{ in-lb} = (\tfrac{1}{2} \times f_c \times k \times j) \times bd^2 = Rbd^2$$

$$R = \tfrac{1}{2} \times 1{,}125 \times 0.428 \times 0.857 = 207$$

$$d^2 = \frac{M}{Rb} = \frac{350{,}000}{207 \times 12} = 141.6,\ d = 11.9 \text{ in. Use 12 in. with}$$

3-in. cover for steel, as steel is on the back side of the wall.

$$A_s = \frac{M}{f_sjd} = \frac{350{,}000}{18{,}000 \times 0.857 \times 12} = 1.89 \text{ sq in. per ft}$$

Use #8 bars 5 in. on centers.

One #8 bar (1 in. round) has an area = 0.785 sq in.

$1\frac{2}{5} \times 0.785 = 1.885$ sq in. per ft ∴ Area and spacing are OK.

$$\Sigma_0 = \frac{V}{ujd} = \frac{4{,}860}{250 \times 0.857 \times 12} = 1.89 \text{ sq in. per in.}$$

Perimeter, one #8 bar = 3.14 sq in. per in. ∴ Bond area is ample.

7.42 Assume 6-in. slab with weight = 75 psf and $f_s = 18{,}000$ psi

$$k = \frac{1{,}350}{1{,}350 + 18{,}000/10} = 0.429$$

$$j = 1 - \frac{k}{3} = 0.857$$

$$R = \tfrac{1}{2} \times 1{,}350 \times 0.429 \times 0.857 = 248$$
$$M = \tfrac{1}{8}(400 + 75) \times 10 \times 10 \times 12 = 71{,}400 \text{ in-lb}$$
$$= Rbd^2 = 248 \times 12 \times d^2$$

$$d^2 = \frac{71{,}400}{248 \times 12} = 24.0$$

$d = 4.88$ in. or 5 in. with $1\frac{1}{4}$ in. for clear cover for steel or slab of $6\frac{1}{4}$-in. thickness.

Slab depth needed for shear without web reinforcement $= \dfrac{V}{vbj}$

$$= \frac{10/2 \times 475}{90 \times 12 \times 0.857} = 2.56 \text{ in.,}\quad d = 5 \text{ in., which is OK.}$$

The minimum amount of tension steel = 0.002 bd = 0.12 sq in. per ft.

But $A_s = \dfrac{M}{f_sjd} = \dfrac{71{,}400}{18{,}000 \times 0.857 \times 5} = 0.93$ sq in. per ft or #6 bars on $5\frac{1}{2}$-in. centers

$$A_s = 12 \times 0.44/5.5 = 0.96 \text{ sq in. per ft, which is OK.}$$

7.43 Let C = moment coefficient for two-way slab (see ACI specifications)

S = length short span

m = ratio of short span to long span

$m = {}^{12}\!/_{30} = 0.40$

w = total uniform load = 75 + 300 = 375 psf

Middle *strips* (four edges discontinuous) $M = CwS^2$

Short span:

a. M positive $= 0.083 \times 375 \times 12 \times 12 \times 12 = +53{,}800$ in-lb

b. M negative $= 0.055 \times 375 \times 1728 = -35{,}700$ in-lb

Long span:

c. M positive $= 0.050 \times 648{,}000 = +32{,}400$ in.

d. M negative $= 0.033 \times 648{,}000 = -21{,}400$ in.

Middle strip width (on long edge) = 30 − 12 = 18 ft

Outer strip width (on long edge) = 12 × ½ = 6 ft

Middle strip width (on short edge) = 12 × ½ = 6 ft

Outer strip width (on short edge) = 6 × ½ = 3 ft

$f_c = 1{,}350$

$k = 0.429$

$j = 0.857$

$R = 248$

$M = Rbd^2$

$$d^2 = \frac{53{,}800}{248 \times 12} = 18.1$$

$d = 4.25$

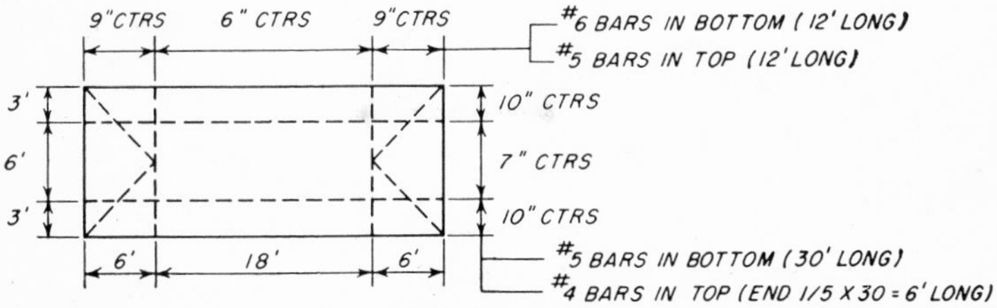

FIG. 7.43

Use $d = 4\frac{1}{4}$ in. and over-all depth

$$= 5\tfrac{1}{2} \text{ in.} > 4 \text{ in.} > \frac{(12 + 30) \times 2 \times 12}{180}$$

$$\text{Maximum shear} = \frac{ws}{3}\left(\frac{3 - m^2}{2}\right) = \frac{375 \times 12}{6}(3 - 0.16)$$
$$= 750 \times 2.84 = 2{,}130 \text{ lb per ft}$$

$$v = \frac{V}{bjd} = \frac{2{,}130}{12 \times 0.857 \times 4\frac{1}{4}} = 49 \text{ psi} < 90 \text{ psi, which is OK.}$$

$$\text{Tension steel} = A_s = \frac{M}{f_sjd} = \frac{M}{18{,}000 \times 0.857 \times 4\frac{1}{4}} = \frac{M}{65{,}600}$$

Center strips:

A_s for
a. = 0.82 sq in. per ft, #6 bars on 6-in. centers (bottom) = 0.88 sq in. per ft
b. = 0.54 sq in. per ft, #5 bars on 6-in. centers (top) = 0.62 sq in. per ft
c. = 0.50 sq in. per ft, #5 bars on 7-in. centers (bottom) = 0.53 sq in. per ft
d. = 0.326 sq in. per ft, #4 bars on 7-in. centers (top) = 0.343 sq in. per ft

Outer strips:

$A_s = \frac{2}{3}A_s$ of center strips or center-to-center spacing = $\frac{3}{2}$ × center spacing of center strips (or less)

7.44 Find neutral axis of beam, where $n = 10$.

$$18y \times \frac{y}{2} = 4 \times 1.27 \times 10(37.5 - y)$$
$$+ 2 \times (0.79 + 1.00) \times 10(34.5 - y)$$
$$y^2 = 5.65(37.5 - y) + 3.98(34.5 - y)$$
$$y^2 + 9.63y = 212 + 137 = 349$$

Complete square:

$$(y + 4.815)^2 = 349 + (4.815)^2 = 372 = (19.265)^2$$
$$y = 19.265 - 4.815 = 14.45 \text{ in.}$$

Moment of inertia:

$$\begin{aligned}
\text{Compression area} &= \tfrac{1}{3} \times 18 \times \overline{14.45}^3 &&= 18{,}100 \text{ in.}^4 \\
\text{Two \#8 and two \#9 bars} &= 35.8 \times \overline{20.05}^2 &&= 14{,}400 \text{ in.}^4 \\
\text{Four \#10 bars} &= 50.8 \times \overline{23.05}^2 &&= \underline{27{,}000 \text{ in.}^4} \\
& && 59{,}500 \text{ in.}^4
\end{aligned}$$

$$\text{Dead weight of beam} = 150 \times \frac{18 \times 40}{144} = 750 \text{ lb per ft}$$

$$\text{Dead-weight moment} = \tfrac{1}{8} \times 750 \times 15 \times 15 \times 12 = 253{,}000 \text{ in-lb}$$

$$\text{If } f_s = 18{,}000 \text{ psi, } f_c = \frac{14.45}{23.05} \times \frac{18{,}000}{10} = 1{,}130 \text{ psi}$$

$$f = \frac{Mc}{I} \text{ or } M = \frac{fI}{c} = \frac{1{,}130 \times 59{,}500}{14.45} = 4{,}650{,}000 \text{ in-lb}$$

$$DLM = \underline{253{,}000 \text{ in-lb}}$$

$$\text{Live load moment} = \frac{PL}{4} = \frac{P \times 15 \times 12}{4} = 4{,}397{,}000 \text{ in-lb}$$

$$P = \mathbf{97{,}600} \text{ lb}$$

Check load for shear and bond.

$$\Sigma_0 = \frac{V}{ujd} \text{ or } V = \Sigma_0 ujd$$

$$\begin{aligned}
\Sigma_0 = 4 \times 3.990 &= 15.96 \\
2 \times 3.544 &= 7.09 \\
2 \times 3.142 &= \underline{6.28} \\
& 29.33 \text{ sq in. per in.}
\end{aligned}$$

$$\begin{aligned}
\text{Maximum } V &= 29.33 \times 300 \times \tfrac{7}{8} \times 36 = 277{,}000 \text{ lb} \\
\text{Dead load } V &= 7.5 \times 750 = \underline{5{,}625} \\
P &= 2 \times 271{,}375 \text{ lb} \\
&= 542{,}800 \text{ lb} > 97{,}600 \text{ lb}
\end{aligned}$$

$$v = \frac{V}{ujd} \text{ or } V = vbjd$$

$$\begin{aligned}
\text{Maximum } V &= 360 \times 18 \times \tfrac{7}{8} \times 36 = 204{,}000 \\
\text{Dead load } V &= \underline{5{,}625} \\
P &= 198{,}375 \times 2 \\
&= 396{,}800 \text{ lb} > 97{,}600 \text{ lb}
\end{aligned}$$

$$\text{Deflection at center line} = \frac{15 \times 12}{800} = 0.225 = \frac{PL^3}{48EI}$$

$$P = \frac{0.225 \times 48 \times 3{,}000{,}000 \times 59{,}500}{15 \times 15 \times 15 \times 12 \times 12 \times 12} = 330{,}000 \text{ lb} > 97{,}600 \text{ lb}$$

7.45 By 1951 ACI specifications:

$f_c = 1{,}125$

$n = 12$

$$k = \frac{1{,}125}{1{,}125 + 18{,}000/12} = 0.429$$

$$j = 1 - \frac{0.429}{3} = 0.857$$

$$R = \frac{f_c}{2} \times j \times k = \frac{1{,}125}{2} \times 0.857 \times 0.429 = 207$$

$$M = \tfrac{1}{8}wl^2 \times 12 = \tfrac{3}{2} \times 1{,}500 \times 20 \times 20 = 900{,}000 \text{ in-lb}$$

$$= R \times bd^2 = \frac{Rd^3}{2}$$

$$d^3 = \frac{900{,}000 \times 2}{207} = 8{,}700,\ d = 20.6 \text{ in.}$$

or use $d = 21$ in. (23 in. over all), $b = 10$ in.

$$A_s = \frac{M}{f_s jd} = \frac{900{,}000}{18{,}000 \times 0.857 \times 21} = 2.78 \text{ sq in.}$$

	Area	Σ_0
One #8 bar =	0.79	3.14
Two #9 bars =	2.00	7.09
	2.79 sq in.	10.23 sq in. per in.

$$\Sigma_0 = \frac{V}{ujd} = \frac{1{,}500 \times 10}{250 \times 0.857 \times 21} = 3.33 \text{ sq in. per in.}$$

(bend up #8 bar into compressed concrete $5\frac{1}{2}$ ft each side of center line of beam)

$$v = \frac{V}{bjd} = \frac{1{,}500 \times 10}{10 \times 0.857 \times 21} = 83.3 \text{ psi} > 75 \text{ psi (for no stirrups)}$$

Minimum stirrup steel = #3 U stirrups on $\frac{d}{2}$ or $10\frac{1}{2}$-in. centers

$2 \times 0.11 \times 18{,}000 = 10(83.3 - 75)S$ or $S = 47.7$ in. $> 10\frac{1}{2}$ in.
∴ Use $10\frac{1}{2}$-in. spacings.

7.46 By 1951 ACI specifications:

At interior support $M = -\frac{wl^2}{10}$, $V = \frac{1.15wl}{2}$

Positive moment in end span $= \frac{wl^2}{14}$, in center span $= \frac{wl^2}{16}$

$$M = \frac{1{,}500 \times 20 \times 20 \times 12}{10} = Rbd^2 = 207 \times \frac{d^3}{2}$$

$d^3 = 720{,}000 \times \frac{2}{207} = 6{,}960, \quad d = 19.1$

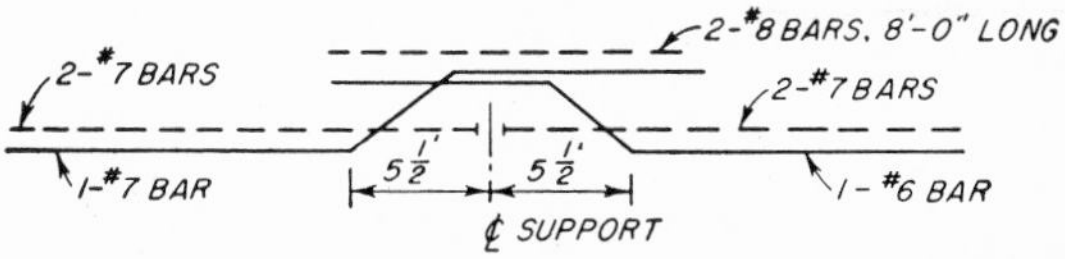

FIG. 7.46

Use $d = 18\frac{3}{4}$($20\frac{1}{2}$ over all), $b = 10$ in.

$$A_s \text{ (over interior support)} = \frac{M}{f_s jd} = \frac{72{,}000}{18{,}000 \times 0.857 \times 18\frac{3}{4}}$$
$= 2.49$ sq in.

Use one #6, one #7, and two #8 bars $= 0.44 + 0.60 + 1.58$
$= 2.62$ sq in.

A_s (mid-interior span) $= \frac{10}{16} \times 2.49 = 1.56$ sq in.

Use two #7 = 1.20
one #6 = 0.44
1.64 sq in.

A_s (mid-outside span) $= \frac{10}{14} \times 2.49 = 1.78$ sq in.

Use three #7 = 1.80 sq in.

$$V = 1.15 \times \frac{1{,}500 \times 20}{10} = 17{,}250 \text{ lb}$$

$$v = \frac{17{,}250}{10 \times 0.857 \times 18\frac{3}{4}} = 105 \text{ psi} > 75 \text{ psi (for no stirrups)}$$

Minimum stirrup steel = #3 U stirrups on $\frac{d}{2}$ or $9\frac{1}{2}$-in. centers throughout beam

$$2 \times 0.11 \times 18{,}000 = 10 \times (105 - 75) \times S$$
$$S = 13.2 \text{ in. } \therefore 9\tfrac{1}{2} \text{ in. OK}$$

7.47 By 1951 ACI specifications: $n = 10$, $f_s = 18{,}000$

$$8y \times \frac{y}{2} + 2 \times (10 - 1) \times 0.60 \times (y - 2)$$
$$= 2 \times 10 \times 1.27(16 - y)$$
$$4y^2 + 10.8(y - 2) = 25.4(16 - y)$$
$$y^2 + 2.7y - 5.4 = 101.6 - 6.35y$$
$$y^2 + 9.05y + (4.525)^2 = 107 + (4.525)^2 = 127.44$$
$$= (11.27)^2$$
$$y = 11.27 - 4.52 = 6.75 \text{ in.}$$

Moment of inertia:

Compression area	$= \frac{1}{3} \times 8 \times 6.75^3$	=	820
Compression steel	$= 10.8 \times 4.75^2$	=	244
Tension steel	$= 25.4 \times 9.25^2$	=	2,176
			3,240 in.^{4}

$$\text{If } f_s = 18{,}000 \text{ psi, } f_c = \frac{6.75}{9.25} \times \frac{18{,}000}{10} = 1{,}312 \text{ psi}$$

$$f = \frac{Mc}{I} \text{ or } M = \frac{fI}{c} = \frac{1{,}312 \times 3{,}240}{6.75} = 630{,}000 \text{ in-lb}$$

This is $> 12 \times 50{,}000$ or 600,000 in-lb. ∴ Beam is OK to carry load.

7.48 By 1951 ACl specifications:

$$f_s = 20{,}000$$
$$f_c = 1{,}687$$
$$n = 8$$
$$k = \frac{1{,}687}{1{,}687 + 20{,}000/8} = 0.403$$
$$j = 1 - \frac{0.403}{3} = 0.866$$
$$R = \frac{f_c}{2} \times j \times k = \frac{1{,}687}{2} \times 0.866 \times 0.403 = 294$$

Assume one line of steel $2\frac{1}{2}$ in. above bottom of beam

$$M = Rbd^2 = 294 \times 24 \times 31.5 \times 31.5 = 7{,}000{,}000 \text{ in-lb}$$

This is less than 12 × 650 ft kips = 7,800,000 in-lb

$$A_s = \frac{M}{f_s \times jd} = \frac{7{,}800{,}000}{20{,}000 \times 0.866 \times 31.5} = 14.3 \text{ sq in.}$$

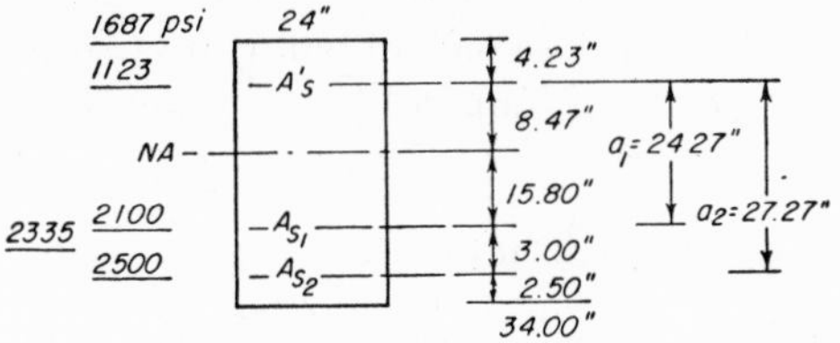

FIG. 7.48

This is too much tension steel for one row and compression steel is also needed.

$d = 31.5$ in.
$kd = 12.7$ in.
$\frac{kd}{3} = 4.23$ in.

Place six #11 bars in bottom row, $A_{s_2} = 9.36$ sq in.

$$M = A_{s_1} \times f_{s_1} \times a_1 + A_{s_2} \times f_{s_2} \times a_2$$

$$7{,}800{,}000 = A_{s_1} \times 2{,}100 \times 8 \times 24.27 + 9.36 \times 2500 \times 8 \times 27.27$$

$$7{,}800{,}000 = 408{,}000 A_{s_1} + 5{,}110{,}000$$

$$A_{s_1} = \frac{2{,}690{,}000}{408{,}000}$$

= 6.58 sq in. Use four #10 bars = 5.08 sq in.
two #8 bars = 1.58 sq in.

	6.66 sq in.
+	9.36 sq in.
Total A_s =	16.02 sq in.

Center of gravity of tension steel (below A_{s_1})

$$= \frac{3 \times 9.36}{16.02} = 1.75 \text{ in.}$$

$jd = (24.27 + 1.75) = 26.02$ in.

f_s (at center of gravity of steel) = 18,700 psi,

$$\text{and } A_S = \frac{7{,}800{,}000}{18{,}700 \times 26.02} = 16.02 \text{ sq in. check}$$

$$M_{(\text{concrete})} = b \times kd \times \frac{f_c}{2} \times jd = 24 \times 12.7 \times \frac{1{,}687}{2} \times 26.02$$

$= 6{,}680{,}000$ in-lb

Additional compression moment $= 1{,}120{,}000$ in-lb

$= A'_s \times (8 - 1) \times 1{,}123 \times 26.02 = 205{,}000A'_s$

$A'_s = 5.47$ sq in. Use one #6 bar $= 0.44$ sq in.

four #10 bars $= 5.08$ sq in.

5.52 sq in.

7.49 $kd = 0.429 \times 21 = 9$ in.

$\frac{kd}{3} = 3$ in.

Use A_{s_2} = three #9 bars

$= 3.00$ sq in.

New moment $= 1{,}200{,}000$ in-lb $= A_{s_1} \times f_{s_1} \times a_1 + A_{s_2} \times f_{s_2} \times a_2$

$= A_{s_1} \times 1{,}188 \times 12 \times 15.5 + 3.00 \times 18{,}000 \times 18$

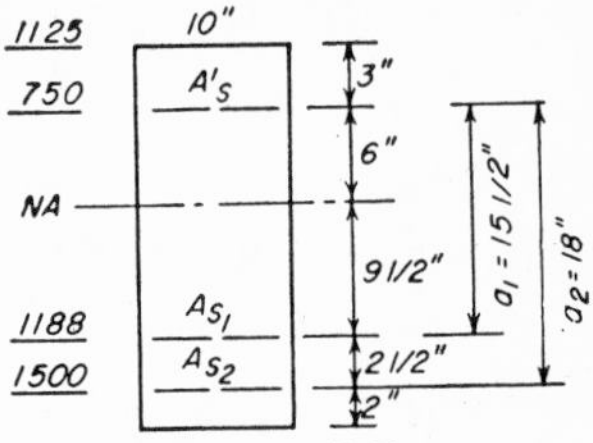

Fig. 7.49

$$A_{s_1} = \frac{1{,}200{,}000 - 972{,}000}{221{,}000} = \frac{228{,}000}{221{,}000} = 1.03 \text{ sq in.}$$

One #6 bar + two #5 bars $= 0.44 + 0.62 = 1.06$ sq in.

Center of gravity of tension steel (below A_{s_1}) $= \frac{2.5 \times 3.00}{4.06}$

$= 1.85$ in.

$jd = (15.5 + 1.85) = 17.35$ in.

$$M_{(\text{concrete})} = 10 \times 9 \times \frac{1{,}125}{2} \times 17.35 = 877{,}000 \text{ in-lb}$$

Additional compression moment $= 323{,}000$ in-lb

$= A'_s(12 - 1) \times 750 \times 17.35$

$$A'_s = \frac{323{,}000}{143{,}000} = 2.26 \text{ sq in.}$$

Use three #8 bars $= 2.37$ sq in. or two #10 bars $= 2.54$ sq in.

$$v = \frac{V}{bjd} = \frac{2{,}000 \times 10}{10 \times 17.35} = 115.3 \text{ psi} > 75 \text{ psi}$$ (for no web steel)

#3 U stirrups, $2 \times 0.11 \times 18{,}000 = 10 \times (115.3 - 75) \times S$

$S = 9.85 \text{ in.} < \frac{d}{2} = 10\frac{1}{2} \text{ in.}$

The end two stirrups should cover 9½ in. each, thereafter use 10½-in. center-to-center spacings.

7.50 $\frac{1}{8}wl^2 = \frac{l}{4} \times \frac{wl}{2} = 200{,}000 \text{ ft-lb}$

$$\frac{wl}{2} = 40{,}000 \text{ lb}$$

$\frac{l}{4} = 5 \text{ ft}, \quad l = 20 \text{ ft},$

$w_T = 4{,}000$ lb per ft,

$w_d = 790$ lb per ft,

$w_L = 535$ psf

Assume that neutral axis falls within slab.

Effective flange width for T beam $= \frac{l}{4} = 5 \text{ ft} = 60 \text{ in.}$

$$60y \times \frac{y}{2} = [(9 - y) + (12 - y) + (15 - y)] \times 4 \times 1.56 \times 10$$

$$30y^2 = 62.4(36 - 3y)$$

$$y^2 = 74.88 - 6.24y$$

$$y^2 + 6.24y + (3.12)^2 = 74.88 + (9.74) = 84.62$$

$$y + 3.12 = \pm 9.20$$

$$y = 6.08 \text{ in. (assumption OK)}$$

I_c $\frac{60}{3} \times 6.08^3 = 4{,}500$

$62.4 \times 2.92^2 = 532$

$62.4 \times 5.92^2 = 2{,}185$

$62.4 \times 8.92^2 = 4{,}960$

$12{,}177 \text{ in.}^4$

$$f_{(\text{concrete})} = \frac{200{,}000 \times 12 \times 6.08}{12{,}177} = 1{,}200 \text{ psi} < 1{,}350,$$

which is OK.

$$f_{(\text{steel})} = \frac{200{,}000 \times 12 \times 8.92 \times 10}{12{,}177} = 17{,}600 \text{ psi}$$

$< 18{,}000$, which is OK.

$$v = \frac{V}{b'jd} = \frac{40{,}000}{22(\frac{2}{3} \times 6.08 + 5.92)} = \frac{40{,}000}{22 \times 9.98} = 182 \text{ psi}$$

$v = >90$ and <360 Stirrups are needed.

$$\text{Spacing} = \frac{d}{2} = \frac{12}{2} = 6 \text{ in. maximum throughout.}$$

$$2 \times A_s \times 18{,}000 = v'bs = (182 - 90) \times 22 \times 6$$

$$A_s = \frac{92 \times 22 \times 6}{2 \times 18{,}000} = 0.337 \text{ sq in.}$$

Use #5 U stirrups 6 in. on centers for end 3 ft
Use #4 U stirrups 6 in. on centers for next 2 ft
Use #3 U stirrups 6 in. on centers for center 10 ft

7.51 Weight per ft $= (2 \times 2 + \frac{1}{2} \times 4) \times 150 = 900$ lb per ft

$M_D = \frac{1}{8} \times 900 \times 40 \times 40 \times 12 = 2{,}160{,}000$ in-lb
$M_L = 172{,}000 \times 12 = 2{,}064{,}000$ in-lb
$M_I = 52{,}000 \times 12 = 624{,}000$ in-lb
$M_T = 4{,}848{,}000$ in-lb

Assuming steel and concrete is stressed to maximum allowable,

$k = 0.403$
$j = 0.866$
$kd = 0.403 \times 21.5 \text{ in.} = 8.65 \text{ in.}$
and $21.50 \text{ in.} - 8.65 \text{ in.} = 12.85 \text{ in.}$

$$\left(\frac{8.65 - 6}{8.65}\right) \times 1{,}350 = 414 \text{ psi}$$

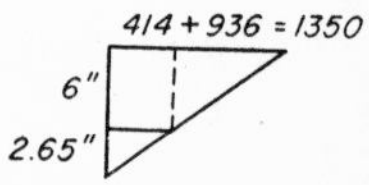

FIG. 7.51

$414 \times 6 = 2{,}484 \times 3 = 7{,}452$

$\frac{936}{2} \times 6 = 2{,}808 \times 2 = 5{,}616$

$5{,}292\ (2.47) = 13{,}068$

Compressive force centers 2.47 in. from top of slab.

Use six #11 bars ($A = 9.36$ sq in.) in bottom row of steel.

Moment carried by #11 bars $= 20{,}000 \times 9.36 \times 19.03$
$= 3{,}560{,}000$ in-lb

Use second row of steel 3 in. above #11 bars.

$$M = 4{,}848{,}000 - 3{,}560{,}000 = 1{,}288{,}000$$
$$= \frac{9.85}{12.85} \times 20{,}000 \times 16.03 A_{S_2}$$

$$A_{S_2} = \frac{1{,}288{,}000 \times 12.85}{16.03 \times 20{,}000 \times 9.85} = 5.24 \text{ sq in.}$$

Use six #8 bars. $A_{S_2} = 4.76$ sq in.

This should be OK as N.A. is higher than figured.
M beam can carry in concrete $= 72 \times 5292 \times 18.03 =$ 6,860,000 in-lb

and no A'_s is needed. $\left[b = 72 \text{ in.} < \frac{l}{4} < (24 + 2 \times 8 \times 6)\right]$

$$72 \times 6(y - 3) = 4.76 \times 10(18.5 - y) + 9.36 \times 10(21.5 - y)$$

$(y - 3) = 2.04 - 0.11y + 4.66 - 0.217y$
$1.327y = 9.70$ and $y = 7.30$ in.

$$\begin{aligned} I = \tfrac{1}{12} \times 72 \times 6 \times 6 \times 6 &= 1{,}296 \\ +72 \times 6 \times 4.30^2 &= 8{,}000 \\ +47.6 \times 11.20^2 &= 5{,}970 \\ +93.6 \times 14.20^2 &= 18{,}900 \\ &\quad 34{,}166 \text{ in.}^4 \end{aligned}$$

$$f_c = \frac{4{,}848{,}000}{34{,}166} \times 7.30 = 1{,}035 \text{ psi}$$

$$f_s = \frac{4{,}848{,}000}{34{,}166} \times 14.20 \times 10 = 20{,}150 \text{ psi, say OK.}$$

Or use four #8 bars + two #9 bars for $A_{S_2} = 5.18$ sq in.

$$jd = 21.5 - 1.0 - 2.25 = 18.25 \text{ in.}$$

$$v = \frac{V}{b'jd} = \frac{40{,}000}{24 \times 18.25} = 91.5 \text{ psi} > 90 \text{ psi (no stirrups)}$$

As this is only slightly above a "no-stirrups-needed" condition, use minimum size stirrups at maximum spacing. Use #3 U stirrups $\frac{d}{2}$ or $\frac{20.5}{2}$ or 10-in. spacings center-to-center

7.52 $f_c = 1{,}686$
$f_s = 20{,}000$
$n = 8$
$k = 0.403$
$j = 0.866$
$R = 294$

$$b \text{ for T beam} = \frac{l}{4} = \frac{16 \times 12}{4} = 48 \text{ in.} < b' + 2 \times (8 \times 4\tfrac{1}{2}) < 96 \text{ in.}$$

Assume dead weight of T beam = 600 lb per ft

$+M = \frac{8}{10} \times (\frac{1}{8} \times 8{,}600 \times 16 \times 16 \times 12)$

$= 2{,}640{,}000$ in-lb

$-M = \frac{1}{5} \times (3{,}300{,}000) = 660{,}000$ in-lb

$M = Rbd^2 = 294 \times 48 \times d^2 = 2{,}640{,}000$ in-lb

$d^2 = 187$, $d = 13.7$ or 14 in., and $kd = 5.67$ in.

As neutral axis lies below slab, A_s' is required.

$d - kd = 14 \text{ in.} - 5.67 \text{ in.} = 8.33$ in.

$$jd = 14 \text{ in.} - 1.89 \text{ in.} = 12.11 \text{ in.}$$

(to bottom row of tension steel, approximate)

$A_s = \dfrac{M}{f_s jd} = \dfrac{2{,}640{,}000}{20{,}000 \times 12.11 \text{ in.}} = 10.9$ sq in. (if all A_s were in one row)

$b' = 24$ in. for six #11 bars in one row.

Use six #11 bars, $A_{s_1} = 9.36$ sq in. in bottom row.

$+M_1 = 9.36 \times 20{,}000 \times 12.11 = 2{,}270{,}000$ in-lb

$+M_2 = 2{,}640{,}000 - 2{,}270{,}000 = 370{,}000$ in-lb

Place A_{s_2} 3 in. above A_{s_1}

$$M_2 = A_{s_2} \times \frac{5.22}{8.33} \times 20{,}000 \times 9.11 = 370{,}000 \text{ in-lb}$$

$$A_{s_2} = \frac{370{,}000}{116{,}500} = 3.18 \text{ sq in.}$$

Use two #6 and four #7 bars, $A_{s_2} = 0.88 + 2.40 = 3.28$ sq in.

Center of gravity steel (below A_{s_2} line) $= \dfrac{3 \times 9.36}{(9.36 + 3.28)}$

$= 2.24$ in. or 0.76 in. above A_{s_1}

New $d = 13.24$ in. and $13.24 - \dfrac{5.67}{3}$

$= 11.35$ in.

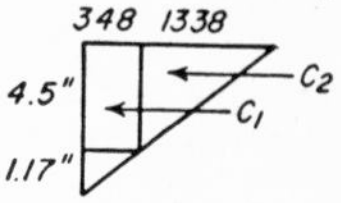

FIG. 7.52a

Center of gravity of compression forces (from top of beam)

	Force	Arm	Moment
$c_1 = 4.5 \times 348 =$	1,566 lb per in.	$\times$ 2.25	= 3,524
$c_2 = 4.5 \times 1{,}338/2 =$	3,010 lb per in.	$\times$ 1.5	= 4,515
	4,576 lb per in.	(1.75)	= 8,039

New jd = 13.24 in. − 1.75 in. = 11.49 in. > 11.35 in. used for getting A_{s_1} and A_{s_2} but say OK

(Actually, A_{s_2} could have been four #6 and two #7 bars for 2.96 sq in.)

$$M_T = 2{,}640{,}000 \text{ in-lb}$$

$$M_{(\text{concrete})} = 4{,}576 \times 48 \times 11.49 = 2{,}520{,}000 \text{ in-lb}$$

$$M \text{ to be supplied by } A'_s = 120{,}000 \text{ in-lb}$$

$$120{,}000 = A'_s \times (8-1) \times \frac{3.92}{5.67} \times 1{,}686 \times 11.49 = 93{,}800A'_s$$

$$A'_s = \frac{120{,}000}{93{,}800} = 1.28 \text{ sq in.}$$

Use two #8 bars and tie the stirrups to these bars.

Steel needed for negative moment $= \dfrac{660{,}000}{20{,}000 \times 12.11} =$ 2.72 sq in. The two #6 bars and the four #7 bars bent up from A_{s_2} are enough (3.28 sq in.).

$$-M = Rb'd^2$$
$$= 294 \times 24 \times 14 \times 14 = 1{,}385{,}000 \text{ in-lb}$$

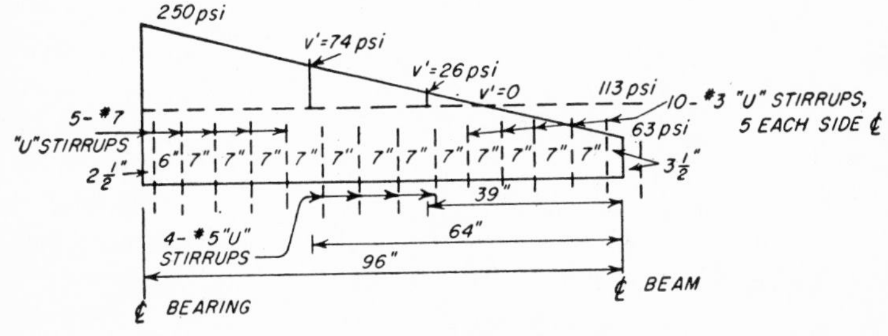

SHEAR DIAGRAM AND STIRRUP ARRANGEMENT

FIG. 7.52b

The concrete of the stem section is OK to carry the 660,000 in-lb of moment.

$$V = 8 \times 8600 = 68{,}800 \text{ lb}$$

$$v(\text{end}) = \frac{V}{b'jd} = \frac{68{,}800}{24 \times 11.49} = 250 \text{ psi} > 113 \text{ psi} < 450 \text{ psi}$$

$\therefore$ OK

Maximum stirrup spacing $= \frac{d}{2} = \frac{14}{2} = 7$ in.

$$2A_sf_s = v'b's, \quad \text{or } v' = \frac{2A_sf_s}{b's} = A_s \times \frac{2 \times 20{,}000}{24 \times 7} = 238A_s$$

For #7 U stirrup $v' = 0.60 \times 238 = 143$ psi, $v = 256$ psi
For #5 U stirrup $v' = 0.31 \times 238 = 74$ psi, $v = 187$ psi
For #3 U stirrup $v' = 0.11 \times 238 = 26$ psi, $v = 139$ psi
Assume v at center line = $\frac{1}{4}v$ at end $= {}^{250}\!/_{4} = 63$ psi

7.53 $\frac{h}{d} = \frac{15 \times 12}{22} = 8.2 < 10$, ∴ Short column

$$P = A_g(0.225f'_c + f_sp_g)$$

$$P = \frac{\pi}{4}(22)^2\left(0.225 \times 2{,}500 + 16{,}000 \times \frac{12 \times 1.56}{A_g}\right)$$

$$P = 380 \times 562.5 + 16{,}000 \times 18.72 = 214{,}000 + 300{,}000$$
$$= 514{,}000 \text{ lb}$$

Spiral steel:

$$p' = 0.45\left(\frac{A_g}{A_c} - 1\right)\frac{f'c}{f's} = \frac{\text{volume spiral wire}}{\text{volume concrete core}}$$

$$p' = 0.45\left(\frac{22 \times 22}{18 \times 18} - 1\right)\frac{2{,}500}{60{,}000} = \frac{0.45}{24}(1.493 - 1)$$
$$= 0.00925$$

Use 1.5 in. pitch for spirals $= < {}^{18}\!/_{6}$ in. < 3 in.

$$0.00925 = \frac{A_{sp} \times 18\pi}{1.5 \times 18 \times 18\pi/4}, \quad A_{sp} = 0.0624 \text{ sq in.}$$

Use #1 wire, Washburn and Moen gage for cold-drawn wire, $A = 0.063$ sq in.

7.54 Try an 18-in. outside diameter column.

$\frac{h}{d} = \frac{14 \times 12}{18} = 9.33 < 10$, ∴ Short column

$$P = A_g(0.225f'_c + f_sp_g)$$
$$300{,}000 = 81\pi \times 562.5 + 20{,}000A_s$$
$$A_s = \frac{300{,}000 - 143{,}000}{20{,}000} = \frac{157{,}000}{20{,}000} = 7.85 \text{ sq in.}$$

Use ten #8 bars, $A = 7.90$ sq in., and center the bars on a 13-in. diameter circle for 4.1-in. center-to-center spacing.

Spiral steel:

$$p' = 0.45\left(\frac{A_g}{A_c} - 1\right)\frac{f'c}{f'_s} = \frac{\text{volume spiral wire}}{\text{volume concrete core}}$$

$$p' = 0.45\left(\frac{18 \times 18}{14 \times 14} - 1\right)\frac{2{,}500}{60{,}000} = \frac{0.45}{24}(1.65 - 1)$$

$$= 0.0122$$

Use 1.67-in. pitch or three turns in 5 in. = $< {}^{14}\!/_{6} < 3$ in.

$$0.0122 = \frac{A_{sp} \times 14\pi}{167 \times {}^{14}\!/_{4} \times 14\pi},\quad A_{sp} = 0.0713 \text{ sq in.}$$

Use #0 wire, Washburn and Moen gage for cold-drawn wire, $A = 0.074$ sq in.

7.55 $\frac{h}{d} = \frac{8 \times 12}{10} = 9.6 < 10$, ∴ Short column.

$$P = 0.80 \times A_g(0.225f'c + f_s p_g)$$

$$100{,}000 = 0.80 \times \frac{\pi}{4}(10)^2(0.225 \times 3{,}000 + 20{,}000p_g)$$

$$1{,}590 = 675 + 20{,}000p_g$$

$$p_g = \frac{915}{20{,}000} = 0.046 > 0.01 < 0.08, \therefore \text{OK}$$

$$A_s = 0.046 \times 78.54 = 3.62 \text{ sq in.}$$

Use six #7 bars equally spaced and with centers on a circle 5 in. in diameter.

Use #2 hoop ties on 10-in. centers $< 16 \times \frac{7}{8} < 48 \times \frac{1}{4}$, ∴ OK

7.56 $P = 0.80A_g(0.225f'_c + f_s p_g)$

$$700{,}000 = 0.80 \times (28 \times 28)(0.225 \times 3{,}000 + 16{,}000p_g)$$

$$1{,}118 = 675 + 16{,}000p_g$$

$$p_g = \frac{443}{16{,}000} = 0.0277 > 0.01 < 0.08, \therefore \text{OK}$$

$$A_s = 0.0277 \times 784 = 21.7 \text{ sq in.}$$

Use four #11 and twelve #10 bars $A_s = 6.24 + 15.26 = 21.50$ sq in., say OK, or else use six #11 and ten #10 bars for 22.06 sq in. Place bars inside a square 24 in. on a side. Place the #11 bars in the corners with three #10 or two #10 and one #11 bars between corners.

Use #4 tie steel on $16 \times 1\frac{1}{4} = 20$-in. centers < 28 in. < $48 \times \frac{1}{2}$, which is OK.

7.57 Assume a 12 WF 65

Area $= A_r = 19.11$ sq in., $d = 12.12$ in., $b = 12$ in.

Diameter of enclosing circle for WF = 17.1 in. Use spiral diameter = 22 in. Diameter of column = 25 in. and

$$A_g = \frac{\pi}{4}(25)^2 = 492 \text{ sq in.}$$

Use twenty-four #8 bars, $A_s = 19.0$ sq in. and $p = \dfrac{19.0}{492} = 0.04$ < 0.08, ∴ OK.

$$A_c = A_g - A_s - A_r = 492 - 19.0 - 19.11 = 454 \text{ sq in.}$$

$$P = 0.225A_cf'_c + f_sA_s + f_rA_r$$

$$P = 0.225 \times 454 \times 3{,}000 + 16{,}000 \times 19 + 16{,}000 \times 19.11$$

$$P = 306{,}000 + 304{,}000 + 306{,}000 = \mathbf{916{,}000}\text{ lb}$$

Core section OK

Spiral steel:

$$p' = 0.45\left(\frac{A_g}{A_c} - 1\right)\frac{f'_c}{f'_s} = \frac{\text{volume spiral wire}}{\text{volume concrete core}}$$

$$p' = 0.45\left(\frac{492}{380} - 1\right)\frac{3{,}000}{60{,}000} = \frac{0.45}{20}(1.292 - 1) = 0.00657$$

Use 2-in. pitch for spirals = $< {}^{22}\!/_{6} < 3$ in., ∴ OK.

$$0.00657 = \frac{A_{sp} \times 22\pi}{2 \times {}^{22}\!/_{4} \times 22\pi}, \quad A_{sp} = 0.0722 \text{ sq in.}$$

Use #0 wire, Washburn and Moen gage for cold-drawn wire, $A = 0.074$ sq in.

7.58 $P = A_rf'_r\left[1 + \dfrac{A_g}{100A_r}\right]$

Assume a 12 WF 65 lb per ft, $r = 3.02$ in.

$d = 12.12$ in.

$b = 12$

$A_r = 19.11$ sq in.

Concrete encasement will form a solid square 18 by 18 in.
$= 324$ sq in.
$A_g = 324 - 19.11 = 305$ sq in.

$$\frac{l}{r} \text{ of WF} = \frac{20 \times 12}{3.02} = 80, \quad f'_r = 17{,}000 - 0.485\left(\frac{l}{r}\right)^2$$

$$f'_r = 17{,}000 - 0.485 \times 6{,}400$$

Allowable unit stress in core $= 17{,}000 - 3{,}100 = 13{,}900$ psi

$$P = 19.11 \times 13{,}900\left[1 + \frac{305}{1{,}911}\right] = 266{,}000 \times 1.16$$

$= \textbf{308,000}$ lb
WF section OK.

7.59 $P = 0.225f'_cA_c + f'_rA_r$

$$f'_r = \left[18{,}000 - \frac{70h}{K}\right]F = \text{allowable unit stress in pipe}$$

Assume a 12-in. extra-strong pipe
K(radius of gyration) $= 4.34$ in., $A_r = 19.24$ sq in.,

$$A_c = \frac{\pi}{4}(11.75)^2 = 108.6 \text{ sq in.}$$

$$F = \frac{\text{yield point of pipe}}{45{,}000} = \frac{33{,}000}{45{,}000} = 0.735 \text{ for bridge steel}$$

(minimum)

$$f'_r = \left[18{,}000 - 70 \times \frac{20 \times 12}{4.34}\right]0.735$$

$$= (18{,}000 - 3870) \times 0.735 = 10{,}400 \text{ psi}$$

$P = 0.225 \times 2000 \times 108.6 + 10{,}400 \times 19.24$
$P = 48{,}800 + 200{,}000 = \textbf{248,800}$ lb $> 240{,}000$ lb
Pipe section OK

7.60 $P' = 0.80A_g(0.225f'_c + f_sp_g)\left(1.30 - 0.03\frac{h}{d}\right)$

$$P' = 0.80 \times 14 \times 14\,(0.225 \times 3{,}000 + 20{,}000 \times \frac{12 \times 0.60}{14 \times 14}\Big)\left(1.30 - 0.03 \times \frac{12 \times 16}{14}\right)$$

$P' = 156.8(675 + 735)(1.30 - 0.412)$
$P' = 156.8 \times 1410 \times 0.888 = \textbf{196,000}$ lb

7.61 $n = 12$

			A				I
Concrete	15 × 24	=	360	×	$15^2/12$	=	6,750 in.^{4}
Steel	6 × (12 − 1)	=	66	×	5.5^2	=	2,000 in.^{4}
			426				8,750 in.^{4}

$$f_c = \frac{170{,}000}{426} \pm \frac{170{,}000 \times 2.5 \times 7.5}{8750} = \frac{N}{A} \pm \frac{Nec}{I}$$

$f_c = 400 \pm 364 = 764$ psi (maximum) and 36 psi (minimum) both compression

Check by ACI specifications.

$$f_c = \frac{N}{A_g}\left[\frac{1 + De/t}{1 + (n-1)p_g}\right] \qquad \frac{e = 2.5}{t = 15} = \frac{1}{6}, \quad p_g = \frac{6}{360} = \frac{1}{60}$$

$$f_c = \frac{170{,}000}{360}\left[\frac{1 + 5.46 \times 1/6}{1 + 11 \times 1/60}\right] \qquad D = \frac{t^2}{2R^2} \text{ and } R^2 = \frac{I}{A}$$

$$= \frac{8{,}750}{426} = 20.6$$

$$D = \frac{15 \times 15}{2 \times 20.6} = 5.46$$

$$f_c = 472\left[\frac{1 + 0.91}{1 + 0.183}\right] = 472 \times \frac{1.91}{1.183} = 764 \text{ psi}$$

The maximum allowable compressive stress

$$= f_p = f_a\left[\frac{t + De}{t + CDe}\right], \text{ but } C = \frac{f_a}{0.45f'_c}$$

$$\text{and} \quad f_a = 0.80\left[\frac{0.225f'_c + f_s p_g}{1 + (n-1)p_g}\right] = 0.80\left(\frac{562.5 + 334}{1.183}\right)$$

$$f_a = \frac{0.80 \times 896.5}{1.183} = 607 \text{ psi, and } C = \frac{607}{0.45 \times 2{,}500} = 0.539$$

$$f_p = 607\left[\frac{15 + 5.46 \times 2.5}{15 + 0.539 \times 13.65}\right] = 607\,\frac{(28.65)}{(22.35)} = 778 \text{ psi} > 764.$$

∴ 764 psi is OK.

7.62 Take $\Sigma M_N = 0$

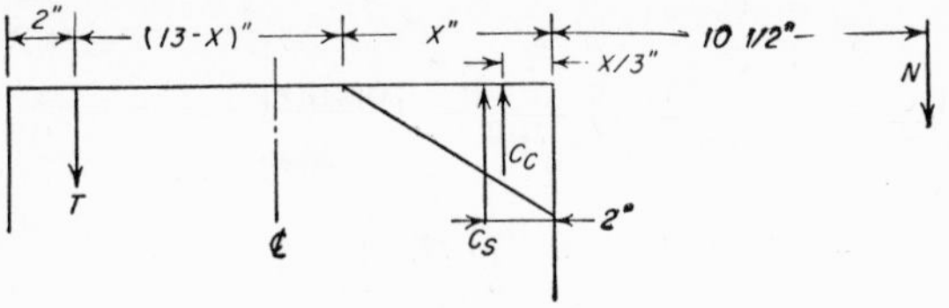

FIG. 7.62

Force	Area	× Intensity	× Arm	× Factor (to simplify products)	= moment
$+C_c$;	$24x \times \frac{f_c}{2}$		$\times (10.5 + x)$	$\times \frac{x}{12f_c}$	$= +x^2(x + 10.5)$
$+C_s$;	$(12 - 1)3 \times \left(\frac{x-2}{x}\right) f_c$		$\times 12.5$	$\times \frac{x}{12f_c}$	$= +34.4(x - 2)$
$-T$;	$12 \times 3 \times \left(\frac{13-x}{x}\right) f_c$		$\times 23.5$	$\times \frac{x}{12f_c}$	$= -70.5(13 - x)$

$$\Sigma M_N = 0 = +x^2(x + 10.5) + 34.4(x - 2) + 70.5(x - 13)$$
$$x^3 + 10.5x^2 + 104.9x - 985.3 = 0$$

Solve for x by trial.

$x = 1,\quad +1 + 10.5 + 105 - 985 = -870$
$x = 10,\quad +1{,}000 + 1{,}050 + 1{,}049 - 985 = +2{,}114$
$x = 5,\quad +125 + 262 + 525 - 985 = -73$
$x = 6,\quad +216 + 378 + 629 - 985 = +238$
$x = 5.26,\quad +145.5 + 290 + 551 - 985.3 = +1.2$, say OK.

$$+C_c = 24 \times 5.26 \times \frac{f_c}{2} = +63.1f_c$$

$$+C_s = 11 \times 3 \times \frac{3.26}{5.26} \times f_c \quad \frac{+20.5f_c}{+83.6f_c}$$

$$-T = 12 \times 3 \times \frac{7.74}{5.26} \times f_c \quad \frac{-53.0f_c}{+30.6f_c}$$

$$+C_c + C_s - T - N = 0$$
$$N = 30.6f_c = 30{,}000$$
$$f_c = 980 \text{ psi} < 0.45f'_c < 1125 \text{ psi}, \therefore \text{OK.}$$
$$f_s \text{ (tension)} = 980 \times \frac{53.0}{3} = 17{,}300 \text{ psi}$$
$$< 18{,}000 \text{ psi}, \therefore \text{OK.}$$

7.63 To allow for weight of footing, use 5,500 psf for soil pressure from column load.

$$\text{Area needed for footing} = \frac{700{,}000}{5{,}500} = 127.3 \text{ sq ft}$$

Use footing 11 ft 4 in. × 11 ft 4 in. = 128.5 sq ft

$$\text{and soil pressure} = \frac{700{,}000}{128.5} = 5450 \text{ psf}$$

Pass a vertical plane xy at the face of the column and take moment of upward pressure on rectangle to right of xy.

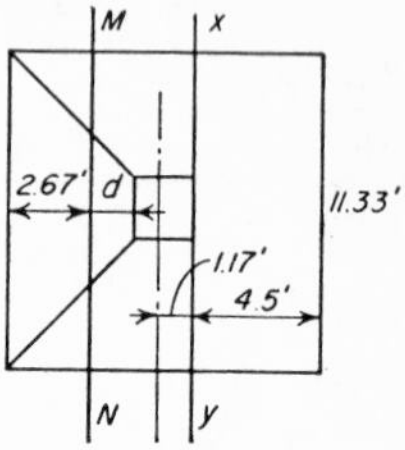

FIG. 7.63

$$M = 11.33 \times 4.5 \times \frac{4.5}{2} \times 5{,}450 \times 12 = 7{,}500{,}000 \text{ in-lb}$$

$$f_c = 1{,}350, \quad k = \frac{1{,}350}{1{,}350 + 16{,}000/10} = 0.456, \; j = 0.848$$

$$R = \frac{1{,}350}{2} \times 0.456 \times 0.848 = 261$$

$$M = Rbd^2 \text{ or } d^2 = \frac{M}{Rb} = \frac{7{,}500{,}000}{261 \times 11.33 \times 12} = 212, \; d = 14.5 \text{ in.}$$

Use d = 22 in. for shear and footing of 26-in. over-all depth. Pass a vertical plane mn d distance from the face of the column. This is the critical section for shear. The trapezoid outward from mn brings shear to mn.

$$V = \frac{11.33 + (28/12 + 2 \times 22/12)}{2} \times 2.67 \times 5{,}450$$

$$= \frac{11.33 + 6.00}{2} \times 2.67 \times 5{,}450 = 126{,}000 \text{ lb}$$

$$v = \frac{V}{bjd} = \frac{126{,}000}{72 \times 0.848 \times 22} = 94 \text{ psi.} > 90 \text{ psi.}$$

Say OK or make d = 23 in. ∴ no stirrups needed.

For two-way reinforced footings, steel is needed for only 85 per cent of moment (each way).

$$A_s = \frac{0.85 \times 7{,}500{,}000}{16{,}000 \times 0.848 \times 22} = 21.4 \text{ sq in.}$$

Use twenty-two #9 bars = **22.00** sq in.

7.64 Use soil pressure from column loads = 5,500 psf.

$$\text{Length of footing} = \frac{700{,}000}{9 \times 5{,}500}$$

$$L = 14.17 \text{ ft}$$

$$M_{xy} = 9 \times \frac{5.91^2}{2} \times 5{,}500 = 862{,}000 \text{ ft-lb}$$

$$M_{PQ} = 14.17 \times \frac{3.33^2}{2} \times 5{,}500 = 432{,}000 \text{ ft-lb}$$

$$d_{(xy)}{}^2 = \frac{M}{Rb} = \frac{862{,}000}{261 \times 9} = 367, \quad d = 19.2 \text{ in.}$$

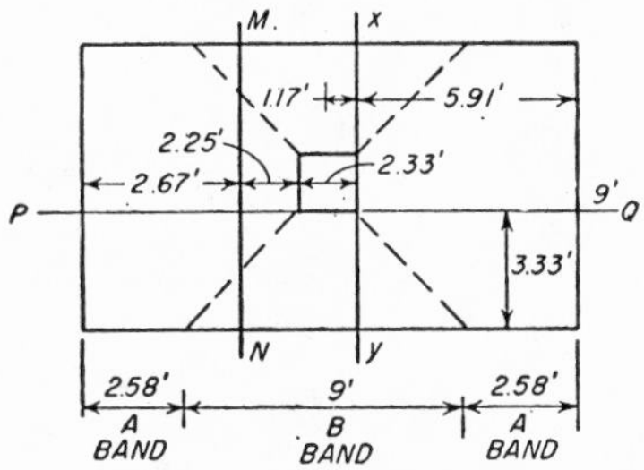

FIG. 7.64

Use d = **27** in., over-all depth = 31 in., with weight under 500 psf.

$$V = 2.58 \times 9 \times 5500 + \frac{(9 + 2 \times 2.25 + 2.33)}{2} \times 1.08 \times 5500$$

$$V = 127{,}800 + 47{,}000 = 174{,}800 \text{ lb}$$

$$v = \frac{V}{bjd} = \frac{174{,}800}{82 \times 0.848 \times 27} = 93 \text{ psi} > 90 \text{ psi.}$$

Say OK or make d = 28 in. ∴ no stirrups needed.

Long steel for 9-ft width:

$$A_s = \frac{M}{f_s jd} = \frac{862{,}000 \times 0.85 \times 12}{16000 \times 0.848 \times 27} = 23.5 \text{ sq in.}$$

Use nineteen #10 bars, A_s = **24.1** sq in.

Short steel for 14-ft 2-in. length

$$A_s = \frac{0.85 \times 432{,}000 \times 12}{16{,}000 \times 0.848 \times 27} = 12.0 \text{ sq in.}$$

$$A_s \text{ for } B \text{ Band} = 12.0 \times \frac{2}{(s+1)} \quad \text{where } s = \frac{14.17}{9} = 1.575$$

$$= 12.0 \times \frac{2}{2.575} = 9.32 \text{ sq in.}$$

Use twelve #8 bars on 9-in. centers
$A_s = 9.48$ sq in.

$$\text{for } A \text{ band} = \frac{12.0 - 8.77}{2} = \frac{3.23}{2} = 1.61 \text{ sq in.}$$

Use three #7 bars on 10-in. centers in each 31-in. end of A band. $A_s =$ **1.80** sq in.

7.65

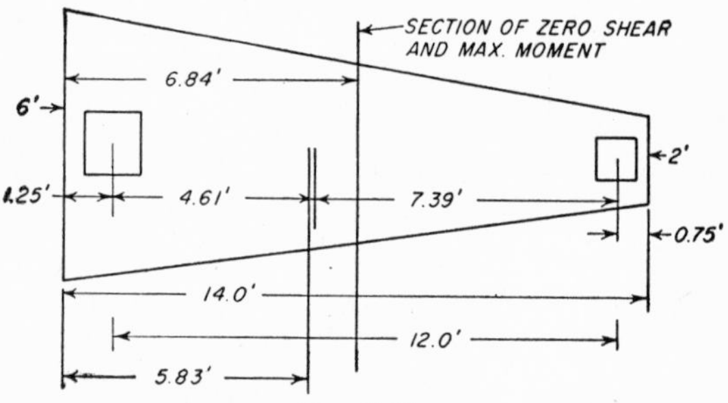

FIG. 7.65

Center-of-gravity distance of column loads from center line 120 kips load $= \dfrac{12 \times 75}{(120 + 75)} = \dfrac{900}{195} = 4.61$ ft

Use 3,500 psf as working pressure on underside of concrete slab from column loads.

$$\text{Area of footing} = \frac{195{,}000}{3{,}500} = 56 \text{ sq ft}$$

Trapezoidal footing 14 ft long, width 2 to 6 ft, and A of 56 sq ft.

Center of gravity of footing from 6 ft end = 5.83 ft

$$2 \times 14 = 28 \times 7 \text{ ft} = 196$$

$$2 \times \frac{14 \times 2}{2} = 28 \times 4.67 \text{ ft} = 130.7$$

$$56\ (5.83 \text{ ft}) = 326.7$$

Place center line of 15 × 15 column 15 in. from 6 ft end of footing

Place center line of 12 × 12 column 9 in. from 2 ft end of footing

The center of gravity of column loads and the center of gravity of upward pressure coincide within 0.03 ft. Say OK

Find distance from left end to point of zero shear

$$6 \times 3{,}500 = 21{,}000 \text{ psf} = 21 \text{ kips per sq ft}$$

Upward pressure varies from 21 kips to 7 kips in 14 ft or by 1 kip per ft

$+21x - 1x^2/2 - 120 = 0$

$+42x - x^2 - 240 = 0$

$x^2 - 42x + (21)^2 = -240 + (21)^2 = +201$

$(x - 21) = \pm\sqrt{201} = \pm 14.16$

$x = +21 - 14.16 = 6.84 \text{ ft} =$ point of maximum moment

$$M_{(\max)} = (21 - 6.84) \text{ kips} \times \frac{6.84^2}{2} + 6.84 \text{ kips} \times \frac{6.84}{2}$$

$$\times \tfrac{2}{3} \times 6.84 - 120 \times 5.59 \text{ ft} = 330.5 + 106.5 - 671$$

$$= 234 \text{ ft-kips}$$

Width at inside face of 15 × 15 column (point *A*)

$$= 6 - \frac{1.87 \times 4}{14} = 6 - 0.54 = 5.46 \text{ ft}$$

Width at inside face of 12 × 12 column (point *B*)

$$= 2 + \frac{1.25 \times 4}{14} = 2 + 0.36 = 2.36 \text{ ft}$$

Width at point of maximum moment $= 6 - \dfrac{6.48 \times 4}{14}$

$$= 6 - 1.95 = 4.05 \text{ ft}$$

Shear at point $A = 21 \times 1.87 - \dfrac{1.87^2 \times 1}{2} - 120$

$= 39.4 - 1.76 - 120 = 82.36$ kips or

$\dfrac{82.36}{5.46} = 15.1$ kips per ft

Shear at point $B = 7 \times 1.25 + 1 \times \dfrac{1.25^2}{2} - 75$

$= 8.75 + 0.78 - 75 = 65.47$ kips or

$\dfrac{65.47}{2.36} = 27.7$ kips per ft

$$k = \frac{1{,}350}{1{,}350 + 18{,}000/10} = 0.429, \quad j = 0.857$$

$$R = \frac{1{,}350}{2} \times 0.857 \times 0.429 = 248$$

$$v = \frac{V}{bjd} \text{ and } d = \frac{V}{vbj} = \frac{27{,}700}{90 \times 12 \times 0.857} = 30 \text{ in.} + 4 \text{ in.}$$

$= 34$ in. over all

weight $= 325$ psf < 500 $\therefore$ OK

Moment concrete could take $= M_c = Rbd^2$

$= 248 \times 4.05 \times 30 \times 30$

$= 905$ ft-kips > 234 ft-kips $\therefore$ OK

$$A_s = \frac{M}{f_s jd} = \frac{234{,}000 \times 12}{18{,}000 \times 0.857 \times 30} = 6.06 \text{ sq in.}$$

Use eight #8 bars, $A =$ **6.28** sq in.

Maximum lateral bending $= 3{,}500 \times \dfrac{2.38^2}{2} \times 12$

$= 119{,}000$ in-lb

$$A_s = \frac{M}{f_s jd} = \frac{119{,}000}{18{,}000 \times 0.857 \times 30} = 0.257 \text{ sq in. per ft}$$

Use #5 bars 12 in. on centers, $A =$ **0.31** sq in per ft

7.66 6 to 12 triangle $= 1, 2, \sqrt{5}$

$$\cos^2\theta = \frac{(2)^2}{5} = 0.80, \quad \sin^2\theta = \frac{(1)^2}{5} = 0.20$$

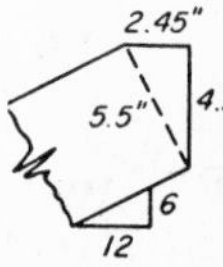

Fig. 7.66

$$N_1 = \frac{1{,}200 \times 380}{1{,}200 \times 0.20 + 380 \times 0.80}$$

$$= \frac{455{,}000}{240 + 304} = \frac{455{,}000}{544} = 836 \text{ psi}$$

$$N_2 = \frac{1{,}200 \times 380}{1{,}200 \times 0.80 + 380 \times 0.20} = \frac{455{,}000}{960 + 76}$$

$$= \frac{455{,}000}{1{,}036} = 439 \text{ psi}$$

Dressed size of timbers = 5.5 × 5.5 in.
A 4-in. diameter washer has 11 sq in. bearing area
Washer bearing = 4,500/11 = 409 psi < 439 psi, ∴ OK

$$6 \text{ by } 6 \text{ bearing against } 6 \text{ by } 6 = \frac{9{,}000}{4.9 \times (5.5 - 1)}$$

$$= \frac{9{,}000}{4.9 \times 4.5} = 408 \text{ psi} < 836 \text{ psi}, \therefore \text{ OK}$$

2 × 2.45 in. = 4.90 in. > 4 in. (diameter of washer)

7.67 4 by 6 bearing on plane of notch in 6 by 6 $= \dfrac{5{,}000}{3.5 \times 5.5}$
= 260 psi < 836 psi (see preceding answer), ∴ OK

7.68 Let N be the load per square foot.
For bearing:

$$V = 1.33 \times 14 \times N \times \tfrac{1}{2} = 9.33N$$

$$s_b = \frac{V}{bl} = \frac{9.33N}{2.62 \times 6} = 380$$

$$N = 641 \text{ psf}$$

For shear:

$$s_s = \frac{3}{2}\frac{V}{A} = \frac{3 \times 9.33N}{2 \times 2.62 \times 11.5} = 120$$

$$N = 259 \text{ psf}$$

For bending:

$$f = \frac{M}{S} = \frac{\tfrac{1}{8}(1.33N) \times 14 \times 14 \times 12}{\tfrac{1}{6} \times 2.62 \times 11.5 \times 11.5} = 1{,}600$$

$$N = 236 \text{ psf}$$

For deflection:

$$\frac{\text{Span}}{360} = \frac{5wl^4}{384EI} = \frac{14 \times 12}{360} = \frac{5(1.33N) \times 14^4 \times 12^3}{384 \times 1{,}600{,}000 \times 2.62 \times 11.5^3/12}$$

$$N = 216 \text{ psf}$$

This is the largest loading to satisfy all four conditions.

7.69 From preceding answer, defection is most critical.

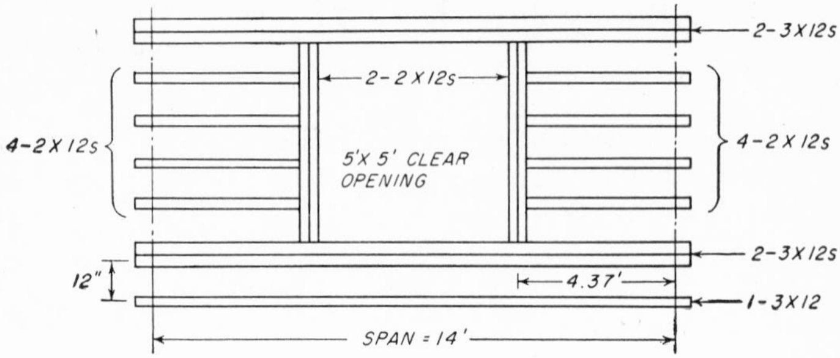

FIG. 7.69

$$\Delta \text{ for one 3 by 12} = \frac{5 \times 250 \times 14^4 \times 1{,}728}{384 \times 1{,}600{,}000 \times 333} = \frac{5wl^4}{384EI}$$

$$= 0.406 \text{ in.} < \text{allowable} = \frac{14 \times 12}{360} = 0.467 \text{ in.}$$

Δ for two concentrated loads on one 3 by 12

$$F = \text{concentrated load} = 2 \times 250 \times \frac{4.37}{2} = 1{,}092 \text{ lb}$$

$$a = 4.37 \text{ ft}$$
$$l = 14 \text{ ft}$$
$$\Delta = \frac{Fa(3l^2 - 4a^2)}{24EI}$$
$$= \frac{1{,}092 \times 4.37(3 \times 14 \times 14 - 4 \times 4.37 \times 4.37)1{,}728}{24 \times 1{,}600{,}000 \times 333}$$
$$= 0.330 \text{ in.} < 0.467 \text{ in.}$$

The two 3 by 12 will have a $\Delta = 0.368$ in. < **0.467 in.**

$$V = 7 \times 250 + 1{,}092 = 2{,}842$$
$$v = \frac{3}{2}\frac{V}{A} = \frac{3 \times 2{,}842}{2 \times 5.25 \times 11.5} = 71 \text{ psi} < 120, \therefore \text{OK}$$
$$f = \frac{(\frac{1}{8} \times 250 \times 14 \times 14 \times 12) + (1{,}092 \times 4.37 \times 12)}{\frac{1}{6} \times 5.25 \times 11.5 \times 11.5}$$
$$= \frac{73{,}500 + 57{,}500}{115.7} = 1{,}132 \text{ psi} < 1{,}600, \therefore \text{OK}$$

7.70 If four 2 by 8s are placed on edge side by side

$$I = 4 \times \tfrac{1}{12} \times 1.62 \times \overline{7.5}^3 = 4 \times 57 = 228 \text{ in.}^4$$

If placed in the form of an I or hollow box of 10.75 in. depth

$$I = \tfrac{1}{12} \times 7.5 \times 10.75^3 - \tfrac{1}{12}(7.5 - 2 \times 1.62) \times 7.5^3$$
$$= 777 - 149 = \mathbf{628} \text{ in.}^4 \text{ (use)}$$

7.71 One 2 by 8, $A = 1.62 \times 7.5 = 12.2$ sq in.

$$Q = \text{statical moment} = 12.2 \times 4.56 + 12.2 \times \frac{3.75}{2}$$
$$= 55.7 + 22.8 = 78.5 \text{ in.}^3$$

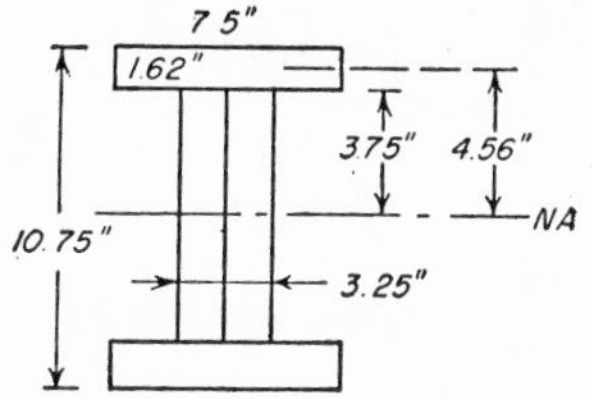

FIG. 7.71

If placed in the form of an I,

$$v = \frac{VQ}{bI} \text{ or } \frac{V}{v} = \frac{bI}{Q} = \frac{3.25 \times 628}{78.5} = \mathbf{260} \text{ sq in.}$$

If placed side by side on edge,

$$v = \frac{3V}{2A} \text{ or } \frac{V}{v} = \tfrac{2}{3}A = \tfrac{2}{3} \times 4 \times 12.2 = \mathbf{32.4} \text{ sq in. (use)}$$

7.72 Dense southern yellow pine has the following properties:

$$E = 1{,}600{,}000 \text{ psi}$$

$$\frac{P}{A} \text{ for } \frac{L}{d} < 10 = 1{,}285 = f_c$$

$$\frac{P}{A} \text{ for } \frac{L}{d} > 10 = 1{,}285C$$

$$k = \frac{\pi}{2}\sqrt{\frac{E}{4f_c}} = \frac{3.14}{2}\sqrt{\frac{1{,}600{,}000}{4 \times 1{,}285}} = 27.8 \text{ or } 28$$

$$C = \left[1 - \frac{1}{3}\left(\frac{L}{kd}\right)^4\right]$$

$$\frac{L}{d} = \frac{6 \times 12}{5.5} = 13.1$$

$$C = \left[1 - \frac{1}{3}\left(\frac{13.1}{28}\right)^4\right] = 0.98$$

$$\text{Allowable } \frac{P}{A} = 1{,}285 \times 0.98 = 1{,}260 \text{ psi}$$

$$N = 1{,}260 \times (5.5 \times 9.5) = 65{,}800 \text{ lb} > 60{,}000 \text{ lb}$$

Use **6 by 10.**

7.73 Try a 6 by 6.

$$\frac{L}{d} = \frac{12 \times 12}{5.5} = 26.2$$

$$C = \left[1 - \frac{1}{3}\left(\frac{26.2}{28}\right)^4\right] = 0.75$$

$$\frac{P}{A} = 1{,}285 \times 0.75 = 963 \text{ psi}$$

$$N = 963 \times (5.5 \times 5.5) = 29{,}100 \text{ lb} > 27{,}000 \text{ lb}$$

∴ **6 by 6** is OK.

7.74 Try four 2 by 10s.

Box is 1.62 + 9.5 = 11.12 by 11.12 in. outside

$$\frac{L}{d} = \frac{12 \times 12}{11.12} = 13$$

$$C = [1 - \tfrac{1}{3}(\tfrac{13}{28})^4] = 0.98$$

$$\text{Allowable } \frac{P}{A} = 1{,}285 \times 0.98 = 1{,}260 \text{ psi}$$

$$N = 4 \times (1.62 \times 9.5) \times 1{,}260 = 77{,}600 \text{ lb} > 75{,}000 \text{ lb}$$

∴ **four 2 by 10s** are OK.

7.75 4 × 8 is 3.62 in. × 7.5 in. dressed size, $A = 27.2$ sq in.
2 × 4 is 1.62 × 3.62 dressed size, $A = 5.89$ sq in.
5.89
38.98 sq in.

Least dimension is (1.62 + 1.62 + 3.62) = 6.86 in. < 7.5 in.

$$\frac{L}{d} = \frac{10 \times 12}{6.86} = 17.5$$

$$C = \left[1 - \frac{1}{3}\left(\frac{17.5}{28}\right)^4\right] = 0.949$$

$$\text{Allowable } \frac{P}{A} = 1{,}285 \times 0.949 = 1{,}220 \text{ psi}$$

$$N = 38.98 \times 1{,}220 = \mathbf{47{,}500} \text{ lb}$$

SECTION EIGHT

8.01–8.25

LAND SURVEYING

8.01

Point	B.S.	H.I.	F.S.	Elevation
B.M. 49	1.37	286.06		284.69
1	4.58	283.71	6.93	279.13
2	8.72	284.05	8.38	275.33
3	11.47	293.36	2.16	281.89
4	10.97	302.50	1.83	291.53
5	7.69	309.78	0.41	302.09
6	5.41	311.35	3.84	305.94
7	8.48	307.91	11.92	299.43
B.M. 50			9.15	298.76
	58.69		44.62	−284.69
	−44.62			→ 14.07
	14.07 ←	Check		

8.02

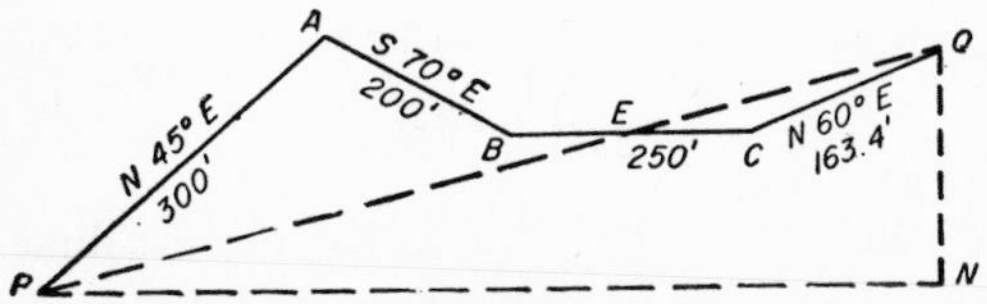

FIG. 8.02

	Distance × sin bearing		= East distance	Distance × cos bearing		= N-S distance
PA	300	0.70711	+212.133	300	0.70711	+212.133
AB	200	0.93969	+187.938	200	0.34202	− 68.404
BC	250	1.00000	+250.000	250	0	0.000
CQ	163.4	0.86603	+141.509	163.4	0.50000	+ 81.700
PN		=	+791.580			+293.833

$\overline{PN}^2 = 626{,}598.8964$
$\overline{NQ}^2 = 50{,}818.2340$
$\overline{PQ}^2 = 677{,}417.1304$

$PQ = 823.05$ ft

$-\ 68.404$
$NQ = +225.429$

$\text{tan cobearing} = \dfrac{225.429}{791.580} = 0.28478$

Cobearing = 15°54′ bearing PQ = N74°06′E

8.03

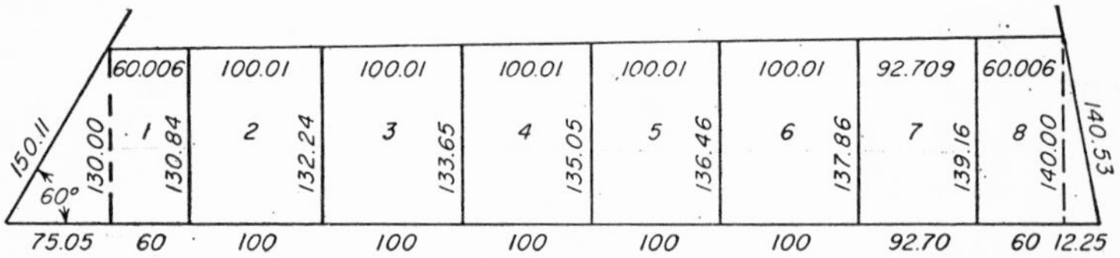

FIG. 8.03

$$150.11 \times \cos 60° = 75.05 \text{ ft}$$
$$150.11 \times \sin 60° = 130.00 \text{ ft}$$
$$140.53 \times \cos 85° = 12.25 \text{ ft}$$
$$140.53 \times \sin 85° = 140.00 \text{ ft}$$
$$75.05 + 60 + 5 \times 100 + 60 + 12.25 = 707.30 \text{ ft}$$

South dimension of lot 7 = 800 − 707.30 = 92.70 ft
Lots 1 to 8 change in vertical dimension (N-S) from 130.00 ft to 140.00 ft in 800 − (75.05 + 12.25) = 712.70 ft

$$\frac{10}{712.70} \times 60 = 0.84 \text{ ft} + 130.00$$
$$= 130.84 \text{ ft east dimension lot 1}$$
$$\frac{10}{712.70} \times 160 = 2.34 + 130.00$$
$$= 132.24 \text{ ft west dimension lot 3}$$

$$\frac{10}{712.70} \times 260 \quad = 3.65 + 130.00$$

$$= 133.65 \text{ ft east dimension lot 3}$$

$$\frac{10}{712.70} \times 560 \quad = 7.86 + 130.00$$

$$= 137.86 \text{ ft west dimension lot 7}$$

$$\frac{10}{712.70} \times 652.70 = 9.16 + 130.00$$

$$= 139.16 \text{ ft east dimension lot 7}$$

North dimension of lots 1 to 8 is longer than the corresponding south dimension by $\frac{10 \times 10}{2 \times 712.70} = 0.07$ ft. Add the following amounts to the south dimensions of lots 1, 3, 7, and 8 to get the north dimensions

$$\text{Lots 1 and 8 add } \frac{0.07}{712.7} \times 60 = 0.006 \text{ ft}$$

$$\text{Lot 3 add } \frac{0.07}{712.7} \times 100 = 0.010 \text{ ft}$$

$$\text{Lot 7 add } \frac{0.07}{712.7} \times 92.7 = 0.009 \text{ ft}$$

8.04 Beginning at the northwest corner of the intersection of South Mountain Avenue and Salter Place in the town of Maplewood, Essex County, N.J., and running along the said Salter Place N62°54′30″E a distance of one hundred ninety seven and ninety eight hundredths (197.98′) feet to an iron pipe in the ground which is the southeast corner of the property; thence turning and running N27°05′30″W a distance of one hundred and thirty eight and ninety five hundredths (138.95′) feet along the land now or formerly belonging to James Martin to an iron pipe at land now or formerly belonging to Joseph Reed; thence turning and running N62°54′30″E along the land of said Reed a distance of exactly fifty (50.00′) feet to an iron pipe at land now or formerly belonging to Charles A. Poe; thence turning and running along the land of said Poe S27°05′30″E a distance of one hundred and thirty eight and ninety five hundredths (138.95′) feet to a drill hole in the concrete drive way at Salter Place; thence turning and running S62°54′30″W along the northwesterly line of Salter Place a distance of exactly fifty (50.00′)

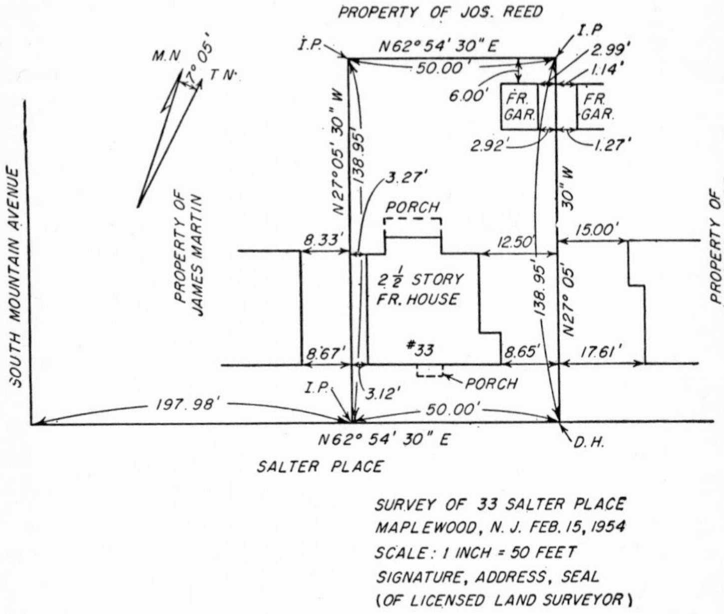

Fig. 8.04

feet to the iron pipe which is the southeast corner of the property; all bearings being magnetic and the parcel containing a calculated area of 6947.50 square feet more or less.

8.05 The plan should show U.S. pierhead and bulkhead lines, any state pierhead and bulkhead lines, high and low water lines, tributary water courses, drainage ditches, etc., and any structures such as piers, wharves, bulkheads, jetties, groins, etc. The survey must conform to any scale and other special requirements established by whatever state department has jurisdiction over riparian properties.

8.06 Temperature correction $= 27 \times 0.0000064 \times 292.59$
$= +0.05$ ft

Slope correction $= 292.59 \times 0.00375 = -1.10$ ft

$$\text{Sag correction} = \frac{L}{24}\left(\frac{wL}{t}\right)^2 = \frac{292.59}{24}\left(\frac{292.59 \times 6/300}{30}\right)^2$$

$$= 12.2 \times (0.195)^2 = -0.46 \text{ ft}$$

Total correction $= +0.05 - 1.56 = -1.51$ ft

True horizontal distance $= 291.08$ ft

8.07 *a.* 1. Sight on the backsight with telescope in the normal position. Plunge telescope through 180° about the horizontal axis, and set foresight point.

2. Swing telescope 180° about vertical axis of transit and sight on backsight. Plunge telescope through 180° about horizontal axis and set foresight point.

3. If there is a difference between the two points set, average them. Repeat for check.

b. 1. Angle should be measured by repetition, with telescope in normal position, by turning from left-hand to right-hand point in clockwise direction.

2. Angle should then be measured by repetition; with telescope in reverse position by turning from right-hand to left-hand point in counterclockwise direction. Average with *b* 1.

3. The horizon should be closed and this closing angle is measured as was the angle in *b* 1 and 2.

4. The sum of the inside and outside (closing) angles should be 360° ± permissible deviation.

c. 1. With telescope direct, sight at peak and then set point in canyon.

2. With telescope inverted, sight at peak and then set point in canyon.

3. The average of the points set in the canyon is the correct point. Repeat for check.

d. Set instrument very nearly one-half way between B.S. and F.S. Keep level bubble well centered at all times.

8.08 Distances and bearings between monuments and/or markers of undisputable permanence take precedence over recorded values. Owner of property is entitled to 144.76 ft.

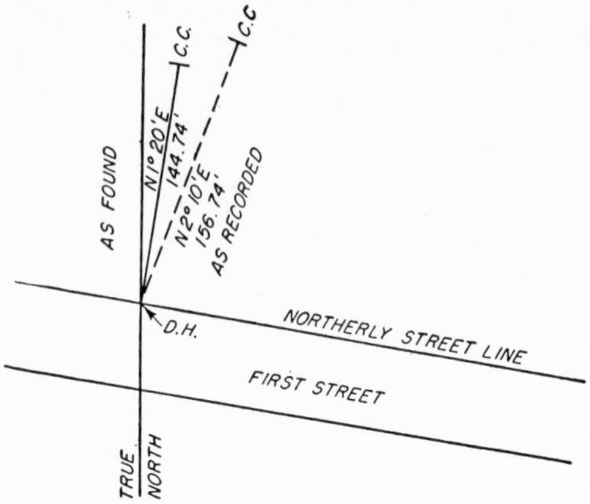

Fig. 8.08

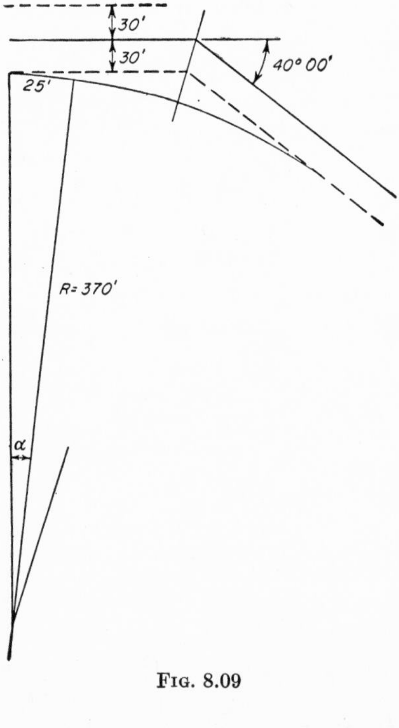

Fig. 8.09

8.09 Central angle for an arc of 25′ $= \alpha = \dfrac{25}{2 \times 370\pi} \times 360°$

$= 3.87° = 3°52'12''$. $(3°52'12'') \times 10 = 38°42'$. Last central angle increment $= 1°18'$

Chord for 25′ arc $= 2 \times 370 \times \sin 1°56'06''$
$= 740 \times 0.03377 =$ **24.99** ft

$\dfrac{1.30°}{3.87°} \times 25 =$ **8.40** ft = last chord

Deflection angles are

1°56.1′	9°40.5′	17°24.9′
3°52.2′	11°36.6′	19°21.0′
5°48.3′	13°32.7′	20°00.0′
7°44.4′	15°28.8′	

8.10 Cross-sectional area at 4 + 00
$= \frac{1}{2} \times 6(16 + 28) + \frac{1}{2} \times 10(4 + 12)$
$= 132 + 80 =$ **212** sq ft

Cross-sectional area at 5 + 00
$= \frac{1}{2} \times 3(13 + 22) + \frac{1}{2} \times 10(2 + 8)$
$= 52.5 + 50 =$ **102.5** sq ft

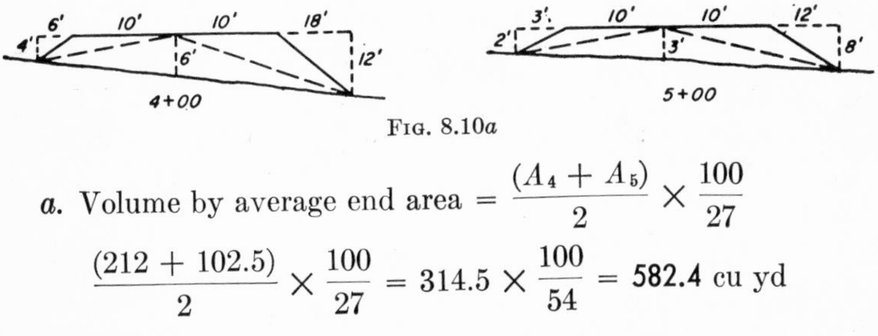

FIG. 8.10*a*

a. Volume by average end area $= \dfrac{(A_4 + A_5)}{2} \times \dfrac{100}{27}$

$$\frac{(212 + 102.5)}{2} \times \frac{100}{27} = 314.5 \times \frac{100}{54} = \textbf{582.4} \text{ cu yd}$$

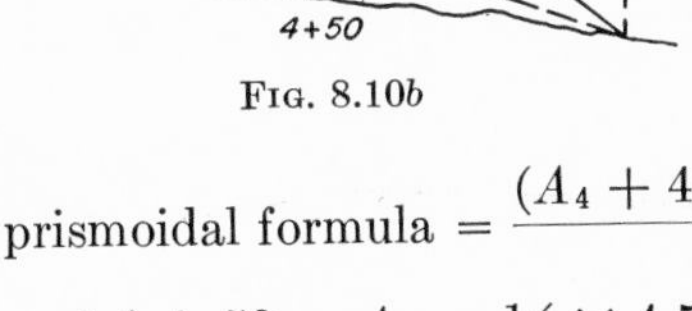

FIG. 8.10*b*

b. Volume by prismoidal formula $= \dfrac{(A_4 + 4Am + A_5)}{6} \times \dfrac{100}{27}$

Cross section at 4 + 50 $= A_m = \frac{1}{2} \times 4.5(14.5 + 25)$
$+ \frac{1}{2} \times 10(3 + 10) = 88.9 + 65 =$ **153.9** sq ft

Volume $= (314.5 + 615.6) \times {}^{100}\!/_{162} =$ **574.1** cu yd

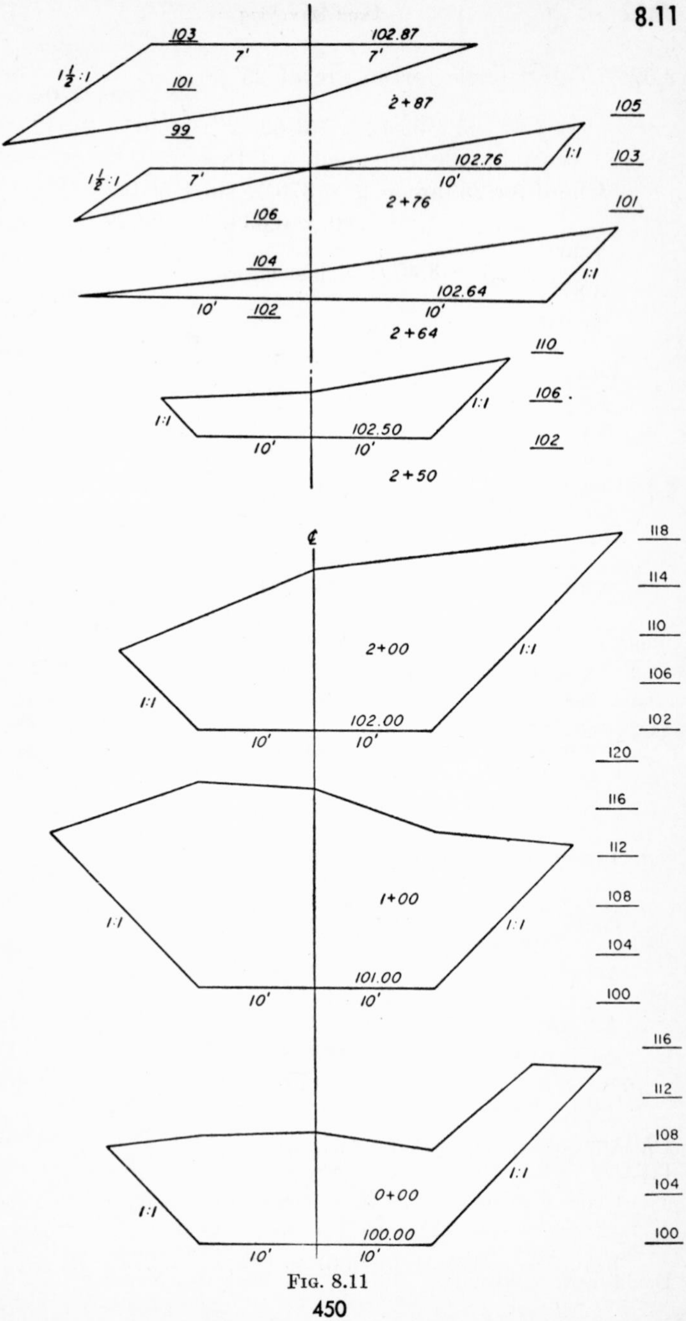

103
102.87
7'
7'
1½:1
101
2+87
99
105
1:1
103
102.76
1½:1
7'
10'
2+76
101
106
104
1:1
102.64
10'
102
10'
2+64
110
106
1:1
1:1
102.50
102
10'
10'
2+50
℄
118
114
110
2+00
1:1
106
1:1
102.00
102
10'
10'
120
116
112
1+00
108
1:1
1:1
104
101.00
100
10'
10'
116
112
108
1:1
104
0+00
1:1
100.00
100
10'
10'

Fig. 8.11

8.12

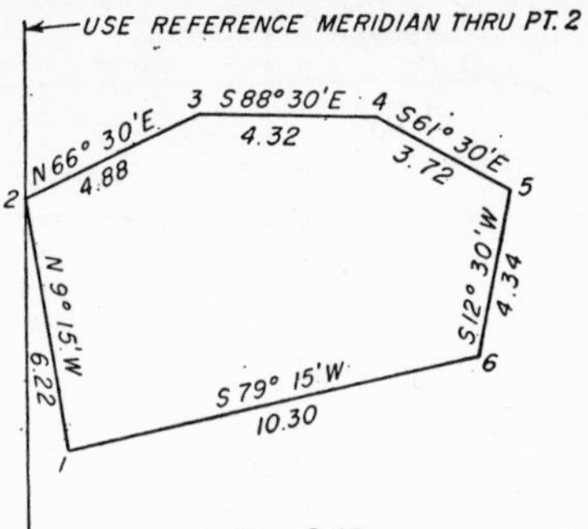

FIG. 8.12

Line	Bearing	Chains	× sin bearing =	W	E
2-3	N66°30′E	4.88	0.91706		+ 4.47
3-4	S88°30′E	4.32	0.99966		+ 4.32
4-5	S61°30′E	3.72	0.87882		+ 3.27
5-6	S12°30′W	4.34	0.21644	− 0.94	
6-1	S79°15′W	10.30	0.98245	−10.12	
1-2	N 9°15′W	6.22	0.16074	− 1.00	
				−12.06	+12.06

No correction needed

Line	Bearing	Chains	× cos bearing =	N	corr.	S	corr.
2-3	N66°30′E	4.88	0.39875	+1.95	−0.01		
3-4	S88°30′E	4.32	0.02618			−0.11	
4-5	S61°30′E	3.72	0.47716			−1.78	
5-6	S12°30′W	4.34	0.97630			−4.24	+0.01
6-1	S79°15′W	10.30	0.18652			−1.92	
1-2	N 9°15′W	6.22	0.98700	+6.14	−0.02		
				+8.09		−8.05	
			Corrected:	+8.06		−8.06	

Line	Corrected latitudes	Corrected departures	DMD	Double area +	Double area −
2-3	+1.94	+ 4.47	+ 4.47	+ 8.672	
3-4	−0.11	+ 4.32	+13.26		− 1.459
4-5	−1.78	+ 3.27	+20.85		− 37.113
5-6	−4.25	− 0.94	+23.18		− 98.515
6-1	−1.92	−10.12	+12.12		− 23.270
1-2	+6.12	− 1.00	+ 1.00	+ 6.120	
				+14.792	−160.357
					+ 14.792

DMD of (2-3) = departure of (2-3)

DMD of (3-4) = DMD of (2-3) + departure of (2-3) + departure of (3-4)

Twice area = 145.565

Double area = latitude × DMD

Area (sq chains) = 72.78

Area (acres) = 7.278

8.13 A parcel of land may be described by:

a. Metes and bounds

b. Stating its location and size in a rectangular system of land subdivision

c. Giving the coordinates of the property corners with reference to a plane coordinate system

d. A deed reference to a description in a previously recorded deed

e. Reference to block and individual property numbers appearing on a recorded map

8.14

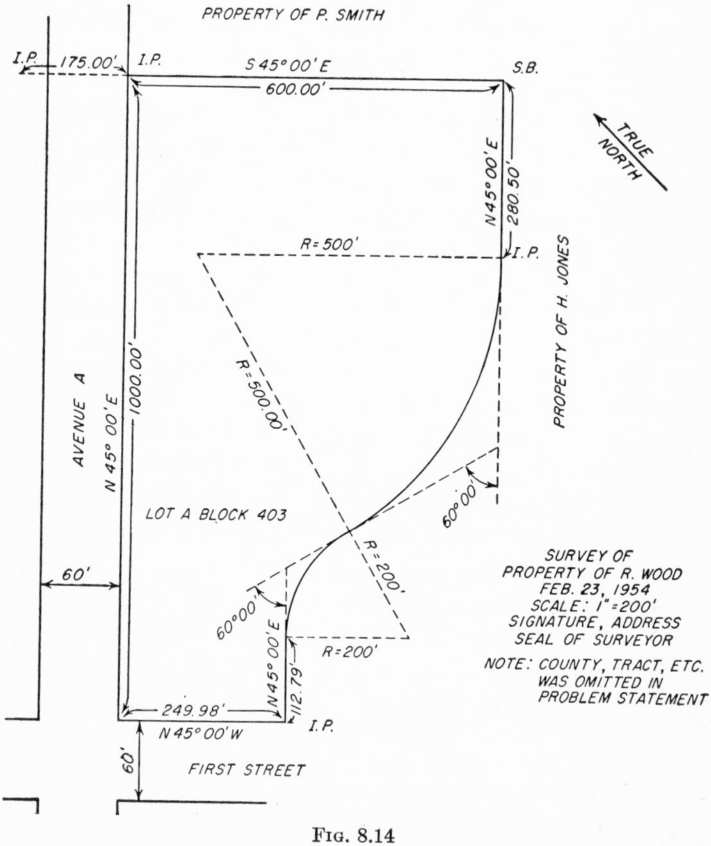

Fig. 8.14

8.15 Beginning at the northeast corner of the intersection of Avenue A and First Street and running along the said Avenue A N45°00′E, which is also the true bearing of Avenue A as shown on a recorded file map No. 62 by E. R. Sullivan dated May 16, 1922, a distance of one thousand (1000.00′) feet to an iron pipe in the ground which is the northwest corner of the property; thence turning and running S45°00′E a distance of six hundred (600.00′) feet along the land now or formerly belonging to Paul Smith to a stone bound at land now or formerly belonging to Harold Jones; thence turning and running S45°00′W along the land of said Jones a distance of 4.25 chains or two hundred eighty and fifty hundredths (280.50′) feet to an iron pipe in the ground; thence continuing along the land of said Jones along a curve to the right of radius five hundred (R = 500.00′) feet a distance along the arc of five hundred twenty three and sixty hundredths (523.60′) feet to a point of reverse curvature, the long chord of said curve being five hundred (500.00′) feet long; thence continuing along the land of said Jones along a curve to the left of radius two hundred (R = 200.00′) feet a distance along the arc of two hundred nine and forty four hundredths (209.44′) feet to a point of tangency, the long chord of said curve being two hundred (200.00′) feet long; thence continuing along the afore-mentioned tangent S45°00′W a distance of one hundred twelve and seventy nine hundredths (112.79′) feet to an iron pipe on the northeasterly side of First Street; thence turning and running along First Street N45°00′W, which is also the true bearing of First Street as shown on a recorded File Map No. 62 previously described, a distance of two hundred forty nine and ninety eight hundredths (249.98′) feet to the point of beginning; all bearings being true bearings and the parcel containing a calculated area of 473,313 square feet more or less.

8.16 $f/i = 100$ and $(F + C) = 1$ ft
Instrument at Sta. M (elev. 372.9), H.I. = 5.0 ft
Elevation of instrument line of sight = 377.9 ft

Point	Rod reading	Vertical angle	Elevation	Horizontal distance
1	8.65	+3°54′	431.7	862 ft
2	7.93	−1°25′ on 3′	355.3	793 ft
3	5.43	−3°57′	335.5	542 ft
4	10.36	+0°48′ on 2′	390.4	1,037 ft

8.17

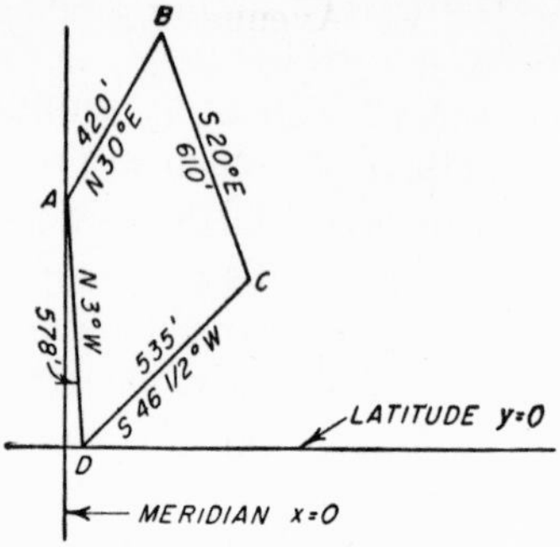

FIG. 8.17

Line	Bearing	Distance	× sin bearing =	W	corr.	E	corr.
AB	N30°E	420	0.50000			210.00	−0.08
BC	S20°E	610	0.34202			208.63	−0.08
CD	S46½°W	535	0.72537	388.07	+0.14		
DE	N3°W	578	0.05234	30.25	+0.01		
				418.32	+0.15	418.63	−0.16
			Corrected	418.47		418.47	

Line	Bearing	Distance	× cos bearing =	N	corr.	S	corr.
AB	N30°E	420	0.86603	363.73	+0.10		
BC	S20°E	610	0.93969			573.21	−0.16
CD	S46½°W	535	0.68835			368.27	−0.11
DE	N 3°W	578	0.99863	577.21	+0.17		
				940.94	+0.27	941.48	−0.27
			Corrected	941.21		941.21	

Line	W-E departure	N-S latitude	*x* coordinate	*y* coordinate
AB	209.92	363.83	*A* = 0	*A* = 577.38
BC	208.55	573.05	*B* = 209.92	*B* = 941.21
CD	388.21	368.16	*C* = 418.47	*C* = 368.16
DE	30.26	577.38	*D* = 30.26	*D* = 0

$$2\text{ Area} = \frac{Xa}{Ya} \times \frac{Xb}{Yb} \times \frac{Xc}{Yc} \times \frac{Xd}{Yd} \times \frac{Xa}{Ya} = (2A_1 - 2A_2)$$

$$\begin{aligned}
Xa \cdot Yb &= 0 \times 941.21 = 0 \\
Xb \cdot Yc &= 209.92 \times 368.16 = 77{,}284 \\
Xc \cdot Yd &= 418.47 \times 0 = 0 \\
Xd \cdot Ya &= 30.26 \times 577.38 = 17{,}472 \\
2A_2 &= 94{,}756 \text{ sq ft} \\
Ya \cdot Xb &= 577.38 \times 209.92 = 121{,}204 \\
Yb \cdot Xc &= 941.21 \times 418.47 = 393{,}868 \\
Yc \cdot Xd &= 368.16 \times 30.26 = 11{,}140 \\
Yd \cdot Xa &= 0 \times 0 = 0 \\
2A_1 &= 526{,}212 \text{ sq ft} \\
2A_2 &= 94{,}756 \\
2\text{ Area} &= 431{,}456 \\
\text{Area} &= 215{,}728 \text{ sq ft}
\end{aligned}$$

With original distances measured only to the nearest foot and with angles measured to only the nearest degree or one-half degree, an area expressed to the nearest square foot is unrealistic. It is better to state the area as 215,700 sq ft.

8.18 1. In measuring:

a. Subtract the correction from the measured (recorded) distance.

b. Add the correction to the measured (recorded) distance.

c. Subtract the correction from the measured (recorded) distance.

d. Add the correction to the measured (recorded) distance.

2. In layout, the point should be moved

a. Out 0.03 ft, as the distance is actually 99.97 ft

b. Back, as the distance is actually 100.01 ft

c. Out, as the distance is actually 99.96 ft

d. Back, as the distance is actually 100.008 ft

8.19 Assume that the sights are long enough to ensure that the vertical cross hair will set upon the point observed without causing angular variation. If the angle is measured once, the accuracy of measurement is probably not closer than ±5 sec, but if the angle is measured by eight repetitions, the total angle divided by eight should produce a measured angle good to 1 sec of angle. There is little point in going beyond eight repetitions for the average observer since personal errors nullify the gain. If one half the readings are made with the telescope in normal position and the other half with the telescope inverted, error due to lack of very close adjustment of the instrument is eliminated. The act of repetition uses angles in different parts of the graduated circle, thus reducing or eliminating very small errors in graduation. Both verniers should be read on each set of readings, thus eliminating eccentricity of the graduated circle. Care should be used so that systematic errors in the clamps are avoided. The tangent screws should be turned against and not with the springs. The instrument should always be turned either clockwise or counterclockwise to avoid any twist in the tripod. Protection of the instrument against sun or wind should be provided for best results. Rapidity of observation reduces eyestrain and increases the accuracy of sighting. Standing too near or too long at one tripod leg may cause settlement of the tripod and nullify other precautions.

8.20 Simpson's rule:

$$A = \frac{d}{3}\,(h_{e_L} + 2\Sigma h_{(\text{odd})} + 4\Sigma h_{(\text{even})} + h_{e_R})$$

	$h_{(\text{odd})}$		$h_{(\text{even})}$
h_3	= 8.9	h_2	= 4.6
h_5	= 10.4	h_4	= 15.3
h_7	= 18.5	h_6	= 13.2
h_9	= 17.6	h_8	= 23.4
h_{11}	= 3.2	h_{10}	= 9.3
$2\Sigma_{(\text{odd})}$	$= 58.6 \times 2 = 117.2$	$4\Sigma_{(\text{even})}$	$= 65.8 \times 4 = 263.2$

$$A = {}^{25}\!/_{3}(0 + 117.2 + 263.2 + 0) = {}^{100}\!/_{12} \times 380.4 = \mathbf{3{,}170}\ \text{sq ft}$$

Trapezoidal rule

$$A = \frac{d}{2}\,(h_{e_L} + 2\Sigma h + h_{e_R})$$

$$= {}^{25}\!/_{2}[0 + 2(58.6 + 65.8) + 0] = {}^{100}\!/_{4} \times 124.4 = \mathbf{3{,}110}\ \text{sq ft}$$

8.21

$$\begin{array}{ll} 3.398 = \text{F.S. on } B & 4.465 = \text{B.S. on } B \\ \underline{-3.148} = \text{B.S. on } A & \underline{-4.035} = \text{F.S. on } A \\ 0.250 & 0.430 \end{array}$$

True difference in elevation between A and B

$$= (0.250 + 0.430) \times \tfrac{1}{2} = 0.340.$$

4.465 − 0.340 = 4.125 = rod reading on A to give level sight with instrument 4.465 ft above B. Move cross hair up.

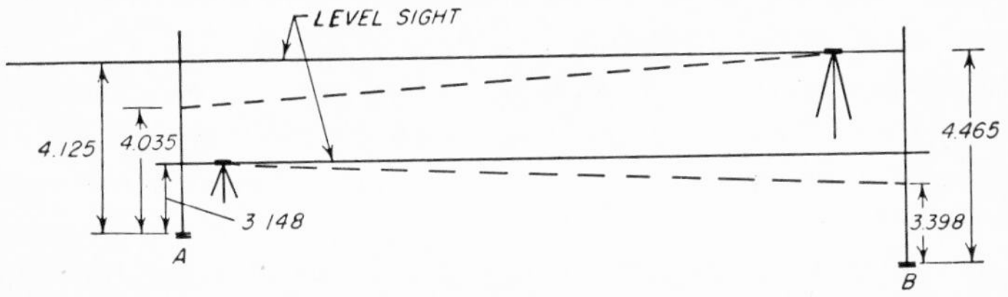

FIG. 8.21

8.22 The survey and plot plan submitted to the client should show the situation as it should be and also the 0.2-ft encroachment as it exists. Many surveyors would show these lines in two colors (e.g., black for the deed description and red for the "as-constructed" condition) on a hard copy, or if a tracing is made the encroachment might be shown as a dotted line. In any case, the plan submitted would be a true description of the existing condition.

The best advice the surveyor can give his client is to consult a lawyer. It is not within a surveyor's province to presume to give legal advice. The courts have continuously frowned on any such attempt on the part of the surveyor.

A condition occurs here which definitely requires legal assistance. A title search may indicate that an easement has been secured from the city. Legal action may involve securing one if none exists. Such action is not simple. The laws of adverse possession do not apply against a municipality. Since the street involves the public interest, public hearings might be required before legislation permitting the encroachment could be passed.

8.23 Even with a carefully adjusted instrument, it is unlikely that the line of sight and the axis of the level tube are truly parallel. It is more likely that the line of sight is inclined slightly up or down. The error in reading is proportional to the distance from the instrument to the rod. If the backsight distance equals the foresight distance, and since one reading is added and the other subtracted, the net result due to the error is zero. It is not necessary that each backsight distance equal each foresight distance. Since the proportionality is a direct similar triangle relationship, it is only required that the sum of the backsight distances equal the sum of the foresight distances.

Curvature of the earth and atmospheric refraction will also enter the problem. Normally, since the correction is about 0.001 ft in 200 ft, it can be ignored. However, on long runs where the aggregate unbalance of backsight and foresight distances is large, this may be a substantial figure. Since the error varies as the square of the distance it is necessary for *exact* work to make *each* backsight distance equal *each* foresight distance. For most work, balancing the aggregate distances gives satisfactory results.

8.24 *a.* The line is construed as running to the definite object since the definite object has a higher call over the distance (see answer to 8.25*c*).

b. "Northerly" in the absence of other information may mean anything from N45°W to N45°E. With other information it may permit one to tie down the bearing to a specific value.

c. Where the "metes and bounds" and the area disagree, the metes and bounds will prevail over the area since it is assumed that as long as the boundaries are visible, the intentions of the contracting parties to the sale is quite evident.

8.25 *a.* (See answer to 8.13.)

b. 1. By "a point of beginning" which should be monumented and referenced by ties or distances along street lines from well-established monuments or easily located and fixed points such as street intersections.

2. Lengths and bearings (preferably true bearings) of each side such that they give a closed traverse. If magnetic bearings are used, the declination of the needle and the date of the survey should be stated.

3. The names of abutting property owners.

4. The area of the property.

5. All buildings and improvements located by offsets from the property lines.
6. All (if any) easements or encroachments.
7. Coordinates of local grid if determined.
8. Direction of true meridian or magnetic meridian and declination.
9. Any town, county, or other political subdivision lines.
10. Street lines, names, and widths where possible.
11. Boundary monuments and lines and ties to same.
12. Any fences, walls, driveways, etc.
13. Title showing location, scale, and date.
14. Signature of surveyor and, where required by law, his address and seal.
15. Lot, plat, block, or other necessary identification.
16. Occupancy of structures and types of structures.

c. In order of decreasing precedence:

1. Natural monuments and boundaries.
2. Artificial monuments.
3. Calls for adjoiners.
4. Courses and distances.
5. Area. One exception is that this item will take precedence over item 4, courses and distances, in cases where a will states that equal or other specified divisions of land to several heirs are intended.

d. A party wall is a wall built along a property line which usually is (but not necessarily so) in the center of the wall. To the surveyor, the wall becomes a physical monument and the center of it becomes the property line whether this checks or does not check with the recorded distances from other points.

SYMBOLS

″	= inch, in., i.; second, sec of angle
″^{2}	= square inch, s.i., sq in., in.^{2}
″^{3}	= cubic inch, c.i., cu in., in.^{3}
″^{4}	= inches 4th, i.^{4}, in.^{4}
′	= foot, ft., f, ft; minute, min of angle
′^{2}	= square foot, s.f., sq ft, ft^2
′^{3}	= cubic foot, c.f., cu ft, ft^3
′^{4}	= feet 4th, f.^{4}, ft^4
I	= moment of inertia (″^{4} or ′^{4})
#	= pound, lb., lb
k	= kip (1,000-pound unit)
T	= ton (2,000-pound unit)
″#	= inch pound, pound inch, i.p., in-lb
′#	= foot pound, pound foot, f.p., ft-lb
′k	= foot kip, kip foot, f.k., ft-kip
p.s.i.	= pounds per square inch, #/″^{2}, psi
p.s.i.a.	= pounds per square inch absolute, #a/″^{2}, psia
p.s.i.g.	= pounds per square inch gage, #g/″^{2}, psig
p.s.f.	= pounds per square foot, #/′^{2}, psf
p.c.i.	= pounds per cubic inch, #/″^{3}, pci
p.c.f.	= pounds per cubic foot, #/′^{3}, pcf
k.s.f.	= kips per square foot, k/′^{2}, ksf
π	= ratio of circumference to diameter of a circle or 3.1416
c.c.	= cubic centimeter, cc
gm	= gram
kg	= kilogram or 1,000 grams
l	= liter, ltr., or 1,000 c.c.
°	= degree of temperature or of angle
°F	= degree Fahrenheit
°R	= degree Rankin [°F (absolute)]
°C	= degree centigrade
°K	= degree Kelvin [°C (absolute)]
h	= hour of time, hr., hr

m = minute of time, min., min; mile(s)
s = second of time, sec
t = time (h, m, s)
m.p.h. = miles per hour, mph
f.p.s. = feet per second, fps
a = acceleration ($'/s^2$) or ft per sec per sec, fps per sec; absolute (abs.) or gage pressure abs.
g = acceleration due to gravity or 32.2 ($'/s^2$); gage (for pressure above atmospheric)
v = velocity (units per sec), f/s or ($'/s$)
v_0 = initial velocity
M = mass or (w/g), weight/gravity
F = force or ma (mass $\times$ acceleration)
f = coefficient of friction
HP = horsepower, hp (33,000 $'^{\#}$/min) or (550 $'^{\#}$/sec)